ELECTRICITY AND MAGNETISM

Series in Physics

Richard M. Sutton

Editor

Oleg D. Jefimenko
WEST VIRGINIA UNIVERSITY

ELECTRICITY AND MAGNETISM

An introduction to the theory of electric and magnetic fields

New York • Appleton-Century-Crofts

Division of Meredith Publishing Company

PREFACE

This book has been written for an advanced undergraduate course in electricity and magnetism offered to students majoring in physics and in related fields. It presupposes a year's course in general physics and one in calculus. It is based on the lectures in electricity and magnetism given by the author for the past nine years and is designed to be readily understood by even the student who will receive only minimal guidance from his instructor.

The book has three main objectives. The first objective is a presentation of the fundamentals of electromagnetic theory reflecting recent developments and applications of the subject. To achieve this objective, considerable amount of modern material is included in the book; operational definitions are introduced for all fundamental electric and magnetic quantities; current and voltage are used as the basic measurables (*mksva* system of units)*; vector analysis is used as a standard mathematical tool; and, which is most important, the theory is presented in a logical rather than in a historical sequence.

The second objective of the book is a rigorous but simple presentation of electromagnetic theory, with emphasis on the internal unity and harmony of the mathematical description of electric and magnetic phenomena. To achieve this objective, the basic structure of the theory is first determined. With the aid of general physical considerations it is made plausible that the theory must be based upon three types of experimental laws: the field laws, the energy laws, and the constitutive laws. At the same time it is deduced from Helmholtz's theorem of vector analysis that a complete set of electric or magnetic field laws need not contain more than two experimentally established correlations, which may be either in a differential form (curl and divergence laws) or in an integral form (circulation and flux laws). On the basis of these considerations the theory is then presented rigorously and simply in a systematic, coherent, and logical manner.

The third objective of the book is to develop in the student a creative ability in the application of electromagnetic theory. For this purpose,

*The formulation of the concepts of electric current, voltage, charge, and electric and magnetic fields is based on ideas developed by R. W. Pohl in his famous lectures on general physics. The electricity and magnetism section of the lectures is described in R. W. Pohl, "Elektrizitätslehre," XIX Auflage, Springer, Berlin (1964).

detailed solutions to a large number of illustrative examples demonstrating various methods and applications of the theory have been incorporated in the book. Furthermore, each chapter, except Chapter 3, has been supplemented by a number of carefully selected problems which should help the student to build up his skill and initiative in practical application of the presented material.

In agreement with modern curricula, the book deals primarily with a detailed exposition of the theory of macroscopic electric and magnetic fields. The book is, however, sufficiently flexible to allow the instructor to add supplementary topics to the course. With this in mind, much subordinate material has been relegated to starred sections, which may be omitted without loss of continuity, and to illustrative examples. The instructor can easily substitute additional material for these sections and examples.

In writing the book, the author has attempted a complete rethinking of the subject matter. The book contains therefore an appreciable amount of original material, most of which has evolved in the process of developing the theory in accordance with the principles outlined in connection with the second objective of the book.

The author is grateful to many of his former students for their encouraging attitude and helpful suggestions. He owes a great debt to his wife Valentina, who patiently typed and proofread the numerous drafts of the manuscript and assisted in the preparation of the lines-of-force photographs appearing in this book.

OLEG D. JEFIMENKO

CONTENTS

Part II   ELECTROMAGNETIC THEORY

13 Energy and Force Relations in the Magnetostatic Field in Vacuum

14 Magnetostatic Field in Material Media

ELECTRICITY AND MAGNETISM

I

MATHEMATICAL
INTRODUCTION

1

PHYSICAL QUANTITIES AND PROPERTIES OF PHYSICAL EQUATIONS

In physics extensive use is made of the possibility of mathematical representation of physical phenomena: physical concepts are designated by symbols, the relationships between concepts are expressed by formulas, and the correlations between phenomena are represented by equations. Physical formulas and equations are characterized by special properties and form a special class of mathematical expressions. The knowledge of these properties is essential for an accurate formulation and intelligent application of physical theories. In the field of electricity and magnetism this knowledge is also needed for the understanding of the relations between different systems of electric and magnetic measurables used in scientific literature. We shall start therefore with a brief discussion of the nature and properties of physical formulas and equations.

1-1. Physical Quantities and Physical Equations

The properties of physical formulas and equations are closely connected with four preliminary procedures which constitute the starting point for a quantitative study of physical phenomena. These procedures are:

(1) selection of *basic*, or *primary*, *measurables* (basic objects of measurements) and specification of properties to be used for their identification

3

(2) selection of instruments for the measurement of basic measurables

(3) selection of standards and units for the calibration of these instruments and

(4) selection of *derived*, or *secondary*, *measurables* and specification of rules for their measurement.

The first of these procedures defines the conceptual contents of the *basic*, or *primary*, *quantities*, while the second and third procedures make it possible to associate a definite magnitude with each of these quantities, thus completing their definition. The fourth procedure consists in selecting certain groups of primary measurements in combination with specified mathematical operations to be performed upon the results of these measurements and defines the *derived*, or *secondary*, *quantities*.

With the aid of these four procedures it is possible to describe various physical phenomena in terms of a few primary quantities (results of single measurements) and a few secondary quantities (results of certain groups of measurements). The experimentally observed correlations between phenomena can then be expressed as correlations between these quantities in the form of algebraic equations.

It is clear that such equations reflect two different things. On one hand, they reflect correlations inherent in the physical phenomena. On the other hand, they reflect our approach to the quantitative description of these phenomena—in particular, our selection of measurables, standards, and units. This selection involves a considerable degree of arbitrariness. In principle, one can express the same set of correlations by using one, two, or any other number of basic measurables of any reasonable kind. The division of measurables into primary and secondary is also arbitrary. The choice of standards and units of measurements is, of course, arbitrary too. As we shall see, this arbitrariness in the selection of measurables, standards, and units is responsible for several remarkable properties of the physically meaningful mathematical expressions.

1-2. Ratio Requirement. Dimensions of Physical Quantities

Let us investigate how physical quantities, formulas, and equations are affected by the possibility of choosing different standards and units of measurements.

Obviously, the correlations between physical phenomena are determined by the very nature of these phenomena and do not depend on our choice of standards or units. Since the correlations between physical phenomena are independent of the choice of standards or units, all equations which describe these correlations must be invariant to a change of the size of the standards or the size of the corresponding units. In particular, the ratio of any two physical quantities each of which represents the same measurable must not depend on the units in terms of which these quantities are expressed (for instance, the ratio of two distances must not depend on whether these distances are measured in feet or in meters). Only those quantities that satisfy this *ratio requirement* are considered physically meaningful. The fact that physical quantities must satisfy the ratio requirement is their characteristic property.

Since the same quantity can be expressed by different numbers, depending on the size of units used, a complete specification of a quantity must contain a statement of the units in terms of which the quantity is measured. If a quantity represents the result of a group of measurements (secondary quantity), it is necessary to state how the number representing the quantity is correlated to each individual unit used for the evaluation of this number.

It has been found that if both the primary and secondary quantities, satisfy the ratio requirement, then the value of any secondary quantity represents a power product of the values of primary quantities. Therefore physical quantities may be written as products of two factors. The first factor is a number (or a symbol standing for a number) and is called the *numerical value* of the quantity. The second factor is a power product of symbols designating basic units or, in a general case, a power product of symbols designating basic measurables; this power product is called the *dimensions* of the quantity and constitutes a formula which shows how the numerical value of the quantity is related to the units of basic measurables. The dimensions of a basic quantity are, of course, only one symbol designating the basic unit or the basic measurable itself. Conceptually different quantities usually have different dimensions, and therefore dimensions are frequently used for identification of quantities. To indicate that only the dimensions but not the numerical value of a quantity are being considered, the symbol designating the quantity is placed between square brackets. For example, $[V]$ means dimensions of the quantity V. The dimensions themselves are usually written in square brackets too; thus if L

designates length and T designates time, the equation $[V] = [LT^{-1}]$ means: the dimensions of V are length divided by time.[1]

1-3. Dimensional Homogeneity of Physical Equations. Dimensional Analysis

As has been stated in the preceding section, all physical equations must be invariant to a change in the size of units. A detailed investigation shows that the necessary and sufficient condition for this invariance is the *dimensional homogeneity* (dimensional uniformity) of the equations, which means that only quantities possessing the same dimensions may be added, subtracted, or equated, and that only pure numbers may serve as exponents or as arguments of trigonometric, hyperbolic, and other similar functions. If equations are dimensionally homogeneous, any change of units cancels out and does not influence the equation. Thus the arbitrariness in the choice of standards and units restricts physical equations to equations homogeneous in dimensions.

This restriction gave rise to a branch of physics called *dimensional analysis*. Dimensional analysis is an aggregate of methods for solving various physical problems on the basis of dimensional considerations by utilizing the property of dimensional homogeneity of physical equations. Dimensional analysis can be used for a variety of purposes, from finding errors in algebraic computations to solving partial differential equations. Two especially useful applications of dimensional analysis are described below. Other applications are demonstrated in Sections 1-4 and 1-5.

A very useful application of dimensional analysis is a method for tracing errors in calculations involving physical quantities. Since physical equations must be homogeneous in dimensions, the dimensions of all the terms connected by equality signs must be the same. Furthermore, all terms connected by plus or minus signs must have the same dimensions, and all exponents and arguments of transcendental functions must be pure numbers. Consequently, if any term obtained in the process of calculation has dimensions different from those of the preceding term, or if it violates dimensional homogeneity in any other manner, then an error has been made in the calculation of this term. By checking the dimensional consistency of calculations one

---

[1] The symbols L and T are used universally to indicate length and time. Another universally used symbol is M, indicating mass.

can find the term in which the error has occurred. Once it is known where the error is, the error can easily be identified and eliminated.

Of course, even if a calculation is dimensionally consistent it still may be wrong for a number of obvious reasons. A dimensional check, however, allows one to detect a surprisingly large number of errors encountered in most types of calculations.

▼

Example 1-3.1   As a result of a certain calculation the following formula has been obtained:

$$R = \frac{R_1 + R_2}{R_1 \cdot R_2}.$$

Determine whether or not this formula is physically meaningful, if R_1, R_2 and R are physical quantities having the same dimensions $[R]$.

To check the formula, we compare the dimensions of the left side with those of the right side. The dimensions of the left side are $[R]$, the dimensions of the right side are $[R_1 + R_2]/[R_1] \cdot [R_2] = [R] \cdot [R]^{-2} = [R]^{-1}$. Thus the formula in question is dimensionally wrong, which indicates that an error has been made in the calculation. (Note that the dimensions of a sum or a difference of two quantities are the same as the dimensions of each quantity alone since only quantities of the same dimensions may be added or subtracted.)

Example 1-3.2   Make a dimensional check of the following calculation:

$$\int x^2 \cos ax \, dx = \frac{2x}{a} \cos ax + \frac{x^2}{a} \sin ax - \frac{2}{a^3} \sin ax,$$

where $[a] = [x]^{-1}$.

Taking into account the fact that $[dx] = [x]$, we see that the dimensions of the last two terms on the right are the same as those of the term (integral) on the left, namely $[x]^3$. The dimensions of the first term on the right are, however, $[x]^2$. Hence, there is an error in this term (a recalculation would reveal that there should be a^2 instead of a in the denominator).

▲

Another very important application of dimensional analysis is a method for determining functional dependences between quantities involved in physical phenomena. According to the fundamental theorem of dimensional analysis—the Buckingham, or "π" theorem—a functional dependence between any physical quantities can always be expressed as

$$\pi_1 = f(\pi_2, \pi_3, \ldots \pi_n),$$

where the π's are independent dimensionless power products built from the quantities involved.[1] In particular, if these quantities are such that only one independent dimensionless power product π_1 can be made from them, then the above formula reduces to $\pi_1 = $ constant. In this case one can find the functional dependence between the quantities by building a dimensionless power product from these quantities and setting the product equal to an undetermined numerical constant.

▼

Example 1-3.3   A beam of electrons of cross-sectional area $S[\text{m}^2]$ and charge density $\rho[\text{amp} \cdot \text{sec} \cdot \text{m}^{-3}]$ is ejected from an electron gun and moves with velocity $v[\text{m} \cdot \text{sec}^{-1}]$. The beam is equivalent to a current I [amp]. Find how this current depends on S, ρ, and v.

We begin by constructing independent dimensionless power products from S, ρ, v, and I. This we do by combining successively the quantity having the most complex dimensions (ρ in the present case) with other quantities, each time eliminating some of the units from the dimensions of the quantity with which we start. To eliminate [amp] from ρ, we use I, obtaining

$$\frac{\rho}{I} \, [\text{sec} \cdot \text{m}^{-3}].$$

To eliminate [sec] from this expression, we use v, obtaining

$$\frac{\rho v}{I} \, [\text{m}^{-2}].$$

To eliminate [m^{-2}] from this expression, we use S, obtaining

$$\frac{\rho v S}{I}.$$

The last expression is a dimensionless power product, π_1. In building it, we have used all quantities given in the problem, and there are no quantities left from which we could build other independent π's. By Buckingham's theorem we then have

$$\frac{\rho v S}{I} = C',$$

where C' is a numerical constant. The dependence which we seek is therefore (we replace C' by $1/C$, for simplicity)

$$I = C\rho v S.$$

---

[1] n power products are called independent if none of the products can be expressed as a power product of any of the remaining $n - 1$ products. Each product has the form $Q_1^\alpha \cdot Q_2^\beta \cdot Q_3^\gamma \cdots$, where Q's are the quantities under consideration.

Example 1-3.4 Find the functional dependence between the period and the length of a simple pendulum, taking into account that the period t depends on the length of the pendulum l and on the acceleration of gravity g.

Since the dimensions of g are

$$[g] = [LT^{-2}],$$

we see by inspection that the functional dependence must be

$$\frac{gt^2}{l} = C', \quad \text{or} \quad t = C\sqrt{\frac{l}{g}},$$

where

$$C = \sqrt{C'}$$

is a numerical constant.

▲

1-4. Dimensional Constants

As we have learned in the preceding section, the basic property of physical equations is their dimensional homogeneity. This property originates from the possibility of choosing between different standards of measurement. Another important property of physical equations is the presence of dimensional constants in them. This property arises from the fact that more than one basic measurable is used in the investigation of physical phenomena.

Adding one more basic measurable to a given set of measurables results in the appearance of at least one new dimensional constant in the equations correlating this new measurable with those already present. Thus in electricity and magnetism the introduction of current and voltage as new basic measurables in addition to length, mass, and time results in the appearance of three new universal dimensional constants:

permittivity of space

$$\varepsilon_0 \left[\frac{\text{current} \cdot \text{time}}{\text{voltage} \cdot \text{length}} \right],$$

permeability of space

$$\mu_0 \left[\frac{\text{voltage} \cdot \text{time}}{\text{current} \cdot \text{length}} \right],$$

and *constant of energy*

$$^0 \left[\frac{\text{mass} \cdot (\text{length})^2}{\text{current} \cdot \text{voltage} \cdot (\text{time})^3} \right]$$

(these constants are not present if electromagnetic phenomena are formulated only in terms of length, mass, and time as is the case when the so-called "electrostatic," "electromagnetic," or "Gaussian" systems of measurables are used).[1]

Similarly, the reduction of basic measurables by one results in the disappearance of at least one dimensional constant from the equations that correlate the eliminated measurable with other measurables. One could, for instance, eliminate mass as a basic measurable in mechanics and consider it as a secondary measurable of dimensions $[(\text{length})^3/(\text{time})^2]$. As a result, the gravitational constant G would disappear from all equations where it is now present (Newton's expression of the gravitational law would be $F = m_1 m_2 / r^2$ rather than $F = G m_1 m_2 / r^2$, as it is usually written).

The significance of dimensional constants is frequently underestimated. Sometimes they are regarded as a nuisance introduced in physics because of the necessity of "taking care of units." Actually, however, dimensional constants originate from experimentally established correlations between physical quantities and may well be regarded as concise formulations of physical laws. Physical laws express certain permanent correlations between quantities. These permanent correlations are usually implicitly represented by the corresponding dimensional constants. When a dimensional constant enters an equation, it makes that equation subject to the corresponding law.

To illustrate this point, let us return to Example 1-3.4. In this example we derived the equation for the period of a pendulum on the basis of dimensional considerations. We know, however, that in order to derive this equation by the usual analytical means, we should start from the law of motion of a particle in the earth's gravitational field. The question arises: how could we obtain the correct formula by merely using dimensional considerations without any reference to the law of gravity? The answer is simple: we actually did use the information contained in the law of gravity by including the constant of gravity g in the set of quantities pertaining to the problem.[2]

Often the statement of a physical law is equivalent to the statement of the existence of a certain dimensional constant. Consider, for

---

[1] For a discussion of various systems of measurables see Section 1-5.

[2] In fact, in Example 1-3.4 we have determined the correlation between time and length for the general case of the motion of a particle in a constant gravitational field specified by g. Thus the formula $t = C\sqrt{l/g}$ describes not only the period of a pendulum but also the time of fall as a function of distance for a freely falling body, the time-distance dependence for a particle moving on an inclined plane, etc.

instance, the well-known Ohm's law for electric conductors. According to this law (in its circuital form), the ratio V/I of the voltage V applied to a conductor and the current I in this conductor has under certain conditions a constant value independent of either V or I. The ratio V/I is called the resistance R of the conductor. Thus Ohm's law states that under certain conditions R is constant, or that there exists a dimensional constant R.

An analysis of dimensional constants characterizing a given physical problem may easily reveal "hidden" correlations that otherwise would not be known without a detailed mathematical investigation of the problem. This is illustrated in the following example.

▼

Example 1-4.1   Find the correlation between the radius of the orbit and the period of revolution of a planet by analyzing the dimensions of the gravitational constant.

Planetary motion is completely determined by Newton's gravitational law, which is represented by the gravitational constant G. Since $[G] = [L^3/MT^2]$, it is obvious that the correlation between the radius of the orbit r, the period of revolution t, and the mass of the system m must be such that $G = Cr^3/mt^2$, where C is a numerical constant. Since m, the mass, is constant for a sun–planet system, this correlation may be written as r^3/t^2 = constant, which is known as Kepler's third law. (See also Problem 1.11.)

▲

1-5. Transformation of Units and Measurables

Since several systems of units and measurables are used in physics, it frequently becomes necessary to convert physical quantities and equations from one system to another. This can be done with the aid of dimensional analysis.

Two kinds of systems of basic measurables are now used in electricity and magnetism: the electro-mechanical systems and the mechanical systems.

The most important representatives of the electro-mechanical systems are the length-mass-time-voltage-current, or the *LMTVI*, system; the length-mass-time-current, or the *LMTI*, system; and the length-mass-time-charge, or the *LMTQ*, system. The fundamental units in the first system are usually the meter, the kilogram, the second, the volt, and the ampere—the *mksva* units. In the second system they are usually the meter, the kilogram, the second, and the ampere—the *mksa* units. In the third system they are usually the meter, the kilogram, the second, and the coulomb—the *mksc* units.

The most important representative of the mechanical systems is the length-mass-time, or the *LMT*, system. The units in this system are usually *cgs*—the centimeter, the gram, and the second, which, for historical reasons, are frequently called the "absolute" units. There are three especially important subdivisions of the *LMT* system: the *electrostatic*, the *electromagnetic*, and the *Gaussian* systems. They differ in the definitions of certain electric and magnetic quantities. The respective units of these quantities are referred to as the *cgs electrostatic*, the *cgs electromagnetic*, and the *cgs Gaussian* units.

To convert an equation to a new system of basic measurables, the symbols designating physical quantities are replaced by the corresponding symbols of the new system, the numerical and dimensional constants are replaced by the corresponding constants of the new system, and additional dimensional constants of the new system are introduced into the equation to make it dimensionally homogeneous in the new system.[1] This method of conversion follows from the fact that all equations describing the same physical phenomenon must exhibit the same functional dependence between the corresponding quantities regardless of the system of basic measurables in which each particular equation is written. Such equations may differ therefore only in the designation of quantities and in the number and kind of constants.

▼
Example 1-5.1   The "Coulomb law" (once thought to be the most fundamental law of electricity) can be expressed in the *LMTVI* system as

$$F = \frac{{}^{\circ}q_1 q_2}{4\pi \varepsilon_0 r^2} \,.$$

Convert this formula to the *LMT* electrostatic system.

Examining the tables of symbols and constants given in Appendix I, (Tables A-1 and A-2), we see that no symbols need be replaced in the above formula, that ° must be replaced by 1, and that ε_0 must be replaced by $1/4\pi$. Coulomb's law in the *LMT* electrostatic system is therefore

$$F = \frac{q_1 q_2}{r^2} \,.$$

---

[1] Tables of corresponding symbols and constants as well as a table of the dimensions of electric and magnetic quantities in various systems are given in Appendix I.

Example 1-5.2 The capacitance of a sphere of radius r is in the LMT Gaussian system (indicated by subscript "g")

$$C_g = r.$$

Express the capacitance of this sphere in the $LMTQ$ system.

Since the relations between the constants of the two systems are $1/4\pi \to \varepsilon_0$, $4\pi \to \mu_0$ (see Table A-2 in Appendix I), we have in the $LMTQ$ system

$$C = (4\pi\varepsilon_0)^\alpha (\mu_0/4\pi)^\beta r,$$

where α and β are exponents, to be determined, which are needed to make this equation dimensionally homogeneous in the $LMTQ$ system. Consulting the table of dimensions (Table A-3 of Appendix I), we see that $\alpha = 1$ and $\beta = 0$ must be used. The capacitance of the sphere in the $LMTQ$ system is therefore

$$C = 4\pi\varepsilon_0 r.$$

Example 1-5.3 The "Maxwell equations" (the most fundamental laws of electromagnetic fields) can be written in the $LMTVI$ system as

$$\nabla \times \mathbf{E} = -\frac{\partial \mathbf{B}}{\partial t}, \qquad \nabla \cdot \mathbf{D} = \rho,$$

$$\nabla \times \mathbf{H} = \mathbf{J} + \frac{\partial \mathbf{D}}{\partial t}, \qquad \nabla \cdot \mathbf{B} = 0.$$

Convert these equations to the LMT Gaussian system (∇ is a differential operator of dimensions $[L^{-1}]$, $\partial/\partial t$ is a time derivative of dimensions $[T^{-1}]$—both remain the same in all systems).

Using the tables of symbols and constants given in Appendix I (Tables A-1 and A-2), we replace the symbols in the above equations and introduce the additional constant c characteristic of the Gaussian system (there are no constants in these equations, so that none can be replaced). We then have, using subscript "g" to indicate the Gaussian system,

$$\nabla \times \mathbf{E}_g = -c^\alpha \frac{\partial \mathbf{B}_g}{\partial t}, \qquad \nabla \cdot (\mathbf{D}_g/4\pi) = c^\beta \rho_g,$$

$$\nabla \times (\mathbf{H}_g/4\pi) = c^\gamma \mathbf{J}_g + c^\delta \frac{\partial (\mathbf{D}_g/4\pi)}{\partial t}, \qquad \nabla \cdot \mathbf{B}_g = 0,$$

where α, β, γ, and δ are exponents, to be determined, which are needed to make the equations dimensionally homogeneous. Examining the dimensions of $\mathbf{E}_g$, $\mathbf{B}_g$, $\mathbf{D}_g$, ρ_g, $\mathbf{H}_g$, and $\mathbf{J}_g$, given in the table of dimensions in Appendix I (Table A-3), we recognize that $\alpha = -1$, $\beta = 0$, $\gamma = -1$, and $\delta = -1$. Thus Maxwell's equations in the Gaussian system are (we are dropping the subscripts "*g*" now)

$$\mathbf{V} \times \mathbf{E} = -\frac{1}{c}\frac{\partial \mathbf{B}}{\partial t}, \qquad\qquad \mathbf{V} \cdot \mathbf{D} = 4\pi\rho,$$

$$\mathbf{V} \times \mathbf{H} = \frac{1}{c}\left(4\pi\mathbf{J} + \frac{\partial \mathbf{D}}{\partial t}\right), \qquad \mathbf{V} \cdot \mathbf{B} = 0.$$

▲

To convert a quantity to new units within the same system of basic measurables, each unit in the dimensions of the quantity is replaced with an equivalent number of new units. To convert a quantity to units of a new system of basic measurables, the units are replaced in the same manner, except that the sign $\triangleq$ ("corresponds") is used in place of the equality sign whenever a quantity expressed in terms of old units is "equated" with a quantity expressed in terms of new units (otherwise dimensionally inhomogeneous equations would result).[1] These methods of conversion are self-evident and require no justification.

▼

Example 1-5.4   The average atmospheric electric field near the earth's surface is $E = 130$ volt/m. What is the magnitude of this field in millivolt/cm?

Since 1 volt $= 10^3$ millivolt and 1 m $= 10^2$ cm, we have

$$E = 130\,\frac{\text{volt}}{\text{m}} = 130\,\frac{1\ \text{volt}}{1\ \text{m}} = 130\,\frac{10^3\ \text{millivolt}}{10^2\ \text{cm}} = 1300\,\frac{\text{millivolt}}{\text{cm}}.$$

Example 1-5.5   The average density of atmospheric electric charge near the earth's surface is $\rho = +3 \cdot 10^{-12}$ amp $\cdot$ sec/m³. Convert this quantity to *cgs* electrostatic units by converting each basic unit.

According to Table A-4 of Appendix I, 1 amp $\triangleq 3 \cdot 10^9$ cm$^{\frac{3}{2}}$ g$^{\frac{1}{2}}$ sec^{-2}. Furthermore, 1 sec $=$ 1 sec and 1 m $= 10^2$ cm. We have therefore

$$\rho = +3 \cdot 10^{-12}\,\frac{\text{amp} \cdot \text{sec}}{\text{m}^3} = +3 \cdot 10^{-12}\,\frac{1\ \text{amp} \cdot 1\ \text{sec}}{(1\ \text{m})^3}$$

$$\triangleq +3 \cdot 10^{-12}\,\frac{3 \cdot 10^9\ \text{cm}^{\frac{3}{2}}\ \text{g}^{\frac{1}{2}}\ \text{sec}^{-2} \cdot 1\ \text{sec}}{(10^2\ \text{cm})^3} = +9 \cdot 10^{-9}\ \text{cm}^{-\frac{3}{2}}\ \text{g}^{\frac{1}{2}}\ \text{sec}^{-1}$$

(this result could be obtained directly from the relation between the units of ρ given in Table A-4).

▲

---

[1] The correlations between units of various systems are given in Appendix I.

PROBLEMS

1.1. Which, if any, of the following expressions are definitely wrong?

$$\text{(a)}\quad R = \frac{R_1 + R_2}{R_1 + 2R_2}, \qquad \text{(b)}\quad E = \frac{q}{4\pi\varepsilon_0 r^3}, \qquad \text{(c)}\quad V = V_0\, e^{-2t},$$

$$\text{(d)}\quad \frac{dV}{dt} = rt\,\frac{d^2E}{dt^2}, \qquad \text{(e)}\quad V = \int E(\sin \pi r)^2 dr + V_0.$$

The dimensions are as follows: $[E] = [\text{volt/m}]$; $[q] = [\text{amp} \cdot \text{sec}]$; $[\varepsilon_0] = [\text{amp} \cdot \text{sec/volt} \cdot \text{m}]$; $[r] = [\text{m}]$; $[V_0] = [V] = [\text{volt}]$; $[t] = [\text{sec}]$.

1.2. The resonance frequency of an L-C circuit depends on the inductance $L[\text{volt} \cdot \text{sec/amp}]$ and the capacitance $C[\text{amp} \cdot \text{sec/volt}]$. By using dimensional considerations, find how this frequency will change if the capacitance is doubled.

1.3. The current in an R-C circuit is given by $I = I_0 e^{-\alpha}$. Find α if it is known that α depends on $R[\text{volt/amp}]$, $C[\text{amp} \cdot \text{sec/volt}]$, and $t[\text{sec}]$, is proportional to t, and does not contain any numerical constants.

1.4. The representation of correlations between quantities by means of dimensionless products results in a reduction of the number of variables (according to a "rule of thumb," the number of independent dimensionless power products which can be formed from a given set of quantities is equal to the number of quantities involved, minus the number of basic measurables in terms of which these quantities are expressed). Taking this into consideration, what is the advantage of using dimensionless products for the experimental determination of correlations between quantities and for the graphical representation of functional dependences?

1.5. Often the number of dimensionless products obtained from a given set of quantities can be made smaller by increasing the number of basic measurables (independent units) in terms of which the quantities are expressed. Use this method to find the functional dependence between the charge $q[q]$ of a parallel-plate capacitor, separation $d[l]$ of the capacitor's plates, area of the plates $A[S]$, and voltage $V[V]$ applied to the capacitor, assuming that the problem is subject to a certain law represented by the constant $\varepsilon_0[ql/SV]$, where S is some independent unit of surface area not equal to l^2. Show that this dependence cannot be obtained by dimensional means if A is measured in units of l^2

1.6. Dimensional analysis can be used for solving certain partial differential equations by reducing them to ordinary differential equations. Apply this method to the following problem. The approximate "telegraph equation" for an underwater cable is

$$CR\,\frac{\partial V}{\partial t} = \frac{\partial^2 V}{\partial x^2},$$

where V is voltage, t is time, x is distance, and C and R are constants. Show that if the voltage V_0 is applied at $t = 0$ to the terminal $x = 0$ of an infinitely long cable, then the voltage at any point x of the cable and at any later time t is given by

$$V = V_0\left(1 - \frac{1}{\sqrt{\pi}} \int_0^\xi e^{-\frac{1}{4}\xi^2} d\xi\right),$$

where $\xi = \sqrt{\dfrac{CR}{t}}\, x$. (Hint: use Buckingham's theorem to express the voltage V as $V_0 f\left(\sqrt{\dfrac{CR}{t}}\, x\right) = V_0 f(\xi)$ and determine the function f by substituting this expression in the telegraph equation.)

1.7. Convert Coulomb's law formula stated in Example 1-5.1 to the *LMTI*, *LMTQ*, *LMT* magnetostatic, and *LMT* Gaussian systems of basic measurables.

1.8. Convert the formula for the capacitance of a sphere stated in Example 1-5.2 to the *LMTVI*, *LMTI*, *LMT* electrostatic, and *LMT* magnetostatic systems of basic measurables.

1.9. Convert Maxwell's equations stated in Example 1-5.3 to the *LMTI*, *LMTQ*, *LMT* electrostatic, and *LMT* electromagnetic systems of basic measurables.

1.10. Taking into account that in the *mksva* system the charge of the electron is $1.6 \cdot 10^{-19}$ amp · sec, what energy in ergs corresponds to 1 electron · volt if the electron is considered as a new unit of charge?

1.11. According to Rutherford's model, an atom may be regarded as a positive nucleus around which electrons rotate like planets around the sun. The force between the nucleus and the electrons is determined by Coulomb's formula stated in Example 1-5.1. (a) By analyzing the dimensions of the single constant ε_0 contained in this formula in the *LMTQ* system, show that the electrons obey Kepler's third law. (b) In the *LMT* electrostatic and *LMT* Gaussian systems, Coulomb's formula contains no constants. Yet, even in these systems one can deduce by means of dimensional analysis that the electrons obey Kepler's third law. How? (Hint: look at the dimensions of electric charge.) (c) Consider Coulomb's formula in the *LMTVI*, *LMTI*, and *LMT* electromagnetic systems and show that in these systems, too, one can deduce by dimensional analysis that the electrons obey Kepler s third law.

Supplementary Reading

Bridgman, P. W.: *Dimensional Analysis*, 2d ed., Yale University Press, New Haven (1931).

LANGHAAR, H. L.: *Dimensional Analysis and Theory of Models*, John Wiley and Sons, New York (1951).

MOON, P. and D. E. SPENCER: "A Modern Approach to Dimensions," *Journal Franklin Institute*, **248,** 495 (1949).

SEDOV, L. I.: *Similarity and Dimensional Methods in Mechanics*, Academic Press, New York (1959).

2

VECTOR ANALYSIS

The mathematical description of electromagnetic phenomena becomes especially simple and clear if it is based on the methods of vector analysis. Vector analysis provides an efficient shorthand for writing relations between physical quantities, and at the same time makes it possible to visualize the physical meaning of these relations distinctly and exactly. As a result, in contemporary physics, and in electromagnetic theory in particular, vector analysis is both a standard mathematical tool and a mode of thought. It is therefore well worth while to develop a familiarity with vector analysis before proceeding to formulate electromagnetic theory. The fundamentals of vector analysis are presented in this chapter.

2-1. Scalars and Vectors

Physical quantities which are not associated with a direction or orientation in space are called *scalars*. They can be adequately specified by the statement of their numerical value and dimensions. Typical examples of scalars are mass, temperature, and energy. Mathematical operations with scalars obey the rules of ordinary algebra and ordinary calculus ("analysis"). Many physical quantities, however, are associated with some direction or orientation and require for their adequate specification the statement of this direction or orientation in addition to the statement of the numerical value and dimensions. Examples of such quantities are moment of inertia, rotation through an angle, force, velocity, and displacement. Some of these directional quantities obey the well-known *polygon law* (*parallelogram law*) of addition. The quantities which obey this law are called *vectors*. Typical examples of vectors are displacement, velocity, force, and rotation through an infinitesimal angle.

Vectors may be represented graphically by means of arrows. The length of the arrow represents the numerical value, or the magnitude, of the vector. The orientation of the arrow shows the direction of the vector.

Algebraically, vectors are designated by bold-face letters in contrast to scalars, which are designated by ordinary letters. Thus, a "vector A" is designated by **A**. The magnitude of **A** is denoted either by the symbol |**A**|, or by the letter A in ordinary type. Mathematical manipulations with vectors obey the rules of *vector algebra* and *vector analysis*.

2-2. Addition and Subtraction of Vectors

As already stated, vectors are added in accordance with the polygon law of addition. A three-dimensional example of vector addition is shown in Fig. 2.1.

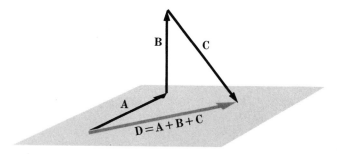

Fig. 2.1   Addition of vectors.

Vectors are subtracted with the aid of the *negative vectors*. The negative vector −**A** is defined as the vector whose magnitude is the same as that of **A**, but whose direction is opposite to the direction of **A**. The *difference* of two vectors **B** and **A** is defined as the sum **B** + (−**A**).

Two vectors are equal if their difference is zero—that is, if they are equal both in direction and in magnitude.

The sum (and difference) of vectors is characterized by the same properties as the sum of scalars: the *commutative property*

$$\mathbf{A} + \mathbf{B} = \mathbf{B} + \mathbf{A},$$

and the *associative property*

$$\mathbf{A} + (\mathbf{B} + \mathbf{C}) = (\mathbf{A} + \mathbf{B}) + \mathbf{C}.$$

These properties may be easily established by examining Fig. 2.2 and Fig. 2.3.

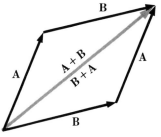

FIG. 2.2   Commutative property of vector addition.

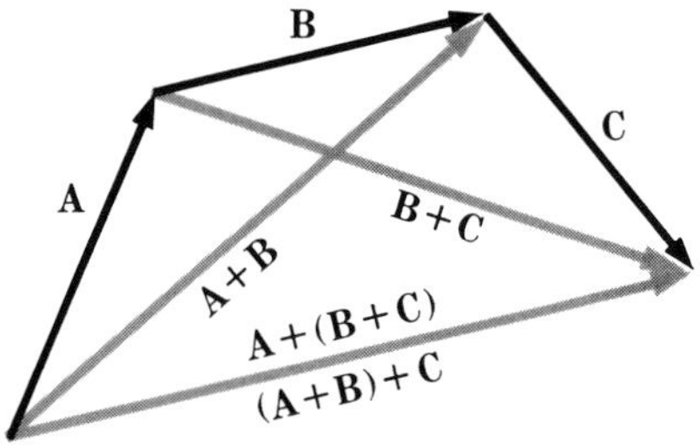

FIG. 2.3   Associative property of vector addition.

2-3. Multiplication of a Vector by a Scalar

The *product n*$\mathbf{A}$ *or* $\mathbf{A}$*n of a vector* $\mathbf{A}$ *and a scalar n* is defined as a vector whose magnitude is equal to $n|\mathbf{A}|$, and whose direction is the same as that of $\mathbf{A}$, if $n > 0$, or opposite to it, if $n < 0$. If $n = 0$, $n\mathbf{A} = 0$.

Graphically, a vector $\mathbf{B} = n\mathbf{A}$ is represented by the arrow whose length is n times the length of the arrow representing vector $\mathbf{A}$ and whose direction is parallel to that of $\mathbf{A}$. Figure 2.4 shows vectors $\mathbf{A}$, $\mathbf{B}$, and $\mathbf{C}$, where $\mathbf{B} = 2\mathbf{A}$ and $\mathbf{C} = -\frac{1}{2}\mathbf{A}$.

As can be demonstrated by graphical construction, the product of a vector by a scalar is *distributive* over addition of the scalars

$$(n + m)\mathbf{A} = n\mathbf{A} + m\mathbf{A}$$

as well as over addition of the vectors

$$n(\mathbf{A} + \mathbf{B}) = n\mathbf{A} + n\mathbf{B}.$$

It is clear, that if two vectors $\mathbf{A}$ and $\mathbf{B}$ are parallel to each other then there exists a relation

$$\mathbf{B} = n\mathbf{A},$$

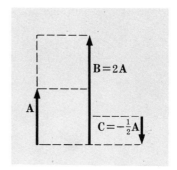

FIG. 2.4 Example of the multiplication of a vector by a scalar.

which may be written more symmetrically as

$$a\mathbf{A} = b\mathbf{B},$$

by setting $n = a/b$. Conversely, the existence of such a relation indicates that either $\mathbf{A}$ and $\mathbf{B}$ are parallel, or that a and b are both equal to zero.

The following example gives an illustration of the methods of vector algebra based on the foregoing definitions.

▼

Example 2-3.1   Show that the medians of a triangle intersect each other at a point of trisection.

Let vectors $\mathbf{a}$ and $\mathbf{b}$ represent the sides BC and AC of the triangle ABC, as shown in Fig. 2.5; let vectors $\mathbf{d}$ and $\mathbf{e}$ represent the medians of this triangle, so that points D and E are the midpoints of $\mathbf{a}$ and $\mathbf{b}$; and let F be the point of intersection of the medians. In the triangle ADC we have

$$\mathbf{e} + \tfrac{1}{2}\mathbf{a} = \mathbf{b}.$$

In the triangle BEC we have

$$\mathbf{d} + \tfrac{1}{2}\mathbf{b} = \mathbf{a}.$$

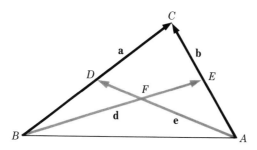

FIG. 2.5 Vector method of proving that the medians of a triangle trisect each other.

The vector FD is some fraction x of the vector $\mathbf{e}$, or $FD = x\mathbf{e}$. Similarly, $FE = y\mathbf{d}$. In the quadrangle $FDCE$ we then have

$$x\mathbf{e} + \tfrac{1}{2}\mathbf{a} = y\mathbf{d} + \tfrac{1}{2}\mathbf{b}.$$

Eliminating $\mathbf{e}$ and $\mathbf{d}$ from this equation by means of the previous two, we obtain

$$x(\mathbf{b} - \tfrac{1}{2}\mathbf{a}) + \tfrac{1}{2}\mathbf{a} = y(\mathbf{a} - \tfrac{1}{2}\mathbf{b}) + \tfrac{1}{2}\mathbf{b},$$

or

$$(-\tfrac{1}{2}x + \tfrac{1}{2} - y)\mathbf{a} = (-\tfrac{1}{2}y + \tfrac{1}{2} - x)\mathbf{b}.$$

But since $\mathbf{a}$ and $\mathbf{b}$ are not parallel, the equation can hold only if

$$-\tfrac{1}{2}x + \tfrac{1}{2} - y = 0 \quad \text{and} \quad -\tfrac{1}{2}y + \tfrac{1}{2} - x = 0.$$

Solving these two equations for x and y, we finally obtain $x = y = \tfrac{1}{3}$, so that F is a point of trisection of each median.

▲

2-4. Representation of Vectors by Means of Scalar Components

It is often desirable to perform mathematical operations with vectors by purely algebraic means, without supplementary geometrical constructions. This can be accomplished by representing both the magnitude and the direction of a vector analytically by certain numbers or by symbols denoting these numbers. The vector itself is represented in this case by a set of scalars.

The possibility of representing a vector by a set of scalars is based upon the fact that any vector $\mathbf{D}$ can be expressed as a linear combination

$$\mathbf{D} = a\mathbf{A} + b\mathbf{B} + c\mathbf{C}$$

of any three vectors $\mathbf{A}$, $\mathbf{B}$, and $\mathbf{C}$, provided that $\mathbf{A}$, $\mathbf{B}$, and $\mathbf{C}$ are not all in one plane (Fig. 2.6). The vectors $a\mathbf{A}$, $b\mathbf{B}$, and $c\mathbf{C}$ are called the *vector components* of $\mathbf{D}$ in the direction of $\mathbf{A}$, $\mathbf{B}$, and $\mathbf{C}$, respectively. Geometrically, they constitute the sides of a parallelepiped with vector $\mathbf{D}$ as a diagonal. The scalars a, b, and c are called the *scalar components* of $\mathbf{D}$ along the directions of $\mathbf{A}$, $\mathbf{B}$, and $\mathbf{C}$. The vectors $\mathbf{A}$, $\mathbf{B}$, and $\mathbf{C}$ which determine the directions of the vector components of $\mathbf{D}$ are called the *basic vectors*. The determination of the components of a vector is called the *resolution* of the vector. For a given set of basic vectors the resolution of a vector is unique—that is, different vectors have different components, and vice versa. Therefore, once the three basic vectors $\mathbf{A}$, $\mathbf{B}$, and $\mathbf{C}$ are given, any vector $\mathbf{D}$ can be uniquely specified by its

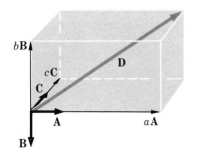

FIG. 2.6 Representation of vector **D** as the sum of three vectors $a\mathbf{A}$, $b\mathbf{B}$, and $c\mathbf{C}$.

vector components $a\mathbf{A}$, $b\mathbf{B}$, and $c\mathbf{C}$, or, which is most important, by its scalar components a, b, and c.

Although any three vectors may serve as basic vectors if they are not all in one plane, the most convenient sets of basic vectors consist of three mutually perpendicular vectors of magnitude (length) 1. Such vectors are called *orthogonal unit vectors*. The most common set of orthogonal unit vectors is the set of *Cartesian* unit vectors. These vectors are customarily designated by the symbols **i**, **j**, and **k** and are the unit vectors in the direction of the positive x-, y-, and z-axis, respectively, of a rectangular system of coordinates.

Any vector **A** (Fig. 2.7) can be expressed in terms of the Cartesian unit vectors as

$$\mathbf{A} = A_x\mathbf{i} + A_y\mathbf{j} + A_z\mathbf{k},$$

where A_x, A_y, and A_z are the scalar components of **A** corresponding to the x-, y-, and z-axis, as indicated by subscripts. As can be seen from

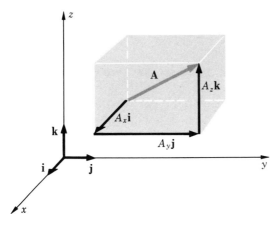

FIG. 2.7   Representation of vector **A** as the sum of its Cartesian components.

Fig. 2.7, A_x, A_y, and A_z represent the magnitudes of the projections of **A** along the directions of the coordinate axes and may be obtained therefore by multiplying the magnitude of **A** by the cosine of the angle between **A** and the respective axis. Thus

$$A_x = A \cos (\mathbf{A}, x), \quad A_y = A \cos (\mathbf{A}, y), \quad A_z = A \cos (\mathbf{A}, z).$$

Conversely, since vector **A** and its components A_x, A_y, and A_z form the diagonal and the sides of a rectangular prism, the magnitude of **A** may be obtained from A_x, A_y, and A_z by the formula

$$A = \sqrt{A_x^2 + A_y^2 + A_z^2}.$$

With the aid of a simple geometrical construction it can be demonstrated that the sum of two vectors

$$\mathbf{A} = A_x\mathbf{i} + A_y\mathbf{j} + A_z\mathbf{k} \quad \text{and} \quad \mathbf{B} = B_x\mathbf{i} + B_y\mathbf{j} + B_z\mathbf{k}$$

can be written as

$$\mathbf{A} + \mathbf{B} = (A_x + B_x)\mathbf{i} + (A_y + B_y)\mathbf{j} + (A_z + B_z)\mathbf{k},$$

so that the addition of vectors reduces to the addition of the corresponding scalar components of these vectors. Similarly, the multiplication of a vector by a scalar reduces to the multiplication of the scalar components of this vector by the scalar:

$$n\mathbf{A} = (nA_x)\mathbf{i} + (nA_y)\mathbf{j} + (nA_z)\mathbf{k}.$$

Thus, the representation of vectors by means of scalar components makes it possible to reduce mathematical operations with vectors to purely algebraic operations with their scalar components, so eliminating the necessity of geometrical constructions for the performance of the calculations.

2-5. Scalar, or Dot, Product of Two Vectors

Two kinds of products of two vectors **A** and **B** are defined in vector algebra. The first kind is called the *scalar, or dot, product* and is denoted as **A · B** (read "**A** dot **B**"). The second kind is called the *vector, or cross, product* and is denoted as **A × B** (read "**A** cross **B**").

The dot product of two vectors is defined as a scalar equal to the product of the magnitudes of these vectors multiplied by the cosine of the angle between them:

$$\mathbf{A} \cdot \mathbf{B} = |\mathbf{A}|\, |\mathbf{B}| \cos (\mathbf{A}, \mathbf{B}).$$

According to this definition, the dot product possesses the *commutative property*

$$\mathbf{A} \cdot \mathbf{B} = \mathbf{B} \cdot \mathbf{A}$$

and, as one can show with the aid of a geometrical construction, also the *distributive property*

$$\mathbf{A} \cdot (\mathbf{B} + \mathbf{C}) = \mathbf{A} \cdot \mathbf{B} + \mathbf{A} \cdot \mathbf{C}.$$

If two vectors $\mathbf{A}$ and $\mathbf{B}$ are perpendicular, $\cos (\mathbf{A}, \mathbf{B}) = 0$, and therefore

$$\mathbf{A} \cdot \mathbf{B} = 0 \qquad (\mathbf{A} \perp \mathbf{B}).$$

If $\mathbf{A}$ is parallel (or antiparallel) to $\mathbf{B}$, $\cos (\mathbf{A}, \mathbf{B}) = \pm 1$, and therefore

$$\mathbf{A} \cdot \mathbf{B} = \pm |\mathbf{A}| |\mathbf{B}| = \pm AB \qquad (\mathbf{A} \parallel \mathbf{B}),$$

where the minus sign holds if $\mathbf{A}$ and $\mathbf{B}$ are antiparallel. The dot product of a vector $\mathbf{A}$ with itself is

$$\mathbf{A} \cdot \mathbf{A} = |\mathbf{A}| |\mathbf{A}| = A^2.$$

The dot products of the Cartesian unit vectors are

$$\mathbf{i} \cdot \mathbf{j} = \mathbf{j} \cdot \mathbf{k} = \mathbf{k} \cdot \mathbf{i} = 0,$$

and

$$\mathbf{i} \cdot \mathbf{i} = \mathbf{j} \cdot \mathbf{j} = \mathbf{k} \cdot \mathbf{k} = 1.$$

For any two vectors,

$$\mathbf{A} = A_x\mathbf{i} + A_y\mathbf{j} + A_z\mathbf{k} \quad \text{and} \quad \mathbf{B} = B_x\mathbf{i} + B_y\mathbf{j} + B_z\mathbf{k},$$

we can write (using the distributive property)

$$\begin{aligned}
\mathbf{A} \cdot \mathbf{B} = {}& (A_x\mathbf{i} + A_y\mathbf{j} + A_z\mathbf{k}) \cdot (B_x\mathbf{i} + B_y\mathbf{j} + B_z\mathbf{k}) \\
= {}& A_xB_x\mathbf{i} \cdot \mathbf{i} + A_xB_y\mathbf{i} \cdot \mathbf{j} + A_xB_z\mathbf{i} \cdot \mathbf{k} + A_yB_x\mathbf{j} \cdot \mathbf{i} + A_yB_y\mathbf{j} \cdot \mathbf{j} \\
& + A_yB_z\mathbf{j} \cdot \mathbf{k} + A_zB_x\mathbf{k} \cdot \mathbf{i} + A_zB_y\mathbf{k} \cdot \mathbf{j} + A_zB_z\mathbf{k} \cdot \mathbf{k}
\end{aligned}$$

and, substituting the above-stated values of the dot products of the unit vectors, we obtain

$$\mathbf{A} \cdot \mathbf{B} = A_xB_x + A_yB_y + A_zB_z.$$

Thus the dot product of two vectors is equal to the sum of the products of the corresponding Cartesian components of these vectors.

The dot product has many applications. By means of the dot product one can easily find angles between vectors; the dot product of a vector and a unit vector gives the component of this vector in the direction represented by the unit vector; the dot product can be used for the solution of many geometrical problems; and, of course, it is extensively used in the description of physical phenomena. An example of the application of the dot product is given below.

▼

Example 2-5.1   Derive the law of cosines for a triangle.

Let vectors **a**, **b**, and **c** represent the sides of the triangle ABC (Fig. 2.8). In this triangle we have

$$\mathbf{a} = \mathbf{b} + \mathbf{c}.$$

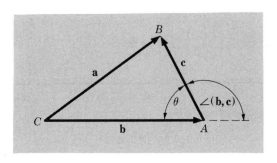

FIG. 2.8   Vector method of deriving the law of cosines for a triangle.

Calculating the dot product **a · a**, we obtain

$$\mathbf{a} \cdot \mathbf{a} = (\mathbf{b} + \mathbf{c}) \cdot (\mathbf{b} + \mathbf{c}) = \mathbf{b} \cdot \mathbf{b} + \mathbf{b} \cdot \mathbf{c} + \mathbf{c} \cdot \mathbf{b} + \mathbf{c} \cdot \mathbf{c},$$

or

$$a^2 = b^2 + bc \cos (\mathbf{b}, \mathbf{c}) + cb \cos (\mathbf{c}, \mathbf{b}) + c^2.$$

But $\angle(\mathbf{b}, \mathbf{c}) = \angle(\mathbf{c}, \mathbf{b}) = 180° - \theta$, and therefore

$$a^2 = b^2 + c^2 - 2bc \cos \theta.$$

▲

2-6. Vector, or Cross, Product of Two Vectors

The vector, or cross, product **A × B** of two vectors **A** and **B** is defined as a vector **C** (Fig. 2.9) whose magnitude is equal to the product of the magnitudes of vectors **A** and **B** multiplied by the sine of the angle between them,

$$|\mathbf{C}| = |\mathbf{A} \times \mathbf{B}| = |\mathbf{A}|\,|\mathbf{B}| \sin (\mathbf{A}, \mathbf{B}),$$

and whose direction is normal to both **A** and **B**, and such that vectors **A**, **B**, and **C** form a *right-handed system* (a system of three vectors **A**, **B**, and **C** is called right-handed if a screw with a right-handed thread will advance in the direction of **C** when turned from **A** to **B** through the smaller angle). The magnitude of the cross product of two vectors is equal to the area of the parallelogram having these vectors as its sides.

Since the rotation which carries **A** to **B** is opposite to that which carries **B** to **A**, the cross product is *not commutative*, but rather

$$\mathbf{A} \times \mathbf{B} = -\mathbf{B} \times \mathbf{A}.$$

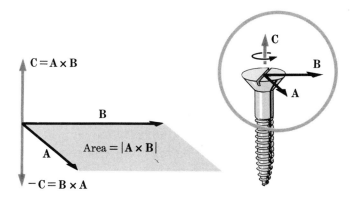

FIG. 2.9 Definition of the cross product of two vectors.

The cross product is, however, *distributive*,

$$\mathbf{A} \times (\mathbf{B} + \mathbf{C}) = \mathbf{A} \times \mathbf{B} + \mathbf{A} \times \mathbf{C},$$

as can be shown by means of a geometrical construction.

If two vectors **A** and **B** are parallel to each other, sin (**A**, **B**) = 0, and therefore

$$\mathbf{A} \times \mathbf{B} = 0 \qquad (\mathbf{A} \parallel \mathbf{B}).$$

In particular, for any **A**

$$\mathbf{A} \times \mathbf{A} = 0.$$

The cross products of the Cartesian unit vectors forming a right-handed system (the only system used in this book) are

$$\mathbf{i} \times \mathbf{i} = \mathbf{j} \times \mathbf{j} = \mathbf{k} \times \mathbf{k} = 0$$

and

$$\mathbf{i} \times \mathbf{j} = \mathbf{k}, \qquad \mathbf{j} \times \mathbf{k} = \mathbf{i}, \qquad \mathbf{k} \times \mathbf{i} = \mathbf{j},$$
$$\mathbf{j} \times \mathbf{i} = -\mathbf{k}, \quad \mathbf{k} \times \mathbf{j} = -\mathbf{i}, \quad \mathbf{i} \times \mathbf{k} = -\mathbf{j}.$$

By using these values of the cross products of the unit vectors, it is possible to express the cross product of two vectors in terms of the components of these vectors. The calculation is similar to that which was done for the dot product, and only the result of it will be given here. If

$$\mathbf{A} = A_x\mathbf{i} + A_y\mathbf{j} + A_z\mathbf{k} \quad \text{and} \quad \mathbf{B} = B_x\mathbf{i} + B_y\mathbf{j} + B_z\mathbf{k},$$

then the product $\mathbf{A} \times \mathbf{B}$ is

$$\mathbf{A} \times \mathbf{B} = \mathbf{i}(A_yB_z - A_zB_y) + \mathbf{j}(A_zB_x - A_xB_z) + \mathbf{k}(A_xB_y - A_yB_x),$$

which can also be written in the determinant notation as

$$\mathbf{A} \times \mathbf{B} = \begin{vmatrix} \mathbf{i} & \mathbf{j} & \mathbf{k} \\ A_x & A_y & A_z \\ B_x & B_y & B_z \end{vmatrix}.$$

Like the dot product, the cross product has many applications in both mathematics and physics. An illustration is given in the following example.

▼

Example 2-6.1   Show that $\sin(\alpha + \beta) = \sin\alpha\cos\beta + \sin\beta\cos\alpha$.
Consider two vectors $\mathbf{A}$ and $\mathbf{B}$ in the xy-plane as shown in Fig. 2.10. They can be written as

$$\mathbf{A} = \mathbf{i}A\cos\alpha - \mathbf{j}A\sin\alpha \quad \text{and} \quad \mathbf{B} = \mathbf{i}B\cos\beta + \mathbf{j}B\sin\beta.$$

Their cross product is by definition

$$\mathbf{A} \times \mathbf{B} = \mathbf{k}AB\sin(\alpha + \beta).$$

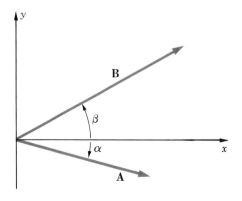

FIG. 2.10   Vector method of determining $\sin(\alpha + \beta)$.

In terms of components, their cross product is

$$\mathbf{A} \times \mathbf{B} = \mathbf{k}(A_x B_y - A_y B_x)$$
$$= \mathbf{k}(A \cos \alpha \, B \sin \beta + A \sin \alpha \, B \cos \beta)$$
$$= \mathbf{k}AB(\cos \alpha \sin \beta + \sin \alpha \cos \beta).$$

Hence

$$\mathbf{k}AB \sin (\alpha + \beta) = \mathbf{k}AB(\cos \alpha \sin \beta + \sin \alpha \cos \beta)$$

and therefore

$$\sin (\alpha + \beta) = \sin \alpha \cos \beta + \sin \beta \cos \alpha.$$

▲

2-7. Multiple Products of Vectors

With the aid of the dot and cross products of two vectors one can build multiple products involving several vectors. Among them, two kinds of triple products are especially important.

One of these products is the *box*, or *triple scalar, product* $\mathbf{A} \cdot (\mathbf{B} \times \mathbf{C})$, whose magnitude represents the volume of a parallelepiped having $\mathbf{A}, \mathbf{B},$ and $\mathbf{C}$ as the edges. This product is invariant to a cyclic permutation of vectors,

$$\mathbf{A} \cdot (\mathbf{B} \times \mathbf{C}) = \mathbf{B} \cdot (\mathbf{C} \times \mathbf{A}) = \mathbf{C} \cdot (\mathbf{A} \times \mathbf{B}),$$

and to an interchange of the dot with the cross,

$$\mathbf{A} \cdot (\mathbf{B} \times \mathbf{C}) = (\mathbf{A} \times \mathbf{B}) \cdot \mathbf{C},$$

but changes sign if any two vectors are interchanged,

$$\mathbf{A} \cdot (\mathbf{B} \times \mathbf{C}) = -\mathbf{A} \cdot (\mathbf{C} \times \mathbf{B}).$$

It is equal to zero if any two of the three vectors are parallel. In particular,

$$\mathbf{A} \cdot (\mathbf{A} \times \mathbf{C}) = 0$$

for any $\mathbf{A}$ and $\mathbf{C}$. These properties of the box product can be easily verified with the aid of a geometrical construction.

Another important triple product is the *triple cross*, or *triple vector, product*,

$$\mathbf{A} \times (\mathbf{B} \times \mathbf{C}),$$

which can also be written as the difference of two other triple products

$$\mathbf{A} \times (\mathbf{B} \times \mathbf{C}) = \mathbf{B}(\mathbf{A} \cdot \mathbf{C}) - \mathbf{C}(\mathbf{A} \cdot \mathbf{B}). \tag{2-7.1}$$

This is one of the most frequently used expansion formulas in both vector algebra and vector analysis ("bac cab" expansion). The proof of this formula is left to Problem 2.6.

2-8. Differentiation and Integration of Vectors

A variable vector **A** is called a *vector function* **A**(s) of a scalar variable s if to every value of s there corresponds a definite value of **A**. The *derivative* of a vector function with respect to a scalar is defined as the limit

$$\frac{d}{ds}\,\mathbf{A}(s) = \lim_{\Delta s \to 0} \frac{\mathbf{A}(s + \Delta s) - \mathbf{A}(s)}{\Delta s}.$$

According to this definition and to the rules of subtraction (addition) of vectors in terms of components, the derivative of **A**(s) can be expressed as

$$\frac{d\mathbf{A}(s)}{ds} = \frac{dA_x(s)}{ds}\,\mathbf{i} + \frac{dA_y(s)}{ds}\,\mathbf{j} + \frac{dA_z(s)}{ds}\,\mathbf{k}.$$

The differentiation of vectors is a limiting process of the operations of subtraction (addition) of vectors and division (multiplication) of vectors by a scalar. Both of these operations obey rules identical with the rules of ordinary algebra. Therefore the rules of differentiation known in ordinary calculus are applicable to expressions involving vectors. For example, if φ, **A**, and **B** are functions of a scalar s, we have

$$\frac{d}{ds}\,(\mathbf{A} + \mathbf{B}) = \frac{d\mathbf{A}}{ds} + \frac{d\mathbf{B}}{ds},$$

$$\frac{d}{ds}\,(\varphi\mathbf{A}) = \frac{d\varphi}{ds}\,\mathbf{A} + \varphi\,\frac{d\mathbf{A}}{ds},$$

$$\frac{d}{ds}\,(\mathbf{A} \cdot \mathbf{B}) = \frac{d\mathbf{A}}{ds} \cdot \mathbf{B} + \mathbf{A} \cdot \frac{d\mathbf{B}}{ds},$$

$$\frac{d}{ds}\,(\mathbf{A} \times \mathbf{B}) = \frac{d\mathbf{A}}{ds} \times \mathbf{B} + \mathbf{A} \times \frac{d\mathbf{B}}{ds}.$$

Partial differentiation is similarly defined for vectors which are functions of several scalar variables. For **A**(x, y, z) the three partial derivatives are

$$\frac{\partial \mathbf{A}}{\partial x} = \frac{\partial A_x}{\partial x}\,\mathbf{i} + \frac{\partial A_y}{\partial x}\,\mathbf{j} + \frac{\partial A_z}{\partial x}\,\mathbf{k},$$

$$\frac{\partial \mathbf{A}}{\partial y} = \frac{\partial A_x}{\partial y}\,\mathbf{i} + \frac{\partial A_y}{\partial y}\,\mathbf{j} + \frac{\partial A_z}{\partial y}\,\mathbf{k},$$

$$\frac{\partial \mathbf{A}}{\partial z} = \frac{\partial A_x}{\partial z}\,\mathbf{i} + \frac{\partial A_y}{\partial z}\,\mathbf{j} + \frac{\partial A_z}{\partial z}\,\mathbf{k},$$

and the total differential is

$$dA = \frac{\partial A}{\partial x}\, dx + \frac{\partial A}{\partial y}\, dy + \frac{\partial A}{\partial z}\, dz.$$

Three types of integrals are especially important in vector analysis: the *scalar line integral* $\int_C A \cdot dl$ of a vector A, the *scalar surface integral* $\int_S A \cdot dS$ of a vector A, and the *volume integral* $\int_v U\, dv$ of a scalar U.

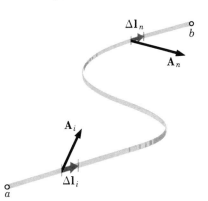

Fig. 2.11 Definition of the scalar line integral.

The line integral $\int_a^b A \cdot dl$ extended from point a to point b along curve C (Fig. 2.11) is defined as the limit

$$\int_a^b A \cdot dl = \lim_{\Delta l \to 0} \sum_i A_i \cdot \Delta l_i,$$

where Δl_i is an element of the curve C taken at the point i in the direction from a to b, and subject to the condition $\sum_i \Delta l_i =$ length of the curve C, while A_i is the value of the vector A at this point.[1]

Taking into account that the line element dl can be expressed in terms of its Cartesian components as

$$dl = dx\mathbf{i} + dy\mathbf{j} + dz\mathbf{k}$$

and using the rules of dot multiplication, we can write

$$\int_a^b A \cdot dl = \int_a^b (A_x dx + A_y dy + A_z dz) = \int_a^b A \cos (A, dl)\, dl. \quad (2\text{-}8.1)$$

---

[1] The scalar line integral has a simple mechanical meaning: if F represents a force, then the integral $\int_a^b F \cdot dl$ represents the work done by this force in moving a particle from point a to point b.

Often line integrals must be evaluated along a closed path. In this case the integral sign is written as $\oint$, and the integral is called the *circulation integral*.

▼

Example 2-8.1   Evaluate $\oint \mathbf{A} \cdot d\mathbf{l}$ along the path shown in Fig. 2.12, if $\mathbf{A} = 2xy\mathbf{i} + x^2\mathbf{j}$.

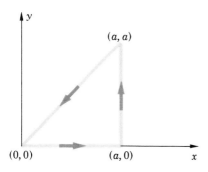

(a, a)

$(0, 0)$ $(a, 0)$ x

FIG. 2.12   Example of the evaluation of a scalar line integral.

The integral can be written as the sum of three integrals corresponding to the three rectilinear portions of the path. Using Eq. (2-8.1), we then have

$$\oint \mathbf{A} \cdot d\mathbf{l} = \int_{0,0}^{a,0} \mathbf{A} \cdot d\mathbf{l} + \int_{a,0}^{a,a} \mathbf{A} \cdot d\mathbf{l} + \int_{a,a}^{0,0} \mathbf{A} \cdot d\mathbf{l}$$

$$= \int_{0,0}^{a,0} (2xy\, dx + x^2\, dy) + \int_{a,0}^{a,a} (2xy\, dx + x^2\, dy) + \int_{a,a}^{0,0} (2xy\, dx + x^2\, dy).$$

Since the first of these three integrals is taken along the x-axis, where $y = 0$ and $dy = 0$, this integral is equal to zero. Since $x = a$ and $dx = 0$ along the second portion of the path, the second integral is

$$\int_0^a a^2\, dy = a^2 y \Big|_0^a = a^3.$$

Finally, since $x = y$ along the third part of the path, the third integral is

$$\int_{a,a}^{0,0} (2x^2\, dx + y^2\, dy) = \frac{2x^3}{3}\Big|_a^0 + \frac{y^3}{3}\Big|_a^0 = -\frac{2a^3}{3} - \frac{a^3}{3} = -a^3.$$

For the complete path we thus obtain

$$\oint \mathbf{A} \cdot d\mathbf{l} = 0 + a^3 - a^3 = 0.$$

▲

The second type of integral frequently used in vector analysis is the scalar surface integral.

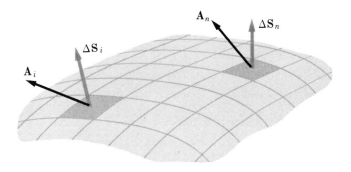

Fig. 2.13   Definition of the scalar surface integral.

As a preliminary step to the definition of the scalar surface integral we shall define the *surface-element vector* $d\mathbf{S}$. The vector $d\mathbf{S}$ (or $\Delta\mathbf{S}$) is defined as a vector whose magnitude at any point of a surface is numerically equal to the infinitesimal element dS of the surface area at this point and whose direction is normal to this element (the sense of the direction of $d\mathbf{S}$ is determined by certain conventions that will be stated later). In terms of Cartesian coordinates, $d\mathbf{S}$ is given by

$$d\mathbf{S} = \pm(dydz\mathbf{i} + dzdx\mathbf{j} + dxdy\mathbf{k}).$$

The scalar surface integral $\int_S \mathbf{A} \cdot d\mathbf{S}$ is defined as the limit

$$\int_S \mathbf{A} \cdot d\mathbf{S} = \lim_{\Delta S \to 0} \sum_i \mathbf{A}_i \cdot \Delta\mathbf{S}_i,$$

where $\Delta\mathbf{S}_i$ is an element of the surface area S taken at the point i (Fig. 2.13), subject to the condition $\sum_i \Delta S_i = S$, while $\mathbf{A}_i$ is the value of the vector $\mathbf{A}$ at this point.

The product $\mathbf{A} \cdot d\mathbf{S}$ is called the *flux* of the vector $\mathbf{A}$ through the surface element dS. The surface integral $\int_S \mathbf{A} \cdot d\mathbf{S}$ represents the total flux of $\mathbf{A}$ through the surface of integration S, and therefore this integral is often called the *flux integral*.

A flux integral can be written in scalar forms:

$$\int_S \mathbf{A} \cdot d\mathbf{S} = \pm\int\int_S (A_x dydz + A_y dzdx + A_z dxdy) = \int_S A\cos(\mathbf{A}, d\mathbf{S})\, dS.$$

$$(2\text{-}8.2)$$

As in the case of line integrals, a surface integral which has to be evaluated over a closed surface is designated by $\oint$. For a closed surface the positive direction of $d\mathbf{S}$ is, by convention, outward with respect to the volume enclosed.

▼

Example 2-8.2   Evaluate $\oint x\mathbf{i} \cdot d\mathbf{S}$ over the surface of a cube of side a (Fig. 2.14).

The surface integral may be split into six integrals corresponding to the six surfaces of the cube. The integrals over four of these surfaces vanish,

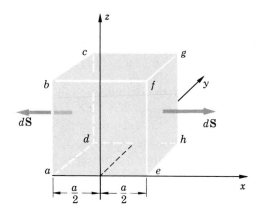

FIG. 2.14   Example of the evaluation of a scalar surface integral.

because cos $(\mathbf{i}, d\mathbf{S})$ is zero for all surfaces other than yz-surfaces. For the first yz-surface, $abcd$, we have

$$\int_{abcd} x\mathbf{i} \cdot d\mathbf{S} = -\int_{abcd} x \, dS.$$

(Minus sign is needed because the direction of the outward normal at this surface is opposite to the direction of $\mathbf{i}$.) Recognizing that x is constant and is equal to $-a/2$ on the surface $abcd$ and taking into account that $\int_{abcd} dS = a^2$, we have

$$\int_{abcd} x\mathbf{i} \cdot d\mathbf{S} = \frac{a}{2}\int_{abcd} dS = \frac{a^3}{2}.$$

Similarly, for the second remaining integral we obtain

$$\int_{efgh} x\mathbf{i} \cdot d\mathbf{S} = \frac{a^3}{2}.$$

Therefore

$$\oint x\mathbf{i} \cdot d\mathbf{S} = a^3.$$

▲

The third type of integral frequently used in vector analysis is the volume integral of a scalar function U: $\int_v U \, dv$. This integral is identical to the triple integral $\iiint U \, dx \, dy \, dz$ used in ordinary calculus.

In addition to the scalar integrals described above, vector integrals of the types $\int_C \mathbf{A} \times d\mathbf{l}$, $\int_S U \, d\mathbf{S}$, $\int_S \mathbf{A} \times d\mathbf{S}$, etc. occur in vector analysis. Their definitions are analogous to the definitions of the line and surface integrals which we have just learned.

2-9. Scalar and Vector Fields

If a quantity Q has a definite value everywhere within a certain region of space, then this region of space is called the *field* of Q. The field of a scalar quantity is called a *scalar field*, and the field of a vector quantity is called a *vector field*. The quantity Q, which determines a scalar or a vector field, is called, respectively, the scalar or vector *point function*.

An example of a scalar field is the temperature field—for instance, a region of space occupied by a heated body. Every point of the temperature field is associated with some definite temperature. An example of a vector field is the velocity field—for instance, a region of space occupied by a moving fluid. Every point of the velocity field is associated with some definite velocity.

Both scalar and vector fields can be represented graphically by means of field maps.

A three-dimensional field map of a scalar quantity U consists of a set of *level surfaces*. Each level surface is a surface at every point of which U has the same value. Different level surfaces correspond to different values of U. A two-dimensional field map of U consists of a set of *level lines*. Each level line is a line at every point of which U has the same value and, again, different level lines correspond to different values of U.

Familiar examples of the two-dimensional maps of scalar fields are weather maps. They show the temperature field of the air at the earth's surface by means of different "isotherms" (level lines joining geographical points of the same temperature) and also show the field of atmospheric pressure at the earth's surface by means of different "isobars" (level lines joining geographical points of the same barometric pressure).

A map of a vector field consists of a set of *field lines*. On the field map of a vector quantity **V**, each field line is a curve such that the tangent at every point of this curve is in the direction of the vector **V** at this point.

Familiar examples of crude vector field maps are the "lines of force" patterns produced by grass seeds in electric fields or by iron filings in magnetic fields (Plates 1–12). In these patterns the field lines are represented by the filaments formed by the seeds or filings.

2-10. Gradient

In studying the field of some scalar function U it is often necessary to know the rate of change of U corresponding to a transition from one point of the field to some other, neighboring point. This information can be obtained with the aid of a vector called the *gradient of the field of U* or, simply, "gradient U" and defined by the formula

$$\text{grad } U = \frac{\partial U}{\partial x}\mathbf{i} + \frac{\partial U}{\partial y}\mathbf{j} + \frac{\partial U}{\partial z}\mathbf{k}. \tag{2-10.1}$$

For any point of the field this vector gives the rate of change of U in the direction normal to the level surface drawn through this point and is oriented in this direction towards the points of larger U.

To demonstrate these properties of grad U, we shall consider the increment of $U(x, y, z)$ corresponding to a transition from a point x, y, z to a point $x + dx, y + dy, z + dz$. This increment is given by the total differential

$$dU = \frac{\partial U}{\partial x}\,dx + \frac{\partial U}{\partial y}\,dy + \frac{\partial U}{\partial z}\,dz.$$

The right side of this formula can be written as a dot product of two vectors:

$$\frac{\partial U}{\partial x}\,dx + \frac{\partial U}{\partial y}\,dy + \frac{\partial U}{\partial z}\,dz$$
$$= \left(\frac{\partial U}{\partial x}\mathbf{i} + \frac{\partial U}{\partial y}\mathbf{j} + \frac{\partial U}{\partial z}\mathbf{k}\right) \cdot (dx\mathbf{i} + dy\mathbf{j} + dz\mathbf{k}).$$

The first of these vectors we recognize as grad U, while the second vector is merely $d\mathbf{l}$—vector joining the point x, y, z with the point $x + dx$, $y + dy, z + dz$. We can write therefore

$$dU = \text{grad } U \cdot d\mathbf{l}. \tag{2-10.2}$$

Suppose now that both points x, y, z and $x + dx, y + dy, z + dz$ belong to the same level surface, so that $d\mathbf{l}$ lies in this surface. Since U is constant on a level surface, dU is then zero, and we have

$$0 = \operatorname{grad} U \cdot d\mathbf{l}.$$

Since both grad U and $d\mathbf{l}$ are assumed to be different from zero, this equation shows that grad U is perpendicular to $d\mathbf{l}$ in this case. By supposition, however, $d\mathbf{l}$ lies in the level surface, and, consequently, grad U must be perpendicular to this surface. To determine the sense of direction and the magnitude of grad U, we shall orient the coordinate axes in such a manner that two of them, say y and z, are tangent to the level surface, while the third one, x, is normal to it. Then we have

$$\operatorname{grad} U = \frac{dU}{dx}\, \mathbf{i},$$

which again shows that grad U is normal to the level surface, and also shows that grad U is directed towards the points of larger U and that the magnitude of grad U is equal to the rate of change of U in the direction normal to the level surface.

Since U at any point of the field changes most rapidly in the direction normal to the level surface drawn through this point, grad U can be interpreted as a vector whose direction and magnitude at any point represent the direction and magnitude of the fastest rate of change of U at this point.

The rate of change of U in a direction s, $\partial U/\partial s$, is called the *directional derivative* of U in the direction of s. This derivative is equal to the component of grad U along s.

A vector field that can be represented as the field of the gradient of a scalar function U is called a *potential*, or *conservative*, *field*, and the function U (or $-U$) is called the *potential* of this field. The level lines and the level surfaces corresponding to a conservative field are called the *equipotential lines* and the *equipotential surfaces*.

▼

Example 2-10.1   Find the gradient of the field of the position function r representing the distance of the points of space from the origin of Cartesian coordinates.

In terms of x, y, and z, r is

$$r = \sqrt{x^2 + y^2 + z^2}$$

so that

$$\text{grad } r = \frac{\partial}{\partial x} \sqrt{x^2 + y^2 + z^2}\,\mathbf{i} + \frac{\partial}{\partial y} \sqrt{x^2 + y^2 + z^2}\,\mathbf{j} + \frac{\partial}{\partial z} \sqrt{x^2 + y^2 + z^2}\,\mathbf{k}$$

$$= \frac{x}{\sqrt{x^2 + y^2 + z^2}}\,\mathbf{i} + \frac{y}{\sqrt{x^2 + y^2 + z^2}}\,\mathbf{j} + \frac{z}{\sqrt{x^2 + y^2 + z^2}}\,\mathbf{k}$$

$$= \frac{1}{\sqrt{x^2 + y^2 + z^2}}\,(x\mathbf{i} + y\mathbf{j} + z\mathbf{k}) = \frac{1}{r}\,(x\mathbf{i} + y\mathbf{j} + z\mathbf{k}).$$

Since the expression in parenthesis represents the vector $\mathbf{r}$, we have

$$\text{grad } r = \frac{\mathbf{r}}{r},$$

or

$$\text{grad } r = \mathbf{r}_u,$$

where $\mathbf{r}_u$ is a unit vector in the direction of r away from the origin.

▲

2-11. Divergence and Curl

Just as the gradient yields important information about scalar fields, two other vector-analytical expressions—*divergence* and *curl*—yield important information about vector fields.

The divergence of the vector field of $\mathbf{V}$ or, simply, "divergence $\mathbf{V}$" is a scalar quantity defined as

$$\text{div } \mathbf{V} = \frac{\partial V_x}{\partial x} + \frac{\partial V_y}{\partial y} + \frac{\partial V_z}{\partial z}. \qquad (2\text{-}11.1)$$

The curl of the vector field of $\mathbf{V}$ or, simply, "curl $\mathbf{V}$" is a vector quantity defined as

$$\text{curl } \mathbf{V} = \mathbf{i}\left(\frac{\partial V_z}{\partial y} - \frac{\partial V_y}{\partial z}\right) + \mathbf{j}\left(\frac{\partial V_x}{\partial z} - \frac{\partial V_z}{\partial x}\right) + \mathbf{k}\left(\frac{\partial V_y}{\partial x} - \frac{\partial V_x}{\partial y}\right).$$
$$(2\text{-}11.2)$$

The origin of the terms "divergence" and "curl" is connected with the study of the motion of fluids. Their physical significance may be illustrated with the aid of the following example. Suppose that water flows in some reservoir from certain points where it is being "produced" to certain points where it is being "consumed." The field of the water velocity $\mathbf{V}$ in this reservoir constitutes a vector field. If we calculated div $\mathbf{V}$ for different points of this field, we would find that div $\mathbf{V}$ is essentially a measure of the amount of water produced or consumed at these points, and that div **V** is zero everywhere except at the points where the water is produced or consumed. Similarly, we would find that curl **V** is a measure of the magnitude and direction of the rotation of the water in the reservoir. Experimentally, curl **V** can be manifested with the aid of a small paddle wheel immersed in the water. The wheel

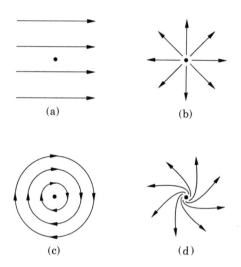

FIG. 2.15   Field lines of a vector field **V** near a point where

(a) div **V** = 0,   curl **V** = 0
(b) div **V** ≠ 0,   curl **V** = 0
(c) div **V** = 0,   curl **V** ≠ 0
(d) div **V** ≠ 0,   curl **V** ≠ 0.

turns when placed at points where curl **V** is not zero. The maximum angular velocity of the wheel is at all points proportional to curl **V** at these points, and the axis of rotation of the wheel is parallel to curl **V** when the wheel is so oriented that its angular velocity is a maximum.

   On field maps, the divergence is usually different from zero only at the points where the field lines originate or disappear, and the curl is usually different from zero only at the points surrounded by closed or spiralling field lines (Fig. 2.15).[1]

   A vector field whose divergence is everywhere zero is called a *solenoidal field*. A vector field whose curl is everywhere zero is called an *irrotational field*.

[1] Note, however, that on the map of the field **V** = $y\mathbf{i}$ all lines are straight, but curl **V** is everywhere different from zero.

▼

Example 2-11.1   Find the divergence and curl of the field of the position vector $\mathbf{r} = x\mathbf{i} + y\mathbf{j} + z\mathbf{k}$.

From the definition of divergence we have

$$\text{div } \mathbf{r} = \frac{\partial x}{\partial x} + \frac{\partial y}{\partial y} + \frac{\partial z}{\partial z} = 3.$$

Similarly, from the definition of curl we have

$$\text{curl } \mathbf{r} = \mathbf{i}\left(\frac{\partial z}{\partial y} - \frac{\partial y}{\partial z}\right) + \mathbf{j}\left(\frac{\partial x}{\partial z} - \frac{\partial z}{\partial x}\right) + \mathbf{k}\left(\frac{\partial y}{\partial x} - \frac{\partial x}{\partial y}\right) = 0.$$

▲

2-12. Operator ∇ ("del")

Operator, or symbolic vector, *del* is denoted by the symbol ∇ and is defined by the expression

$$\nabla = \mathbf{i}\frac{\partial}{\partial x} + \mathbf{j}\frac{\partial}{\partial y} + \mathbf{k}\frac{\partial}{\partial z}.$$

A "multiplication" of a scalar U or a vector $\mathbf{V}$ by this symbolic vector produces, respectively, the gradient of U or the divergence and curl of $\mathbf{V}$:

$$\nabla U = \mathbf{i}\frac{\partial U}{\partial x} + \mathbf{j}\frac{\partial U}{\partial y} + \mathbf{k}\frac{\partial U}{\partial z} = \text{grad } U,$$

$$\nabla \cdot \mathbf{V} = \frac{\partial V_x}{\partial x} + \frac{\partial V_y}{\partial y} + \frac{\partial V_z}{\partial z} = \text{div } \mathbf{V},$$

$$\nabla \times \mathbf{V} = \mathbf{i}\left(\frac{\partial V_z}{\partial y} - \frac{\partial V_y}{\partial z}\right) + \mathbf{j}\left(\frac{\partial V_x}{\partial z} - \frac{\partial V_z}{\partial x}\right)$$

$$+ \mathbf{k}\left(\frac{\partial V_y}{\partial x} - \frac{\partial V_x}{\partial y}\right) = \text{curl } \mathbf{V}.$$

It is often more convenient to express the gradient, the divergence, and the curl by means of the operator ∇ rather than by means of the previously introduced symbols. We shall use this operator frequently, writing

$$\nabla U \text{ instead of grad } U,$$
$$\nabla \cdot \mathbf{V} \text{ instead of div } \mathbf{V},$$
$$\nabla \times \mathbf{V} \text{ instead of curl } \mathbf{V}.$$

With the aid of the operator ∇ one can simplify many vector-analytical calculations. Since ∇ is both a symbolic vector and a differential operator, the rules for the calculations of expressions involving ∇ are a combination of the rules of vector algebra and vector differentiation. These rules can be summarized as follows:

(1) If ∇ precedes a sum $\sum a_i X_i$, where the a_i's are constants and the X_i's are point functions representing scalar or vector fields,[1] then

$$\nabla(\sum a_i X_i) = \sum a_i \nabla X_i.$$

(2) If ∇ precedes a product of point functions X, Y, and Z, then the calculation is done in two steps. First, the product is rewritten as the sum

$$\nabla(XYZ) = \nabla XY_c Z_c + \nabla X_c YZ_c + \nabla X_c Y_c Z,$$

where the original order of all the symbols is preserved and ∇ is applied to only one function in each product, different for each product, while the remaining functions are treated as constants, as indicated by the subscript "c." (This is called "differentiation by parts.") Second, the calculation is completed by transforming each product according to the rules of vector algebra so that all functions with subscript "c" precede ∇, and the subscripts are then dropped.

▼

Example 2-12.1

$$\text{div } (U\mathbf{V}) = \nabla \cdot (U\mathbf{V}) = \nabla \cdot U\mathbf{V}_c + \nabla \cdot U_c\mathbf{V} = \nabla U \cdot \mathbf{V}_c + U_c\nabla \cdot \mathbf{V}$$
$$= \mathbf{V} \cdot \nabla U + U\nabla \cdot \mathbf{V} = \mathbf{V} \cdot \text{grad } U + U \text{ div } \mathbf{V}.$$

Example 2-12.2

$$\text{div } (\mathbf{V} \times \mathbf{W}) = \nabla \cdot (\mathbf{V} \times \mathbf{W}) = \nabla \cdot \mathbf{V} \times \mathbf{W}_c + \nabla \cdot \mathbf{V}_c \times \mathbf{W}$$
$$= \nabla \times \mathbf{V} \cdot \mathbf{W}_c - \nabla \cdot \mathbf{W} \times \mathbf{V}_c = \nabla \times \mathbf{V} \cdot \mathbf{W}_c - \nabla \times \mathbf{W} \cdot \mathbf{V}_c$$
$$= \mathbf{W}_c \cdot \nabla \times \mathbf{V} - \mathbf{V}_c \cdot \nabla \times \mathbf{W} = \mathbf{W} \cdot \nabla \times \mathbf{V} - \mathbf{V} \cdot \nabla \times \mathbf{W}$$
$$= \mathbf{W} \cdot \text{curl } \mathbf{V} - \mathbf{V} \cdot \text{curl } \mathbf{W}.$$

Here we have used the properties of the box product of three vectors.

▲

Operator ∇ can operate upon itself as $(\nabla \cdot \nabla)$, $(\nabla \times \nabla)$, and $\nabla(X)$, where (X) is an expression already containing ∇. The first of these operations results in a new operator called the *Laplacian operator*, ∇^2,

$$(\nabla \cdot \nabla) = \nabla^2 = \frac{\partial^2}{\partial x^2} + \frac{\partial^2}{\partial y^2} + \frac{\partial^2}{\partial z^2}.$$

---

[1] X_i incorporates $\cdot$ or $\times$ in the case of vector fields.

The expression $\nabla^2 U$ is called the *Laplacian* of U. The second operation, $(\nabla \times \nabla)$, according to Section 2-6, produces a zero. The third operation depends on the nature of (X). A typical example of this operation is $\nabla \times (\nabla \times \mathbf{V})$; the application of the expansion formula (2-7.1) to this expression results in an important vector identity

$$\nabla \times (\nabla \times \mathbf{V}) = \nabla(\nabla \cdot \mathbf{V}) - \nabla^2 \mathbf{V}. \tag{2-12.1}$$

2-13. Fundamental Properties of Vector Fields

The fundamental properties of vector fields may be summarized with the aid of the following vector-analytical theorems.[1]

Gauss's Theorem. The flux integral of a vector point function $\mathbf{A}$ extended over a closed surface S is equal to the volume integral of div $\mathbf{A}$ extended over the volume bounded by the surface S

$$\oint \mathbf{A} \cdot d\mathbf{S} = \int \nabla \cdot \mathbf{A} \, dv. \tag{2-13.1}$$

Stokes's Theorem. The circulation integral of a vector point function $\mathbf{A}$ extended along a closed curve C is equal to the scalar surface integral of curl $\mathbf{A}$ extended over any surface bounded by the curve C

$$\oint \mathbf{A} \cdot d\mathbf{l} = \int \nabla \times \mathbf{A} \cdot d\mathbf{S}. \tag{2-13.2}$$

Helmholtz's Theorem. A vector field $\mathbf{V}$ is uniquely determined by its divergence and curl, $\nabla \cdot \mathbf{V}$ and $\nabla \times \mathbf{V}$, if they are given throughout all space and if $\mathbf{V}$ approaches zero at infinity at least as $1/(\text{distance})^2$, or, as one says, $\mathbf{V}$ is "regular at infinity."

Poisson's Theorem. A vector field $\mathbf{V}$, regular at infinity, can be expressed in terms of its divergence and curl as

$$\mathbf{V} = -\frac{1}{4\pi} \int_{\text{All space}} \frac{\nabla(\nabla \cdot \mathbf{V}) - \nabla \times (\nabla \times \mathbf{V})}{r} \, dv'. \tag{2-13.3}$$

Corollary: A vector field $\mathbf{V}$, regular at infinity, whose curl and divergence are zero outside a finite region of space, can be expressed as

$$\mathbf{V} = -\nabla \varphi + \nabla \times \mathbf{A}, \tag{2-13.4}$$

[1] Special considerations may be needed when applying these theorems to discontinuous fields. Proof of the theorems and a discussion of their limitations can be found in most texts on vector analysis. For simplicity, we do not always state these theorems and corollaries here in their most complete or most general forms, but instead use the forms ordinarily employed in physics texts.

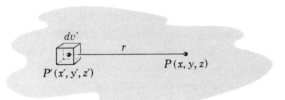

FIG. 2.16   Explanation of symbols used in Poisson integrals. The distance between the points P' and P is $r = \sqrt{(x - x')^2 + (y - y')^2 + (z - z')^2}$.

where φ, called the *scalar potential* of $\mathbf{V}$, is given by

$$\varphi = \frac{1}{4\pi} \int_{\text{All space}} \frac{\nabla \cdot \mathbf{V}}{r} \, dv' + \varphi_0, \qquad (2\text{-}13.5)$$

and $\mathbf{A}$, called the *vector potential* of $\mathbf{V}$, is given by

$$\mathbf{A} = \frac{1}{4\pi} \int_{\text{All space}} \frac{\nabla \times \mathbf{V}}{r} \, dv' + \mathbf{A}_0, \qquad (2\text{-}13.6)$$

φ_0 and $\mathbf{A}_0$ being arbitrary constants.[1] We shall call the integrals in Eqs. (2-13.3), (2-13.5), and (2-13.6) the *Poisson integrals*;[2] in them r represents the distance from the point $P'(x', y', z')$ where the volume element of integration, dv', is located to the point $P(x, y, z)$ where $\mathbf{V}$, φ, or $\mathbf{A}$ is being determined (Fig. 2.16).

Mathematical manipulations with vector fields frequently require applications of the operator ∇ to expressions of the type

$$\frac{f(x', y', z')}{\sqrt{(x - x')^2 + (y - y')^2 + (z - z')^2}},$$

occurring in Poisson integrals. When applying ∇ to such expressions one should keep in mind that they can be differentiated with respect to the primed coordinates as well as with respect to the unprimed coordinates. Whenever an explicit statement of the variables of differentiation is needed, one uses the primed operator ∇' to indicate an operation with respect to the primed coordinates and the ordinary operator ∇ to indicate an operation with respect to the unprimed

---

[1] $\mathbf{A}_0$ can be also a gradient of any scalar function. Since the curl of a gradient is zero, the choice of this function has no effect on $\mathbf{V}$ calculated from Eq. (2-13.4).

[2] In mathematical literature, the term "Poisson integral" is used for integrals of a different type.

coordinates. Similarly, if an explicit statement of the direction of radius vectors occurring in Poisson integrals is needed, one uses the primed vectors $\mathbf{r}'$ and $\mathbf{r}'_u$ to indicate a direction towards the point x', y', z', and the ordinary vectors $\mathbf{r}$ and $\mathbf{r}_u$ to indicate a direction towards the point x, y, z.

Designating an unspecified scalar or vector function $f(x', y', z')$ together with an appropriate multiplication sign by (X), and using the above notations, we have the following two operational relations:

$$\nabla' \frac{(X)}{r} = \frac{\nabla'(X)}{r} + \mathbf{r}_u \frac{(X)}{r^2} , \qquad (2\text{-}13.7)$$

where we have used the identity $\nabla' \dfrac{1}{r} = -\dfrac{\mathbf{r}'_u}{r^2} = \dfrac{\mathbf{r}_u}{r^2}$, and

$$\nabla \frac{(X)}{r} = -\mathbf{r}_u \frac{(X)}{r^2} . \qquad (2\text{-}13.8)$$

Combining these two relations, we obtain another useful relation:

$$\frac{\nabla'(X)}{r} = \nabla \frac{(X)}{r} + \nabla' \frac{(X)}{r} . \qquad (2\text{-}13.9)$$

▼

Example 2-13.1   Using Gauss's theorem, evaluate the integral $\oint x\mathbf{i} \cdot d\mathbf{S}$ over the surface of a cube of side a and compare the result with that of Example 2-8.2.

Since $\nabla \cdot (x\mathbf{i}) = 1$, we have by Gauss's theorem

$$\oint x\mathbf{i} \cdot d\mathbf{S} = \int \nabla \cdot (x\mathbf{i}) \, dv = \int dv = a^3.$$

The same result was obtained in Example 2-8.2 by direct integration.

Example 2-13.2   Using Stokes's theorem, evaluate the integral $\oint \mathbf{A} \cdot d\mathbf{l}$, where $\mathbf{A} = 2xy\mathbf{i} + x^2\mathbf{j}$, along the path shown in Fig. 2.12 and compare the result with that of Example 2-8.1.

The curl of $\mathbf{A}$ is

$$\nabla \times (2xy\mathbf{i} + x^2\mathbf{j}) = \mathbf{k}(2x - 2x) = 0,$$

so that by Stokes's theorem

$$\oint (2xy\mathbf{i} + x^2\mathbf{j}) \cdot d\mathbf{l} = \int \nabla \times (2xy\mathbf{i} + x^2\mathbf{j}) \cdot d\mathbf{S} = 0.$$

The same result was obtained in Example 2-8.1.

Example 2-13.3   Show that $\int \nabla U \, dv = \oint U \, d\mathbf{S}$.

Applying Gauss's theorem to the product $\mathbf{C}U$ where $\mathbf{C}$ is an arbitrary constant vector, we have

$$\int \nabla \cdot (\mathbf{C}U) \, dv = \oint \mathbf{C}U \cdot d\mathbf{S}.$$

Since $\nabla \cdot (\mathbf{C}U) = \mathbf{C} \cdot \nabla U$, we have, factoring $\mathbf{C}$ out from under the integral sign,

$$\mathbf{C} \cdot \int \nabla U \, dv = \mathbf{C} \cdot \oint U \, d\mathbf{S}.$$

Since $\mathbf{C}$ is arbitrary, this equation can hold only if (see Problem 2.12)

$$\int \nabla U \, dv = \oint U \, d\mathbf{S}.$$

Example 2-13.4   Show that $\int \nabla \times \mathbf{V} \, dv = -\oint \mathbf{V} \times d\mathbf{S}$.

Applying Gauss's theorem to the product $\mathbf{C} \times \mathbf{V}$ where $\mathbf{C}$ is an arbitrary constant vector, we have

$$\int \nabla \cdot (\mathbf{C} \times \mathbf{V}) \, dv = \oint \mathbf{C} \times \mathbf{V} \cdot d\mathbf{S}.$$

Since $\nabla \cdot (\mathbf{C} \times \mathbf{V}) = -\mathbf{C} \cdot (\nabla \times \mathbf{V})$, and since $\mathbf{C} \times \mathbf{V} \cdot d\mathbf{S} = \mathbf{C} \cdot \mathbf{V} \times d\mathbf{S}$, we obtain, factoring $\mathbf{C}$ out from under the integral sign,

$$-\mathbf{C} \cdot \int \nabla \times \mathbf{V} \, dv = \mathbf{C} \cdot \oint \mathbf{V} \times d\mathbf{S}.$$

Since $\mathbf{C}$ is arbitrary, this equation can hold only if

$$\int \nabla \times \mathbf{V} \, dv = -\oint \mathbf{V} \times d\mathbf{S}.$$

Example 2-13.5   Simplify $\nabla' \cdot \dfrac{\mathbf{V}}{r}$ and $\nabla' \times \dfrac{\mathbf{V}}{r}$.

Substituting $(\mathbf{X}) = \cdot\mathbf{V}$ and $(\mathbf{X}) = \times\mathbf{V}$ in Eq. (2-13.7), we have

$$\nabla' \cdot \frac{\mathbf{V}}{r} = \frac{\nabla' \cdot \mathbf{V}}{r} + \mathbf{r}_u \cdot \frac{\mathbf{V}}{r^2} \quad \text{and} \quad \nabla' \times \frac{\mathbf{V}}{r} = \frac{\nabla' \times \mathbf{V}}{r} + \mathbf{r}_u \times \frac{\mathbf{V}}{r^2}.$$

Example 2-13.6   Prove the corollary to Poisson's theorem.

Rewriting Poisson's theorem in terms of the primed operators (to avoid ambiguity) and using Eq. (2-13.9), we have

$$\mathbf{V} = -\frac{1}{4\pi}\int\frac{\boldsymbol{\nabla}'(\boldsymbol{\nabla}'\cdot\mathbf{V}) - \boldsymbol{\nabla}'\times(\boldsymbol{\nabla}'\times\mathbf{V})}{r}\,dv'$$

$$= -\frac{1}{4\pi}\int\boldsymbol{\nabla}\left(\frac{\boldsymbol{\nabla}'\cdot\mathbf{V}}{r}\right)dv' - \frac{1}{4\pi}\int\boldsymbol{\nabla}'\left(\frac{\boldsymbol{\nabla}'\cdot\mathbf{V}}{r}\right)dv'$$

$$+ \frac{1}{4\pi}\int\boldsymbol{\nabla}\times\left(\frac{\boldsymbol{\nabla}'\times\mathbf{V}}{r}\right)dv' + \frac{1}{4\pi}\int\boldsymbol{\nabla}'\times\left(\frac{\boldsymbol{\nabla}'\times\mathbf{V}}{r}\right)dv',$$

where all integrals are extended over all space. The second and the fourth integrals in the last expression can be transformed into surface integrals by the formulas of Examples 2-13.3 and 2-13.4. This gives

$$\int\boldsymbol{\nabla}'\left(\frac{\boldsymbol{\nabla}'\cdot\mathbf{V}}{r}\right)dv' = \oint\frac{\boldsymbol{\nabla}'\cdot\mathbf{V}}{r}\,d\mathbf{S}'$$

and

$$\int\boldsymbol{\nabla}'\times\left(\frac{\boldsymbol{\nabla}'\times\mathbf{V}}{r}\right)dv' = -\oint\left(\frac{\boldsymbol{\nabla}'\times\mathbf{V}}{r}\right)\times d\mathbf{S}'.$$

Now, $\boldsymbol{\nabla}'\cdot\mathbf{V}$ and $\boldsymbol{\nabla}'\times\mathbf{V}$, by the statement of the corollary, are different from zero only within a limited region of space. The surface of integration in the above surface integrals encloses, however, all space and thus is outside the region where $\boldsymbol{\nabla}'\cdot\mathbf{V}$ and $\boldsymbol{\nabla}'\times\mathbf{V}$ differ from zero. Hence $\boldsymbol{\nabla}'\cdot\mathbf{V}$ and $\boldsymbol{\nabla}'\times\mathbf{V}$ are zero everywhere on this surface, and the integrals vanish. We therefore obtain

$$\mathbf{V} = -\frac{1}{4\pi}\int_{\text{All space}}\boldsymbol{\nabla}\left(\frac{\boldsymbol{\nabla}'\cdot\mathbf{V}}{r}\right)dv' + \frac{1}{4\pi}\int_{\text{All space}}\boldsymbol{\nabla}\times\left(\frac{\boldsymbol{\nabla}'\times\mathbf{V}}{r}\right)dv'.$$

But the ordinary operator $\boldsymbol{\nabla}$ in these integrals can be factored out because the integration is done over the primed coordinates, upon which $\boldsymbol{\nabla}$ does not operate. Hence we have

$$\mathbf{V} = -\boldsymbol{\nabla}\left(\frac{1}{4\pi}\int_{\text{All space}}\frac{\boldsymbol{\nabla}'\cdot\mathbf{V}}{r}\,dv'\right) + \boldsymbol{\nabla}\times\left(\frac{1}{4\pi}\int_{\text{All space}}\frac{\boldsymbol{\nabla}'\times\mathbf{V}}{r}\,dv'\right).$$

Dropping the primes on $\boldsymbol{\nabla}'$ and designating the expressions in parentheses by $\varphi - \varphi_o$ and $\mathbf{A} - \mathbf{A}_o$, where φ_o and $\mathbf{A}_o$ are arbitrary constants, we then obtain the corollary to Poisson's theorem.

▲

2-14. Vector Wave Fields and Retarded Quantities*

Until now we have made no distinction between time-dependent and time-independent fields. Certain time-dependent fields have,

* This section is not essential for the understanding of the material presented in the chapters preceding Chapter 15. The study of this section may therefore be postponed until Chapter 15 is taken up.

however, special characteristic properties the knowledge of which is essential for an adequate mathematical treatment of these fields. An especially important time-dependent field is the *vector wave field*.

The vector wave field is the field of a vector **V** which satisfies the *general wave equation*

$$\mathbf{V} \times \mathbf{V} \times \mathbf{V} + \frac{1}{c^2} \frac{\partial^2 \mathbf{V}}{\partial t^2} = \mathbf{K}(x, y, z, t), \qquad (2\text{-}14.1)$$

where **K** is some vector function of space and time which, for simplicity, will be assumed here to be zero outside a finite region of space (this differential equation constitutes a mathematical expression for a wave-like disturbance that propagates in space with the speed c).

An important special property of a vector wave field is that this field can be represented not only by the ordinary Poisson integral of Eq. (2-13.3) and ordinary potentials defined in the preceding section, but also by the *retarded Poisson integral* and *retarded potentials*, as stated in the following theorem.

Wave Field Theorem.[1] A vector field **V** satisfying Eq. (2-14.1) and vanishing at infinity can be represented by the retarded Poisson integral as

$$\mathbf{V} = -\frac{1}{4\pi} \int\limits_{\text{All space}} \frac{[\mathbf{V}(\mathbf{V} \cdot \mathbf{V}) - \mathbf{K}]}{r} \, dv'. \qquad (2\text{-}14.2)$$

(*Note:* the brackets in this and in the following integrals are the "retardation symbol" to be explained below.)

Corollary I. A vector field **V** satisfying Eq. (2-14.1), vanishing at infinity, and having zero divergence outside a finite region of space can be represented by the retarded scalar potential φ^* and the retarded vector potential **A*** as

$$\mathbf{V} = -\nabla\varphi^* + \nabla \times \mathbf{A}^*, \qquad (2\text{-}14.3)$$

with φ^* and **A*** given by

$$\varphi^* = \frac{1}{4\pi} \int\limits_{\text{All space}} \frac{[\mathbf{V} \cdot \mathbf{V} + K_1]}{r} \, dv' + \varphi_{\circ}^* \qquad (2\text{-}14.4)$$

and

$$\mathbf{A}^* = \frac{1}{4\pi} \int\limits_{\text{All space}} \frac{[\mathbf{K}_2]}{r} \, dv' + \mathbf{A}_{\circ}^*, \qquad (2\text{-}14.5)$$

where K_1 and $\mathbf{K}_2$ are the ordinary potentials of the function **K** of

---

[1] See the footnote on page 42.

Eq. (2-14.1) (so that $\mathbf{K} = -\nabla K_1 + \nabla \times \mathbf{K}_2$), both vanishing at infinity, and φ_0^* and $\mathbf{A}_0^*$ are arbitrary constants.

Corollary II. A vector field $\mathbf{V}$ satisfying Eq. (2-14.1), vanishing at infinity, and having zero divergence outside a finite region of space can be represented by the retarded scalar potential φ^* and the retarded vector $\mathbf{W}^*$ as

$$\mathbf{V} = -\nabla\varphi^* + \mathbf{W}^*, \tag{2-14.6}$$

with

$$\varphi^* = \frac{1}{4\pi} \int_{\text{All space}} \frac{[\nabla \cdot \mathbf{V}]}{r}\, dv' + \varphi_0^* \tag{2-14.7}$$

and

$$\mathbf{W}^* = \frac{1}{4\pi} \int_{\text{All space}} \frac{[\mathbf{K}]}{r}\, dv' + \mathbf{W}_0^*, \tag{2-14.8}$$

where φ_0^* and $\mathbf{W}_0^*$ are arbitrary constants.

In order to clarify the meaning of the above expressions let us compare Eq. (2-14.2) with Eq. (2-13.3). As one can see, these equations are similar, except that the integral of Eq. (2-14.2) contains the retardation symbol [ ] that is not present in the integral of Eq. (2-13.3). This symbol indicates a special space and time dependence of the quantities to which it is applied and is defined by the identity

$$[f] \equiv f(x', y', z', t - r/c).$$

Therefore, whereas Eq. (2-13.3), written for a time dependent field, has the form

$$\mathbf{V}(x, y, z, t) = \frac{1}{4\pi} \int_{\text{All space}} \frac{\mathbf{f}(x', y', z', t)}{r}\, dv',$$

Eq. (2-14.2) has the form

$$\mathbf{V}(x, y, z, t) = \frac{1}{4\pi} \int_{\text{All space}} \frac{\mathbf{f}(x', y', z', t - r/c)}{r}\, dv'.$$

The basic difference between these equations is in the time dependence of the integrands appearing in the two integrals. In the first integral, the value of the integrand is that which the integrand has at the instant t for which $\mathbf{V}$ is being determined. In the second integral, on the other hand, the value of the integrand is *not* that which the integrand has at the instant t, but that which it *had* at some earlier instant $t' = t - r/c$, or, as one says, the integrand is retarded.

The integrals of retarded quantities are mathematical expressions reflecting the phenomenon of "finite signal speed"—that is, the fact that a certain time, $t = r/c$, must elapse before the result of some occurance at the point x', y', z' can be felt at the point x, y, z separated from the point x', y', z' by a distance r. The fact that wave fields can be expressed in terms of the retarded integrals is therefore plausible, since in wave fields physical effects are carried by waves, and waves propagate with finite speed.

Mathematical manipulations with wave fields frequently require applications of the operator ∇ to retarded point functions. When applying ∇ to such functions, one should take into account that they depend on space coordinates not only explicitly, but also implicitly through $r = \sqrt{(x - x')^2 + (y - y')^2 + (z - z')^2}$ appearing in the re- tarded time $t' = t - r/c$. One also should take into account that ∇ may operate with respect to x, y, z coordinates as well as with respect to x', y', z' coordinates. Finally, one should take into account that a ∇ operation may be performed upon a retarded point function taken at the instant $t = $ constant as well as at the instant $t' = t - r/c = $ constant (the latter operation is identical with the corresponding operation upon the same *unretarded* function, combined with the *subsequent* "retardation" of the resulting quantity by replacing in this quantity t by $t - r/c$).

In order to avoid ambiguities with ∇ operations we shall employ special notations, as follows. If an operation is to be performed with respect to primed coordinates, we shall use the primed operator ∇' in writing this operation. If an operation upon a retarded function is to be performed considering $t - r/c$ as being constant, we shall denote the operation as $[\nabla X]$ or $[\nabla' X]$, placing both the operator and the function upon which it operates between the retardation brackets. As before, we shall use the ordinary operator ∇ for operations with respect to unprimed coordinates, and we shall use the ordinary notations $\nabla[X]$ or $\nabla'[X]$ for operations upon retarded functions when these operations are to be performed considering t, rather than $t - r/c$, as being constant.

We shall now derive several useful operational equations for retarded functions.

Let us consider the operation $\partial[X]/\partial x'\big|_{y', z', t}$, where $[X]$ is some retarded scalar or vector point function.[1] Taking into account that retarded functions depend on x', y', and z' not only directly, but also indirectly through r, we can write

$$\frac{\partial[X]}{\partial x'}\bigg|_{y', z', t} = \frac{\partial[X]}{\partial x'}\bigg|_{y', z', t-r/c} + \frac{\partial[X]}{\partial(t - r/c)}\bigg|_{x', y', z'} \cdot \frac{\partial(t - r/c)}{\partial x'}.$$

[1] The notation $\big|_{y', z', t}$ means "y', z', t are held constant."

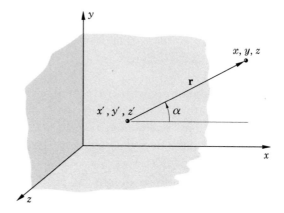

FIG. 2.17   The direction cosine of **r** with respect to the x-axis is $\cos \alpha = (x - x')/r$.

We can simplify the last term of this expression by observing that

$$\frac{\partial[X]}{\partial(t - r/c)}\bigg|_{x',y',z'} = \frac{\partial[X]}{\partial t}\bigg|_{x',y',z'},$$

and that

$$\frac{\partial(t - r/c)}{\partial x'} = \frac{x - x'}{cr} = \frac{\cos \alpha}{c},$$

where $\cos \alpha$ is the direction cosine of **r** with respect to the x-axis (Fig. 2.17). We then obtain

$$\frac{\partial[X]}{\partial x'}\bigg|_{y',z',t} = \frac{\partial[X]}{\partial x'}\bigg|_{y',z',t-r/c} + \frac{\cos \alpha}{c} \frac{\partial[X]}{\partial t}\bigg|_{x',y',z'}.$$

Analogous expressions can be obtained also for $\partial[X]/\partial y'|_{x',z',t}$ and for $\partial[X]/\partial z'|_{x',y',t}$. If we now multiply these expressions by **i**, **j**, and **k**, respectively, and then add them together, we obtain the following operational equation

$$\nabla'[X] = [\nabla'X] + \frac{\mathbf{r}_u}{c} \frac{\partial[X]}{\partial t}, \qquad (2\text{-}14.9)$$

where $\mathbf{r}_u = \mathbf{i} \cos \alpha + \mathbf{j} \cos \beta + \mathbf{k} \cos \gamma$ is the unit vector directed along r toward the point x, y, z.

    In a similar manner we can obtain the corresponding equation for the unprimed ∇ (assuming that X does not explicitly depend on x, y, z)

$$\nabla[X] = -\frac{\mathbf{r}_u}{c}\frac{\partial[X]}{\partial t}. \qquad (2\text{-}14.10)$$

Combining Eqs. (2-14.10) and (2-14.9), we obtain an equation correlating one unprimed ∇ operation with two primed ∇ operations

$$[\nabla'X] = \nabla[X] + \nabla'[X]. \qquad (2\text{-}14.11)$$

Using this equation, we obtain the correlation

$$\nabla\frac{[X]}{r} = -\frac{\mathbf{r}_u[X]}{r^2} + \frac{\nabla[X]}{r} = \frac{\mathbf{r}'_u[X]}{r^2} + \frac{[\nabla'X]}{r} - \frac{\nabla'[X]}{r},$$

and, combining the first and the last term of the last expression, we obtain a useful equation

$$\frac{[\nabla'X]}{r} = \nabla\frac{[X]}{r} + \nabla'\frac{[X]}{r}. \qquad (2\text{-}14.12)$$

▼

Example 2-14.1   Transform $\nabla' \cdot [\mathbf{F}]$ into an expression with $[\nabla' \cdot \mathbf{F}]$. Using Eq. (2-14.9), we have

$$\nabla' \cdot [\mathbf{F}] = [\nabla' \cdot \mathbf{F}] + \frac{\mathbf{r}_u}{c} \cdot \frac{\partial[\mathbf{F}]}{\partial t}.$$

Example 2-14.2   Transform $\nabla \times [\mathbf{F}]$ into operations with respect to the primed coordinates, if $[\mathbf{F}]$ is a function of x', y', z', and t'. Using Eq. (2-14.11), we have

$$\nabla \times [\mathbf{F}] = [\nabla' \times \mathbf{F}] - \nabla' \times [\mathbf{F}].$$

Example 2-14.3   Prove Corollary I to the wave field theorem, assuming that $\nabla \cdot \mathbf{V}$, K_1, and $\mathbf{K}_2$ are zero outside a finite region of space.

The proof of this corollary is analogous to the proof of the corollary to Poisson's theorem (Example 2-13.6). Rewriting Eq. (2-14.2) in terms of primed operators, expressing $\mathbf{K}$ as $\mathbf{K} = -\nabla K_1 + \nabla \times \mathbf{K}_2$, and using Eq. (2-14.12), we have

$$\mathbf{V} = -\frac{1}{4\pi}\int \frac{[\nabla'(\nabla' \cdot \mathbf{V}) - \mathbf{K}]}{r}\, dv'$$

$$= -\frac{1}{4\pi}\int \frac{[\nabla'(\nabla' \cdot \mathbf{V}) + \nabla'K_1 - \nabla' \times \mathbf{K}_2]}{r}\, dv'$$

$$= -\frac{1}{4\pi}\int \nabla\frac{[\nabla' \cdot \mathbf{V} + K_1]}{r}\, dv' - \frac{1}{4\pi}\int \nabla'\frac{[\nabla' \cdot \mathbf{V} + K_1]}{r}\, dv'$$

$$+ \frac{1}{4\pi}\int \nabla \times \frac{[\mathbf{K}_2]}{r}\, dv' + \frac{1}{4\pi}\int \nabla' \times \frac{[\mathbf{K}_2]}{r}\, dv'.$$

The second and the fourth integrals of the last expression can be transformed into surface integrals by formulas of Examples 2-13.3 and 2-13.4. This gives

$$\int \boldsymbol{\nabla}' \frac{[\boldsymbol{\nabla}' \cdot \mathbf{V} + K_1]}{r} \, dv' = \oint \frac{[\boldsymbol{\nabla}' \cdot \mathbf{V} + K_1]}{r} \, d\mathbf{S}'$$

and

$$\int \boldsymbol{\nabla}' \times \frac{[\mathbf{K}_2]}{r} \, dv' = -\oint \frac{[\mathbf{K}_2]}{r} \times d\mathbf{S}'.$$

But since $\boldsymbol{\nabla} \cdot \mathbf{V}$, K_1, and $\mathbf{K}_2$ are zero outside a finite region of space, while the surface integrals are taken over all space, the integrals vanish. We thus have

$$\mathbf{V} = -\frac{1}{4\pi} \int \boldsymbol{\nabla} \frac{[\boldsymbol{\nabla}' \cdot \mathbf{V} + K_1]}{r} \, dv' + \frac{1}{4\pi} \int \boldsymbol{\nabla} \times \frac{[\mathbf{K}_2]}{r} \, dv'.$$

Factoring $\boldsymbol{\nabla}$ out from under the integral signs and designating the resulting integrals by $\varphi^* - \varphi_\circ^*$ and $\mathbf{A}^* - \mathbf{A}_\circ^*$, we obtain Corollary I to the wave field theorem.

Example 2-14.4   Prove Corollary II to the wave field theorem.
    As in the preceding example, we have

$$\mathbf{V} = -\frac{1}{4\pi} \int \frac{[\boldsymbol{\nabla}'(\boldsymbol{\nabla}' \cdot \mathbf{V}) - \mathbf{K}]}{r} \, dv' = -\frac{1}{4\pi} \int \boldsymbol{\nabla} \frac{[\boldsymbol{\nabla}' \cdot \mathbf{V}]}{r} \, dv'$$

$$-\frac{1}{4\pi} \int \boldsymbol{\nabla}' \frac{[\boldsymbol{\nabla}' \cdot \mathbf{V}]}{r} \, dv' + \frac{1}{4\pi} \int \frac{[\mathbf{K}]}{r} \, dv'.$$

The second integral of the last expression is, as before, zero. We thus have

$$\mathbf{V} = -\frac{1}{4\pi} \int \boldsymbol{\nabla} \frac{[\boldsymbol{\nabla}' \cdot \mathbf{V}]}{r} \, dv' + \frac{1}{4\pi} \int \frac{[\mathbf{K}]}{r} \, dv'$$

$$= -\boldsymbol{\nabla}\left(\frac{1}{4\pi} \int \frac{[\boldsymbol{\nabla}' \cdot \mathbf{V}]}{r} \, dv'\right) + \frac{1}{4\pi} \int \frac{[\mathbf{K}]}{r} \, dv'.$$

Designating the first integral by $\varphi^* - \varphi_\circ^*$ and the second integral by $\mathbf{W}^* - \mathbf{W}_\circ^*$, we obtain Corollary II to the wave field theorem.   ▲

2-15. Vector Expressions in Curvilinear Orthogonal Coordinates

Many physical problems require the use of *curvilinear orthogonal* coordinates for their solution. The most frequently used curvilinear orthogonal coordinates are the circular cylindrical coordinates (Fig. 2.18) and the spherical coordinates (Fig. 2.19). The three unit vectors in the system of circular cylindrical coordinates are $\mathbf{z}_u$, $\mathbf{r}_u$, and $\boldsymbol{\theta}_u$; they point in the direction of increasing z, r, and θ, respectively. Similarly, in the system of spherical coordinates the unit vectors are $\mathbf{r}_u$, $\boldsymbol{\theta}_u$, and $\boldsymbol{\phi}_u$; they point in the direction of increasing r, θ, and ϕ.

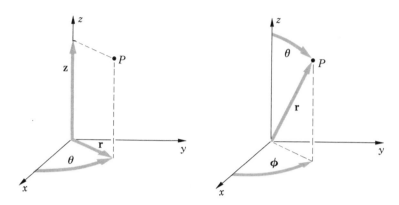

FIG. 2.18   Cylindrical coordinates.   FIG. 2.19   Spherical coordinates.

The expressions of vector algebra developed for the system of Cartesian coordinates can be extended to an arbitrary system of orthogonal coordinates. So, for instance, in any system defined by a set of three orthogonal unit vectors $\mathbf{a}_1$, $\mathbf{a}_2$, and $\mathbf{a}_3$ the dot product can be written as

$$\mathbf{A} \cdot \mathbf{B} = A_1 B_1 + A_2 B_2 + A_3 B_3, \qquad (2\text{-}15.1)$$

and the cross product can be written as

$$\mathbf{A} \times \mathbf{B} = \begin{vmatrix} \mathbf{a}_1 & \mathbf{a}_2 & \mathbf{a}_3 \\ A_1 & A_2 & A_3 \\ B_1 & B_2 & B_3 \end{vmatrix}, \qquad (2\text{-}15.2)$$

which follows directly from the definition of these products.

Also, the expressions of vector analysis defined for the system of Cartesian coordinates can be extended to an arbitrary system of orthogonal coordinates. The expressions for the gradient, divergence, curl, and Laplacian in the three most common coordinate systems are given in Table 2-I. The method for obtaining vector analytical expressions in general orthogonal coordinate systems is described below.

Let us first consider the gradient. Since grad U is a vector whose component in any direction represents the rate of change of U in that direction, we can write

$$\nabla U = \frac{\partial U}{\partial s_1} \mathbf{a_1} + \frac{\partial U}{\partial s_2} \mathbf{a_2} + \frac{\partial U}{\partial s_3} \mathbf{a_3},$$

where ∂s_1, ∂s_2, ∂s_3 are the differential elements of distance in the directions of the unit vectors $\mathbf{a_1}$, $\mathbf{a_2}$, and $\mathbf{a_3}$, respectively. Obviously, these differential elements are not always equal to the increments of the corresponding coordinates. For example, in the spherical system of coordinates the element of distance in the direction of $\mathbf{\theta}_u$ is $r\,d\theta$, rather than $d\theta$. In general, if q_1, q_2, and q_3 are the three coordinates of an orthogonal system, then the corresponding differential elements of distance ds_1, ds_2, ds_3 can be expressed as

$$ds_1 = h_1 dq_1, \qquad ds_2 = h_2 dq_2, \qquad ds_3 = h_3 dq_3,$$

where h_1, h_2, and h_3 are some multipliers ("metric coefficients"), functions of q_1, q_2, and q_3. The general expression for grad U in any orthogonal system of coordinates is therefore

$$\nabla U = \frac{\partial U}{h_1\,\partial q_1} \mathbf{a_1} + \frac{\partial U}{h_2\,\partial q_2} \mathbf{a_2} + \frac{\partial U}{h_3\,\partial q_3} \mathbf{a_3}.$$

Before deriving general expressions for divergence and curl, we shall prove that the divergence and curl of a vector field are independent of the system of coordinates used for their representation (the gradient, of course, is also independent of the system of coordinates, as follows from the fact that the gradient represents the rate of change of a function in the direction of the fastest change).

TABLE 2–I
Vector Operations in Cartesian, Cylindrical, and Spherical Coordinates

Cartesian Coordinates	Cylindrical Coordinates

Line elements:

dx, dy, dz	$dr, r\,d\theta, dz$

Components of gradient:

$\mathrm{grad}_x\, U = \dfrac{\partial U}{\partial x}$	$\mathrm{grad}_r\, U = \dfrac{\partial U}{\partial r}$
$\mathrm{grad}_y\, U = \dfrac{\partial U}{\partial y}$	$\mathrm{grad}_\theta\, U = \dfrac{1}{r}\dfrac{\partial U}{\partial \theta}$
$\mathrm{grad}_z\, U = \dfrac{\partial U}{\partial z}$	$\mathrm{grad}_z\, U = \dfrac{\partial U}{\partial z}$

Divergence:

$\mathrm{div}\,\mathbf{A} = \dfrac{\partial A_x}{\partial x} + \dfrac{\partial A_y}{\partial y} + \dfrac{\partial A_z}{\partial z}$	$\mathrm{div}\,\mathbf{A} = \dfrac{1}{r}\dfrac{\partial}{\partial r}(rA_r) + \dfrac{1}{r}\dfrac{\partial A_\theta}{\partial \theta} + \dfrac{\partial A_z}{\partial z}$

TABLE 2–I (Continued)

Components of curl:

$$\text{curl}_x \, \mathbf{A} = \frac{\partial A_z}{\partial y} - \frac{\partial A_y}{\partial z} \qquad\qquad \text{curl}_r \, \mathbf{A} = \frac{1}{r}\frac{\partial A_z}{\partial \theta} - \frac{\partial A_\theta}{\partial z}$$

$$\text{curl}_y \, \mathbf{A} = \frac{\partial A_x}{\partial z} - \frac{\partial A_z}{\partial x} \qquad\qquad \text{curl}_\theta \, \mathbf{A} = \frac{\partial A_r}{\partial z} - \frac{\partial A_z}{\partial r}$$

$$\text{curl}_z \, \mathbf{A} = \frac{\partial A_y}{\partial x} - \frac{\partial A_x}{\partial y} \qquad\qquad \text{curl}_z \, \mathbf{A} = \frac{1}{r}\left[\frac{\partial}{\partial r}(rA_\theta) - \frac{\partial A_r}{\partial \theta}\right]$$

Laplacian:

$$\nabla^2 U = \frac{\partial^2 U}{\partial x^2} + \frac{\partial^2 U}{\partial y^2} + \frac{\partial^2 U}{\partial z^2} \qquad\qquad \nabla^2 U = \frac{1}{r}\frac{\partial}{\partial r}\left(r\frac{\partial U}{\partial r}\right) + \frac{1}{r^2}\frac{\partial^2 U}{\partial \theta^2} + \frac{\partial^2 U}{\partial z^2}$$

Spherical coordinates

Line elements:

$$dr, \; r\,d\theta, \; r\sin\theta\,d\phi$$

Components of gradient:

$$\text{grad}_r \, U = \frac{\partial U}{\partial r}$$

$$\text{grad}_\theta \, U = \frac{1}{r}\frac{\partial U}{\partial \theta}$$

$$\text{grad}_\phi \, U = \frac{1}{r\sin\theta}\frac{\partial U}{\partial \phi}$$

Divergence:

$$\text{div} \, \mathbf{A} = \frac{1}{r^2}\frac{\partial(r^2 A_r)}{\partial r} + \frac{1}{r\sin\theta}\frac{\partial(\sin\theta\,A_\theta)}{\partial \theta} + \frac{1}{r\sin\theta}\frac{\partial A_\phi}{\partial \phi}$$

Components of curl:

$$\text{curl}_r \, \mathbf{A} = \frac{1}{r\sin\theta}\left[\frac{\partial(\sin\theta\,A_\phi)}{\partial \theta} - \frac{\partial A_\theta}{\partial \phi}\right]$$

$$\text{curl}_\theta \, \mathbf{A} = \frac{1}{r}\left[\frac{1}{\sin\theta}\frac{\partial A_r}{\partial \phi} - \frac{\partial(rA_\phi)}{\partial r}\right]$$

$$\text{curl}_\phi \, \mathbf{A} = \frac{1}{r}\left[\frac{\partial(rA_\theta)}{\partial r} - \frac{\partial A_r}{\partial \theta}\right]$$

Laplacian:

$$\nabla^2 U = \frac{1}{r^2}\frac{\partial}{\partial r}\left(r^2\frac{\partial U}{\partial r}\right) + \frac{1}{r^2\sin\theta}\frac{\partial}{\partial \theta}\left(\sin\theta\frac{\partial U}{\partial \theta}\right) + \frac{1}{r^2\sin^2\theta}\frac{\partial^2 U}{\partial \phi^2} \; .$$

Let us apply Gauss's theorem (2-13.1) to a very small volume element Δv. As Δv goes to zero, the volume integral approaches $(\mathbf{V} \cdot \mathbf{A}) \Delta v$, and we obtain for $\mathbf{V} \cdot \mathbf{A}$

$$\mathbf{V} \cdot \mathbf{A} = \lim_{\Delta v \to 0} \frac{\oint \mathbf{A} \cdot d\mathbf{S}}{\Delta v} , \qquad (2\text{-}15.3)$$

which is an expression obviously independent of any system of coordinates. Similarly, applying the relation derived in Example 2-13.4 to a very small volume element Δv, we obtain for $\mathbf{V} \times \mathbf{A}$

$$\mathbf{V} \times \mathbf{A} = - \lim_{\Delta v \to 0} \frac{\oint \mathbf{A} \times d\mathbf{S}}{\Delta v} , \qquad (2\text{-}15.4)$$

which shows that the curl of a vector field is also independent of the choice of coordinates.

The above two formulas are considered to be the definitions of divergence and curl in general orthogonal coordinate systems and are used for obtaining differential formulas for divergence and curl in these systems.

The expression for divergence in terms of general orthogonal curvilinear coordinates is obtained from Eq. (2-15.3) by evaluating the integral $\oint \mathbf{A} \cdot d\mathbf{S}$ over the surface of an infinitesimal volume element $dv = h_1 dq_1 \cdot h_2 dq_2 \cdot h_3 dq_3$ and by dividing this integral by dv. The result is

$$\mathbf{V} \cdot \mathbf{A} = \frac{1}{h_1 h_2 h_3} \left[\frac{\partial}{\partial q_1} (h_2 h_3 A_1) + \frac{\partial}{\partial q_2} (h_3 h_1 A_2) + \frac{\partial}{\partial q_3} (h_1 h_2 A_3) \right] .$$

The expression for curl in terms of general orthogonal curvilinear coordinates is similarly obtained from Eq. (2-15.4) by evaluating the integral $\oint \mathbf{A} \times d\mathbf{S}$ over the surface of an infinitesimal volume element dv and by dividing this integral by dv. The result is

$$\mathbf{V} \times \mathbf{A} = \begin{vmatrix} \dfrac{\mathbf{a}_1}{h_2 h_3} & \dfrac{\mathbf{a}_2}{h_3 h_1} & \dfrac{\mathbf{a}_3}{h_1 h_2} \\[2mm] \dfrac{\partial}{\partial q_1} & \dfrac{\partial}{\partial q_2} & \dfrac{\partial}{\partial q_3} \\[2mm] h_1 A_1 & h_2 A_2 & h_3 A_3 \end{vmatrix} .$$

The Laplacian of a scalar is obtained by combining the above expressions for the divergence and gradient. The result is

$$\nabla^2 U = \mathbf{V} \cdot \mathbf{V} U = \frac{1}{h_1 h_2 h_3} \left[\frac{\partial}{\partial q_1} \left(\frac{h_2 h_3}{h_1} \frac{\partial U}{\partial q_1} \right) + \frac{\partial}{\partial q_2} \left(\frac{h_3 h_1}{h_2} \frac{\partial U}{\partial q_2} \right) \right. $$
$$\left. + \frac{\partial}{\partial q_3} \left(\frac{h_1 h_2}{h_3} \frac{\partial U}{\partial q_3} \right) \right] .$$

From these general equations the explicit expressions for the gradient, divergence, curl, and Laplacian may be readily determined for any system of orthogonal coordinates.

2-16. Vector Identities

We shall conclude this chapter by tabulating various especially important vector-analytical identities. In these identities φ and U are scalar point functions; $\mathbf{A}$, $\mathbf{B}$, and $\mathbf{V}$ are vector point functions; X is a scalar or vector point function of primed coordinates and incorporates an appropriate multiplication sign.

Identities for the calculation of gradient

(V-1)
$$\nabla(\varphi U) = \varphi \nabla U + U \nabla \varphi$$

(V-2)
$$\nabla(\mathbf{A} \cdot \mathbf{B}) = (\mathbf{A} \cdot \nabla)\mathbf{B} + \mathbf{A} \times (\nabla \times \mathbf{B})$$
$$+ (\mathbf{B} \cdot \nabla)\mathbf{A} + \mathbf{B} \times (\nabla \times \mathbf{A})$$

(V-3)
$$\nabla\varphi(U_1 \cdots U_n) = \sum_{i=1}^{n} \frac{\partial \varphi}{\partial U_i} \nabla U_i$$

Identities for the calculation of divergence

(V-4)
$$\nabla \cdot (\varphi \mathbf{A}) = \varphi \nabla \cdot \mathbf{A} + \mathbf{A} \cdot \nabla \varphi$$

(V-5)
$$\nabla \cdot (\mathbf{A} \times \mathbf{B}) = \mathbf{B} \cdot \nabla \times \mathbf{A} - \mathbf{A} \cdot \nabla \times \mathbf{B}$$

(V-6)
$$\nabla \cdot \mathbf{A}(U_1 \cdots U_n) = \sum_{i=1}^{n} \frac{\partial \mathbf{A}}{\partial U_i} \cdot \nabla U_i$$

Identities for the calculation of curl

(V-7)
$$\nabla \times (\varphi \mathbf{A}) = \varphi \nabla \times \mathbf{A} + \nabla\varphi \times \mathbf{A}$$

(V-8)
$$\nabla \times (\mathbf{A} \times \mathbf{B}) = (\mathbf{B} \cdot \nabla)\mathbf{A} + \mathbf{A}(\nabla \cdot \mathbf{B})$$
$$- (\mathbf{A} \cdot \nabla)\mathbf{B} - \mathbf{B}(\nabla \cdot \mathbf{A})$$

(V-9)
$$\nabla \times \mathbf{A}(U_1 \cdots U_n) = \sum_{i=1}^{n} \nabla U_i \times \frac{\partial \mathbf{A}}{\partial U_i}$$

Repeated application of ∇

(V-10)
$$\nabla \cdot (\nabla \times \mathbf{A}) = 0$$

(V-11)
$$\nabla \times \nabla U = 0$$

(V-12)
$$\nabla \times (\nabla \times \mathbf{A}) = \nabla(\nabla \cdot \mathbf{A}) - \nabla^2 \mathbf{A}$$

(V-13)
$$\nabla^2(\nabla \times \mathbf{A}) = \nabla \times (\nabla^2 \mathbf{A})$$

(V-14)
$$\nabla^2(\nabla\varphi) = \nabla(\nabla^2\varphi)$$

Identities for the calculation of line and surface integrals

(V-15) $\oint \mathbf{A} \cdot d\mathbf{l} = \int \nabla \times \mathbf{A} \cdot d\mathbf{S}$ (Stokes's theorem)

(V-16) $\oint U \, d\mathbf{l} = \int d\mathbf{S} \times \nabla U$

(V-17) $\oint \mathbf{A}(\mathbf{B} \cdot d\mathbf{l}) = \int d\mathbf{S} \times [(\nabla \cdot \mathbf{B})\mathbf{A} + (\mathbf{B} \cdot \nabla)\mathbf{A}]$

(V-18) $\oint \mathbf{A} \times d\mathbf{l} = \int \nabla \cdot \mathbf{A} \, d\mathbf{S} - \int \nabla(\mathbf{A} \cdot d\mathbf{S})$

Identities for the calculation of surface and volume integrals

(V-19) $\oint \mathbf{A} \cdot d\mathbf{S} = \int \nabla \cdot \mathbf{A} \, dv$ (Gauss's theorem)

(V-20) $\oint U \, d\mathbf{S} = \int \nabla U \, dv$

(V-21) $\oint \mathbf{A} \times d\mathbf{S} = - \int \nabla \times \mathbf{A} \, dv$

(V-22) $\frac{1}{2} \oint A^2 d\mathbf{S} - \oint \mathbf{A}(\mathbf{A} \cdot d\mathbf{S}) = \int [\mathbf{A} \times (\nabla \times \mathbf{A}) - \mathbf{A}(\nabla \cdot \mathbf{A})] \, dv$

(V-23) $\oint \mathbf{A}(\mathbf{B} \cdot d\mathbf{S}) = \int [(\nabla \cdot \mathbf{B})\mathbf{A} + (\mathbf{B} \cdot \nabla)\mathbf{A}] \, dv$

The following identities are called the first, second, and third Green's theorem, respectively:

(V-24) $\oint U_1 \nabla U_2 \cdot d\mathbf{S} = \int (U_1 \nabla^2 U_2 + \nabla U_1 \cdot \nabla U_2) \, dv$

(V-25) $\oint (U_1 \nabla U_2 - U_2 \nabla U_1) \cdot d\mathbf{S} = \int (U_1 \nabla^2 U_2 - U_2 \nabla^2 U_1) \, dv$

(V-26) $\oint \nabla U \cdot d\mathbf{S} = \int \nabla^2 U \, dv$

Poisson's theorem

(V-27) $\mathbf{V} = -\frac{1}{4\pi} \int_{\text{All space}} \frac{\nabla(\nabla \cdot \mathbf{V}) - \nabla \times (\nabla \times \mathbf{V})}{r} \, dv'$

Operations with ∇ in Poisson integrals

(V-28) $\nabla' \frac{(\mathrm{X})}{r} = \frac{\nabla'(\mathrm{X})}{r} + \mathbf{r}_u \frac{(\mathrm{X})}{r^2}$ (V-29) $\nabla \frac{(\mathrm{X})}{r} = -\mathbf{r}_u \frac{(\mathrm{X})}{r^2}$

(V-30) $\frac{\nabla'(\mathrm{X})}{r} = \nabla \frac{(\mathrm{X})}{r} + \nabla' \frac{(\mathrm{X})}{r}$

Vector wave field theorem

(V-31) $$\mathbf{V} = -\frac{1}{4\pi} \int\limits_{\text{All space}} \frac{[\mathbf{\nabla}(\mathbf{\nabla} \cdot \mathbf{V}) - \mathbf{K}]_{\text{ret}}}{r} \, dv'$$

Operations with $\mathbf{\nabla}$ in retarded Poisson integrals

(V-32) $$\mathbf{\nabla}'[\mathrm{X}]_{\text{ret}} = [\mathbf{\nabla}'\mathrm{X}]_{\text{ret}} + \frac{\mathbf{r}_u}{c} \frac{\partial [\mathrm{X}]_{\text{ret}}}{\partial t}$$

(V-33) $$\mathbf{\nabla}[\mathrm{X}]_{\text{ret}} = -\frac{\mathbf{r}_u}{c} \frac{\partial [\mathrm{X}]_{\text{ret}}}{\partial t}$$

(V-34) $$[\mathbf{\nabla}'\mathrm{X}]_{\text{ret}} = \mathbf{\nabla}[\mathrm{X}]_{\text{ret}} + \mathbf{\nabla}'[\mathrm{X}]_{\text{ret}}$$

(V-35) $$\frac{[\mathbf{\nabla}'\mathrm{X}]_{\text{ret}}}{r} = \mathbf{\nabla}\frac{[\mathrm{X}]_{\text{ret}}}{r} + \mathbf{\nabla}'\frac{[\mathrm{X}]_{\text{ret}}}{r}$$

Vector operations in the form independent of coordinate systems

(V-36) $\mathbf{\nabla}U = \lim\limits_{\Delta v \to 0} \dfrac{\oint U \, d\mathbf{S}}{\Delta v}$ (V-37) $\mathbf{\nabla} \cdot \mathbf{A} = \lim\limits_{\Delta v \to 0} \dfrac{\oint \mathbf{A} \cdot d\mathbf{S}}{\Delta v}$

(V-38) $$\mathbf{\nabla} \times \mathbf{A} = -\lim\limits_{\Delta v \to 0} \frac{\oint \mathbf{A} \times d\mathbf{S}}{\Delta v}$$

(V-39) $$\nabla^2 U = \lim\limits_{\Delta v \to 0} \frac{\oint \mathbf{\nabla}U \cdot d\mathbf{S}}{\Delta v}$$

PROBLEMS

2.1. Show by vector methods that the diagonals of a parallelogram bisect each other.

2.2. Show by vector methods that the line which joins one vertex of a parallelogram with the midpoint of an opposite side intersects a diagonal in a point of trisection.

2.3. Show by vector methods that the diameter of a circle subtends a right angle at any point of the circumference.

2.4. Using vector methods derive the formulas

$$\sin (\alpha - \beta) = \sin \alpha \cos \beta - \cos \alpha \sin \beta,$$
$$\cos (\alpha \pm \beta) = \cos \alpha \cos \beta \mp \sin \alpha \sin \beta.$$

2.5. Using vector methods derive the law of sines for a triangle.

2.6. Prove the identity

$$\mathbf{A} \times (\mathbf{B} \times \mathbf{C}) = \mathbf{B}(\mathbf{A} \cdot \mathbf{C}) - \mathbf{C}(\mathbf{A} \cdot \mathbf{B}).$$

2.7. Show that the components of a vector $\mathbf{B}$ in the direction parallel and perpendicular to a vector $\mathbf{A}$ are given by

$$\mathbf{B}_{\|} = \frac{(\mathbf{A} \cdot \mathbf{B})\mathbf{A}}{A^2}, \qquad \mathbf{B}_{\perp} = \frac{(\mathbf{A} \times \mathbf{B}) \times \mathbf{A}}{A^2}.$$

2.8. Show that the solution of the two simultaneous vector equations $\mathbf{x} \cdot \mathbf{a} = b$ and $\mathbf{x} \times \mathbf{a} = \mathbf{c}$ can be written as

$$\mathbf{x} = \frac{b\mathbf{a} + \mathbf{a} \times \mathbf{c}}{a^2}.$$

2.9. Show that the solution of the vector equation

$$x\mathbf{a} + y\mathbf{b} + z\mathbf{c} = \mathbf{d}$$

can be written as

$$x = \frac{\mathbf{d} \cdot \mathbf{b} \times \mathbf{c}}{\mathbf{a} \cdot \mathbf{b} \times \mathbf{c}}, \qquad y = \frac{\mathbf{a} \cdot \mathbf{d} \times \mathbf{c}}{\mathbf{a} \cdot \mathbf{b} \times \mathbf{c}}, \qquad z = \frac{\mathbf{a} \cdot \mathbf{b} \times \mathbf{d}}{\mathbf{a} \cdot \mathbf{b} \times \mathbf{c}},$$

and determine the geometrical significance of this solution.

2.10. Find the projection of the vector $\mathbf{A} = 3\mathbf{i} + \mathbf{j} - 8\mathbf{k}$ upon the vector $\mathbf{B} = 2\mathbf{i} + 2\mathbf{j} + \mathbf{k}$.

2.11. Find the angle between vectors $\mathbf{A}$ and $\mathbf{B}$ if

$$\mathbf{A} = \mathbf{j} + \mathbf{k} \quad \text{and} \quad \mathbf{B} = \mathbf{i} + \mathbf{j}.$$

2.12. Show that if $\mathbf{C} \cdot \mathbf{B} = \mathbf{C} \cdot \mathbf{A}$ for any $\mathbf{C}$, then $\mathbf{B} \equiv \mathbf{A}$.

2.13. Show that $\oint d\mathbf{l}$ is always zero.

2.14. Show that $\oint d\mathbf{S}$ is always zero.

2.15. Show that grad $U(r) = \dfrac{dU}{dr} \mathbf{r}_u$.

2.16. Show that for any potential field $\mathbf{F} = -\nabla \varphi$

$$\int_a^b \mathbf{F} \cdot d\mathbf{l} = \varphi_a - \varphi_b \quad \text{and} \quad \oint \mathbf{F} \cdot d\mathbf{l} = 0,$$

where φ_a and φ_b are the values of the potential φ at the points a and b, respectively.

2.17. Find curl $(xy\mathbf{i} + yz\mathbf{j} + zx\mathbf{k})$.

2.18. Find the curl and the divergence of $r\mathbf{r}$.

2.19. Prove the identity (V-2).

2.20. Prove the identity (V-8).

2.21. Show that in spherical coordinates $\nabla \cdot \mathbf{r}_u = \dfrac{2}{r}$.

2.22. Show that $\nabla \times f(r)\mathbf{r}_u$ is always zero.

2.23. Find the curl and the divergence of the vector

$$\mathbf{V} = \frac{\mathbf{r}}{r} \ln \frac{c}{r}.$$

2.24. Find the curl and the divergence of the vector

$$\mathbf{V} = \mathbf{A}(x, y, z) \sin [U(x, y, z)].$$

2.25. Prove that in spherical coordinates $(\mathbf{A} \cdot \nabla)\mathbf{r} = \mathbf{A}$.

2.26. Show that $\nabla^2(\nabla\varphi) = \nabla(\nabla^2\varphi)$.

2.27. Show that $\nabla^2(\nabla \times \mathbf{A}) = \nabla \times (\nabla^2\mathbf{A})$.

2.28. Show that $\nabla^2(\varphi U) = \varphi\nabla^2 U + 2(\nabla\varphi) \cdot (\nabla U) + U\nabla^2\varphi$.

2.29. Prove the identity (V-16).

2.30. Prove the identity (V-18) by applying Stokes's theorem to the vector $\mathbf{A} \times \mathbf{C}$, where $\mathbf{C}$ is an arbitrary constant vector.

2.31. Prove the identity (V-23) by applying Gauss's theorem to $A_x\mathbf{B}$, $A_y\mathbf{B}$, and $A_z\mathbf{B}$. Then prove the identity (V-17).

2.32. Prove the identity (V-22) by using identities (V-23), (V-20), and (V-2).

2.33. Derive the three Green's theorems from Gauss's theorem.

2.34. Show that $\oint \nabla \times \mathbf{A} \cdot d\mathbf{S} = \oint \nabla U \times d\mathbf{S}$ for any $\mathbf{A}$ and U.

2.35. Show that grad U can be expressed as

$$\nabla U = \lim_{\Delta v \to 0} \frac{\oint U \, d\mathbf{S}}{\Delta v}.$$

2.36. Show that the distance r_{12} between any two points P_1 and P_2 may be expressed as $|\mathbf{r}_1 - \mathbf{r}_2|$, where $\mathbf{r}_1$ and $\mathbf{r}_2$ are the vectors connecting the origin of coordinates with the points P_1 and P_2, respectively. Then show that the vector $\mathbf{r}_{12}$ directed from point P_1 to point P_2 may be expressed in terms of the coordinates of the two points as

$$\mathbf{r}_{12} = (x_2 - x_1)\mathbf{i} + (y_2 - y_1)\mathbf{j} + (z_2 - z_1)\mathbf{k}.$$

2.37. Show that for $c \to \infty$, the vector wave field theorem reduces to Poisson's theorem, and the corollaries to the vector wave field theorem reduce to the corollary to Poisson's theorem if $\nabla \times \mathbf{V} = 0$ outside a finite region of space.

2.38. Show that for $c \to \infty$, the identity (V-35) reduces to the identity (V-30).

2.39. Show that for $c \to \infty$, the identities (V-32), (V-33), and (V-34) reduce to correct expressions for the corresponding unretarded operations.

2.40. Using the correlation $\mathbf{A} = n\mathbf{B}$ for two parallel vectors, derive the differential equation for the field lines of a map of a vector field $\mathbf{V}$

$$\frac{dx}{V_x} = \frac{dy}{V_y} = \frac{dz}{V_z}.$$

2.41. A solid body rotates with angular velocity $\boldsymbol{\omega}$ about a symmetry axis. Show that within the body

$$\nabla \times \mathbf{v} = 2\boldsymbol{\omega} \, ,$$

where $\mathbf{v}$ is the linear velocity of a point in the body.

2.42. Show that in the vicinity of the point (x_0, y_0, z_0) the Taylor series for the function $\mathbf{F}(x', y', z')$ can be expressed as

$$\mathbf{F}(x', y', z') = \mathbf{F}(x_0, y_0, z_0) + (\mathbf{h} \cdot \nabla')\mathbf{F}(x_0, y_0, z_0) + \frac{1}{2!} (\mathbf{h} \cdot \nabla')^2\mathbf{F}(x_0, y_0, z_0) +$$

$$\frac{1}{3!} (\mathbf{h} \cdot \nabla')^3\mathbf{F}(x_0, y_0, z_0) + \ldots,$$

where $\mathbf{h}$ is the vector from the point (x_0, y_0, z_0) to the point (x', y', z').

SUPPLEMENTARY READING

BRAND, L.: *Vector Analysis,* John Wiley and Sons, New York (1957).

DAVIS, H. F.: *Introduction to Vector Analysis,* Allyn and Bacon, Boston (1961).

SCHWARTZ, M., GREEN, S., and RUTLEDGE, W. A. *Vector Analysis,* Harper and Brothers, New York (1960).

SPIEGEL, M. R.: *Outline of Theory and Problems of Vector Analysis,* Schaum, New York (1959).

II

ELECTROMAGNETIC THEORY

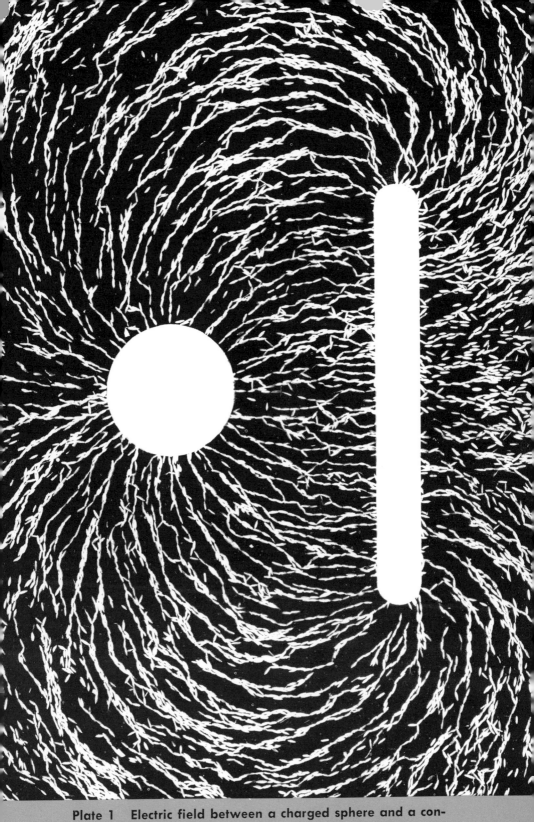

Plate 1 Electric field between a charged sphere and a conducting plate. (Plates 1 to 9 are lines-of-force pictures formed by grass seeds. Plates 10, 11, and 12 are lines-of-force pictures formed by iron fillings.)

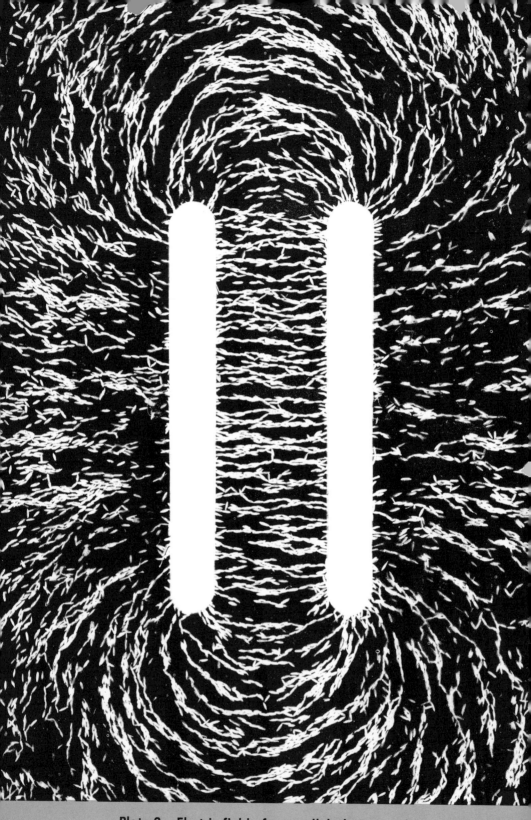

Plate 2   Electric field of a parallel-plate capacitor.

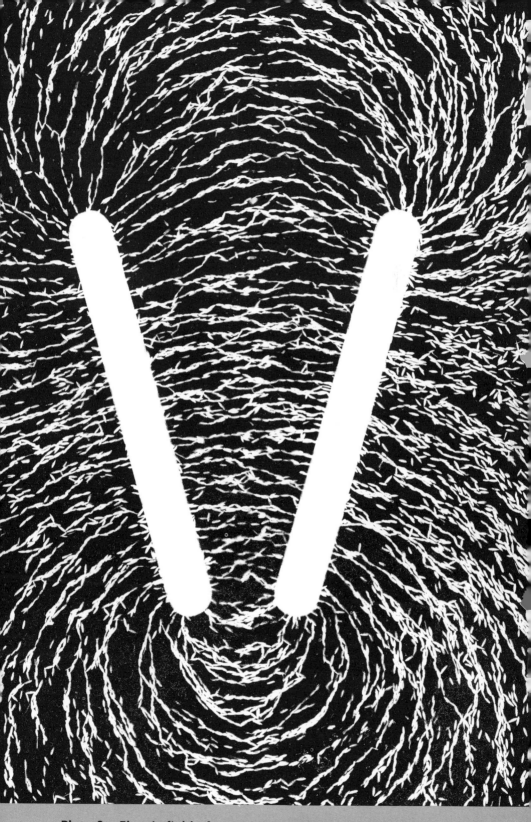

Plate 3   Electric field of a capacitor with nonparallel plates.

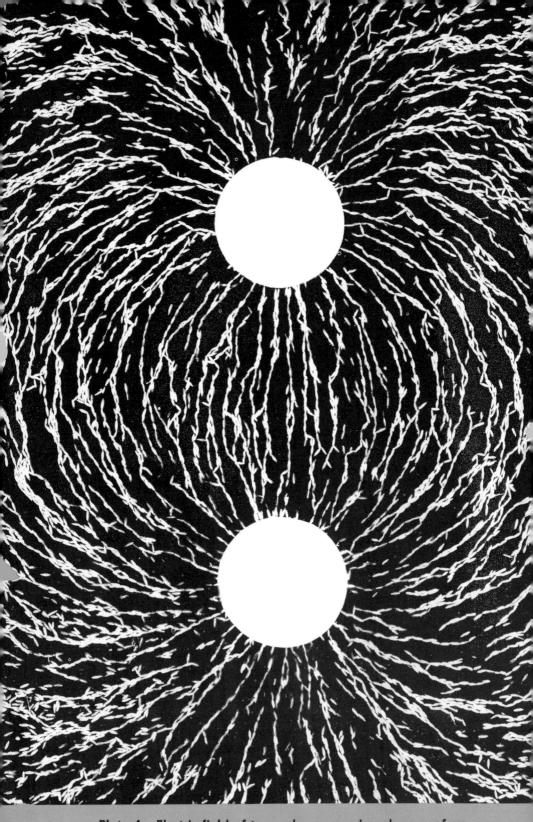

Plate 4   Electric field of two spheres carrying charges of opposite sign.

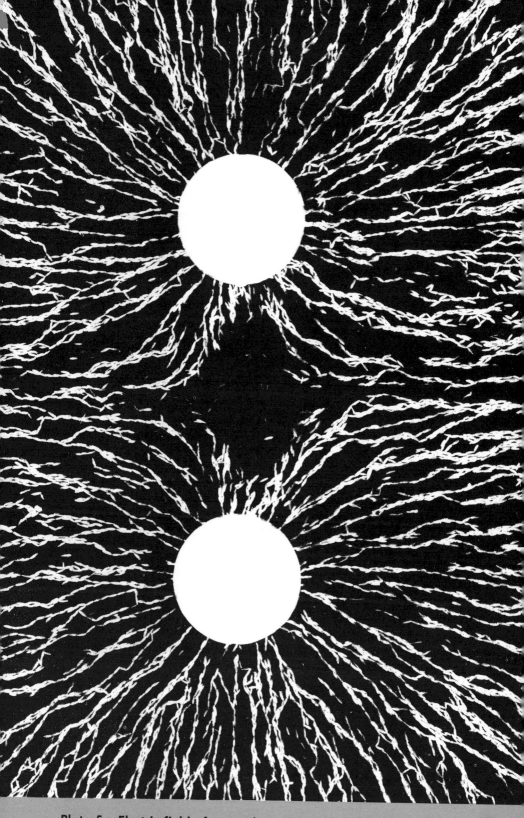

Plate 5   Electric field of two spheres carrying charges of the same sign.

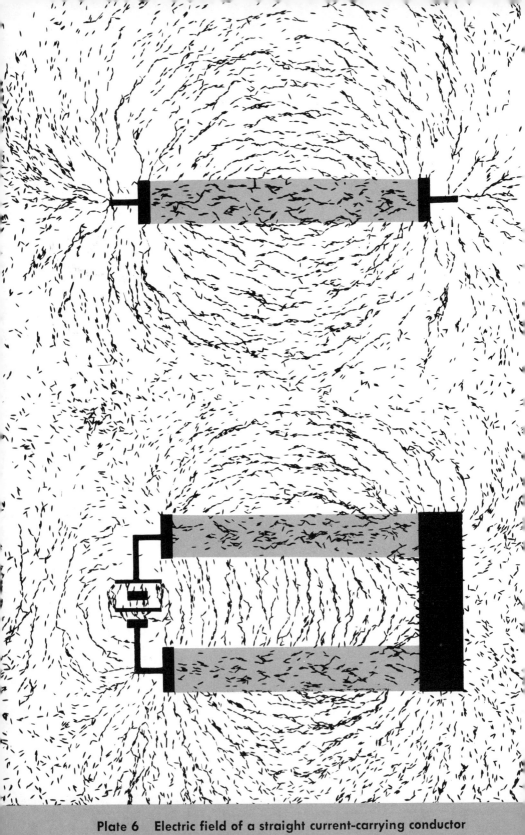

Plate 6   Electric field of a straight current-carrying conductor (above) and of two shorted current-carrying conductors (below).

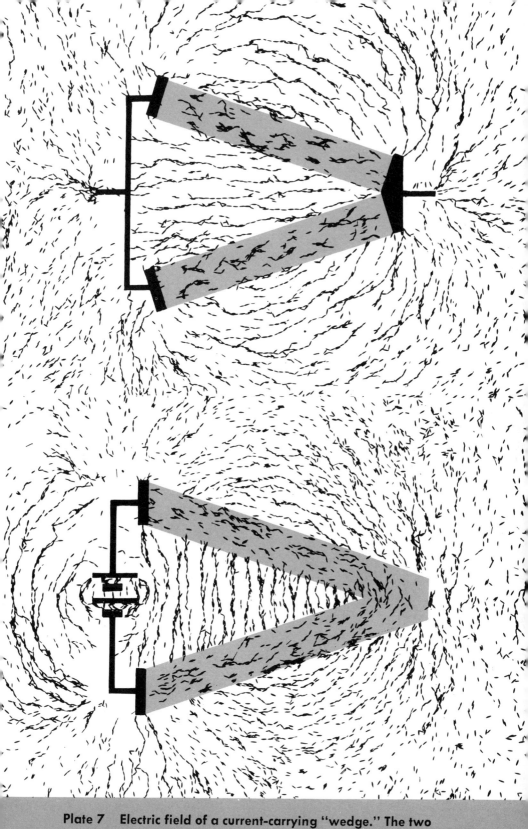

Plate 7   Electric field of a current-carrying "wedge." The two halves are connected in parallel (above) and in series (below).

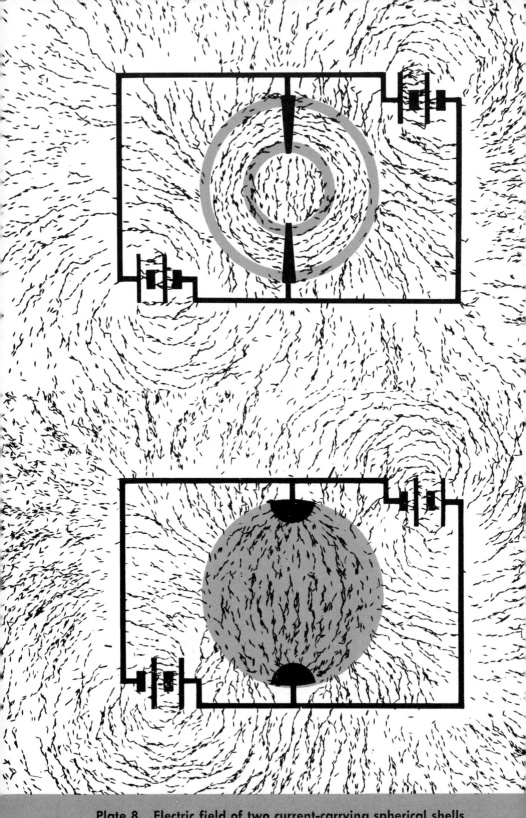

Plate 8   Electric field of two current-carrying spherical shells
(above) and of a current-carrying sphere (below) with two-
pole connections.

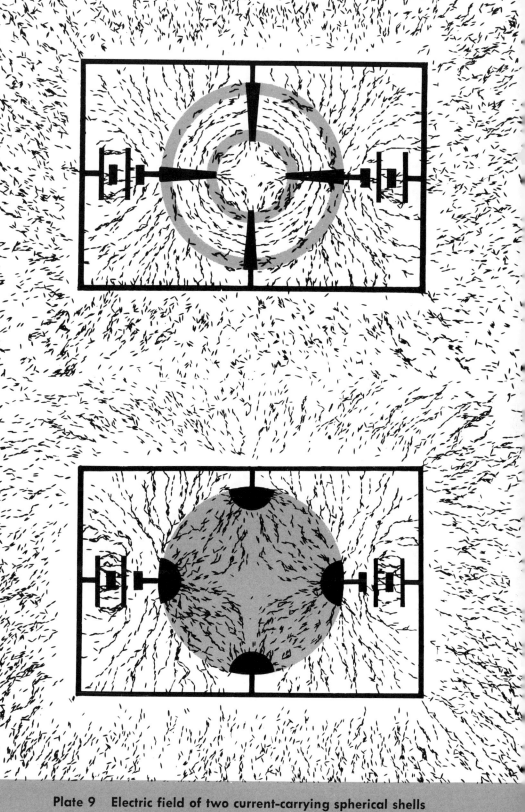

Plate 9   Electric field of two current-carrying spherical shells (above) and of a current-carrying sphere (below) with four-pole connections.

Plate 10　Magnetic field of a spherical magnet (dipole field).

Plate 11   Magnetic field of a short bar-magnet (dipole field).

Plate 12 Magnetic field of two short bar-magnets (quad-rupole field).

3

QUANTITATIVE
INVESTIGATION OF
ELECTRIC AND MAGNETIC
PHENOMENA

In spite of the enormous variety of presently known physical phenomena, most of them can be interpreted as the necessary consequence of only a few fundamental interdependences between physical quantities. These fundamental interdependences are called *fundamental laws*. The determination of these laws in the domain of electric and magnetic phenomena, the study of their immediate consequences, and the study of methods of their application to the solution of concrete physical problems is the main task of electromagnetic theory. There are many ways in which electromagnetic theory can be developed and presented. In this chapter we shall discuss the path chosen in this book.

3-1. Landmarks in the History of Macroscopic Electromagnetic Theory

The systematic study of electric and magnetic phenomena began about the year 1600 when William Gilbert published his book *De Magnete* in which he described his experiments in electricity and magnetism and introduced the word "electricity." The mathematical analysis of electric and magnetic phenomena began, however, only late in the eighteenth century when Charles Coulomb, on the basis of careful measurements, postulated in 1785 his famous force law for electric charges

$$F = k \frac{q_1 q_2}{r^2}$$

(F is the force, k is a constant of proportionality, q_1 and q_2 are the charges, and r is the separation between them). The striking similarity of Coulomb's law to Newton's gravitational law gave rise to mechanical theories of electricity and magnetism which adopted the mathematical apparatus previously developed for gravitational systems. In these "action at a distance" theories, Coulomb's law for electric charges and a similar law for magnetic poles were regarded as the principal laws, and all electric and magnetic phenomena were thought to be deducible from them. The action-at-a-distance theories were not fruitful, however, and helped little towards a better understanding or utilization of electricity and magnetism.

Drastic changes in the interpretation of electric and magnetic phenomena were brought about by Michael Faraday, who founded the concepts of electric and magnetic fields. During the years 1821–1848, he performed and studied a number of electric and magnetic experiments and came to the conclusion that the carriers of electric and magnetic actions were the regions of space around electric charges and magnets. These regions of space, or "fields," could be represented by field-line models.

In 1855, James Clerk Maxwell translated Faraday's ideas about electric and magnetic fields into a mathematical form. Later he succeeded in generalizing the basic facts of macroscopic electromagnetism into a set of fundamental laws for electromagnetic fields. A direct mathematical consequence of these laws was the equations indicating the existence of electromagnetic waves propagating with the velocity of light. In 1886, such waves were discovered by Heinrich Hertz, and this discovery was the first triumph of the "field theory" of electric and magnetic phenomena.

Faraday-Maxwell's field theory, clarified, perfected, and expanded by many other physicists, constitutes the contemporary electromagnetic theory of macroscopic systems. The presentation of the fundamentals of this theory is the main purpose of this book.

3-2. Three Types of Basic Electric and Magnetic Laws

We shall develop the electromagnetic theory in three steps. First of all, in agreement with the considerations presented in Chapter I, we shall select basic measurables, instruments, and standards for the quantitative investigation of electric and magnetic phenomena. Then we shall study elementary groups of these phenomena in the order of increasing complexity and shall obtain the corresponding sets of elementary fundamental laws capable of explaining all individual phenomena within the limits of each group. Finally we shall combine these sets of elementary fundamental laws into one set of general fundamental laws capable of explaining all presently known macroscopic electromagnetic phenomena.

We shall need three types of fundamental electric and magnetic laws, as follows.

Field Laws. The two most important objects of study in the domain of electric and magnetic phenomena are the electric and magnetic vector fields. Therefore we shall need a set of fundamental laws representing the properties of these fields. We shall call these laws *field laws.*

Two questions now arise: (1) what kind of correlations should these laws represent? (2) how many correlations are sufficient for a unique specification of the fields under consideration?

An answer to both these questions is given by Helmholtz's theorem of vector analysis. According to this theorem, a vector field is uniquely determined by its curl and its divergence (provided that the field is regular at infinity, which is almost always the case). A complete set of field laws for a vector field will be obtained therefore once the divergence equation, or the *divergence law*, and the curl equation, or the *curl law*, are found for all points of the field under consideration.

This set of *differential laws* can be replaced, however, by an equivalent set of *integral laws*. Indeed, by Gauss's theorem, a divergence equation $\nabla \cdot \mathbf{V} = U$ valid for all points of space can be expressed as a flux integral equation $\oint \mathbf{V} \cdot d\mathbf{S} = \int U \, dv$ valid for all regions of space, and vice versa. Similarly, by Stokes's theorem, a curl equation $\nabla \times \mathbf{V} = \mathbf{W}$ valid for all points of space can be expressed as a circulation integral equation $\oint \mathbf{V} \cdot d\mathbf{l} = \int \mathbf{W} \cdot d\mathbf{S}$ valid for all regions of space, and vice versa. Therefore the circulation integral equation, or the *circulation law*, and the flux integral equation, or the *flux law*, constitute a complete alternative set of field laws uniquely specifying a vector field.

Divergence, curl, circulation, and flux laws are the laws upon which we shall base the theory of electric and magnetic fields.

Interaction Laws. Field laws determine the properties of fields but do not give any information about the electric and magnetic interactions between particles or bodies. These interactions play, however, a very important role in electric and magnetic phenomena. Therefore we shall also need magnetic and electric *interaction laws*.

The most general electric and magnetic interaction laws must be applicable to all possible systems of particles or bodies and must be independent of any specific system, structure, or configuration. As we shall see, it is possible to obtain such general interaction laws in the form of energy equations, or *energy laws*, expressed in terms of electric and magnetic fields. The energy laws are the laws upon which we shall base the theory of electric and magnetic interactions.

Constitutive, or *Auxiliary*, *Laws*. We shall study electric and magnetic phenomena in various material media. The laws reflecting electric and magnetic properties of the media are called *constitutive*, or *auxiliary*, laws. They are the third type of basic laws that we shall need.[1]

3-3. Basic Measurables in Electricity and Magnetism

At the time when the first quantitative investigations of electric and magnetic phenomena were conducted, no electric or magnetic instruments were known. Almost all quantitative information had to be obtained through measurements of mechanical quantities with the aid of mechanical instruments.[2] For a long time the three mechanical measurables—length, mass, and time—were used as the only basic measurables and were even believed to constitute the ultimate system of basic measurables.

Later it was found that electric and magnetic phenomena could be investigated much more easily with the aid of special electric and magnetic instruments. It was also found that the description of these phenomena became much simpler and clearer if new electric or magnetic basic measurables were used together with the old mechanical ones. Finally, it was realized that there can be no ultimate system of basic measurables and that one should therefore use the system which serves its purpose best.[3]

---

[1] The constitutive laws are not as fundamental as the field laws and the interaction laws. When the electromagnetic properties of matter are investigated on a microscopic scale, the differences in many macroscopic electromagnetic phenomena reflected by the constitutive laws appear as the differences in the atomic and molecular structure of various physical bodies rather than as the differences in the nature of electromagnetic phenomena occurring in these bodies.

[2] Compare with footnote 1 on page 71.

[3] The common systems of basic measurables are described in Section 1-5.

Modern scientists obtain their knowledge about electric and magnetic phenomena mainly through the measurements of two electric quantities—current and voltage—and use current meters and voltage meters as basic tools for experimental investigations of these phenomena. In fact, measurements of current and voltage are the basic sources of quantitative information in almost any branch of modern experimental sciences. It is therefore natural to adopt formally current and voltage as the new basic measurables and to use them alongside with other basic measurables such as, for instance, length, mass (or force), and time. This system of five basic measurables (the *LMTVI* system) is now generally used in experimental physics and is also most appropriate for the mathematical representation of physical phenomena. It is the system which we shall use throughout this book.[1]

3-4. Current as a Basic Measurable

In order to use current and voltage as basic measurables, we must first of all specify the properties that are attributed to them and that are used for their identification and qualitative definition.

The characteristic properties of that which we call current, or, more accurately, *electric current*, can be demonstrated with the aid of the three following experiments.

Magnetic Property. If a wire is placed near a compass needle and is then connected to the terminals of a battery, the needle deflects from its initial position, just as it would if a magnet were placed near it. This magnetic action is attributed to the electric current produced in the wire by the battery and is regarded as the first characteristic property of electric current.

Thermal Property. If several turns of wire are wound around a thermometer, and the wire is connected to a battery, the thermometer shows that the wire heats up. Also, this thermal action is attributed to the current in the wire and is regarded as the second characteristic property of current.

[1] It must be emphasized that the separation of measurables into basic and secondary is merely a matter of practical expedience and has nothing to do with the establishment of ranks or priorities of some physical quantities or concepts relative to others. Thus, for instance, the fact that we consider here current, rather than charge, as a basic measurable does not mean that we regard current as a quantity more (or less) important or fundamental than charge; it merely means that we regard a direct measurement of current as more expedient or convenient than that of charge.

Chemical Property. If two wires are inserted in a glass containing water, and if one end of each wire is then connected to a battery, small bubbles of gas begin to rise from the submerged ends of the wires. As the two previous effects, this chemical action too is attributed to electric current and is regarded as its third characteristic property.

On the basis of these three experiments we shall define electric current qualitatively as that which manifests itself by the magnetic, thermal, and chemical action in the manner described above.[1]

A closer examination of the chemical action of electric current in water shows that the current decomposes water into its components: oxygen and hydrogen. In this process oxygen is liberated at the surface of one wire while hydrogen is liberated at the surface of the other wire. Thus the two wires and therefore the two terminals of the battery to which the wires are connected cause different chemical effects. This means that the two terminals of a battery are electrically different. By international agreement, the hydrogen-delivering terminal is called the *negative terminal* and is designated by the − sign; the oxygen-delivering terminal is called the *positive terminal* and is designated by the + sign.

The difference between the two terminals of a battery expresses itself also in the magnetic action of electric current. If in the experiment with the compass needle the battery connections of the wire were reversed, so that the end previously connected to the + terminal is now connected to the − terminal, and the end previously connected to the − terminal is now connected to the + terminal, the compass needle would change its deflection by 180 degrees. This effect is interpreted by assigning a direction to the electric current (as the word "current" indicates) and is attributed to the reversal of the current in the wire that takes place when the connections of the wire are reversed. By convention, the current outside the battery is considered as being always directed from the positive to the negative terminal.

Current Meters. Ballistic Current Meters. Like any basic measurable, electric current must be defined quantitatively by specifying the instruments with which it can be measured.

All three characteristic properties of current can be used for its measurement. One can construct current meters, or *galvanometers,*

---

[1] A definition in physics is never an explanation. A qualitative definition is merely the statement of a verbal convention; a quantitative definition is the statement of the rules of measurements or calculations.

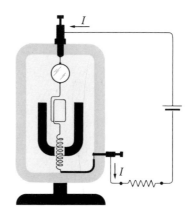

FIG. 3.1 D'Arsonval galvanometer.
This galvanometer utilizes the magnetic
property of electric current.

based on the magnetic, thermal, or chemical action of the electric
current.[1] The most widely used current meters are, however, based on
magnetic action.

A typical current meter based on the magnetic action of electric
current is the d'Arsonval meter shown in Fig. 3.1. In this meter the
current causes an angular deflection of the coil placed between the
poles of a magnet and is measured by this deflection. The deflection
of the coil is indicated on a scale either by a pointer or, in more
sensitive instruments, by a beam of light reflected from a mirror
attached to the coil.

An important property of the d'Arsonval meter is that it can also
be used as a *ballistic current meter*, that is, as an instrument that measures
directly the current × time integral, or the *current-impulse integral*, $\int I\,dt$.

The international unit of electric current is the *ampere*. A current
of n amperes may be defined as the current that liberates $n \times 1.1180$
milligrams of silver from an aqueous solution of $AgNO_3$ in one second.[2]
A current meter calibrated in amperes is called an *ammeter*.

[1] Strictly speaking, to these three actions, or properties, of current one should
add the property of causing a characteristic physiological sensation which makes it
possible to "feel" the current. Strange as it may seem, this property of current can
also be used for electric measurements—for instance, for measurements in bridge
circuits employing the "null method." In fact, it is reported that two centuries ago
Henry Cavendish by "feeling" the current determined the relative conductivity
of different substances with accuracy unsurpassed for almost one hundred years.
This, incidentally, shows clearly that a quantitative study of physical phenomena is
possible without mechanical instruments or devices.

[2] See the footnote on page 73.

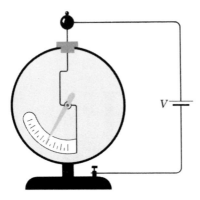

FIG. 3.2 Braun electrometer. This electrometer utilizes the force-producing property of voltage.

3-5. Voltage as a Basic Measurable

The characteristic properties of that which we call *voltage* can be demonstrated with the aid of the following two experiments.

Force-Producing Property. If two pieces of aluminum foil suspended by threads one near the other are connected by two wires to the terminals of a battery, these pieces attract each other (the battery should have several hundred individual cells in order to make the motion of the foil visible under class-room conditions). If the battery is changed, the force of attraction changes. The ability of a battery to produce force is attributed to the voltage generated by the battery, and the force-producing property is regarded as the first characteristic property of voltage.

Current-Producing Property. If a wire is connected to the terminals of a battery, electric current is produced in the wire. If the battery is changed, the current changes. Also the ability of a battery to produce current is attributed to the voltage generated by the battery. The current-producing property is therefore regarded as the second characteristic property of voltage.

On the basis of these two experiments we shall define the voltage qualitatively as that which manifests itself by the force and current action in the manner described above.

Voltage Meters. Ballistic Voltage Meters. For the quantitative definition of voltage we must specify the instruments with which it can be measured.

Both characteristic properties of voltage can be used for its measurement. Voltage meters based on the force-producing property of voltage are called *electrostatic voltage meters,* or *electrometers.* A typical electrostatic voltage meter is the Braun electrometer shown in Fig. 3.2. In this electrometer a light aluminum pointer is attached to a metal rod which is inserted into a metal chamber. If a voltage is applied between the rod and the chamber, the pointer is attracted to the wall of the chamber that it faces and diverges from the rod. The deflection of the pointer is read on a scale and is a measure of the applied voltage.

With the voltage meters based on the current-producing property of voltage, voltage is measured by the current that it produces. These voltage meters are in principle ordinary current meters calibrated, however, in units of voltage rather than in units of current. The most widely used voltage meter of this type is the d'Arsonval meter already described. The d'Arsonval meter can also be used as a *ballistic voltage meter* to measure the *voltage-impulse integral* $\int V \, dt$.

The international unit of voltage is the *volt.* A voltage of n volts may be defined as $1/1.0186$ of the voltage produced by n Cd-Hg standard (Weston Normal) cells connected in series.[1] A voltage meter calibrated in volts is called a *voltmeter.*

---

[1] For the legal definition of the volt and the ampere in the United States the reader is referred to the publications of the National Bureau of Standards.

4

ELECTROSTATIC FIELD
IN VACUUM

We shall now begin the study of the elementary groups of electric and magnetic phenomena. In this chapter we shall study electric fields associated with stationary electric charges in vacuum and shall familiarize ourselves with the basic properties of these fields as well as with some typical problems involving these properties.

4-1. Electric Charges

Let us connect one terminal of a ballistic galvanometer to a terminal of a battery (Fig. 4.1). If we now take a small metal plate attached to a plastic handle (test plate), touch with this plate the open terminal of the battery, and then move the plate over to the open terminal of the galvanometer, we find that the galvanometer registers a current impulse at the moment when the plate touches its terminal.[1]

Thus we can transport from the battery to the galvanometer something which produces a current impulse in the galvanometer. This transportable "something" has been named *electric charge*. The charge is called *positive* if it comes from the positive terminal of a battery and is called *negative* if it comes from the negative terminal.

Let us now repeat the experiment on charge transportation, this time using a double plate consisting of two equal test plates laid one

[1] The battery should have several hundred individual cells to make the effect visible under classroom conditions.

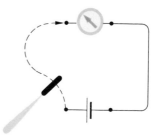

FIG. 4.1   Electric charges can be transported
on a test plate.

over the other. If after touching the battery we separate the two
plates, thus dividing the charge equally between them, we find that
the galvanometer, when touched by each plate separately, registers
only half as strong a current impulse as that which it registers when
touched by the two plates when they are not separated. This means
that electric charge can be measured by the current impulse produced
by it.

Using this result, we shall define electric charge quantitatively as
follows: *an electric charge q is measured by and is equal to the current impulse*
∫I dt that it produces. We thus have

$$q = \int I \, dt. \tag{4-1.1}$$

According to this definition, the units of the electric charge are amp · sec
(these units are usually called "coulomb").

If, continuing our experiments with charges, we completely dis-
connect the galvanometer from the battery and use two test plates for
the simultaneous transportation of a positive charge to one terminal
of the galvanometer and a negative charge to the other terminal, we
find that the galvanometer registers the same current impulse which it
registered when one of its terminals was connected to the battery. This
shows that the wire connecting the galvanometer to the battery per-
forms the same function as a test plate does: it transports charges from
the battery to the galvanometer, or "conducts" them.

Substances and bodies capable of conducting electric charges well
are called *conductors*. Substances and bodies that do not conduct
electric charges well are called *insulators*, or *dielectrics*.

A fundamental property of the electric charge is the property of
conservation. Experiments show that no net electric charge can be
created or destroyed. Electric charges can be only separated or
combined, positive and negative charges always appearing or dis-
appearing in equal quantities.

Many electric and magnetic phenomena depend on how electric charges are distributed in the free space and in the interior of material bodies. The distribution of electric charges is described with the aid of the *volume charge density*, the *surface charge density*, and the *line charge density*. The volume charge density ρ is defined as

$$\rho = \frac{dq}{dv},\tag{4-1.2}$$

where dq is the charge contained in the infinitesimal volume element dv. The surface charge density σ is defined as

$$\sigma = \frac{dq}{dS},\tag{4-1.3}$$

where dq is the charge contained in the infinitesimal surface element of area dS. The line charge density λ is similarly defined as

$$\lambda = \frac{dq}{dl},\tag{4-1.4}$$

where dq is the charge contained in the infinitesimal length element dl.

Electric phenomena associated with stationary charge distributions are called *electrostatic phenomena*, and electric systems in which there are no moving charges and no currents are called *electrostatic systems*.

4-2. Electric Field and Electric Field Vector E

Let us take two metal plates supported by insulating stands, place them opposite each other, and charge them by connecting each plate to a terminal of a battery. If we then charge a small pith ball suspended on an insulating string and place this pith ball between the two plates, we find that in the space between the plates the ball deflects from its normal vertical position (Fig. 4.2). This deflection of the ball is attributed to a special force acting on the electric charge carried by the ball. It is called the *electric force*. A region of space where an electric charge at rest experiences electric force (such as the region between the two charged plates) is called an *electric field*.

Electric fields surround all electric charges and accompany all charged bodies. Electric fields of various characteristics can be obtained by using appropriately arranged charge distributions or by using charged bodies of various shapes. Especially convenient for this purpose

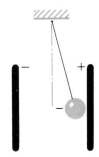

FIG. 4.2 A charged pith ball pendulum deflects in an electric field.

are pairs of oppositely charged conductors; such pairs are called *condensers*, or *capacitors*.

An electric field can be made "visible" by sprinkling small, elongated, poorly-conducting particles (grass seeds, for example) on a glass plate placed in the field. In the electric field the particles arrange themselves in regular chain-like filaments, thus making a picture of the "electric lines of force" (Plates 1 − 9; Figs. 4.3, 4.4, 4.5, 6.13, 7.1).

Different electric fields can be quantitatively compared with each other by means of an electric-field-indicator, or an *electroscope*. An example of a simple electroscope is the charged pith ball suspended from a string which we used for demonstrating electric force (Fig. 4.2). If two electric fields produce the same deflection of an electroscope, the fields are considered equal (subject to proper orientation of the electroscope, as will be clear from the following discussion).

The study of various electric fields by means of electroscopes and lines-of-force pictures shows that the simplest electric field is the field

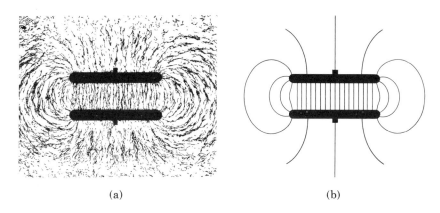

(a)   (b)

FIG. 4.3 (a) Electric lines of force in the field of a parallel plate capacitor. (b) Electric field map for the same capacitor.

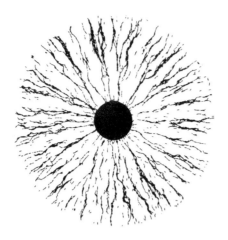

FIG. 4.4 Electric lines of force around an isolated uniformly charged sphere.

inside a thin parallel-plate capacitor; that is, the field between two parallel, oppositely charged conducting plates placed close to each other (Fig. 4.3). Except near the edges of the capacitor, this field is *homogeneous:* it causes the same deflection of an electroscope no matter at what point of the field the electroscope is placed, and its lines of force are straight, parallel lines.

If, using an electroscope, we compare the fields between the plates of different thin parallel-plate capacitors, we find that the fields between the plates of all those capacitors which have the same ratio

$$\frac{\text{voltage between the plates}}{\text{distance between the plates}}$$

cause equal deflections of the electroscope regardless of any other

FIG. 4.5 Electric lines of force around an uncharged sphere in an external electric field.

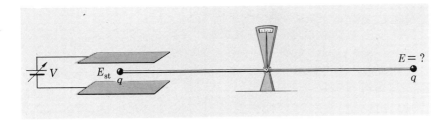

FIG. 4.6   Electric fields can be measured by comparison with a standard electric field.

characteristics of the capacitors. This ratio can be used therefore as the measure of the electric field inside a thin parallel-plate capacitor.

Since the field between the plates of a thin parallel-plate capacitor has a well defined structure, is easily reproducible, and can be used conveniently for establishing standard laboratory conditions for experiments with electric fields, we shall adopt this field as the *standard electric field* E_s and, in agreement with the ratio stated above, shall define its magnitude as

$$E_s = \frac{V}{d}, \tag{4-2.1}$$

where V is the voltage between the two plates and d is their separation.

The magnitude of any electric field can be defined in terms of the magnitude of the standard field. We shall define it as follows: *the magnitude of an arbitrary electric field E is measured by and is equal to the magnitude of the standard electric field E_s which exactly equalizes the field E.* The units of an electric field are, according to this definition, volt/m.

The principle of measurement of an arbitrary electric field is illustrated in Fig. 4.6.[1] The standard field is on the left; it is adjusted by means of a variable voltage source until the balance arm carrying on its ends two equal test charges, one of which is in the standard field while the other is in the unknown field, comes to equilibrium.

---

[1] The method of the direct field measurement shown in Fig. 4.6 is seldom used in practice. Instead, electric fields are usually measured indirectly by first determining the effect of the standard field upon some charge carrier and then comparing this effect with the effect produced upon the same charge carrier by the field that is being measured. In this manner, for instance, atomic electric fields are measured by first determining the behavior of elementary charged particles in a standard electric field (Millikan's oil-drop experiment, mass spectrographs) and then comparing this behavior with the behavior of identical particles in the atomic fields.

Electric fields are vector fields. With each point of an electric field one can associate the *electric field vector* **E**, whose magnitude is equal to the magnitude of the electric field at this point and whose direction is the same as the direction of the force experienced by a test charge placed at this point (by convention, the test charge must be positive). In a thin parallel-plate capacitor, for example, **E** is directed along a normal drawn from the positive to the negative plate.

It has been found that maps of electric vector fields (see page 36) are closely represented by pictures of the electric lines of force (filaments of elongated particles on a glass plate) produced by the same fields (Fig. 4.3). The easily obtainable pictures of the electric lines of force are therefore often used as approximate maps of the electric fields.

4-3. Displacement Field and Displacement Vector D

Let us again take two large metal plates on insulating stands, place them near each other, and charge them by connecting each plate to opposite terminals of a battery. Let us then take two small test plates with insulating handles (such as we used for transporting electric charges), press them one against the other, insert them in the space between the large plates, and separate them there. If we now take out these test plates and touch with them the terminals of a ballistic galvanometer, the galvanometer registers a current impulse, indicating in this way that the test plates became charged. Thus we can charge two originally uncharged conducting plates, initially in contact with

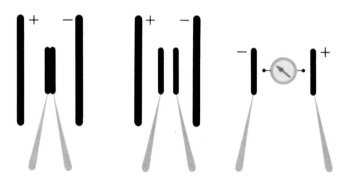

FIG. 4.7   Test plates can be charged by induction.

each other, by merely separating them in the space between two charged plates (Fig. 4.7). This process of charging is called *charging by electric induction*, or *charging by displacement of charge*. The region of space where this process of charging can take place (such as the region between the two charged plates) is called the *field of electric induction*, or the *displacement field*. Experiments show that the displacement field is intimately related to the electric field defined in the preceding section and can be produced by the same means as the latter.

If we measure charges induced on small test plates of different sizes we find that, as long as all plates are inserted at the same point of the field and are oriented to acquire the greatest induced charge, the induced surface charge density

$$\sigma_i = \frac{\text{charge induced on a test plate}}{\text{surface area occupied by charge}}$$

is the same for all plates. Therefore the induced surface charge density can be used as the measure of the displacement field and may be used for the quantitative definition of this field. Utilizing this possibility we shall define the displacement field quantitatively as follows: *the magnitude of the displacement field at a given point is measured by and is equal to the surface charge density induced on a test plate inserted at this point and oriented to acquire the greatest induced charge.* We shall designate the magnitude of the displacement field by the symbol D and shall call it, for brevity, the *displacement*. The units of D are, according to this definition, amp · sec/m².

In practice, the test plates for the measurement of displacement are usually built in the form of a parallel-plate capacitor permanently connected to a ballistic galvanometer which is calibrated directly in terms of the induced surface charge density. For the measurement, the capacitor is either turned through 90°, as in the case of the "flip capacitor" shown in Fig. 4.8, or its plates are rotated with respect to each other by 90°, as in the case of the "field mill" shown in Fig. 4.9. Test capacitors of these types are frequently used for studying the earth's electric field, both as ground and airborne instruments.

Displacement fields are vector fields also. With each point of a displacement field one can associate the *displacement vector* **D** whose magnitude is equal to the displacement at this point and whose direction is along the normal drawn from the negative to the positive test plate when the plates are oriented to acquire the greatest induced charge (this sense of the direction of **D** is merely a convention).

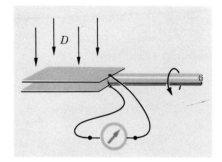
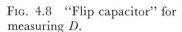
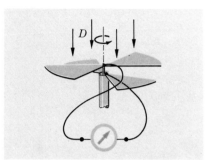

FIG. 4.8 "Flip capacitor" for measuring D.

FIG. 4.9 "Field mill" for measuring D.

To determine the direction of **D** when using a flip capacitor, one orients the axis of rotation so that the induced current impulse becomes zero. The axis of rotation will then be parallel to **D**. The axis of rotation of a field mill, however, will be parallel to **D** when the mill is oriented so that the current impulse becomes a maximum.

It is customary to use the expression "electric field" as a general term for designating both the electric field proper, defined in the preceding section, and the displacement field. When using this expression in such a general sense, we shall refer to both the displacement vector **D** and the electric field vector **E** as the electric field vectors.

As we shall see later, the electric field vectors **E** and **D** have their magnetic counterparts: the magnetic field vectors **H** and **B**. The definitions of these magnetic vectors are analogous to those of the electric vectors. In order to emphasize this important analogy, the definitions of all four vectors **E**, **D**, **H**, and **B** are given in parallel form in Table 4-I.

4-4. Fundamental Electrostatic Field Laws

The laws of physics are established by means of generalizations of numerous and various experimental data, rather than by means of any single measurement, experiment, or observation. The most that a single measurement, experiment, or observation can accomplish is to suggest the possibility of the existence of a law. One should not therefore be surprised if the initial experiments from which the laws of

physics are first deduced are sometimes crude and not entirely convincing. Their function is merely to make a law appear plausible.
This is the only function of the experiments which we shall use for the
deduction of the fundamental electric and magnetic laws. The proof
of the correctness of these laws lies not in the initial experiments
themselves, but rather in the agreement of all the known consequences
of these laws with the experimental data within the limits of experimental errors imposed upon these data by the available techniques of
measurements.

The fundamental laws of the electrostatic field in vacuum may be
deduced as follows.

The Circulation (Curl) Law. If we compare various electrostatic
lines-of-force pictures obtained by the method described in Section 4-2,
we shall find that all these pictures have one remarkable property in
common: there are no closed lines of force in any of these pictures;
all lines of force begin and end on charged bodies. As we already
know, the absence of closed lines is also the characteristic property of
most vector field maps for fields whose curl is zero. Since the lines-of-
force pictures are the maps (however crude) of the corresponding
electrostatic vector fields, we must suspect that the curl of the electrostatic field is always zero:

$$\nabla \times \mathbf{E} = 0. \qquad (4\text{-}4.1a)$$

By Stokes's theorem of vector analysis, it must then also be that

$$\oint \mathbf{E} \cdot d\mathbf{l} = 0. \qquad (4\text{-}4.1b)$$

The validity and generality of these two equations have been
confirmed by all presently known phenomena involving electrostatic
fields. According to Section 3-2, these equations therefore represent a
fundamental electrostatic field law, in its differential and integral
forms, respectively.

The Flux (Divergence) Law. Another fundamental law of the
electrostatic field may be deduced from Faraday's well known
ice-pail experiment. This experiment shows that a charge placed
inside a conducting enclosure always induces an equally large charge of
opposite sign on the inner surface of the enclosure. Since the charge on
a surface is equal to the integral of the surface charge density extended
over this surface, and since the induced surface charge density on a
conducting surface is the measure of the displacement D at this surface,[1]

---

[1] Because each surface element can be regarded as a test plate for measuring D.

TABLE 4-I

Definitions of Electric and Magnetic Field Vectors

(Basic electric measurables and units: voltage [volt], current [amp])

Electric Field	Magnetic Field
Qualitative definition of the electric field:	**Qualitative definition of the magnetic field:**
A region of space where electric charges at rest experience electric forces.	*A region of space where permanent magnets at rest experience magnetic forces.*
Definition of the standard electric field:	**Definition of the standard magnetic field:**
The field inside a thin parallel-plate capacitor,	*The field inside a long coil,*

Electric Field:

$$E_s = \frac{V}{d} \cdot \qquad [E] = \left[\frac{\text{volt}}{\text{m}}\right]$$

Magnetic Field:

$$H_s = \frac{nI}{l} \cdot \qquad [H] = \left[\frac{\text{amp}}{\text{m}}\right]$$

Definition of the electric field vector E:

*A vector in the direction of the force acting on a small positive test charge. The magnitude of **E** is measured in terms of*

$$\frac{\text{voltage}}{\text{plate separation}}$$

Definition of the magnetic field vector H:

*A vector in the direction indicated by the north pole of a small compass needle. The magnitude of **H** is measured in terms of*

$$\frac{\text{current} \cdot \text{turns}}{\text{length}}$$

of a thin parallel-plate capacitor whose field exactly equalizes the field that is measured. Example:

of a long coil whose field exactly equalizes the field that is measured. Example:

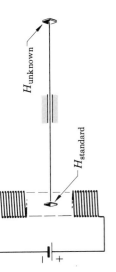

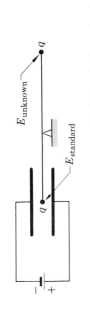

Definition of the induction vector **B** (magnetic flux density vector):

*A vector "causing" induced voltage in a test wire or a test coil. The magnitude of **B** is measured in terms of*

$$\frac{induced\ voltage\ impulse}{area}$$

*of a small, one-turn test coil (test loop). The direction of **B** is normal to the test coil axis when the test coil is oriented so that the induced voltage impulse has its maximum value.*

$$[B] = \left[\frac{volt \cdot sec}{m^2}\right]$$

Example:

Definition of the displacement vector **D** (electric flux density vector):

*A vector "causing" induced surface charges on a test plate or a test capacitor. The magnitude of **D** is measured in terms of*

$$\frac{induced\ charge}{area}$$

*of a small test plate (test capacitor). The direction of **D** is normal to the plane of the test plate when the plate is oriented so that the induced charge has its maximum value.*

$$[D] = \left[\frac{amp \cdot sec}{m^2}\right]$$

Example:

85

Faraday's ice-pail experiment suggests the following correlation:

$$q_{\text{enclosed}} = -q_{\text{induced}} = -\oint \sigma \, dS = \oint D \, dS.$$

Replacing q_{enclosed} in this equation by the integral of the charge density ρ extended over the enclosed volume, $q_{\text{enclosed}} = \int \rho \, dv$, and writing the surface integral as a flux integral, we obtain

$$\oint \mathbf{D} \cdot d\mathbf{S} = \int \rho \, dv, \qquad (4\text{-}4.2a)$$

where $d\mathbf{S}$ is directed along the outward normal to the surface of integration. Although we have deduced this equation from experiments with closed conducting surfaces (enclosures), it has been found to hold for any closed surface whatsoever, be it a real material surface or an imaginary geometrical construction (an imaginary closed surface over which $\oint \mathbf{D} \cdot d\mathbf{S}$ is evaluated is called a *Gaussian surface*). By Gauss's theorem of vector analysis it must then also be that

$$\nabla \cdot \mathbf{D} = \rho. \qquad (4\text{-}4.2b)$$

The validity and generality of these two equations have been confirmed by all presently known phenomena involving displacement fields. Therefore, according to Section 3-2, these equations, too, represent a fundamental electric field law, in its integral and differential forms, respectively. The integral form of this law, Eq. (4-4.2a), is called *Gauss's law of electrostatics*.

Additional experiments show that both the electrostatic $\mathbf{E}$ and electrostatic $\mathbf{D}$ fields are always regular at infinity [approach zero at infinity at least as $1/(\text{distance})^2$].

The Displacement Law. The set of field laws that we have found thus far is not as yet complete, since we do not have the circulation (curl) law for $\mathbf{D}$ and the flux (divergence) law for $\mathbf{E}$. These laws can be obtained, however, from the ones that we already have, if the correlation between the vectors $\mathbf{E}$ and $\mathbf{D}$ is known. This correlation can be determined by making simultaneous measurements of $\mathbf{E}$ and $\mathbf{D}$ in various electric fields. On the basis of such measurements it has been found that in vacuum the vectors $\mathbf{E}$ and $\mathbf{D}$ are bound to each other by the equation

$$\mathbf{D} = \varepsilon_0 \mathbf{E}, \qquad (4\text{-}4.3)$$

where ε_0 is an experimentally determined universal constant, called the permittivity of space; its value is $8.854 \times 10^{-12} \, \text{amp} \cdot \text{sec}/\text{volt} \cdot \text{m}$.

The correlation expressed by this equation is called the *displacement law*. The displacement law is a constitutive law and, in the above form, is valid for electric fields in vacuum (and, practically, also in air) but is not valid for electric fields inside material media, as we shall see later.

Our set of electrostatic laws is now completed. By using the displacement law in combination with the field laws for **E** and **D** determined previously, we can obtain the curl (circulation) as well as the divergence (flux) equations for both vectors **E** and **D**. Thus, according to Helmholtz's theorem of vector analysis, we have a complete set of equations uniquely specifying the vector fields **E** and **D**. This means that if somehow we find an expression for **E** or **D** which for a given electrostatic system in vacuum satisfies all three equations[1] (4-4.1), (4-4.2), and (4-4.3) at all points of space and is regular at infinity, we may be sure that this expression is correct and that the field represented by this expression is the only possible field for the system under consideration.

Several examples on the application of the fundamental electrostatic field laws for the solution of various problems are given below.

▼

Example 4-4.1   A charge q is uniformly distributed throughout a spherical region of radius a (so that $\rho = 0$ for $r > a$ and $\rho = 3q/4\pi a^3$ for $r \leq a$). Find **E** for all points of space.

In order to find the electric field in the space surrounding the charge-filled region, we describe a concentric spherical Gaussian surface S of radius r around this region, as shown in Fig. 4.10a. Applying Gauss's law to this surface, we have

$$\oint \mathbf{D} \cdot d\mathbf{S} = \int \rho \, dv = q_{\text{enclosed}} = q.$$

By the symmetry of the system, the field must be spherically symmetric.[2] The displacement vector **D** must therefore be radial and its magnitude must be the same at all points of the surface S. Since **D** and $d\mathbf{S}$ are in this case parallel, so that $\mathbf{D} \cdot d\mathbf{S} = D \, dS$, and since D is constant on S, so that D can be factored out from under the integral sign, we have

$$\oint \mathbf{D} \cdot d\mathbf{S} = \oint D \, dS = D \oint dS = D4\pi r^2 = q,$$

---

[1] We refer to either of the two equations (4-4.1a) and (4-4.1b) as to Eq. (4-4.1). The same holds for all other equations denoted as "a" and "b."

[2] See Example 4-4.4.

or

$$D = \frac{q}{4\pi r^2}.$$

Using now the displacement law $\mathbf{D} = \varepsilon_0 \mathbf{E}$ and taking into account that $\mathbf{D}$ is in the radial direction, we obtain

$$\mathbf{E} = \frac{q}{4\pi\varepsilon_0 r^2}\, \mathbf{r}_u \qquad (r \geq a). \qquad (4\text{-}4.4)$$

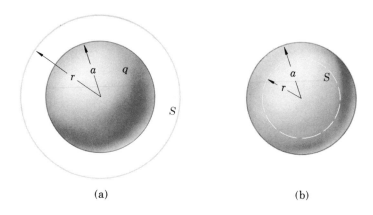

(a)   (b)

Fig. 4.10   (a) Gaussian surface outside a spherical charge distribution. (b) Gaussian surface inside the same charge distribution.

In order to find the electric field inside the charge-filled region, we construct a concentric spherical Gaussian surface S of radius r inside the region, as shown in Fig. 4.10b. Applying Gauss's law to this surface, we have

$$\oint \mathbf{D} \cdot d\mathbf{S} = \int \rho\, dv.$$

As before, $\mathbf{D}$ is parallel to $d\mathbf{S}$ and constant on S, so that the surface integral is

$$\oint \mathbf{D} \cdot d\mathbf{S} = D \oint dS = D4\pi r^2.$$

Since ρ is constant throughout the volume enclosed by S and is equal to $3q/4\pi a^3$, the volume integral is

$$\int \rho\, dv = \rho \int dv = \rho\, \frac{4}{3}\, \pi r^3 = \frac{3q}{4\pi a^3} \cdot \frac{4}{3}\, \pi r^3 = q\, \frac{r^3}{a^3}.$$

We thus have

$$D4\pi r^2 = q\, \frac{r^3}{a^3},$$

or

$$D = \frac{qr}{4\pi a^3}.$$

Using now the displacement law and taking into account that $\mathbf{D}$ is radial, we obtain

$$\mathbf{E} = \frac{qr}{4\pi\varepsilon_0 a^3}\mathbf{r}_u \qquad (r \leq a). \tag{4-4.5}$$

Example 4-4.2   A uniformly distributed charge q forms a long circular rod of length l. Find $\mathbf{E}$ near the surface of the rod far from the rod's ends.

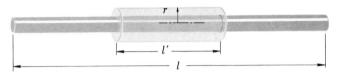

Fig. 4.11   Gaussian surface around a charged rod.

Describing a cylindrical Gaussian surface of radius r and length l' coaxial with the rod, as shown in Fig. 4.11, we can write

$$\oint \mathbf{D} \cdot d\mathbf{S} = q_{\text{enclosed}} = \frac{q}{l} l'.$$

By the symmetry of the system the field is radial (except near the rod's ends), so that if the Gaussian surface is constructed sufficiently far from the ends of the rod, $\mathbf{D}$ on this surface is everywhere radial. Thus on the cylindrical portion of the Gaussian surface $\mathbf{D}$ is perpendicular to the surface, so that $\mathbf{D} \cdot d\mathbf{S} = D \, dS$, while on the two plane ends of the Gaussian surface the field is parallel to the surface, so that $\mathbf{D} \cdot d\mathbf{S} = 0$. We obtain therefore

$$\frac{q}{l} l' = \oint \mathbf{D} \cdot d\mathbf{S} = \underset{\substack{\text{Cylindrical} \\ \text{portion}}}{\int \mathbf{D} \cdot d\mathbf{S}} + \underset{\substack{\text{Plane} \\ \text{ends}}}{\int \mathbf{D} \cdot d\mathbf{S}} = \underset{\substack{\text{Cylindrical} \\ \text{portion}}}{\int D \, dS}.$$

Furthermore, by the symmetry of the system, the field must be constant on the cylindrical portion of the Gaussian surface, so that D in the last integral can be factored out, and therefore

$$\frac{q}{l} l' = D \underset{\substack{\text{Cylindrical} \\ \text{portion}}}{\int dS} = D \cdot 2\pi r l',$$

or

$$D = \frac{q}{2\pi r l}.$$

Using the displacement law, designating q/l as λ (charge per unit length), and taking into account the direction of $\mathbf{E}$, we obtain then

$$\mathbf{E} = \frac{\mathbf{D}}{\varepsilon_0} = \frac{\lambda}{2\pi\varepsilon_0 r}\,\mathbf{r}_u.$$

Example 4-4.3   A spherical region of radius R is filled with charge in such a manner that the electric field inside this region is $\mathbf{E} = (E_0/R^2)r\mathbf{r}$, where $\mathbf{r}$ is the radius vector drawn from the center of the region, and E_0 is a constant. Find the charge density in the region.

According to the divergence and displacement laws, the charge density is

$$\rho = \mathbf{\nabla}\cdot\mathbf{D} = \mathbf{\nabla}\cdot(\varepsilon_0\mathbf{E}) = \varepsilon_0\mathbf{\nabla}\cdot\mathbf{E}.$$

Substituting $\mathbf{E}$, we have

$$\rho = \varepsilon_0\mathbf{\nabla}\cdot\left(\frac{E_0}{R^2}\,r\mathbf{r}\right) = \varepsilon_0\frac{E_0}{R^2}\,\mathbf{\nabla}\cdot(r\mathbf{r}).$$

Differentiating by parts (see vector identity V-4) and remembering that $\mathbf{\nabla}\cdot\mathbf{r} = 3$ and $\mathbf{\nabla}r = \mathbf{r}_u$ (see Examples 2-11.1 and 2-10.1), we obtain

$$\rho = \varepsilon_0\frac{E_0}{R^2}(r\mathbf{\nabla}\cdot\mathbf{r} + \mathbf{r}\cdot\mathbf{\nabla}r) = \varepsilon_0\frac{E_0}{R^2}(3r + \mathbf{r}\cdot\mathbf{r}_u)$$

and, since $\mathbf{r}\cdot\mathbf{r}_u = r$,

$$\rho = \varepsilon_0\frac{4E_0}{R^2}\,r.$$

Example 4-4.4   In solving the problem of Example 4-4.1 we used intuitive considerations of symmetry. Therefore there is some doubt that the solution is correct. Verify the solution.

According to Helmholtz's theorem of vector analysis and the basic electrostatic laws, there is only one correct function for the electric field of any charge distribution, and in order to be correct this function must satisfy the following three conditions: (1) it must be regular at infinity, (2) it must have everywhere zero curl, and (3) it must satisfy everywhere the divergence equation

$$\mathbf{\nabla}\cdot\mathbf{D} = \rho, \quad\text{or}\quad \mathbf{\nabla}\cdot(\varepsilon_0\mathbf{E}) = \rho,$$

where ρ is the density of the charge distribution. These three conditions constitute a criterion for the correctness of an expression for $\mathbf{E}$, so that if they are satisfied by the solution under consideration, the solution is correct.

Examining the solution in question, we see that it satisfies the first condition, since according to Eq. (4-4.4) $\mathbf{E}$ is proportional to $1/r^2$ for $r > a$.

Taking the curl of Eqs. (4-4.4) and (4-4.5), we find that the solution also satisfies the second condition, because it yields $\mathbf{\nabla}\times\mathbf{E} = 0$ for all points of space. Indeed, from Eq. (4-4.4) we have for $r > a$ (using vector identity V-7 and remembering that $\mathbf{V} \times \mathbf{r} = 0$ and $\mathbf{r}_u \times \mathbf{r} = 0$)

$$\mathbf{V} \times \mathbf{E} = \mathbf{V} \times \left(\frac{q}{4\pi\varepsilon_0 r^2}\mathbf{r}_u\right) = \frac{q}{4\pi\varepsilon_0}\mathbf{V} \times \left(\frac{\mathbf{r}}{r^3}\right)$$

$$= \frac{q}{4\pi\varepsilon_0}\left[\frac{1}{r^3}\mathbf{V} \times \mathbf{r} + \mathbf{V}\left(\frac{1}{r^3}\right) \times \mathbf{r}\right]$$

$$= \frac{q}{4\pi\varepsilon_0}\left(\frac{1}{r^3}\mathbf{V} \times \mathbf{r} - \frac{3\mathbf{r}_u}{r^4} \times \mathbf{r}\right) = \frac{q}{4\pi\varepsilon_0}(0 - 0) = 0.$$

From Eq. (4-4.5) we similarly have for $r \leq a$

$$\mathbf{V} \times \mathbf{E} = \mathbf{V} \times \left(\frac{qr}{4\pi\varepsilon_0 a^3}\mathbf{r}_u\right) = \frac{q}{4\pi\varepsilon_0 a^3}\mathbf{V} \times \mathbf{r} = 0.$$

Finally, taking the divergence of Eqs. (4-4.4) and (4-4.5), we find that the solution satisfies also the third condition. Indeed, from Eq. (4-4.4) we have for $r > a$ (using vector identity V-4 and remembering that $\mathbf{V} \cdot \mathbf{r} = 3$)

$$\mathbf{V} \cdot (\varepsilon_0 \mathbf{E}) = \mathbf{V} \cdot \left(\frac{\varepsilon_0 q}{4\pi\varepsilon_0 r^2}\mathbf{r}_u\right) = \frac{q}{4\pi}\mathbf{V} \cdot \left(\frac{\mathbf{r}}{r^3}\right) = \frac{q}{4\pi}\left[\frac{1}{r^3}\mathbf{V} \cdot \mathbf{r} + \mathbf{V}\left(\frac{1}{r^3}\right) \cdot \mathbf{r}\right]$$

$$= \frac{q}{4\pi}\left(\frac{3}{r^3} - \frac{3\mathbf{r}_u}{r^4} \cdot \mathbf{r}\right) = \frac{q}{4\pi}\left(\frac{3}{r^3} - \frac{3r}{r^4}\right) = 0,$$

which is the correct value of ρ for $r > a$. From Eq. (4-4.5) we similarly have for $r \leq a$

$$\mathbf{V} \cdot (\varepsilon_0 \mathbf{E}) = \mathbf{V} \cdot \left(\frac{\varepsilon_0 qr}{4\pi\varepsilon_0 a^3}\mathbf{r}_u\right) = \frac{q}{4\pi a^3}\mathbf{V} \cdot \mathbf{r} = \frac{3q}{4\pi a^3},$$

which is the correct value of ρ for $r \leq a$.

Thus the solution obtained in Example 4-4.1 satisfies the conditions which constitute a criterion for the correctness of an expression for $\mathbf{E}$ and is therefore correct.

Example 4-4.5   A certain charge distribution has a region within which the charge has everywhere the same density ρ. A spherical cavity is made in this region by removing the charge originally present at the location of the cavity without disturbing the rest of the charge. The cavity is centered about the point where the electric field originally was $\mathbf{E}_c$. Find how the presence of the cavity affects this field.

The effect of the cavity can be determined by regarding the zero charge density in the cavity as being made up of two equally large charge densities of opposite polarity, ρ and $-\rho$. The field at the center of the cavity is then the sum of three fields: (a) the field due to the charge of density ρ located within the cavity, (b) the field due to the charge of density $-\rho$ located within the cavity, and (c) the field due to the charge located outside the cavity. Now, the sum of the first and the third fields is just $\mathbf{E}_c$, since if the cavity were filled with charge of density ρ, the original charge distribution is restored. The second field is zero, since by symmetry or by Eq. (4-4.5), the field at the center of a spherical charge distribution of uniform density is zero. The sum of all three fields is thus $\mathbf{E}_c$, so that a spherical cavity made in a region of uniform charge density does not affect the field at the point about which the cavity is centered. This, incidentally, allows one to make the so-called *cavity definition* of the electric field inside a charge-filled region. According to this definition the field in a charge-filled region is the field measured at the center of a spherical cavity whose dimensions are small compared to the distance over which the charge density changes appreciably.

Example 4-4.6   Show that a unidirectional electrostatic field $\mathbf{E}$ cannot vary in a direction normal to the direction of the field.

Let us assume that the field is directed along the x-axis of the rectangular system of coordinates, so that

$$\mathbf{E} = E_x\mathbf{i}.$$

Since, by the fundamental law, the curl of an electrostatic field is always zero, we have

$$\mathbf{\nabla} \times \mathbf{E} = \mathbf{\nabla} \times (E_x\mathbf{i}) = \mathbf{j}\frac{\partial E_x}{\partial z} - \mathbf{k}\frac{\partial E_x}{\partial y} = 0,$$

and since a vector may be equal to zero only if all its components are equal to zero, we obtain

$$\frac{\partial E_x}{\partial z} = 0 \quad \text{and} \quad \frac{\partial E_x}{\partial y} = 0.$$

These two equations show that E_x and therefore $\mathbf{E}$, which is equal to $E_x\mathbf{i}$, cannot vary in the direction of either z or y, thus proving that a unidirectional field $\mathbf{E}$ cannot vary in a direction normal to the direction of the field.

▲

4-5. Calculation of Electrostatic Fields from Charge Distributions

The method of calculating electrostatic fields by direct application of Gauss's law (as in examples 4-4.1 and 4-4.2) is limited to fields of very simple structure, because only then the equation $\oint \mathbf{D} \cdot d\mathbf{S} = \int \rho \, dv$ can be easily solved for $\mathbf{D}$. There are other methods, however, based on immediate consequences of the basic electrostatic laws, which can be used for calculating fields of arbitrary structure. One of the most important of these methods is the method of calculating electrostatic fields from the corresponding charge distributions by direct integration. This method can be deduced from the basic electrostatic laws, Eqs. (4-4.1), (4-4.2), and (4-4.3), combined with Poisson's theorem of vector analysis, Eq. (2-13.3), as follows.

Applying Poisson's theorem to the field vector $\mathbf{E}$, we have

$$\mathbf{E} = -\frac{1}{4\pi} \int_{\text{All space}} \frac{\nabla'(\nabla' \cdot \mathbf{E}) - \nabla' \times (\nabla' \times \mathbf{E})}{r} \, dv',$$

where we are using primed operators to avoid ambiguity in the transformations that follow. By the curl law, Eq. (4-4.1a), $\nabla' \times \mathbf{E}$ for an electrostatic field is always zero, while by the divergence law, Eq. (4-4.2b), and by the displacement law, Eq. (4-4.3), $\nabla' \cdot \mathbf{E}$ is just ρ/ε_0. We can write therefore

$$\mathbf{E} = -\frac{1}{4\pi\varepsilon_0} \int_{\text{All space}} \frac{\nabla'\rho}{r} \, dv'. \tag{4-5.1}$$

Let us now apply to the integrand the vector identity (V-28). We have

$$\frac{\nabla'\rho}{r} = \nabla' \frac{\rho}{r} - \frac{\rho}{r^2} \mathbf{r}_u,$$

so that

$$\mathbf{E} = -\frac{1}{4\pi\varepsilon_0} \int_{\text{All space}} \nabla' \frac{\rho}{r} \, dv' + \frac{1}{4\pi\varepsilon_0} \int_{\text{All space}} \frac{\rho\mathbf{r}_u}{r^2} \, dv'. \tag{4-5.2}$$

The first integral can be transformed into a surface integral by means of the vector identity (V-20), which gives

$$\int_{\text{All space}} \nabla' \frac{\rho}{r} \, dv' = \oint_{\text{All space}} \frac{\rho}{r} \, d\mathbf{S}'. \tag{4-5.3}$$

In all cases of practical interest, however, ρ vanishes outside a finite region of space, and since the surface of integration in the surface integral on the right encloses all space and thus lies outside the region where ρ differs from zero, the surface integral is zero. Therefore the volume integral on the left is also zero, and we obtain

$$\mathbf{E} = \frac{1}{4\pi\varepsilon_0} \int_{\text{All space}} \frac{\rho\mathbf{r}_u}{r^2} \, dv'. \tag{4-5.4}$$

Thus the electrostatic field is determined by the distribution of electric charge and can be calculated with the aid of Eq. (4-5.4) if this distribution is known everywhere in space. In this equation r is the distance between the charge element $\rho \, dv'$ and the point where the field is being determined (this point is called the *point of observation;* the points where the charge elements $\rho \, dv'$ are located are called the *source points*).[1] The unit vector $\mathbf{r}_u$ is directed from the source points x', y', z' towards the observation point x, y, z.

The integral of Eq. (4-5.4) can be simplified in certain cases of special charge distributions. The most common of such charge distributions are the following ones.

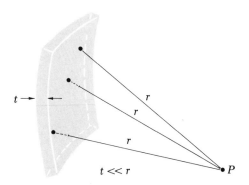

Fig. 4.12   Definition of the surface charge.

Surface Charge. Often charge is confined to a layer-shaped region whose thickness t is much smaller than the distances r from the points of this region to the point of observation (Fig. 4.12). In this case the charge distribution is called a *surface charge.* For this type of charge distribution the variation of r with the depth of the source points inside the layer may be neglected. Integrating over the depth of the layer, we have then

$$\int \frac{\rho \mathbf{r}_u}{r^2} \, dv' = \iint \frac{\rho \mathbf{r}_u}{r^2} \, dS' dt' = \int \frac{\mathbf{r}_u}{r^2} \left(\int \rho \, dt' \right) dS' = \int \frac{\sigma \mathbf{r}_u}{r^2} \, dS',$$

where $\sigma = \int \rho \, dt' = dq/dS'$ is the charge per unit surface area of the layer, and dS' is the element of the surface area. This gives for the field

$$\mathbf{E} = \frac{1}{4\pi\varepsilon_0} \int \frac{\sigma \mathbf{r}_u}{r^2} \, dS'. \tag{4-5.5}$$

Thus in the case of a charge layer whose thickness is much smaller than r, the charge element $\rho \, dv'$ may be replaced by $\sigma \, dS'$ and the volume

[1] Note that r in this equation can never be equal to zero because, by the definition of $\mathbf{E}$, only a test charge ("field-experiencing charge") but not a "field-producing" charge $\rho \, dv'$ can be located at $r = 0$ (that is, at the point of observation x, y, z).

integral may be replaced by the surface integral over the area of the layer.

Line Charge. Another frequently encountered case of special charge distributions is the charge distribution confined to a cylindrical region whose cross section d is much smaller than the distances r from the points of this region to the point of observation (Fig. 4.13). In this case the charge distribution is called a *line charge*. For this type of charge

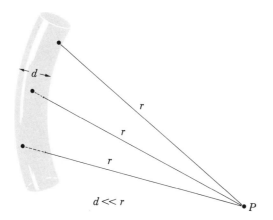

FIG. 4.13   Definition of the line charge.

distribution the variation of r over the cross section of the charge-filled region may be neglected. Taking the integral over the cross-sectional area S of this region in much the same manner as in the case of the surface charge, we obtain the expression

$$\mathbf{E} = \frac{1}{4\pi\varepsilon_0} \int \frac{\lambda \mathbf{r}_u}{r^2} \, dl', \tag{4-5.6}$$

where λ is the charge per unit length of the charge distribution, $\lambda = \int \rho \, dS' = dq/dl'$, and the integral is extended over the length of the charge-filled region. Thus in this case the charge element $\rho \, dv'$ may be replaced by $\lambda \, dl'$ and the volume integral may be replaced by the line integral.

Point Charge. By far the most important case of special charge distributions is the charge restricted to a region in which all linear dimensions are much smaller than the distances from the points of this region to the point of observation (Fig. 4.14). In this case all points of the charge-filled region may be considered as lying approximately at the same distance from the point of observation, so that r and $\mathbf{r}_u$ in the

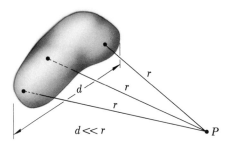

Fig. 4.14   Definition of the point charge.

integral of Eq. (4-5.4) may be considered constant and may be factored out from under the integral sign. We then have

$$\mathbf{E} = \frac{1}{4\pi\varepsilon_0} \int \frac{\rho \mathbf{r}_u}{r^2} \, dv' = \frac{\mathbf{r}_u}{4\pi\varepsilon_0 r^2} \int \rho \, dv',$$

or

$$\mathbf{E} = \frac{q}{4\pi\varepsilon_0 r^2} \mathbf{r}_u, \qquad (4\text{-}5.7)$$

where $q = \int \rho \, dv'$ is the total charge contained in the charge-filled region. This type of charge distribution is called the *point charge*, and the field associated with it is called the *point charge field*, or the *Coulomb field*.

It must be understood that "point charge" is merely a term used for designating a localized charge distribution viewed from a distance large compared with the linear dimensions of this distribution, similar to the term "light point," which is frequently used in reference to stars. In neither case does the word "point" describe the structure or the constitution of the object; instead, it reflects the attitude of the observer towards this object. The same holds also for line and surface charges.

The relative nature of the concept of point charge (as well as that of surface and line charges) may be illustrated as follows. Let us describe a sphere of radius $r_0 > \frac{1}{2}d$ around the charge distribution shown in Fig. 4.15, and let us call this sphere the *sphere of approximation*. We shall agree that for all points outside this sphere the ratio d/r is negligible while for all points inside this sphere this ratio is not negligible. Therefore in the region outside the sphere of approximation the charge distribution may be regarded as a point charge, and Eq. (4-5.7) may be used for the calculation of $\mathbf{E}$; inside the sphere of approximation the distribution may not be regarded as a point charge, and Eq. (4-5.4) must be used for the calculation of $\mathbf{E}$. The radius of the sphere of approximation is determined by the requirement

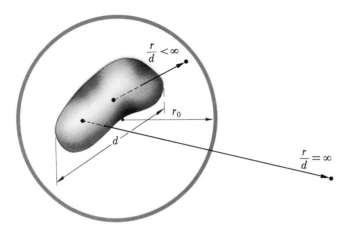

FIG. 4.15   A charge distribution is considered to be a point charge from a distance $r > r_0$ but not from a distance $r < r_0$. Note that in physics a ratio b/a may be considered *infinite* if b is much larger than a.

that the values for E obtained from the point charge formula (4-5.7) for points on this sphere may not deviate from the exact values obtained from Eq. (4-5.4) by more than is considered acceptable in each particular problem. The radius r_0 must be increased if greater accuracy is required, and may be made smaller if lesser accuracy is acceptable. In any case, however, the point charge formula (4-5.7) may be used only for $r > r_0 > \frac{1}{2}d$.

The three equations (4-5.4), (4-5.5), and (4-5.6) are frequently written as a single equation

$$\mathbf{E} = \frac{1}{4\pi\varepsilon_0} \int \frac{\mathbf{r}_u}{r^2}\, dq, \tag{4-5.8}$$

where the charge element dq is equal to $\rho\, dv'$, $\sigma\, dS'$, or $\lambda\, dl'$, depending on the type of the charge distribution under consideration.

For actual calculations the vector equations above may be expressed as scalar equations for the components of $\mathbf{E}$. Thus, for instance, multiplying and dividing the integrand of Eq. (4-5.8) by r and observing that $r\mathbf{r}_u = \mathbf{r} = (x - x')\mathbf{i} + (y - y')\mathbf{j} + (z - z')\mathbf{k}$, we have

$$E_x = \frac{1}{4\pi\varepsilon_0} \int \frac{(x - x')}{r^3}\, dq \tag{4-5.9}$$

$$E_y = \frac{1}{4\pi\varepsilon_0} \int \frac{(y - y')}{r^3}\, dq \tag{4-5.10}$$

$$E_z = \frac{1}{4\pi\varepsilon_0} \int \frac{(z - z')}{r^3}\, dq. \tag{4-5.11}$$

In the same manner we can obtain scalar forms of Eqs. (4-5.7), (4-5.6), (4-5.5), and (4-5.4).

▼

Example 4-5.1   Find the electric field vector **E** at a distance R from the axis of a straight, thin rod carrying a uniformly distributed line charge of density λ and obtain the limiting value of the field for a very long rod.[1]

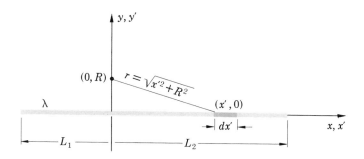

FIG. 4.16   Calculation of the electric field outside a thin charged rod.

Let the rod lie in the x-direction, and let the point of observation be on the y-axis at a distance R from the origin. Let the ends of the rod be at the distances L_1 and L_2 from the origin as shown in Fig. 4.16. From Eqs. (4-5.9), (4-5.10), and (4-5.11) we then have (using $dq = \lambda\, dx'$)

$$E_x = -\frac{\lambda}{4\pi\varepsilon_0} \int_{-L_1}^{+L_2} \frac{x'}{(x'^2 + R^2)^{3/2}}\, dx'$$

$$E_y = +\frac{\lambda}{4\pi\varepsilon_0} \int_{-L_1}^{+L_2} \frac{R}{(x'^2 + R^2)^{3/2}}\, dx'$$

$$E_z = 0.$$

The first of these equations gives

$$E_x = \frac{\lambda}{4\pi\varepsilon_0}\, \frac{1}{\sqrt{x'^2 + R^2}}\Bigg|_{-L_1}^{+L_2} = \frac{\lambda}{4\pi\varepsilon_0}\left(\frac{1}{\sqrt{L_2^2 + R^2}} - \frac{1}{\sqrt{L_1^2 + R^2}}\right).$$

The second equation gives

$$E_y = \frac{\lambda}{4\pi\varepsilon_0 R}\, \frac{x'}{\sqrt{x'^2 + R^2}}\Bigg|_{-L_1}^{+L_2} = \frac{\lambda}{4\pi\varepsilon_0 R}\left(\frac{L_2}{\sqrt{L_2^2 + R^2}} + \frac{L_1}{\sqrt{L_1^2 + R^2}}\right).$$

[1] A "thin" rod is a rod whose radius is much smaller than the distance from the rod to the point of observation. A "long" rod is a rod whose length is much greater than this distance. Note that all expressions like long, thin, small, large, slender, infinite, infinitesimal, etc., are statements of relative dimensions or magnitudes of quantities involved in the physical system at hand and should therefore be understood as relative, rather than absolute, characteristics of these quantities.

If the rod is very long ($R \ll L_1$, and $R \ll L_2$), then R can be neglected in comparison with L_1 and L_2. In this case the expression in parenthesis for E_x becomes zero, and so E_x becomes zero. The expression in parenthesis for E_y becomes equal to 2, which gives $E_y = \lambda/2\pi\varepsilon_0 R$. Thus at all points whose distance R from the rod is such that $R \ll L_1$ and $R \ll L_2$, the electric field of the rod is practically radial. In vector form it may be expressed as

$$\mathbf{E} = \frac{\lambda}{2\pi\varepsilon_0 R}\mathbf{R}_u,$$

where $\mathbf{R}_u$ is the unit vector in the direction of increasing R (observe that this is the same result that we obtained in Example 4-4.2 by using Gauss's law).

Example 4-5.2   Find the electric field on the axis of a thin circular ring of radius a carrying a uniformly distributed charge q and then estimate the axial distance from the ring beyond which the ring may be regarded as a point charge if the greatest admissible error for E is 1%.

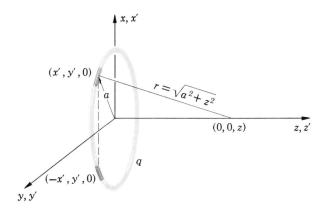

FIG. 4.17   Calculation of the electric field on the axis of a charged ring.

Let the axis of the ring be the z-axis, with the origin at the center of the ring (Fig. 4.17). Using Eqs. (4-5.9), (4-5.10), and (4-5.11), we have

$$E_x = -\frac{1}{4\pi\varepsilon_0}\oint \frac{x'}{r^3}\,dq$$

$$E_y = -\frac{1}{4\pi\varepsilon_0}\oint \frac{y'}{r^3}\,dq$$

$$E_z = +\frac{1}{4\pi\varepsilon_0}\oint \frac{z}{r^3}\,dq.$$

The first of these integrals is zero, since to every charge element dq located at the distance x' from the y-axis, there corresponds an element dq located at the distance $-x'$ from the y-axis, and r is the same for both elements. Therefore $E_x = 0$. Similarly, the second integral is zero, so that $E_y = 0$. In the last integral z and r are constant, so that

$$E_z = \frac{1}{4\pi\varepsilon_0} \frac{z}{r^3} \oint dq = \frac{1}{4\pi\varepsilon_0} \frac{z}{(a^2 + z^2)^{3/2}} q.$$

We finally obtain therefore

$$\mathbf{E} = \frac{qz}{4\pi\varepsilon_0(a^2 + z^2)^{3/2}} \mathbf{k}.$$

In order to estimate the distance beyond which the ring may be regarded as a point charge, we expand E in a power series of z,

$$E = \frac{q}{4\pi\varepsilon_0 z^2}\left(1 + \frac{a^2}{z^2}\right)^{-3/2} = \frac{q}{4\pi\varepsilon_0 z^2} - \frac{q}{4\pi\varepsilon_0 z^2} \cdot \frac{3a^2}{2z^2} + \cdots.$$

The first term in this series is the point charge field, which we shall designate as E_0; the remaining terms represent the deviation ΔE of E_0 from the exact field E. The relative error resulting from using E_0 instead of E is in the first approximation

$$\frac{\Delta E}{E_0} = \frac{3a^2}{2z^2},$$

and since the greatest admissible error is 1%, or 0.01, we have for the smallest z beyond which the ring may be regarded as a point charge

$$\frac{3a^2}{2z_{\min}^2} \approx 0.01, \quad \text{or} \quad z_{\min} \approx 12a.$$

Example 4-5.3   Find the electric field on the axis of a thin, uniformly charged disk of radius a and total charge q and then estimate the axial distance from the disk beyond which the disk may be regarded as a point charge if the greatest admissible error for E is 1%.

Let the axis of the disk be the z-axis with the origin at the center of the disk (Fig. 4.18). Using the same symmetry considerations as in the preceding example, we conclude that $E_x = E_y = 0$. Dividing the disk in elementary rings of radius R and width dR, we then obtain from Eq. (4-5.11) (using $dq = \sigma\, dS'$)

$$E_z = \frac{\sigma}{4\pi\varepsilon_0} \int \frac{z}{r^3} dS' = \frac{\sigma}{4\pi\varepsilon_0} \int_0^a \frac{z2\pi R\, dR}{(R^2 + z^2)^{3/2}}$$

$$= -\frac{\sigma}{2\varepsilon_0} \frac{z}{\sqrt{R^2 + z^2}}\Big|_0^a = \frac{\sigma}{2\varepsilon_0}\left(1 - \frac{z}{\sqrt{a^2 + z^2}}\right),$$

and, since $\sigma\pi a^2 = q$, we finally obtain

$$\mathbf{E} = \frac{q}{2\pi\varepsilon_0 a^2}\left(1 - \frac{z}{\sqrt{a^2 + z^2}}\right)\mathbf{k}.$$

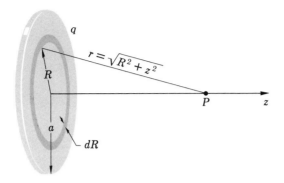

FIG. 4.18   Calculation of the electric field on the axis of a charged disk.

(valid only for $z > 0$ because after substituting the limits we have used $\sqrt{z^2} = +z$).

Expanding E in a power series for z, we obtain as in the preceding example

$$E = \frac{q}{2\pi a^2 \varepsilon_0}\left[1 - \left(1 + \frac{a^2}{z^2}\right)^{-1/2}\right]$$

$$= \frac{q}{2\pi a^2 \varepsilon_0}\left[1 - 1 + \frac{a^2}{2z^2} - \frac{1 \cdot 3}{2 \cdot 4}\frac{a^4}{z^4} + \cdots\right]$$

$$= \frac{q}{4\pi \varepsilon_0 z^2} - \frac{q}{4\pi \varepsilon_0 z^2}\frac{3a^2}{4z^2} + \cdots.$$

The smallest z beyond which the field of the disk may be calculated from the point charge formula with an error smaller than 1% is therefore

$$\frac{3a^2}{4z_{\min}^2} \approx 0.01, \quad \text{or} \quad z_{\min} \approx 9a.$$

▲

4-6. Calculation of Electrostatic Fields from Charge Inhomogeneities

The determination of the electrostatic field **E** associated with a given charge distribution ρ is one of the most fundamental problems of electrostatics. In the last section we solved this problem in its general form by deriving Eq. (4-5.4) which can be used to calculate **E** whenever ρ is given. In this section we shall discuss an alternative solution of the problem—a solution which reveals remarkable new correlations between electrostatic fields and electric charges.

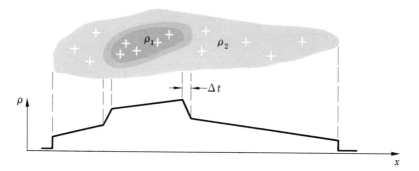

FIG. 4.19 Example of a charge distribution with abruptly changing density. Electric field of such a charge distribution can be calculated from a special formula.

Let us examine Eq. (4-5.1) which we obtained from Poisson's theorem in the preceding section,

$$\mathbf{E} = -\frac{1}{4\pi\varepsilon_0} \int_{\substack{\text{All space}}} \frac{\nabla'\rho}{r}\, dv'. \tag{4-5.1}$$

The remarkable feature of this equation is that it correlates the electric field with the *gradient* of the charge distribution rather than with the charge distribution itself. Hence, the equation may be interpreted as indicating that the electric field is associated not with the electric charge as such, but rather with the inhomogeneities in the distribution of the charge (a homogeneous, or uniform, charge distribution has zero gradient). As we shall see presently, this point of view is useful for analyzing and solving certain types of electrostatic problems.

For practical applications, Eq. (4-5.1) can be transformed into a somewhat different form, which will be more convenient to use in the case of a discontinuous charge distribution—that is, when the charge density changes abruptly from a value ρ_1 to another value ρ_2 across a thin boundary layer, as shown in Fig. 4.19. For a charge distribution of this type, the integral of Eq. (4-5.1) can be split into two integrals

$$\int_{\substack{\text{All space}}} \frac{\nabla'\rho}{r}\, dv' = \int_{\substack{\text{Boundary layer}}} \frac{\nabla'\rho}{r}\, dv' + \int_{\substack{\text{Remaining space}}} \frac{\nabla'\rho}{r}\, dv'. \tag{4-6.1}$$

Let the thickness of the boundary layer be Δt. Since the layer is thin, $\nabla'\rho$ for the layer can be written as

$$\nabla'\rho = \frac{\Delta\rho}{\Delta t}\,\mathbf{n}_u = \frac{\rho_2 - \rho_1}{\Delta t}\,\mathbf{n}_{12},$$

where $\mathbf{n}_u = \mathbf{n}_{12}$ is a unit vector normal to the layer and pointing from ρ_1 to ρ_2 ($\mathbf{\nabla}'\rho$ is normal to the layer because, by supposition, ρ experiences its *maximum* change across the layer). The volume element dv' of the layer can be written as $dv' = \Delta t\, dS'$, where dS' is a surface element of the boundary. The integral over the boundary layer is therefore

$$\int_{\text{Boundary layer}} \frac{\mathbf{\nabla}'\rho}{r}\, dv' = \int_{\text{Boundary}} \frac{\rho_2 - \rho_1}{r\,\Delta t}\, \mathbf{n}_{12}\, \Delta t\, dS'$$

$$= \int_{\text{Boundary}} \frac{\rho_2 - \rho_1}{r}\, d\mathbf{S}'_{12}, \qquad (4\text{-}6.2)$$

where we have denoted $\mathbf{n}_{12}\, dS'$ as $d\mathbf{S}'_{12}$.

Combining Eqs. (4-6.2), (4-6.1), and (4-5.1), we then obtain

$$\mathbf{E} = \frac{1}{4\pi\varepsilon_0} \int_{\text{Boundary}} \frac{\rho_1 - \rho_2}{r}\, d\mathbf{S}'_{12} - \frac{1}{4\pi\varepsilon_0} \int_{\text{Remaining space}} \frac{\mathbf{\nabla}'\rho}{r}\, dv'. \quad (4\text{-}6.3)$$

This equation becomes especially simple in the case of a constant (uniform) charge distribution surrounded by charge-free space. In this case we may set $\rho_1 = \rho$, $\rho_2 = 0$, and $d\mathbf{S}'_{12} = d\mathbf{S}'$, where $d\mathbf{S}'$ points from the charge distribution into the surrounding space. Since ρ is constant, $\mathbf{\nabla}'\rho$ in the last integral is zero, and the integral vanishes. We therefore obtain

$$\mathbf{E} = \frac{\rho}{4\pi\varepsilon_0} \oint_{\text{Boundary}} \frac{d\mathbf{S}'}{r}. \qquad (4\text{-}6.4)$$

Thus in the case of a constant charge distribution confined to a limited region of space, the electrostatic field is completely determined by the density of the charge and shape of the surface bounding this distribution. The direction of the field is then determined solely by the orientation of the surface elements, each surface element contributing to the field only in the direction of its normal.

▼
Example 4-6.1   Show that if an eccentric or asymmetric cavity is made around a field-free point within a uniform charge distribution, an electric field will appear at this point and will be proportional to the size (linear dimensions) of the cavity.

Since the point under consideration is initially field-free, and the charge distribution is uniform, the field, after the cavity is made, will be entirely due to the surface of the cavity, or, by Eq. (4-6.4),

$$E = \frac{\rho}{4\pi\varepsilon_0} \oint_{\text{Cavity}} \frac{d\mathbf{S}'}{r} .$$

Since the surface of the cavity is not symmetric about the point under consideration, the contributions of different surface elements to the total field, in general, will not cancel each other, and the field will be different from zero. Finally, since for a given point of observation the surface integral in the above equation depends only on the geometry of the cavity, and since the dimensions of this integral are [area/distance] = [distance], the integral must be proportional to the size (length, width, or any other characteristic linear dimension) of the cavity. Hence the electric field also must be proportional to the size of the cavity.

Example 4-6.2   Find **E** at an external axial point close to a base of a very long, uniformly charged cylinder of radius a and charge density ρ (Fig. 4.20).

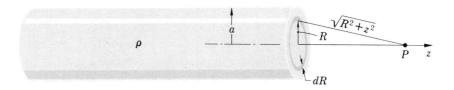

FIG. 4.20   Calculation of the electric field on the axis of a charged cylinder.

By Eq. (4-6.4), the field is

$$E = \frac{\rho}{4\pi\varepsilon_0} \oint_{\text{Boundary}} \frac{d\mathbf{S}'}{r} .$$

The surface integral can be split into three integrals

$$\oint_{\text{Boundary}} \frac{d\mathbf{S}'}{r} = \int_{\text{Near base}} \frac{d\mathbf{S}'}{r} + \int_{\text{Curved surface}} \frac{d\mathbf{S}'}{r} + \int_{\text{Far base}} \frac{d\mathbf{S}'}{r} .$$

The integral over the far base may be neglected since the base is very far from the point of observation, and its contribution to the total field at this point is therefore much smaller than the contribution of the near base. The integral over the curved surface produces no field on the axis, since to every surface element on one side of the axis there corresponds an equal and opposite element on the opposite side. To evaluate the integral over the near base, we subdivide this base in elementary rings of radius R and width dR. Then we have $d\mathbf{S}' = \mathbf{k}2\pi R\, dR$ and $r = \sqrt{R^2 + z^2}$ (Fig. 4.20), so that

$$\int_{\text{Near base}} \frac{d\mathbf{S}'}{r} = \mathbf{k}\int_0^a \frac{2\pi R\, dR}{\sqrt{R^2 + z^2}} = \mathbf{k}2\pi\sqrt{R^2 + z^2}\Big|_0^a$$

$$= 2\pi(\sqrt{a^2 + z^2} - z)\mathbf{k}.$$

The field is therefore

$$\mathbf{E} = \frac{\rho}{2\varepsilon_0}(\sqrt{a^2 + z^2} - z)\mathbf{k}. \tag{4-6.5}$$

Example 4-6.3   A spherical cavity is made about an internal axial point at a distance d from the center of a uniformly charged disk of charge density ρ, thickness $2t$, and radius a (Fig. 4.21). Find $\mathbf{E}$ at the center of the cavity and obtain the limiting value of $\mathbf{E}$ for a very large disk $(a \gg t)$.

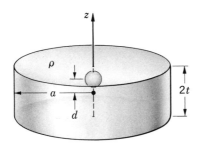

FIG. 4.21   Calculation of the electric field in a spherical cavity located in a charged disk.

The surface of the cavity makes no contribution to the field at its center, since a spherical surface produces only a radial field, all components of which meet in the center and cancel each other.   Likewise, the curved surface of the disk makes no contribution.   Hence only the flat surfaces of the disk are responsible for the field at the point under consideration. The contribution of one such surface to the field at an axial point is given by Eq. (4-6.5).   Applying Eq. (4-6.5) to the two surfaces of the disk, we obtain

$$\mathbf{E} = \frac{\rho}{2\varepsilon_0}[\sqrt{a^2 + (t - d)^2} - \sqrt{a^2 + (t + d)^2} + 2d]\mathbf{k}.$$

For a very large disk, $a \gg t$, and we may neglect $(t + d)$ and $(t - d)$ in the radicals.   We obtain then

$$\mathbf{E} = \frac{\rho d}{\varepsilon_0}\mathbf{k}.$$

Example 4-6.4   A cylindrical cavity of length l and radius a is made in a uniformly charged sphere of charge density ρ, as shown in Fig. 4.22. Find $\mathbf{E}$ at the center of the sphere and check whether the result agrees with that of Example 4-6.1.

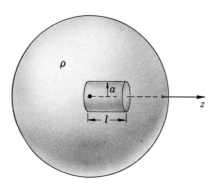

FIG. 4.22   Calculation of the electric field in a cylindrical cavity located in a charged sphere.

By symmetry, only the two bases of the cavity contribute to the field. Using Eq. (4-6.5), we have

$$\mathbf{E} = \frac{\rho}{2\varepsilon_0} [\sqrt{a^2} - (\sqrt{a^2 + l^2} - l)]\mathbf{k},$$

or

$$\mathbf{E} = \frac{\rho}{2\varepsilon_0} l\left[1 + \frac{a}{l} - \sqrt{1 + \left(\frac{a}{l}\right)^2}\right]\mathbf{k},$$

which for a given "shape factor" a/l is proportional to the length of the cavity, as it should be by Example 4-6.1.

▲

PROBLEMS

4.1. A test plate acquires a charge q when touched to a terminal of a battery. If the plate is then touched to an uncharged, insulated conductor, a fraction f of this charge is transferred to it. Show that the maximum total charge that can be transported from the battery to the conductor by repeatedly bringing the plate in contact with the battery and the conductor is

$$Q_{\max} = \frac{fq}{1 - f}.$$

4.2. The radius of the spherical electrode of a van de Graaff generator is 1 m. Electric charge is delivered to it by a moving belt at the constant rate of 10^{-6} amp. The field around the electrode may be considered radially symmetric. Determine the frequency of sparks originating on this electrode, assuming that a spark occurs when the field reaches $3 \cdot 10^6$ volt/m, that a spark completely discharges the electrode, and that no other discharge processes are possible.

4.3. Taking into account that air becomes conducting when the electric field in it reaches about $3 \cdot 10^6$ volt/m, determine the radius of the smallest sphere that can carry a charge of 1 amp · sec in air.

4.4. Show that a unidirectional electrostatic field in a charge-free space must be constant.

4.5. Find the charge distribution that produces the field

$$\mathbf{E} = \frac{E_0}{a^3} r^2 \mathbf{r}, \qquad 0 < r < a$$

and

$$\mathbf{E} = 0, \qquad r > a,$$

where E_0 and a are constants, and r is a radius vector in spherical coordinates.

4.6. Show that the electric field of an infinite plane-parallel slab of charge of density ρ and thickness t for points inside and outside the slab is, respectively,

$$E = \frac{\rho z}{\varepsilon_0} \quad \text{and} \quad E = \frac{\rho t}{2\varepsilon_0},$$

where z is the distance from the midplane of the slab.

4.7. The charges q and $-q$ are uniformly distributed over two concentric spherical shells of radius a and b, respectively $(a < b)$. Find the electric field vector $\mathbf{E}$ associated with these charges in the regions $r < a$, $a < r < b$, and $r > b$.

4.8. Charge q is distributed throughout a spherical volume of radius a with the density $\rho = kr^\alpha$, where k and α are constants and r is the distance from the center of the volume. Find $\mathbf{E}$ at all points of space and plot E against the distance from the center for $\alpha = -1$, $\alpha = 0$, and $\alpha = +1$.

4.9. Show that the electric field of a spherically symmetric charge distribution $\rho(r)$ at any point $r = r_0$ depends only on the charge inside the spherical region of radius r_0 and is the same as if the total charge of the region were concentrated at the center, $r = 0$.

4.10. Electric charge is uniformly distributed with density ρ throughout the volume of an infinitely long circular cylinder of radius a. Show that the electric field vector at a distance r from the axis of the charge-filled region is

$$\mathbf{E} = \frac{\rho a^2}{2\varepsilon_0 r} \mathbf{r}_u, \qquad r \geq a,$$

$$\mathbf{E} = \frac{\rho r}{2\varepsilon_0} \mathbf{r}_u, \qquad r \leq a.$$

4.11. The average fair-weather electric field of the earth has been found to vary with the altitude h above the earth's surface according to the empirical formula

$$\mathbf{E} = -E_0(ae^{-\alpha h} + be^{-\beta h})\mathbf{h}_u,$$

where E_0, a, b, α, and β are constants ($E_0 = 130$ volt/m, $a = 0.69$, $b = 0.31$, $\alpha = 3.5$ km^{-1}, $\beta = 0.23$ km^{-1}). (a) Derive the equation for the charge density ρ in the earth's atmosphere. (b) Plot E and ρ against h and give the values of E and ρ at $h = 0$, $h = 10$ km, and $h = 20$ km. (c) Assuming that the earth's charge is confined to the earth's surface, find the surface charge density and the total charge of the earth.

4.12. Show that if the maximum admissible error in E is $(100/n)\%$, then the distance from an arbitrary charge distribution beyond which this distribution may be regarded as a point charge is always less than $2na$, where a is the distance between the two extreme points of this distribution.

4.13. Show that if the maximum admissible error in E is $(100/n)\%$, then the largest distance from a straight uniform line charge within which this line charge may be regarded as *infinitely long* is approximately

$$\frac{a}{\sqrt{2n}},$$

and show that the smallest distance beyond which this line-charge may be regarded as a *point charge* is approximately

$$na,$$

where a is the length of the line charge.

4.14. In the quantum-mechanical model, a normal hydrogen atom consists of a positive nucleus of charge q located at the center of a negative electron cloud of density

$$\rho = -\frac{q}{\pi a_0^3} e^{-2r/a_0},$$

where a_0 is a constant, and r is the distance from the center. Using this model, find the electric field $\mathbf{E}$ of a hydrogen atom, plot E against r, and determine the numerical values of the field for $r = 0.5a_0$, $r = a_0$, and $r = 2a_0$ if $q = 1.6 \cdot 10^{-19}$ amp $\cdot$ sec and $a_0 = 0.53 \cdot 10^{-10}$ m.

4.15. A thin hemispherical shell carries a uniformly distributed charge of surface density σ. Show that the electric field at the center of curvature of the shell is

$$E = \frac{\sigma}{4\varepsilon_0}.$$

4.16. Show that if a small hole is punched through the wall of a thin, uniformly charged spherical shell whose surface charge density is σ, then the field near the center of the hole will be

$$E = \frac{\sigma}{2\varepsilon_0}.$$

4.17. A spherical cavity of radius a is made within a uniformly charged sphere of radius b, the center of the cavity being at a distance c from the center of the sphere. Find the electric field associated with this charge distribution for all points of space.

4.18. Show that the electric field at an external axial point of a thin, uniformly charged cylinder of charge density ρ, radius a, and length $2l$ is

$$\mathbf{E} = \frac{\rho a^2 l}{2\varepsilon_0(z^2 - l^2)} \mathbf{k},$$

where z is the distance from the center of the cylinder $(z \gg a)$. Then show that the cylinder may be considered a point charge if $z \gg l$.

4.19. A charge distribution has the form of a very large disk of thickness $3d$ consisting of three equally thick layers of uniform charge density ρ_1, ρ_2, and ρ_3. A cubical cavity is made at the center of the central layer (ρ_2), two surfaces of the cavity being parallel to the flat surfaces of the disk. Show that the electric field at the center of the cavity is

$$\mathbf{E} = \frac{(\rho_1 - \rho_3)d}{2\varepsilon_0} \mathbf{k},$$

where $\mathbf{k}$ is a unit vector along the axis of the disk pointing from ρ_1 to ρ_3.

4.20. A uniform charge distribution of density ρ forms a very long, thin-walled, cylindrical tube of radius a and wall thickness t. Show that $\mathbf{E}$ at an axial point near an end of the tube is

$$\mathbf{E} = \frac{\rho a t}{2\varepsilon_0\sqrt{a^2 + z^2}} \mathbf{k},$$

where z is the axial distance measured outward from the same end of the tube.

4.21. A uniform charge distribution of density ρ forms a very long cylinder of radius a. One end of the cylinder has a spherical depression of radius $b > a$, the center of curvature of the depression lying at the point P of the cylinder's axis. Show that $\mathbf{E}$ at P is

$$\mathbf{E} = \frac{\rho a^2}{4\varepsilon_0 b} \mathbf{k},$$

where $\mathbf{k}$ is along the axis, away from the charge.

4.22. Show by means of dimensional analysis, or otherwise, that if an electrostatic system consisting of a charge distribution and a point of observation expands slowly so that all linear dimensions of the system increase n times, the field at the point of observation decreases n^2 times.

4.23. An electrostatic system is studied by means of a small-scale model whose total charge and linear dimensions are, respectively, m and n times the charge and dimensions of the actual system. Show that the electric field at a point of the model is mn^{-2} times the field at the corresponding point of the actual system.

4.24. Suppose that we are located at the center (field-free region) of a very large, uniform, spherical cloud of positive charge. Show that what we consider to be negative charges may then be interpreted merely as holes in this cloud.

4.25. Using the result of Problem 2.40, show that the field lines of two parallel, equal line charges of opposite polarity form a system of circles.

4.26. Using basic laws, show that electrostatic fields satisfy the reciprocal relation

$$\int_{\text{All space}} \rho_1 \mathbf{E}_2 \, dv = - \int_{\text{All space}} \rho_2 \mathbf{E}_1 \, dv,$$

where $\mathbf{E}_1$ is the electric field associated with the charge distribution ρ_1, and $\mathbf{E}_2$ is the electric field associated with the charge distribution ρ_2, both charge distributions being confined to a finite region of space.

5

ELECTROSTATIC POTENTIAL

An electrostatic field can be described not only by vector quantities **E** and **D** but also by a scalar quantity: the electrostatic potential φ. The electrostatic potential φ is intimately related to the electrostatic field vector **E**, and one can be derived from the other. However, φ is frequently easier to measure and (as a scalar quantity) easier to compute than **E**, so that it is frequently more convenient to describe an electrostatic field by means of φ rather than by means of **E** (or **D**). The basic properties and applications of the electrostatic potential are discussed in this chapter.

5-1. Electrostatic Potential

According to the corollary to Poisson's theorem of vector analysis, any vector field whose curl is zero can be expressed as the gradient of a scalar potential. Therefore, since the curl of the electrostatic field is always zero, the electrostatic field can always be expressed as

$$\mathbf{E} = -\nabla\varphi. \qquad (5\text{-}1.1)$$

The potential φ defined by this formula is called the *electrostatic potential*. The unit of the electrostatic potential is the volt.

The electrostatic potential is a scalar point function and determines a scalar field associated with the electrostatic vector field **E**. By the basic property of the gradient, **E** is at every point of the field perpendicular to the equipotential surface (surface of constant φ) drawn

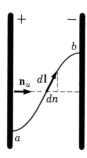

FIG. 5.1　Calculation of the potential difference between the plates of a parallel-plate capacitor.

through this point and, being the *negative* gradient of φ, points in the direction of *decreasing* φ.

If we take the scalar line integral of $\mathbf{E}$ along an arbitrary line connecting any two points a and b, we obtain, using Eqs. (5-1.1) and (2-10.2),

$$\int_a^b \mathbf{E} \cdot d\mathbf{l} = -\int_a^b \nabla\varphi \cdot d\mathbf{l} = -\int_a^b d\varphi = \varphi_a - \varphi_b. \qquad (5\text{-}1.2)$$

Thus the scalar line integral of the electrostatic field vector $\mathbf{E}$ evaluated between any two points is independent of the path of integration and is equal to the difference of the electrostatic potentials, or the *potential difference*, between these points. This correlation can be used for determining φ at any point a if a reference potential φ_c at some reference point c is known. We then have from the last equation

$$\varphi_a = \int_a^c \mathbf{E} \cdot d\mathbf{l} + \varphi_c. \qquad (5\text{-}1.3)$$

The physical significance of φ can be deduced by calculating the potential difference between the plates of a thin parallel-plate capacitor. According to Section 4-2, $\mathbf{E}$ in such a capacitor is

$$\mathbf{E} = \frac{V}{d}\,\mathbf{n}_u,$$

where V is the voltage between the plates, d is the separation of the plates, and $\mathbf{n}_u$ is a unit vector directed along a normal from the positive to the negative plate. Integrating $\mathbf{E}$ along an arbitrary line from a point a on the positive plate to a point b on the negative plate and observing that $\mathbf{n}_u \cdot d\mathbf{l}$, by the definition of the dot product, is equal to dn—length increment in the direction of $\mathbf{n}_u$ (Fig. 5.1)—we obtain

$$\varphi_a - \varphi_b = \int_a^b \mathbf{E} \cdot d\mathbf{l} = \int_a^b \frac{V}{d}\,\mathbf{n}_u \cdot d\mathbf{l} = \frac{V}{d}\int_a^b dn = \frac{V}{d}\,d = V.$$

Thus the potential difference between the two plates is equal to the voltage between them. Since any electrostatic field may be subdivided into small homogeneous regions in each of which the field may be regarded as produced by a small, thin parallel-plate capacitor, we conclude that the equality of the potential difference and voltage,

$$\varphi_a - \varphi_b = V_{ab}, \tag{5-1.4}$$

is a general correlation valid for any two points of an electrostatic field.

In order to measure the voltage between points where no conducting boundaries are present, special devices known as *probes* are placed at these points, and the voltage between the probes is then measured. Examples of probes are a sharp point, a piece of radioactive substance, a burning candle, and a "water dropper" (water-filled container with a small hole from which water drips). Probes make the space around them slightly conducting, so that the voltage in this space can be measured in essentially the same manner as in conducting bodies.

From Eq. (5-1.4) several important conclusions about conducting bodies in the presence of electrostatic fields can be made.

First of all, since voltage and potential difference are equivalent quantities, all conducting bodies under electrostatic conditions must be equipotential bodies. Otherwise voltage would be present between various points of the same conducting body, and due to the current-producing property of voltage, current would be produced in the body, thus violating the condition that no current may be present in an electrostatic system.

From this and from the fact that the electrostatic field vector **E** at any point of an equipotential surface is perpendicular to the surface, it follows that under electrostatic conditions **E** at any point of a conducting surface is perpendicular to it. And since **E** (in vacuum) has the same direction as **D**, **D** is also perpendicular to a conducting surface under these conditions.

Now, according to Section 4-3, the direction of **D** is at any point perpendicular to the plane of the test plate which measures D at this point. But since under electrostatic conditions **D** at the surface of a conductor is perpendicular to the surface, any surface element of a conductor under electrostatic conditions may be regarded as a test plate for measuring D at the location of this surface element. Therefore the surface charge density at any point of a conducting surface in an electrostatic system is equal to the displacement D at this point. Taking into account the sense of the direction of **D**, we can write this correlation as

$$\mathbf{D} = \sigma \mathbf{n}_u,\tag{5-1.5}$$

where $\mathbf{n}_u$ is a unit vector normal to the conducting surface and pointing from the conductor into the surrounding space. Combining this equation with the displacement law, we obtain the corresponding equation for **E**,

$$\mathbf{E} = \frac{\sigma}{\varepsilon_0}\mathbf{n}_u.\tag{5-1.6}$$

A useful special case of this equation is the equation correlating σ and E of a thin parallel-plate capacitor. In such a capacitor $E = V/d$, where V is the voltage applied to the plates and d is the distance between them. The surface charge density on the inner surfaces of the capacitor's plates is then by Eq. (5-1.6)

$$\sigma = \varepsilon_0 \frac{V}{d}.\tag{5-1.7}$$

▼
Example 5-1.1   A voltage V is applied to a thin parallel-plate capacitor of plate separation d. Find the potential at an arbitrary point in the space between the plates, taking a point on the positive plate as the reference point.

Let the reference point be the origin of a rectangular system of coordinates, with the x-axis lying in the direction of the normal drawn from the positive to the negative plate (Fig. 5.2). The electric field in the capacitor is then $\mathbf{E} = (V/d)\mathbf{i}$. Integrating from a point x, y, z to the origin and designating the reference potential as φ_0, we have by Eq. (5-1.3)

$$\varphi(x,y,z) = \int_{x,y,z}^{0} \mathbf{E} \cdot d\mathbf{l} + \varphi_0 = \int_{x,y,z}^{0} \frac{V}{d}\mathbf{i} \cdot d\mathbf{l} + \varphi_0 = \frac{V}{d}\int_{x,y,z}^{0} \mathbf{i} \cdot d\mathbf{l} + \varphi_0.$$

Since $\mathbf{i} \cdot d\mathbf{l} = dx$, the integral is a function of x only, and we obtain

$$\varphi(x) = \frac{V}{d}\int_{x}^{0} dx + \varphi_0$$

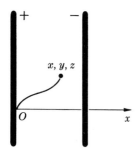

FIG. 5.2   Calculation of the potential in a parallel-plate capacitor.

and finally

$$\varphi(x) = -\frac{V}{d}x + \varphi_0.$$

Example 5-1.2   For all points of space find the potential associated with the spherical charge of Example 4-4.1, taking as the reference potential $\varphi_\infty = 0$.

For points in the space outside the charge-filled region $(r \geq a)$ we have, using Eqs. (5-1.3) and (4-4.4),

$$\varphi(r) = \int_r^\infty \mathbf{E} \cdot d\mathbf{l} + \varphi_\infty = \int_r^\infty \frac{q}{4\pi\varepsilon_0 r^2}\mathbf{r}_u \cdot d\mathbf{l} + 0.$$

But $\mathbf{r}_u \cdot d\mathbf{l} = dr$, so that

$$\varphi(r) = \frac{q}{4\pi\varepsilon_0}\int_r^\infty \frac{dr}{r^2} = -\frac{q}{4\pi\varepsilon_0}\frac{1}{r}\Big|_r^\infty,$$

or

$$\varphi(r) = \frac{q}{4\pi\varepsilon_0 r} \qquad (r \geq a). \tag{5-1.8}$$

The calculation of the potential inside the charge-filled region $(r \leq a)$ is a little more complicated because, according to Example 4-4.1, two different expressions for $\mathbf{E}$ must be used in the line integral. The line integral must be split therefore in two parts: one for the path inside the charge-filled region, the other for the path outside this region. Using Eqs. (5-1.3), (4-4.5), and (4-4.4), we then have

$$\varphi(r) = \int_r^a \mathbf{E}_\text{inside} \cdot d\mathbf{l} + \int_a^\infty \mathbf{E}_\text{outside} \cdot d\mathbf{l}$$

$$= \int_r^a \frac{qr}{4\pi\varepsilon_0 a^3}\mathbf{r}_u \cdot d\mathbf{l} + \int_a^\infty \frac{q}{4\pi\varepsilon_0 r^2}\mathbf{r}_u \cdot d\mathbf{l}$$

$$= \frac{q}{4\pi\varepsilon_0 a^3}\int_r^a r\,dr + \frac{q}{4\pi\varepsilon_0}\int_a^\infty \frac{dr}{r^2}$$

$$= \frac{q}{4\pi\varepsilon_0 a^3}\frac{r^2}{2}\Big|_r^a - \frac{q}{4\pi\varepsilon_0}\frac{1}{r}\Big|_a^\infty,$$

which finally reduces to

$$\varphi(r) = \frac{q}{8\pi\varepsilon_0 a^3}(3a^2 - r^2) \qquad (r \leq a). \tag{5-1.9}$$

Example 5-1.3   Find the external potential near the surface of the charged rod of Example 4-4.2 taking as the reference potential $\varphi(r_0) = 0$, where r_0 is the distance to the reference point from the axis of the rod.

By the symmetry of the problem, the potential is a function of r only, and we have according to Eq. (5-1.3)

$$\varphi(r) = \int_r^{r_0} E \, dr.$$

Substituting E from Example 4-4.2, we obtain

$$\varphi(r) = \int_r^{r_0} \frac{\lambda}{2\pi\varepsilon_0 r} \, dr = \frac{\lambda}{2\pi\varepsilon_0} \ln r \Big|_r^{r_0},$$

or

$$\varphi(r) = -\frac{\lambda}{2\pi\varepsilon_0} \ln r + \frac{\lambda}{2\pi\varepsilon_0} \ln r_0.$$

Example 5-1.4   The potential associated with a certain spherically symmetric charge distribution is

$$\varphi = \frac{q}{4\pi\varepsilon_0 r} e^{-\alpha r}.$$

Find the electric field of this distribution.

According to Eq. (5-1.1) and vector identities (V-1) and (V-3), the field is

$$\mathbf{E} = -\nabla\varphi = -\frac{q}{4\pi\varepsilon_0} \left(\frac{1}{r} \nabla e^{-\alpha r} + e^{-\alpha r} \nabla \frac{1}{r} \right)$$

$$= \frac{q}{4\pi\varepsilon_0} \left(\frac{\alpha}{r} e^{-\alpha r} \mathbf{r}_u + e^{-\alpha r} \frac{\mathbf{r}_u}{r^2} \right),$$

or

$$\mathbf{E} = \frac{q(1 + \alpha r)}{4\pi\varepsilon_0 r^2} e^{-\alpha r} \mathbf{r}_u.$$

▲

5-2. Capacitance

An important problem of electrostatics is the calculation of the potential or voltage associated with a given charge distribution. In the next section we shall solve this problem in its general form. In this section we shall consider a special case of the problem: the calculation of potentials of charged conductors and voltages between charged conductors with the aid of a special quantity called *capacitance*.

Capacitance is defined for single conductors and also for capacitors (a capacitor is a system of two conductors carrying equally large charges of opposite sign).

The *capacitance of a conductor* is defined as the ratio of the charge carried by the conductor to the potential of the conductor

$$C = \frac{q}{\varphi}, \qquad (5\text{-}2.1)$$

where the potential is measured with respect to $\varphi_\infty = 0$.

The *capacitance of a capacitor* is defined as the ratio of the charge residing on one of the two conductors forming the capacitor to the voltage between these conductors

$$C = \frac{q}{V}. \qquad (5\text{-}2.2)$$

As will be shown in the next chapter,[1] the capacitance of a single, isolated conductor or capacitor (in a vacuum) depends only on the shape and the size of the conductor or capacitor and so constitutes a constant characterizing this conductor or capacitor. Therefore, once the capacitance of a given conductor or capacitor has been determined, the potential of the conductor or the voltage of the capacitor can be found immediately from Eq. (5-2.1) or Eq. (5-2.2) if the corresponding charge is known (conversely, the charge can be found if the potential or voltage is known). The problem of calculating the potential of a charged conductor or voltage of a charged capacitor reduces therefore to that of determining the capacitance of the conductor or capacitor under consideration.[2]

The units of capacitance are amp · sec/volt (these units are usually called "farad").

▼

Example 5-2.1   Find the capacitance of a single, isolated conducting sphere of radius a.

Assuming that the sphere carries a charge q, we find by using Gauss's law (as in Example 4-4.1)

$$\mathbf{D} = \frac{q}{4\pi r^2} \mathbf{r}_u.$$

Using the displacement law, we find

$$\mathbf{E} = \frac{q}{4\pi \varepsilon_0 r^2} \mathbf{r}_u.$$

---

[1] See Example 6-2.2 and Section 6-7.

[2] The proportionality of charge and voltage in a capacitor allows one to measure charges by means of electrostatic voltmeters. The charge is then $q = CV$, where C is the capacitance of the voltmeter and V is the voltage indicated by it. Since the capacitance of these voltmeters is very small, even a small charge produces a large voltage in them. Their sensitivity for charge measurement is therefore very high and can exceed the sensitivity of ballistic galvanometers considerably.

By Eq. (5-1.3), the potential of the sphere with respect to $\varphi_\infty = 0$ is then

$$\varphi_a = \int_a^\infty \mathbf{E} \cdot d\mathbf{l} = \int_a^\infty \frac{q}{4\pi\varepsilon_0 r^2} \, dr = -\left.\frac{q}{4\pi\varepsilon_0 r}\right|_a^\infty = \frac{q}{4\pi\varepsilon_0 a}. \qquad (5\text{-}2.3)$$

Using now the capacitance equation (5-2.1), we obtain

$$C = \frac{q}{\varphi_a} = \frac{q4\pi\varepsilon_0 a}{q},$$

or

$$C = 4\pi\varepsilon_0 a.$$

Example 5-2.2   Find the capacitance of a spherical capacitor consisting of an inner sphere of external radius a and an outer sphere, concentric with the first, of internal radius b (Fig. 5.3).

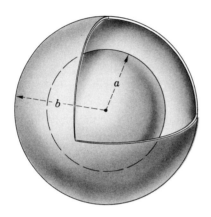

FIG. 5.3 Spherical capacitor. A section of the outer sphere is cut out to make the inner sphere visible.

Assuming a charge q on the inner sphere, we repeat the first three steps of the preceding example (except that the line integral is taken now between the limits a and b). This gives for the voltage between the spheres

$$V_{ab} = \int_a^b \mathbf{E} \cdot d\mathbf{l} = \frac{q}{4\pi\varepsilon_0}\left(\frac{1}{a} - \frac{1}{b}\right).$$

The capacitance is therefore, by Eq. (5-2.2),

$$C = \frac{q}{V_{ab}} = 4\pi\varepsilon_0\left(\frac{1}{a} - \frac{1}{b}\right)^{-1},$$

or

$$C = 4\pi\varepsilon_0 \frac{ab}{b - a}.$$

Example 5-2.3   Find the capacitance per unit length of a cylindrical capacitor consisting of two very long concentric cylinders of radius a and b (Fig. 5.4).

Describing a cylindrical Gaussian surface of radius r and length l coaxial with the two cylinders and assuming that the inner cylinder

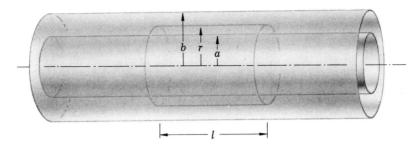

FIG. 5.4   Cylindrical capacitor. A Gaussian surface is shown between the two cylinders which form the capacitor.

carries a charge λ per unit length, we have (compare with Example 4-4.2)

$$\mathbf{D} = \frac{\lambda}{2\pi r}\,\mathbf{r}_u.$$

Using the displacement law, we find

$$\mathbf{E} = \frac{\lambda}{2\pi\varepsilon_0 r}\,\mathbf{r}_u.$$

This gives for the voltage between the cylinders

$$V_{ab} = \int_a^b \mathbf{E}\cdot d\mathbf{l} = \int_a^b \frac{\lambda}{2\pi\varepsilon_0 r}\,dr = \frac{\lambda}{2\pi\varepsilon_0}\ln\frac{b}{a}.$$

The capacitance per unit length, $C_l = \lambda/V_{ab}$, is therefore

$$C_l = 2\pi\varepsilon_0 \frac{1}{\ln\,(b/a)}.$$

Example 5-2.4   Find the capacitance of a parallel-plate capacitor of plate separation d and area A neglecting the "edge effects"—that is, assuming that the field is homogeneous everywhere between the plates and suddenly becomes zero at the edges of the capacitor (Fig. 5.5).

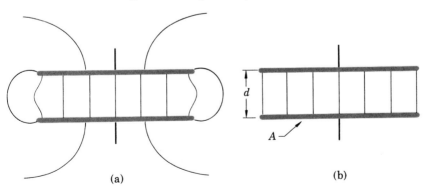

(a)   (b)

FIG. 5.5   (a) Electric field of a parallel-plate capacitor. (b) Idealized electric field of the same capacitor obtained by neglecting edge effects.

If the edge effects are neglected, the density of surface charge on the plates is constant. By Eqs. (4-1.3) and (5-1.7) we then have for the charge on the positive plate

$$q = \sigma A = \varepsilon_0 \frac{V}{d} A,$$

and, substituting q in Eq. (5-2.2), we obtain

$$C = \varepsilon_0 \frac{A}{d} .$$

▲

5-3. Calculation of Electrostatic Potential from Charge Distribution

We shall now obtain the fundamental formula which correlates electrostatic potential with electric charge. According to the corollary to Poisson's theorem of vector analysis, the electrostatic potential, which we have defined by the equation

$$\mathbf{E} = -\nabla\varphi, \qquad (5\text{-}1.1)$$

can be expressed as

$$\varphi = \frac{1}{4\pi} \int_{\text{All space}} \frac{\nabla \cdot \mathbf{E}}{r} dv' + \varphi_\text{o}.$$

Since by the displacement law and the divergence law

$$\nabla \cdot \mathbf{E} = \frac{1}{\varepsilon_0} \nabla \cdot \mathbf{D} = \frac{1}{\varepsilon_0} \rho,$$

we obtain

$$\varphi = \frac{1}{4\pi\varepsilon_0} \int_{\text{All space}} \frac{\rho}{r} dv' + \varphi_\text{o}. \qquad (5\text{-}3.1)$$

Thus the electrostatic potential is determined by the distribution of electric charge and can be calculated directly from this distribution by means of Eq. (5-3.1).

The constant φ_o in Eq. (5-3.1) is an arbitrary reference potential. The arbitrariness of φ_o follows from Eq. (5-1.1) which defines the electrostatic potential; since the gradient of any constant is zero, the presence of an additive constant in the expression for φ has no effect upon $\mathbf{E}$ obtained from this expression. In the case of a finite charge distribution, φ_o is usually set equal to zero, so that φ will be zero when $r \to \infty$—that is, at points very distant from the charge distribution.

When φ_0 is set equal to zero the potential is said to be evaluated *with respect to infinity.* Quite often φ_0 is given a value which makes the potential of the ground (earth) equal to zero; the potential is then said to be evaluated *with respect to the ground.* In general, φ_0 is selected so that the potential φ becomes zero at some convenient reference point, and φ is then said to be evaluated with respect to this point. Unless otherwise stated, we shall always use $\varphi_0 = \varphi_\infty = 0$—that is, we shall always evaluate the electrostatic potential with respect to infinity.

It follows from a comparison of Eq. (5-3.1) with Eq. (4-5.4) and an examination of Eqs. (4-5.5), (4-5.6), and (4-5.7) that Eq. (5-3.1) reduces to

$$\varphi = \frac{1}{4\pi\varepsilon_0} \int \frac{\sigma}{r} dS' + \varphi_0 \qquad (5\text{-}3.2)$$

for a surface charge distribution,

$$\varphi = \frac{1}{4\pi\varepsilon_0} \int \frac{\lambda}{r} dl' + \varphi_0 \qquad (5\text{-}3.3)$$

for a line charge distribution, and

$$\varphi = \frac{q}{4\pi\varepsilon_0 r} + \varphi_0 \qquad (5\text{-}3.4)$$

for a point charge (the potential expressed by this formula is called *Coulomb's potential*).

The three equations (5-3.1), (5-3.2), and (5-3.3) are frequently written as a single equation

$$\varphi = \frac{1}{4\pi\varepsilon_0} \int \frac{dq}{r} + \varphi_0, \qquad (5\text{-}3.5)$$

where the charge element dq is equal to $\rho\,dv'$, $\sigma\,dS'$, or $\lambda\,dl'$, depending on the type of the charge distribution under consideration.

▼
Example 5-3.1   Find the electrostatic potential on the axis of a thin, uniformly charged, circular ring of radius a carrying a charge q (Fig. 5.6) and then estimate the axial distance from the ring beyond which the ring may be regarded as a point charge if the greatest admissible error for φ is 1%.[1]

---

[1] The relative error for φ is meaningful only when a fixed reference point is used. If the reference point is changed, the value of φ changes, and hence the value of the relative error changes. As already stated, we are using $\varphi_0 = \varphi_\infty = 0$.

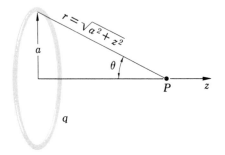

FIG. 5.6   Calculation of the electrostatic potential on the axis of a charged ring.

From Eq. (5-3.5) we have

$$\varphi = \frac{1}{4\pi\varepsilon_0} \int \frac{dq}{r} = \frac{1}{4\pi\varepsilon_0 r} \int dq,$$

or

$$\varphi = \frac{q}{4\pi\varepsilon_0 r} = \frac{q}{4\pi\varepsilon_0 \sqrt{a^2 + z^2}}.$$

In order to estimate the distance beyond which the ring may be regarded as a point charge, we expand φ in the power series of z,

$$\varphi = \frac{q}{4\pi\varepsilon_0 z}\left(1 + \frac{a^2}{z^2}\right)^{-1/2} = \frac{q}{4\pi\varepsilon_0 z} - \frac{q}{4\pi\varepsilon_0 z} \cdot \frac{a^2}{2z^2} + \cdots.$$

The first term in this series is the point charge potential φ'; the remaining terms represent its deviation $\Delta\varphi$ from the exact potential φ. The relative error resulting from using the point charge potential instead of the exact one is in the first approximation

$$\frac{\Delta\varphi}{\varphi'} = \frac{a^2}{2z^2}.$$

Since the greatest admissible error is 1%, or 0.01, we have for the smallest z beyond which the ring may be regarded as a point charge (as far as the potential is concerned)

$$\frac{a^2}{2z_{\min}^2} \approx 0.01, \quad \text{or} \quad z_{\min} \approx 7a.$$

Example 5-3.2   Find the electrostatic potential on the axis of a thin, uniformly charged, circular disk of radius a and surface charge density σ (Fig. 5.7) and then estimate the axial distance from the disk beyond which the disk may be regarded as a point charge if the greatest admissible error for φ is 1%.

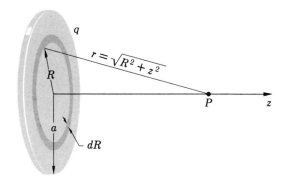

FIG. 5.7   Calculation of electrostatic potential on the axis of a charged disk.

Dividing the disk in elementary rings of radius R and width dR and using Eq. (5-3.2), we have

$$\varphi = \frac{1}{4\pi\varepsilon_0} \int \frac{\sigma}{r}\, dS' = \frac{1}{4\pi\varepsilon_0} \int_0^a \frac{\sigma 2\pi R\, dR}{\sqrt{R^2 + z^2}} = \frac{\sigma}{2\varepsilon_0} \sqrt{R^2 + z^2}\, \Big|_0^a,$$

or

$$\varphi = \frac{\sigma}{2\varepsilon_0} (\sqrt{a^2 + z^2} - z).$$

Expanding the potential in the power series for z and noting that the total charge of the disk is $q = \sigma\pi a^2$, we obtain as in the preceding example

$$\begin{aligned}
\varphi &= \frac{q}{2\pi a^2 \varepsilon_0}\, z\left[\left(1 + \frac{a^2}{z^2}\right)^{1/2} - 1\right] \\
&= \frac{q}{2\pi a^2 \varepsilon_0}\, z\left(1 + \frac{1}{2}\frac{a^2}{z^2} - \frac{1}{2\cdot 4}\frac{a^4}{z^4} + \cdots - 1\right) \\
&= \frac{q}{4\pi\varepsilon_0 z} - \frac{q}{4\pi\varepsilon_0 z}\cdot\frac{a^2}{4z^2} + \cdots.
\end{aligned}$$

The smallest z beyond which the potential may be calculated from the point charge formula with an error smaller than 1% is therefore

$$\frac{a^2}{4z_{\min}^2} \approx 0.01, \quad \text{or} \quad z_{\min} \approx 5a.$$

Example 5-3.3   Two conducting spheres of radius a and b, each carrying a charge q, are separated by a distance $R \gg a,b$. What, approximately, will be the potential and the final charge on each sphere after they are connected by a fine, conducting wire?

We shall find an approximate solution assuming the following idealized conditions: (a) the charge distribution and the field of each sphere are radially symmetric; (b) each sphere can be regarded as a point charge from the location of the other sphere; (c) no charge is residing on the wire. With these assumptions an approximate solution of the problem may be obtained as follows.

In the final state the potentials on the surfaces of both spheres must be the same,

$$\varphi_a = \varphi_b,$$

because only then will there be no voltage along the wire and therefore no current in the wire (initially the potentials of the spheres are different; after the spheres are connected, a certain amount of charge will move from one sphere to the other until the whole system becomes an equipotential system). The potential at the surface of each sphere may be regarded as the sum of two partial potentials: the potential due to the charge residing on the same sphere and the potential due to the charge residing on the other sphere. According to assumption (a), the former is given by Eq. (5-2.3); the latter, according to assumption (b), is given by the point charge potential, Eq. (5-3.4). Using these formulas, we have (designating the charges of the two spheres by q_a and q_b)

$$\varphi_a = \frac{q_a}{4\pi\varepsilon_0 a} + \frac{q_b}{4\pi\varepsilon_0 R},$$

$$\varphi_b = \frac{q_b}{4\pi\varepsilon_0 b} + \frac{q_a}{4\pi\varepsilon_0 R}.$$

Furthermore, since the total charge is conserved, we have according to the assumption (c),

$$q_a + q_b = 2q.$$

Combining these four equations and solving for q_a, q_b, φ_a, and φ_b, we obtain

$$q_a = \frac{2q(R-b)a}{(R-b)a + (R-a)b},$$

$$q_b = \frac{2q(R-a)b}{(R-b)a + (R-a)b},$$

$$\varphi_a = \varphi_b = \frac{2q(R^2 - ab)}{4\pi\varepsilon_0 R[(R-b)a + (R-a)b]}.$$

Example 5-3.4   A certain charge distribution has a region within which the charge has everywhere the same density ρ. A spherical cavity of radius a is made in this region, the center of the cavity being at the point where the potential originally was φ_c. Find the potential at this point after the cavity is made.

The zero charge density in the cavity can be regarded as two equally large charge densities of opposite polarity, ρ and $-\rho$. By Eq. (5-3.1), the potential at the center of the cavity is then

$$\varphi = \frac{1}{4\pi\varepsilon_0} \int_{\substack{\text{External} \\ \text{region}}} \frac{\rho_e}{r} \, dv' + \frac{1}{4\pi\varepsilon_0} \int_{\text{Cavity}} \frac{\rho}{r} \, dv' - \frac{1}{4\pi\varepsilon_0} \int_{\text{Cavity}} \frac{\rho}{r} \, dv',$$

where the first integral is taken over the region of space external to the cavity (ρ_e is the density of charge in this region). The first two terms of this expression give just the potential φ_c associated with the initial charge distribution. We can therefore write for the potential at the center of the cavity

$$\varphi = \varphi_c - \frac{1}{4\pi\varepsilon_0} \int_{\text{Cavity}} \frac{\rho}{r} \, dv'.$$

Since ρ is constant, it can be factored out from under the integral sign. By symmetry, the volume element dv' can be written as $dv' = 4\pi r^2 dr$. Therefore

$$\varphi = \varphi_c - \frac{\rho}{4\pi\varepsilon_0} \int_0^a \frac{4\pi r^2}{r} \, dr,$$

or

$$\varphi = \varphi_c - \frac{\rho a^2}{2\varepsilon_0}.$$

It is interesting to note that although the cavity affects the potential at the center of the cavity, it does not affect the electric field there, as was shown in Example 4-4.5.

▲

5-4. Representation of Electrostatic Potential in Terms of Multipole Potentials

Multipole is a collective term for certain point charge systems which, in the order of increasing complexity, are called the monopole (one-pole), the dipole (two-pole), the quadrupole (four-pole), the octupole (eight-pole), etc. These names are derived from the number of point charges, or "poles," comprising a given multipole. The number of poles in a multipole is always 2^n, where n, called the *order* of the multipole can be 0, 1, 2, or any other positive integer.

The simplest multipole is that of the order 0, or the *monopole*. The monopole is merely a point charge under a new name.

The multipole of the next higher complexity is the multipole of the order 1, or the *dipole* (Fig. 5.8). The dipole is an arrangement of two monopoles, or point charges, of opposite polarity and equal magnitude separated from each other by a small distance Δl_1 (in the theory of

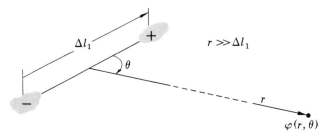

FIG. 5.8   Electric dipole.

multipoles a distance is considered small if it is negligible compared to
the distance from the location of the multipole to the point of observation).

A still more complex multipole is the multipole of the order 2, or
the *quadrupole* (Fig. 5.9). The quadrupole is an arrangement of two
parallel dipoles of opposite polarity,[1] but equal otherwise, separated
from each other by a small distance Δl_2.

In general, now, a multipole of the order n, or a 2^n-pole, is an
arrangement of two multipoles of the order $n - 1$, or 2^{n-1}-poles, having
opposite polarity, having the same orientation in space, and separated
from each other by a small distance Δl_n.

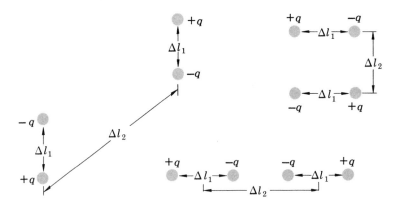

FIG. 5.9   Examples of electric quadrupoles.

[1] Two similar and similarly oriented multipoles are said to be of opposite
polarity if the sign of each charge in one multipole is opposite to the sign of the
similarly located charge in the other multipole. For a given point of observation,
the sign of a multipole is determined by the sign of the potential produced by
the multipole.

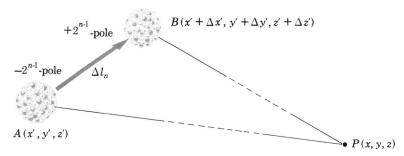

$+2^{n-1}$-pole

$B(x' + \Delta x', y' + \Delta y', z' + \Delta z')$

-2^{n-1}-pole Δl_n

$A(x', y', z')$

$P(x, y, z)$

FIG. 5.10   A 2^n-pole is generated from two 2^{n-1}-poles.

The potential of a 2^n-pole can be expressed in terms of the potentials of the two 2^{n-1}-poles from which the 2^n-pole is made up. Let a negative 2^{n-1}-pole be located at a point $A(x', y', z')$, as shown in Fig. 5.10. Let a similar positive 2^{n-1}-pole be located at a point $B(x' + \Delta x', y' + \Delta y', z' + \Delta z')$ separated from the point A by a small distance Δl_n. Let the potentials produced by these 2^{n-1}-poles be $-\varphi_{n-1}^{(A)}$ and $\varphi_{n-1}^{(B)}$, respectively, where the superscripts indicate the location and the subscripts indicate the order of the multipoles by which the potentials are produced. The two 2^{n-1}-poles together form a 2^n-pole, whose potential φ_n is just the sum of the potentials produced by the two 2^{n-1}-poles. At a point of observation $P(x, y, z)$ we then have

$$\varphi_n = \varphi_{n-1}^{(B)} - \varphi_{n-1}^{(A)}.$$

The difference $\varphi_{n-1}^{(B)} - \varphi_{n-1}^{(A)}$ can be regarded as the increment of the function $\varphi_{n-1}(x', y', z')$ associated with a shift of the source point x', y', z' from A to B. Since the distance Δl_n between the points A and B is small, this increment may be written as the differential

$$\Delta \varphi_{n-1} = \varphi_{n-1}^{(B)} - \varphi_{n-1}^{(A)}.$$

But according to Eq. (2-10.2), this differential can be expressed as

$$\Delta \varphi_{n-1} = \Delta \mathbf{l}_n \cdot \mathbf{\nabla}' \varphi_{n-1} = \Delta l_n \frac{\partial' \varphi_{n-1}}{\partial l_n},$$

where $\Delta \mathbf{l}_n$ is the length element vector drawn from A to B, and where the prime indicates that the differentiation is done with respect to the source point coordinates x', y', z'.[1] Thus we obtain for the potential of a 2^n-pole

$$\varphi_n = \Delta \mathbf{l}_n \cdot \mathbf{\nabla}' \varphi_{n-1}, \quad \text{or} \quad \varphi_n = \Delta l_n \frac{\partial' \varphi_{n-1}}{\partial l_n}. \qquad (5\text{-}4.1a, b)$$

[1] The derivative $\partial' \varphi_{n-1}/\partial l_n$ is the derivative of the function φ_{n-1} with respect to a length increment in the direction of $\Delta \mathbf{l}_n$. It is called the "directional derivative" of φ_{n-1} and, as one can verify by means of a geometrical construction, is equal to the component of $\mathbf{\nabla}' \varphi_{n-1}$ along the direction of $\Delta \mathbf{l}_n$.

Applying either one of these formulas successively to multipoles of different orders, starting with the dipole, we can express the potential of any multipole in terms of the monopole (point charge) potential

$$\varphi_0 = \frac{q}{4\pi\varepsilon_0 r}.$$

Using Eq. (5-4.1b), we obtain for a dipole $(n = 1)$

$$\varphi_1 = \Delta l_1 \frac{\partial'\varphi_0}{\partial l_1} = \Delta l_1 \frac{\partial'}{\partial l_1}\left(\frac{q}{4\pi\varepsilon_0 r}\right),$$

or

$$\varphi_1 = \frac{q\Delta l_1}{4\pi\varepsilon_0} \frac{\partial'}{\partial l_1}\left(\frac{1}{r}\right). \tag{5-4.2}$$

For a quadrupole $(n = 2)$, we then have

$$\varphi_2 = \Delta l_2 \frac{\partial'\varphi_1}{\partial l_2} = \Delta l_2 \frac{\partial'}{\partial l_2}\left[\frac{q\Delta l_1}{4\pi\varepsilon_0} \frac{\partial'}{\partial l_1}\left(\frac{1}{r}\right)\right],$$

or

$$\varphi_2 = \frac{q\Delta l_2 \Delta l_1}{4\pi\varepsilon_0} \frac{\partial'^2}{\partial l_2 \partial l_1}\left(\frac{1}{r}\right). \tag{5-4.3}$$

By induction, the potential of a 2^n-pole is therefore

$$\varphi_n = \frac{q\Delta l_n \Delta l_{n-1} \cdots \Delta l_1}{4\pi\varepsilon_0} \frac{\partial'^n}{\partial l_n \partial l_{n-1} \cdots \partial l_1}\left(\frac{1}{r}\right).$$

The potential of a 2^n-pole can be found from the formula

$$\varphi_n = \frac{p^{(n)}}{4\pi\varepsilon_0 n!} \frac{\partial'^n}{\partial l_n \partial l_{n-1} \cdots \partial l_1}\left(\frac{1}{r}\right), \tag{5-4.4}$$

where the differentiation is with respect to the source point coordinates and

$$p^{(n)} = n! \, q\Delta l_n \Delta l_{n-1} \cdots \Delta l_1. \tag{5-4.5}$$

The quantity $p^{(n)}$ is called the *multipole moment*. It is positive if $\Delta \mathbf{l}_n$ is directed from a 2^{n-1}-pole with a negative moment to a 2^{n-1}-pole with a positive moment.

If a multipole consists of point charges lying on one single axis, the multipole is called an *axial multipole*. For an axial multipole all Δl's are along the axis, so that if we take this axis as the z-axis, we have

$$\varphi_{n(\text{axial})} = \frac{p^{(n)}}{4\pi\varepsilon_0 n!} \frac{\partial^n}{\partial z'^n}\left(\frac{1}{r}\right). \tag{5-4.6}$$

This formula can be transformed into a more convenient one by means of the following considerations. Observe that the dimensions of

r are [length] and the dimensions of z'^n are [length]^n. Hence the dimensions of the quantity $\dfrac{1}{n!}\dfrac{\partial^n}{\partial z'^n}\left(\dfrac{1}{r}\right)$ are [length]$^{-(n+1)}$, which is the same as the dimensions of $1/r^{n+1}$. Therefore we can write

$$\frac{1}{n!}\frac{\partial^n}{\partial z'^n}\left(\frac{1}{r}\right) = \frac{P_n}{r^{n+1}}, \tag{5-4.7}$$

where P_n is a dimensionless coefficient. This coefficient occurs in many physical formulas and is called the *Legendre polynomial of the first kind.*

TABLE 5-I

Legendre Polynomials of the First (P_n) and Second (Q_n) Kind.[a]

n	$P_n(\mu)$	$Q_n(\mu)$
0	1	$\frac{1}{2}\ln\dfrac{1+\mu}{1-\mu}$
1	μ	$\frac{1}{2}\mu\ln\dfrac{1+\mu}{1-\mu} - 1$
2	$\frac{1}{2}(3\mu^2 - 1)$	$\frac{1}{4}(3\mu^2 - 1)\ln\dfrac{1+\mu}{1-\mu} - \frac{3}{2}\mu$
3	$\frac{1}{2}(5\mu^3 - 3\mu)$	$\frac{1}{2}P_3(\mu)\ln\dfrac{1+\mu}{1-\mu} - \frac{5}{3}P_2(\mu) - \frac{1}{6}$

[a] μ stands for $\cos\theta$.

The values of P_n for different n can be obtained from Eq. (5-4.7) by differentiating $1/r$ and can be tabulated for future reference. The values of P_0, P_1, P_2, and P_3 are given in Table 5-I.[1] For $n \geq 1$, all P_n's can be expressed as functions of $\cos\theta$, where θ is the angle between the z-axis (or a polar axis in general) and the radius vector drawn from the source point x', y', z' to the point of observation x, y, z.

Using Eq. (5-4.7), we can rewrite Eq. (5-4.6) as

$$\varphi_{n(\text{axial})} = \frac{p^{(n)}}{4\pi\varepsilon_0}\frac{P_n}{r^{n+1}}. \tag{5-4.8}$$

With the aid of this formula and a table of P_n's, the potential of any axial multipole having a known multipole moment $p^{(n)}$ can be found immediately.

---

[1] Table 5-I contains also Legendre polynomials of the *second kind* used in the "method of harmonics" (Section 6.3).

Next to the point charge, the most frequently encountered multipole is the dipole ($n = 1$). The dipole moment $p^{(1)}$ is by Eq. (5-4.5) just $q\Delta l_1$. It is customary to designate the dipole moment simply as p, without the superscript. The potential of a dipole, φ_1, is then, by Eq. (5-4.8) and Table 5-I,

$$\varphi_{\text{dipole}} = \frac{p}{4\pi\varepsilon_0}\frac{\cos\theta}{r^2},\tag{5-4.9}$$

where θ is the angle between r and the axis of the dipole as shown in Fig. 5.8. The potential of a dipole oriented in an arbitrary manner can be best found from Eq. (5-4.1a). Using this equation, we have

$$\varphi_{\text{dipole}} = \Delta\mathbf{l}_1 \cdot \mathbf{\nabla}'\varphi_0 = \Delta\mathbf{l}_1 \cdot \mathbf{\nabla}'\left(\frac{q}{4\pi\varepsilon_0 r}\right) = \frac{q\Delta\mathbf{l}_1}{4\pi\varepsilon_0} \cdot \mathbf{\nabla}'\left(\frac{1}{r}\right).$$

The product $q\Delta\mathbf{l}_1$ is called the *dipole moment vector* $\mathbf{p}$. It is directed from the negative to the positive charge of a dipole. By means of $\mathbf{p}$, the dipole potential can be written in any of the following forms:

$$\varphi_{\text{dipole}} = \frac{\mathbf{p}}{4\pi\varepsilon_0} \cdot \mathbf{\nabla}'\left(\frac{1}{r}\right) = -\frac{\mathbf{p}}{4\pi\varepsilon_0} \cdot \mathbf{\nabla}\left(\frac{1}{r}\right) = \frac{\mathbf{p}\cdot\mathbf{r}_u}{4\pi\varepsilon_0 r^2} = \frac{\mathbf{p}\cdot\mathbf{r}}{4\pi\varepsilon_0 r^3}.$$

$$\text{(5-4.10a, b, c, d)}$$

Since $\mathbf{p} = p_x\mathbf{i} + p_y\mathbf{j} + p_z\mathbf{k}$ and $\mathbf{r} = (x - x')\mathbf{i} + (y - y')\mathbf{j} + (z - z')\mathbf{k}$, the last expression for φ_{dipole} can be written in terms of rectangular coordinates as

$$\varphi_{\text{dipole}} = \frac{1}{4\pi\varepsilon_0 r^3}[p_x(x - x') + p_y(y - y') + p_z(z - z')].\tag{5-4.11}$$

By taking the gradient of a multipole potential, the electric field of the multipole can be found:

$$\mathbf{E}_n = -\mathbf{\nabla}\varphi_n.\tag{5-4.12}$$

Thus, for instance, from Eq. (5-4.9) we have, using the expression for the gradient in spherical coordinates (Table 2-I),

$$\mathbf{E}_{\text{dipole}} = -\mathbf{\nabla}\varphi_{\text{dipole}} = -\frac{p}{4\pi\varepsilon_0}\left[\frac{\partial}{\partial r}\left(\frac{\cos\theta}{r^2}\right)\mathbf{r}_u + \frac{\partial}{r\partial\theta}\left(\frac{\cos\theta}{r^2}\right)\mathbf{\theta}_u\right],$$

or

$$\mathbf{E}_{\text{dipole}} = \frac{p}{2\pi\varepsilon_0}\frac{\cos\theta}{r^3}\mathbf{r}_u + \frac{p}{4\pi\varepsilon_0}\frac{\sin\theta}{r^3}\mathbf{\theta}_u.\tag{5-4.13}$$

The magnitude of the dipole field is then

$$E = \sqrt{E_r^2 + E_\theta^2} = \frac{p}{4\pi\varepsilon_0 r^3}\sqrt{4\cos^2\theta + \sin^2\theta},$$

or

$$E = \frac{p}{4\pi\varepsilon_0 r^3} \sqrt{1 + 3\cos^2\theta}. \qquad (5\text{-}4.14)$$

▼

Example 5-4.1   Find the potential produced at a point $P(r, \theta)$ by the

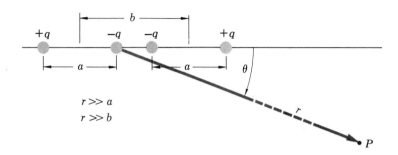

FIG. 5.11   Calculation of the potential produced by a linear quadrupole.

For a quadrupole, $n = 2$. The moment of the quadrupole under consideration is, by Eq. (5-4.5), $2qab$. The potential is then, by Eq. (5-4.8) and Table 5-I,

$$\varphi_{2(\text{axial})} = \frac{qab}{4\pi\varepsilon_0} \frac{3\cos^2\theta - 1}{r^3}.$$

Example 5-4.2   Find the potential produced at the point $P(x, y, 0)$ by the square quadrupole shown in Fig. 5.12.

The moment of this quadrupole is, by Eq. (5-4.5), $2qa^2$. The potential,

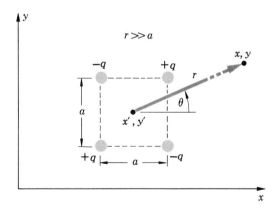

FIG. 5.12   Calculation of the potential produced by a square quadrupole.

by Eq. (5-4.4), is

$$\varphi_{2(\text{square})} = \frac{2qa^2}{4\pi\varepsilon_0 2!} \frac{\partial^2}{\partial y' \partial x'}\left(\frac{1}{r}\right)$$

$$= \frac{qa^2}{4\pi\varepsilon_0} \frac{\partial}{\partial y'}\left(\frac{x-x'}{r^3}\right) = \frac{3qa^2}{4\pi\varepsilon_0} \frac{(x-x')(y-y')}{r^5} = \frac{3qa^2}{4\pi\varepsilon_0} \frac{\cos\theta\sin\theta}{r^3},$$

where we have used $r = \sqrt{(x-x')^2 + (y-y')^2 + (z-z')^2}$.

Example 5-4.3   Find the quadrupole moment of a system of two positive charges q separated by a distance $2a$ and a negative charge $-2q$ placed midway between them (Fig. 5.13).

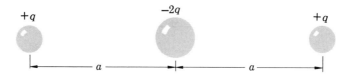

FIG. 5.13   Example of the calculation of a quadrupole moment.

The system may be regarded as a linear quadrupole formed by two dipoles of moment qa separated from each other by a distance a. Hence, by Eq. (5-4.5), the quadrupole moment of the system is $2qa^2$.

Example 5-4.4   Express the electric field of an arbitrarily oriented dipole located at $x' = y' = z' = 0$ in terms of rectangular coordinates.

Since $\mathbf{E}_{\text{dipole}} = -\boldsymbol{\nabla}\varphi_{\text{dipole}}$, we obtain by differentiating Eq. (5-4.11):

$$E_x = -\frac{p_x}{4\pi\varepsilon_0 r^3} + \frac{3(p_x x^2 + p_y yx + p_z zx)}{4\pi\varepsilon_0 r^5},$$

$$E_y = -\frac{p_y}{4\pi\varepsilon_0 r^3} + \frac{3(p_x xy + p_y y^2 + p_z zy)}{4\pi\varepsilon_0 r^5},$$

$$E_z = -\frac{p_z}{4\pi\varepsilon_0 r^3} + \frac{3(p_x xz + p_y yz + p_z z^2)}{4\pi\varepsilon_0 r^5}.$$

Example 5-4.5   Find the value of the Legendre polynomial $P_n(\cos\theta)$ for $\theta = 0$.

If $\theta = 0$, the point of observation x, y, z lies on the z-axis, so that $r = z - z'$. In this case we have, by Eq. (5-4.7),

$$P_n(\cos\theta) = P_n(1) = \frac{(z-z')^{n+1}}{n!}\frac{\partial^n}{\partial z'^n}\left(\frac{1}{z-z'}\right).$$

But

$$\frac{\partial^n}{\partial z'^n}\left(\frac{1}{z-z'}\right) = \frac{\partial^{n-1}}{\partial z'^{n-1}}\left[\frac{1}{(z-z')^2}\right]$$

$$= \frac{\partial^{n-2}}{\partial z'^{n-2}}\left[\frac{2\cdot 1}{(z-z')^3}\right] = \cdots = \frac{n!}{(z-z')^{n+1}}.$$

Therefore

$$P_n(1) = 1.$$

▲

5-5. Expansion of Electrostatic Potential in a Series of Multipole Potentials★

The introduction of the multipole concept into the theory of electric phenomena results in a new method for expressing the potential of a charge distribution. This method can be stated in the form of the following *multipole theorem:* the electrostatic potential of a charge distribution in the space outside an imaginary sphere enclosing this distribution can be expressed as a convergent series of multipole potentials.

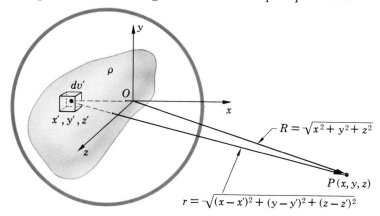

FIG. 5.14   The potential of a charge distribution can be expressed as a series of multipole potentials if the point of observation is outside an imaginary sphere enclosing the charge distribution.

To prove this theorem, let us place a system of rectangular coordinates in or near some charge distribution, as shown in Fig. 5.14. Let R be the distance between the point of observation $P(x, y, z)$ and the origin of the coordinates O, so that $R = \sqrt{x^2 + y^2 + z^2}$. Let r be the

★ This section may be omitted without loss of continuity.

distance between the point of observation and a source point x', y', z', so that $r = \sqrt{(x - x')^2 + (y - y')^2 + (z - z')^2}$. If the point of observation is outside an imaginary sphere enclosing the charge distribution, the quantity

$$\frac{1}{r} = \frac{1}{\sqrt{(x - x')^2 + (y - y')^2 + (z - z')^2}}$$

can be expanded in a convergent power series of x', y', z' about O. By Taylor's theorem of calculus, this series is

$$\frac{1}{r} = \frac{1}{R} - \left[x' \frac{\partial}{\partial x}\left(\frac{1}{R}\right) + y' \frac{\partial}{\partial y}\left(\frac{1}{R}\right) + z' \frac{\partial}{\partial z}\left(\frac{1}{R}\right) \right]$$

$$+ \frac{1}{2!}\left[x'^2 \frac{\partial^2}{\partial x^2}\left(\frac{1}{R}\right) + y'^2 \frac{\partial^2}{\partial y^2}\left(\frac{1}{R}\right) + z'^2 \frac{\partial^2}{\partial z^2}\left(\frac{1}{R}\right) \right.$$

$$+ x'y' \frac{\partial^2}{\partial x\, \partial y}\left(\frac{1}{R}\right) + y'x' \frac{\partial^2}{\partial y\, \partial x}\left(\frac{1}{R}\right) + y'z' \frac{\partial^2}{\partial y\, \partial z}\left(\frac{1}{R}\right)$$

$$\left. + z'y' \frac{\partial^2}{\partial z\, \partial y}\left(\frac{1}{R}\right) + z'x' \frac{\partial^2}{\partial z\, \partial x}\left(\frac{1}{R}\right) + x'z' \frac{\partial^2}{\partial x\, \partial z}\left(\frac{1}{R}\right) \right] - \cdots.$$

If we substitute this series into the Poisson integral for electrostatic potential, factor out all derivatives from under the integral signs (the derivatives are not functions of primed coordinates), and then replace the derivatives by those with respect to x', y', z', we obtain

$$\varphi(x, y, z) = \frac{1}{4\pi\varepsilon_0} \int \frac{\rho}{r}\, dv' = \frac{1}{4\pi\varepsilon_0 R} \int \rho\, dv' + \left[\frac{1}{4\pi\varepsilon_0} \frac{\partial}{\partial x'}\left(\frac{1}{r}\right)_{r=R} \int x'\rho\, dv' \right.$$

$$\left. + \cdots \right] + \left[\frac{1}{4\pi\varepsilon_0 2!} \frac{\partial^2}{\partial x'^2}\left(\frac{1}{r}\right)_{r=R} \int x'^2\rho\, dv' + \cdots \right.$$

$$\left. + \frac{1}{4\pi\varepsilon_0 2!} \frac{\partial^2}{\partial x'\, \partial y'}\left(\frac{1}{r}\right)_{r=R} \int x'y'\rho\, dv' + \cdots \right] + \cdots . \quad (5\text{-}5.1)$$

By Eq. (5-3.4), the first term of this expression is just the point charge potential (monopole potential) that would be produced at P if the total charge of the distribution, $q = \int \rho\, dv'$, were concentrated at the origin. By Eqs. (5-4.4) and (5-4.5), the terms in the first bracket are the potentials that would be produced at P if three dipoles oriented along the x, y, and z axes and having the moments

$$p_x = \int x'\rho\, dv', \qquad p_y = \int y'\rho\, dv', \qquad p_z = \int z'\rho\, dv' \quad (5\text{-}5.2)$$

were placed at the origin. Similarly, the terms in the second bracket are the potentials that would be produced at P if nine appropriately oriented quadrupoles of moments

$$p_{xx} = \int x'^2 \rho \, dv' \qquad p_{xy} = \int x'y' \rho \, dv' \qquad p_{xz} = \int x'z' \rho \, dv'$$

$$p_{yx} = \int y'x' \rho \, dv' \qquad p_{yy} = \int y'^2 \rho \, dv' \qquad p_{yz} = \int y'z' \rho \, dv' \quad (5\text{-}5.3)$$

$$p_{zx} = \int z'x' \rho \, dv' \qquad p_{zy} = \int z'y' \rho \, dv' \qquad p_{zz} = \int z'^2 \rho \, dv'$$

were placed at the origin. As the same line of reasoning can be continued to include still higher multipoles, we see that the multipole theorem stated above is true.

An important consequence of the multipole theorem is that as far as the electrostatic potential outside a charge distribution is concerned, a charge distribution may be *replaced* by a system of multipoles whose moments are given by Eqs. (5-5.2) and (5-5.3), and by similar equations for higher multipoles.[1] The number of multipoles in such a system depends largely on the accuracy with which the potential must be represented. For a charge distribution in which the charge density has everywhere the same sign, the multipoles that must be included in the system can be determined as follows. Examining the dimensions of the quantities involved in Eq. (5-5.1), we recognize that the potential contributed by a 2^n-pole to the total potential of the system is approximately $qa^n/4\pi\varepsilon_0 R^{n+1}$, where q is the total charge and a is the average linear dimension of the charge distribution under consideration. The ratio of the potential of a 2^n-pole to the potential of the point charge q (dominant potential of the system) is then approximately $(a/R)^n$. Therefore no multipoles of an order higher than n need be included in the system unless the accuracy of the total potential must exceed $(a/R)^n \cdot 100\%$.

▼

Example 5-5.1   Construct a system of multipoles reproducing the potential of a uniformly charged cube of total charge q and side $2a$ so that the error in the potential does not exceed 1% at $R \geq 10a$, where R is the distance between the center of the cube and the point of observation.

Since for $(1/10)^n \leq 1\%$, n needs not be larger than 2, no multipoles beyond the quadrupoles are needed. Let the cube be oriented as shown in

---

[1] Axially symmetric charge distributions may also be replaced by axial multipoles which are all confined to the axis of symmetry (see Section 6-4).

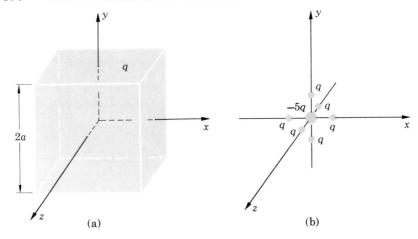

Fɪɢ. 5.15   The potential of a charged cube can be approximated by a cluster of point charges.

Fig. 5.15a. By Eq. (5-5.2), the dipole moments are

$$p_x = \int x' \rho \, dv' = 4\rho a^2 \int_{-a}^{+a} x' dx' = 0,$$

and similarly

$$p_y = 0, \qquad p_z = 0.$$

By Eq. (5-5.3), the quadrupole moments are

$$p_{xx} = \int x'^2 \rho \, dv' = 4\rho a^2 \int_{-a}^{+a} x'^2 \, dx' = \rho \frac{8a^5}{3} = \tfrac{1}{3} q a^2,$$

and similarly

$$p_{yy} = \tfrac{1}{3} q a^2, \qquad p_{zz} = \tfrac{1}{3} q a^2.$$

All other quadrupole moments are zero, by symmetry (for example, $p_{xy} = \int x'y' \rho \, dv' = \rho \int x'y' dv' = 0$ because to every positive $x'y'$ there corresponds an equally large negative $x'y'$). Hence the system of multipoles that we are seeking consists merely of a point charge q and three axial quadrupoles placed at the origin. By Eq. (5-4.5), the moment of an axial quadrupole can be written as $p^{(2)} = 2 q(\Delta l)^2$, so that for Δl of p_{xx}, p_{yy}, and p_{zz} in the present case we can write

$$\tfrac{1}{3} q a^2 = 2q(\Delta l)^2,$$

or

$$\Delta l = \frac{a}{\sqrt 6}.$$

By Example 5-4.3, the quadrupole on the x-axis (p_{xx}) can then be constructed by placing a negative charge $-2q$ at the origin and two positive charges q

at the points $x = \pm a/\sqrt{6}$. The quadrupoles on the y and z axes are constructed in the same manner. The final multipole system is shown in Fig. 5.15b. The total charge at the origin is $Q = q - 6q = -5q$. Each charge on the axes is q, each is placed at the distance $a/\sqrt{6}$ from the origin.

▲

Problems

5.1. Taking into account that air becomes conducting when an electric field in it reaches about $3 \cdot 10^6$ volt/m, determine the radius of the smallest sphere that can be charged in air to a potential of 10^6 volts.

5.2. A spherical conductor of radius a carrying a charge q_a is surrounded by a thin, concentric spherical conductor of radius b carrying a charge q_b. Find the potential produced by these conductors at all points of space.

5.3. A certain electric field is given by $\mathbf{E} = E_0 R^2 \mathbf{r}/r^3$ for $r \geq R$ and $\mathbf{E} = E_0 r \mathbf{r}/R^2$ for $r \leq R$, where E_0 and R are constants, and $\mathbf{r}$ is a radius vector in spherical coordinates. Show that the potential in this field is

$$\varphi = E_0 \frac{R^2}{r}, \qquad\qquad r \geq R,$$

$$\varphi = \frac{1}{3} E_0 R \left(4 - \frac{r^3}{R^3} \right), \qquad r \leq R.$$

5.4. Taking as the reference potential $\varphi(r_0) = 0$, show that the potential due to a charge of uniform density ρ forming an infinitely long cylinder of radius $a < r_0$ is, in cylindrical coordinates,

$$\varphi = -\frac{\rho a^2}{2\varepsilon_0} \ln r + \frac{\rho a^2}{2\varepsilon_0} \ln r_0, \qquad r \geq a,$$

$$\varphi = \frac{\rho}{4\varepsilon_0} (a^2 - r^2) + \frac{\rho a^2}{2\varepsilon_0} \ln \frac{r_0}{a}, \qquad r \leq a,$$

and find the voltage between the axis and the surface of the charge-filled region.

5.5. Using the data of Problem 4.11, derive the equation for the potential φ of the earth's electric field with respect to the ground, plot φ against the altitude h, and give the values of φ at $h = 1, 10$, and 20 km.

5.6. An infinite slab of charge has a charge density ρ and thickness t. Find the potential at all points of space, using the midplane of the slab as the reference plane.

5.7. Using the data of Problem 4.14, find the potential of a normal hydrogen atom at all points of space.

5.8. A voltage V is applied between two concentric conducting spheres of radius a and b $(a < b)$. Show that if the outer sphere is grounded, the potential in the space between the spheres is

$$\varphi(r) = V \frac{(b-r)a}{(b-a)r}.$$

5.9. A voltage V is applied between two coaxial conducting cylinders of radius a and b $(a < b)$. Neglecting end effects, show that if the outer cylinder is grounded, the potential in the space between the cylinders is

$$\varphi(r) = V \frac{\ln b - \ln r}{\ln b - \ln a}.$$

5.10. The plates of a thin parallel-plate capacitor of area A are separated by a distance d. Show that if a sheet of metal of thickness t is inserted between the plates, the capacitance is increased by the amount

$$\Delta C = \frac{\varepsilon_0 t A}{d(d-t)}.$$

5.11. A capacitor is made of two metal spheres of radii a and b which are separated by a distance $d \gg a, b$. Show that the capacitance of this capacitor is approximately

$$C = 4\pi\varepsilon_0 \left(\frac{1}{a} + \frac{1}{b} - \frac{2}{d} \right)^{-1}.$$

5.12. Show that for a given voltage the electric field at the surface of the inner sphere of a concentric spherical capacitor is least if the radius of this sphere is one-half the internal radius of the outer sphere.

5.13. Show that for a given voltage the electric field at the surface of the inner cylinder of a coaxial cylindrical capacitor is least if the radius of this cylinder is $1/e$ of the internal radius of the outer cylinder (neglect end effects).

5.14. A capacitor is made of three conducting thin-walled concentric spheres of radii a, b, and c $(a < b < c)$. The inner and the outer spheres are connected by a fine insulated wire passing through a small hole in the intermediate sphere. Show that the capacitance of this capacitor is

$$C = 4\pi\varepsilon_0 \left(\frac{ab}{b-a} + \frac{cb}{c-b} \right)$$

and find how the electric charge placed on the sphere b distributes itself between the two surfaces of the sphere.

5.15. Show that if the inner conductor in Problem 5.2 is connected by a fine insulating conducting wire passing through a small hole in the outer conductor to a distant uncharged conducting sphere of radius c, the sphere will acquire a charge which in the first approximation is

$$q_c = \frac{q_a b + q_b a}{b(a+c)} c.$$

5.16. A thin rod carrying a uniformly distributed charge q is bent to form the arc of a circle of radius r. Show that the potential at the center of the circle is

$$\varphi = \frac{q}{4\pi\varepsilon_0 r}$$

and that this potential is the same as the potential at the center of a thin, uniformly charged, hemisphere of radius r carrying the charge q.

5.17. Show that the potential due to a straight uniform line charge of length $2L$ and density λ lying along the x-axis of a rectangular system of coordinates, with the center at the origin, is

$$\varphi(x, y, z) = \frac{\lambda}{4\pi\varepsilon_0} \ln \frac{(x + L) + \sqrt{(x + L)^2 + y^2 + z^2}}{(x - L) + \sqrt{(x - L)^2 + y^2 + z^2}}.$$

5.18. Show that the potential at a point on the circumference of a uniform circular disk of surface charge density σ and radius a is

$$\varphi = \frac{\sigma a}{\pi\varepsilon_0}.$$

5.19. Find the electric field produced by a thin, straight rod of length $2L$ carrying a charge q, by using the potential found in Problem 5.17.

5.20. The electrodes of a certain discharge tube have the form of a thin parallel-plate capacitor of plate separation d. The potential in the space between these electrodes has been found to have the form

$$\varphi = V(x/d)^\alpha,$$

where x is the distance from the negative plate, V is the voltage between the electrodes, and α is a constant. (a) Find the electric field vector in the space between the electrodes. (b) Find the space charge density in this space. (c) Find the surface charge density on the electrodes.

5.21. The potential φ in a certain discharge tube, as measured with the aid of probes, is shown in Fig. 5.16, as a function of the distance from the positive electrode. Using this curve for φ, obtain the corresponding curves for the electric field vector **E** and for the space charge density ρ in this tube (assume that the field is a function of the distance along the tube only).

5.22. Show that the potential measured at a point of the model described in Problem 4.23 is mn^{-1} times the potential at the corresponding point of the actual system.

5.23. Derive Eq. (5-4.9) directly, by adding the potentials of the point charges which make up the dipole.

5.24. Under certain idealized conditions the electric field outside a spherical artificial satellite has the potential expressed in spherical coordinates centered at the center of the satellite

$$\varphi = A \frac{\cos\theta}{r^2} - B \frac{1}{r^3}(3\cos^2\theta - 1),$$

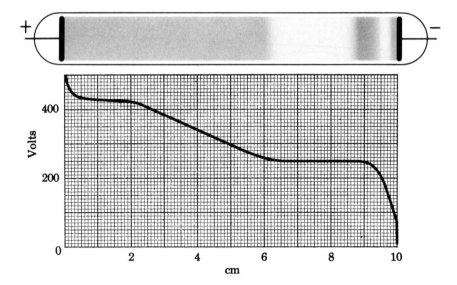

FIG. 5.16 Distribution of electric potential in a discharge tube. From a curve like this, the electric field and charge distribution in the tube can be determined by graphical analysis.

where A and B are constants. With the aid of Section 5-4, show that this potential can be attributed to a system of multipoles and find the multipole moments of this system.

5.25. Show that the electrostatic potential of any unconfined spherically symmetric charge distribution in the space outside the distribution is the same as if the total charge q of the distribution were concentrated at its center, and show that the formula

$$\varphi = \frac{q}{4\pi\varepsilon_0 r}$$

is true for the external potential of all unconfined spherically symmetric charge distributions. Then do the next problem.

5.26. A conducting sphere of radius a carrying a charge q is confined within a larger conducting sphere of inner radius b and outer radius b'. The centers of the spheres coincide. Show that the potential of the system is

$$\varphi = \frac{q}{4\pi\varepsilon_0 r} \quad \text{for} \quad r \geq b',$$

$$\varphi = \frac{q}{4\pi\varepsilon_0 b'} \quad \text{for} \quad b \leq r \leq b',$$

and

$$\varphi = \frac{q}{4\pi\varepsilon_0 r b b'} (bb' - rb' + rb) \quad \text{for} \quad a \leq r \leq b.$$

5.27. Using Eqs. (5-4.10d) and (5-3.11), show that the electric field of a dipole can be expressed as

$$\mathbf{E}_{\text{dipole}} = \frac{1}{4\pi\varepsilon_0 r^5} [3(\mathbf{p} \cdot \mathbf{r})\mathbf{r} - \mathbf{p}r^2].$$

5.28. ★ Verify the results of Example 5-4.3 by using Eq. (5-5.3).

5.29. ★ A point charge $2q$ is placed at the center of a ring charge $-q$ of radius a. (a) Determine φ for $R > a$ up to but not including terms in R^4 using the expansion formula for φ. (b) Show by direct calculation that this φ is correct for any point on the symmetry axis. (c) Find and sketch a symmetrical arrangement of point charges (multipoles) that would produce the same potential as the actual charge distribution does up to the terms in R^4.

5.30. ★ Construct a system of multipoles reproducing the potential of a uniformly charged square plate of total charge q and side $2a$ so that the error in the potential does not exceed 0.1% at $R \geq 10a$, where R is the distance from the center of the plate.

5.31. ★ Find the surface charge of an artificial satellite using the potential given in Problem 5.24, then find the dipole and quadrupole moments of this charge using formulas of Section 5-5, and finally show that these moments agree with those found in Problem 5.24.

5.32. ★ Show that for a charge distribution whose total charge is zero, the dipole moment of the distribution is a characteristic constant and does not depend on the location of a rectangular system of coordinates used for the calculation of the dipole moment.

5.33. ★ Show that for a charge distribution whose total charge is not zero, one can always find a point for the origin of a system of rectangular coordinates such that the dipole moment of the distribution would be zero (this point is called the *center of charge* of the distribution).

★ This problem is based on the material presented in Section 5-5.

6

SPECIAL METHODS
FOR THE SOLUTION
OF ELECTROSTATIC
PROBLEMS

The general methods for solving electrostatic problems which we used in the preceding chapters are not always practicable. Therefore various special, more expedient methods have been developed for solving certain types of frequently encountered electrostatic problems. In this chapter we shall study some of the most common methods of this type.

6-1. Poisson's and Laplace's Equations

Combining the divergence law, Eq. (4-4.2b), with the displacement law, Eq. (4-4.3), and replacing $\mathbf{E}$ with $-\nabla\varphi$ by means of Eq. (5-1.1), we obtain

$$\rho = \nabla \cdot \mathbf{D} = \nabla \cdot (\varepsilon_0\mathbf{E}) = \varepsilon_0\nabla \cdot \mathbf{E} = -\varepsilon_0\nabla \cdot \nabla\varphi = -\varepsilon_0\nabla^2\varphi,$$

or

$$\nabla^2\varphi = -\frac{\rho}{\varepsilon_0}. \tag{6-1.1}$$

This differential equation is called *Poisson's equation*. As far as the calculation of φ is concerned, Poisson's equation is of little use if ρ is known everywhere in space, because in this case φ can be obtained directly from the Poisson integral (5-3.1), which is the solution of Poisson's equation for this particular case (see Problem 6.6). However, while the Poisson integral can be used for calculating φ only if ρ is known everywhere in space, Poisson's equation can be used for calculating φ even if

ρ is known only in a limited region of space, provided that certain additional data concerning φ, called *boundary conditions*, are available for the boundary of this region. And, of course, Poisson's equation can be used for determining ρ if φ is known.

A special case of Poisson's equation is *Laplace's equation*

$$\nabla^2\varphi = 0, \tag{6-1.2}$$

to which Poisson's equation reduces in charge-free regions. Laplace's equation is especially useful for determining the electrostatic potential in charge-free space surrounding charged conductors, which is one of the most frequently encountered electrostatic problems.

▼

Example 6-1.1   A voltage V is applied to a thin parallel-plate capacitor of plate separation d filled with a cloud of charge of constant density ρ (Fig. 6.1). Find the potential inside the capacitor with respect to the positive plate, find the electric field vector **E** inside the capacitor, and find the surface charge density σ on the inner surfaces of the plates.

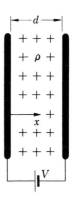

FIG. 6.1   Electrostatic potential in a capacitor filled with charge can be found from Poisson's equation.

The geometry of the problem is such that φ can vary only in the direction normal to the plates. Let this direction be the direction of the x-axis, and let the positive plate lie in the yz-plane of a rectangular system of coordinates. Since φ is then a function of x only, Poisson's equation for this problem reduces to

$$\frac{d^2\varphi}{dx^2} = -\frac{\rho}{\varepsilon_0}.$$

The boundary conditions are:

(1) at $x = 0$, $\varphi = \varphi_0$;

(2) at $x = d$, $\varphi = -V + \varphi_0$.

Integrating the Poisson equation, we obtain

$$\frac{d\varphi}{dx} = -\frac{\rho x}{\varepsilon_0} + C_1,$$

$$\varphi = -\frac{\rho x^2}{2\varepsilon_0} + C_1 x + C_2,$$

where C_1 and C_2 are constants of integration. Substituting the first boundary condition in the last equation, we have

$$C_2 = \varphi_0.$$

Substituting the second boundary condition in the same equation, we have

$$-V + \varphi_0 = -\frac{\rho d^2}{2\varepsilon_0} + C_1 d + \varphi_0,$$

so that

$$C_1 = -\frac{V}{d} + \frac{\rho d}{2\varepsilon_0}.$$

The potential in the space between the plates is therefore

$$\varphi = -\frac{\rho x^2}{2\varepsilon_0} + \left(\frac{\rho d}{2\varepsilon_0} - \frac{V}{d}\right)x + \varphi_0$$

(observe that for $\rho = 0$ this expression becomes the same as the one obtained in Example 5-1.1).

The electric field between the plates may be found by taking the negative gradient of φ, and after a rearrangement of terms we obtain

$$\mathbf{E} = \left[\frac{V}{d} + \frac{\rho}{2\varepsilon_0}(2x - d)\right]\mathbf{i}.$$

The surface charge density on the inner surfaces of the plates is equal to the magnitude of the displacement $\mathbf{D}$, or $\varepsilon_0 \mathbf{E}$, at these surfaces. For the positive plate, $x = 0$, we obtain from the last equation

$$\sigma = \varepsilon_0 \frac{V}{d} - \frac{\rho d}{2}.$$

For the negative plate, $x = d$, we obtain, reversing the sign,

$$\sigma = -\varepsilon_0 \frac{V}{d} - \frac{\rho d}{2}.$$

Example 6-1.2   Show that the electrostatic potential of a point charge (Coulomb's potential) satisfies Laplace's equation.

The point charge potential is, by Eq. (5-3.4),

$$\varphi = \frac{q}{4\pi\varepsilon_0 r} + \varphi_o.$$

Using the expression for the Laplacian in spherical coordinates (Table 2-I) and observing that the point charge potential is a function of r only, we have

$$\nabla^2 \varphi = \nabla^2 \frac{q}{4\pi\varepsilon_0 r} = \frac{q}{4\pi\varepsilon_0} \nabla^2 \frac{1}{r} = \frac{q}{4\pi\varepsilon_0} \frac{1}{r^2} \frac{\partial}{\partial r}\left[r^2 \frac{\partial}{\partial r}\left(\frac{1}{r}\right)\right]$$

$$= -\frac{q}{4\pi\varepsilon_0} \frac{1}{r^2} \frac{d}{dr}\left(r^2 \frac{1}{r^2}\right) = 0$$

(observe that, by the definition of a point charge, r is always larger than zero, so that the effect of $r = 0$ on the above expressions need not be investigated).

▲

6-2. Uniqueness of Solution of Electrostatic Problems

The most important special methods for the solution of electrostatic problems are based on the fact that electrostatic potential in charge-free space must satisfy Laplace's equation and on the three *uniqueness theorems* presented below.

Uniqueness Theorem I. There can be only one distribution of electrostatic potential which in a limited region of space satisfies Laplace's equation and reduces to prescribed values at the boundaries of the region.

To prove this theorem, let us assume that there can be two distributions of the potential, φ_1 and φ_2, both of which satisfy Laplace's equation and reduce to the same prescribed values at the boundaries of the region under consideration (Fig. 6.2). On the boundaries we then have $\varphi_1 = \varphi_2$, or

$$\varphi_1 - \varphi_2 = 0 \qquad \text{(boundaries)}. \tag{6-2.1}$$

Since φ_1 and φ_2 satisfy Laplace's equation, we have everywhere within the region $\nabla^2\varphi_1 = 0$ and $\nabla^2\varphi_2 = 0$, so that

$$\nabla^2(\varphi_1 - \varphi_2) = 0 \qquad \text{(region)}. \tag{6-2.2}$$

If we now substitute Eqs. (6-2.1) and (6-2.2) into the first Green's theorem of vector analysis

$$\int (U_1\nabla^2 U_2 + \nabla U_1 \cdot \nabla U_2)\,dv = \oint U_1\nabla U_2 \cdot d\mathbf{S} \tag{V-24}$$

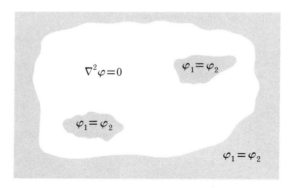

FIG. 6.2   To prove Uniqueness Theorem I, we assume that there can be two potentials satisfying Laplace's equation and identical boundary conditions. The assumption leads to a contradiction.

we obtain (setting $U_1 = U_2 = \varphi_1 - \varphi_2$)

$$\int_{Region} (\varphi_1 - \varphi_2) \nabla^2 (\varphi_1 - \varphi_2) dv + \int_{Region} [\nabla(\varphi_1 - \varphi_2)]^2 dv$$

$$= \sum_{Boundaries} \left[\oint (\varphi_1 - \varphi_2) \mathbf{\nabla}(\varphi_1 - \varphi_2) \cdot d\mathbf{S} \right], \quad (6\text{-}2.3)$$

where the surface integral of (V-24) is expressed as the sum of the surface integrals over individual boundaries of the region. But by Eq. (6-2.1) each of these surface integrals vanishes, and by Eq. (6-2.2) the first volume integral of Eq. (6-2.3) vanishes. We therefore obtain

$$\int_{Region} [\nabla(\varphi_1 - \varphi_2)]^2 dv = 0. \quad (6\text{-}2.4)$$

Since $[\nabla(\varphi_1 - \varphi_2)]^2$ is the square of a real quantity and therefore cannot be negative anywhere, Eq. (6-2.4) can hold only if $\mathbf{\nabla}(\varphi_1 - \varphi_2)$ is zero everywhere in the region under consideration. But then $\varphi_1 - \varphi_2$ must be constant throughout this region, and since, by supposition, $\varphi_1 - \varphi_2$ is zero at the boundaries, $\varphi_1 - \varphi_2$ must be zero everywhere in the region, and hence

$$\varphi_1 = \varphi_2 \quad \text{(region)}.$$

Both φ_1 and φ_2 represent therefore the same distribution of the electrostatic potential, and no other distribution which satisfies Laplace's equation and is compatible with the boundary conditions stated in the theorem is possible. This proves the theorem.

The boundary conditions referred to in the above theorem (the requirement that φ has prescribed values on the boundary of the region under consideration) are frequently encountered in practice. We shall call them *boundary conditions of the first kind.*

Uniqueness Theorem II. There can be only one distribution of electrostatic potential which in an infinite region of space external to a finite system of conductors satisfies Laplace's equation, is compatible with total charge of each conductor, assumes constant values on all conductors, and reduces to a prescribed value at some reference point.[1]

To prove this theorem, let us again assume that there can be two distributions, φ_1 and φ_2, compatible with the conditions stated in the theorem. As before, φ_1 and φ_2 satisfy Eqs. (6-2.2) and (6-2.3), but the surface integrals in Eq. (6-2.3) are now extended over the surfaces of all conductors, and one surface integral is extended over an imaginary surface enclosing all space (all these surfaces form the boundaries of the region under consideration):

$$\sum_{\substack{\text{Boundaries}}} \left[\oint (\varphi_1 - \varphi_2) \, \mathbf{V}(\varphi_1 - \varphi_2) \cdot d\mathbf{S} \right] = \oint_{\substack{\text{All space}}} (\varphi_1 - \varphi_2) \, \mathbf{V}(\varphi_1 - \varphi_2) \cdot d\mathbf{S}$$

$$+ \sum_{\substack{\text{Conductors}}} \left[\oint (\varphi_1 - \varphi_2) \, \mathbf{V}(\varphi_1 - \varphi_2) \cdot d\mathbf{S} \right].$$

As we shall now show, these surface integrals vanish.

Consider first the integral over the surface enclosing all space. Suppose that the average distance from the conductors to this surface is R. Since R is much larger than the dimensions of the region occupied by the conductors, all the conductors may be regarded as a single point charge when viewed from this surface. The potentials φ_1 and φ_2 on this surface may be regarded then as point charge potentials, and the gradients $-\mathbf{V}\varphi_1$ and $-\mathbf{V}\varphi_2$ may be regarded as point charge fields. But since φ_1 and φ_2 are both compatible with the charges of the conductors, it follows that $-\mathbf{V}\varphi_1 = (Q/4\pi\varepsilon_0 R^2)\mathbf{R}_u$ and $-\mathbf{V}\varphi_2 = (Q/4\pi\varepsilon_0 R^2)\mathbf{R}_u$, where Q is the total charge of all conductors. The quantity $\mathbf{V}(\varphi_1 - \varphi_2)$, which is equal to $\mathbf{V}\varphi_1 - \mathbf{V}\varphi_2$, is therefore zero, and hence the integral is zero.

Consider now the integrals over the surfaces of conductors. Since φ_1 and φ_2 are constant on the surface of each conductor, $\varphi_1 - \varphi_2$ may be factored out from under the integral sign. For each conductor we

---

[1] One usually makes $\varphi_\infty = 0$ in all distributions. Therefore the last condition is usually fulfilled automatically and is ignored.

then have

$$\oint (\varphi_1 - \varphi_2) \nabla(\varphi_1 - \varphi_2) \cdot d\mathbf{S} = (\varphi_1 - \varphi_2) \oint \nabla(\varphi_1 - \varphi_2) \cdot d\mathbf{S}.$$

If we now multiply and divide the last integral by ε_0 and observe that $\varepsilon_0 \nabla \varphi_1 = -\mathbf{D}_1$ and $\varepsilon_0 \nabla \varphi_2 = -\mathbf{D}_2$, where $\mathbf{D}_1$ and $\mathbf{D}_2$ are the displacement vectors corresponding to the potentials φ_1 and φ_2, we obtain

$$\oint (\varphi_1 - \varphi_2) \nabla(\varphi_1 - \varphi_2) \cdot d\mathbf{S} = \frac{1}{\varepsilon_0} (\varphi_1 - \varphi_2) \oint (\mathbf{D}_2 - \mathbf{D}_1) \cdot d\mathbf{S}$$

$$= \frac{1}{\varepsilon_0} (\varphi_1 - \varphi_2) \left(\oint \mathbf{D}_2 \cdot d\mathbf{S} - \oint \mathbf{D}_1 \cdot d\mathbf{S} \right).$$

But by Gauss's law and by the requirement that φ_1 and φ_2 are both compatible with the charges of the conductors, each of the last two integrals represents the same total charge of the conductor under consideration, and hence the difference of these integrals is zero. Therefore the surface integral on the left is also zero. Since this reasoning applies to any conductor of the system, the surface integrals over the surfaces of all the conductors are zero.

Finally, by Eq. (6-2.2), the first volume integral of Eq. (6-2.3) is also zero. Thus, as before, we obtain Eq. (6-2.4) and conclude that $\varphi_1 - \varphi_2$ is constant throughout the region under consideration. But then, since $\varphi_1 = \varphi_2$ at the reference point so that $\varphi_1 - \varphi_2 = 0$ there, $\varphi_1 - \varphi_2$ must be zero throughout the region, and hence $\varphi_1 = \varphi_2$ everywhere in the region. Therefore φ_1 and φ_2 represent the same distribution of electrostatic potential, and as before, no other distribution satisfying Laplace's equation and compatible with the boundary conditions stated in the theorem is possible. The theorem is thus proved.

The boundary conditions referred to in this theorem (the requirement that φ is compatible with prescribed charges on conductors and assumes constant values on them) are frequently encountered in practice. We shall call them *boundary conditions of the second kind*.

Uniqueness Theorem III. There can be only one distribution of electrostatic potential which in a region of space external to a system of charged conductors satisfies Laplace's equation, reduces to prescribed values on the outer boundary of the region and on some of the conductors, is compatible with the charges carried by the remaining conductors, and assumes constant values on them.

Since this theorem follows directly from the first two, its formal proof will be left to the reader. The boundary conditions stated in this theorem constitute what we shall call *boundary conditions of the third kind*.

The property of electrostatic potential to satisfy Laplace's equation in charge-free regions of space and to have only one possible distribution compatible with the boundary conditions of the types stated above constitutes a powerful criterion for establishing the correctness of expressions representing the electrostatic potential in a charge-free region of space. Indeed, as it follows from these properties, all that is needed for establishing that a particular expression correctly represents the electrostatic potential in such a region is to verify that this expression satisfies Laplace's equation throughout the region and satisfies the boundary conditions on the periphery of the region. Hence, if by any sort of mathematical procedure, artifice, or intuition we find an expression for electrostatic potential that in a charge-free region of space satisfies Laplace's equation and fits all required boundary conditions, we may be sure that this expression is correct and that the potential represented by it is, under these boundary conditions, the only possible potential for the region. Therefore a problem on the determination of electrostatic potential in a charge-free region is considered solved if an expression is obtained that satisfies this correctness criterion, no matter by what means or manipulations the expression has been obtained.

The methods of obtaining expressions for an electrostatic potential which are capable of satisfying the above correctness criterion have two major variations. The first variation is the construction of expressions capable of satisfying the given boundary conditions from the expressions known to satisfy Laplace's equation. Examples of this variation are the *method of harmonics* and the *method of images*. The second variation is the construction of expressions capable of satisfying Laplace's equation from the expressions known to satisfy the boundary conditions. Examples of this variation are the *method of axial expansion* and the *method of curvilinear squares*. These four methods will be discussed in the four following sections.

The uniqueness theorems which we have just presented are a special case of more general uniqueness theorems for the electrostatic potential in charged-filled regions of space. In such regions the potential satisfies Poisson's, rather than Laplace's, equation. These more general theorems are therefore stated with reference to Poisson's equation, but otherwise are almost identical with the theorems presented above. The proof of these theorems is also almost identical with the proof presented above.

The uniqueness theorems for electrostatic potential in charge-filled regions of space are, in turn, a special case of the general uniqueness theorems for an electrostatic field. These theorems can be stated as follows.

Uniqueness Theorem A. There can be only one electrostatic field **E** which at all points of space satisfies the basic field laws, (4-4.1a), (4-4.2b), (4-4.3), and is regular at infinity (this is merely the Helmholtz theorem applied to an electrostatic field).

Uniqueness Theorem B. There can be only one electrostatic field **E** which in a limited region of space satisfies the basic field laws, (4-4.1a), (4-4.2b), (4-4.3), and whose normal component reduces to prescribed values at the boundaries of the region.

Uniqueness Theorem C. There can be only one electrostatic field **E** which in a space external to a finite system of conductors satisfies the basic field laws, (4-4.1a), (4-4.2b), (4-4.3), is compatible with total charge of each conductor, is everywhere perpendicular to the surfaces of the conductors, and is regular at infinity.

Uniqueness Theorem D. There can be only one electrostatic field **E** which satisfies the basic field laws, (4-4.1a), (4-4.2b), (4-4.3), and whose potential satisfies the boundary conditions of the first, second, or third kind.

Uniqueness Theorem E. The theorems A, B, and C hold also for a limited region of space if the tangential component of **E** assumes prescribed values on the outer boundary of the region, regardless of any other conditions for **E** on or outside the boundary.[1]

The proof of these theorems is the same as that of the uniqueness theorems for electrostatic potential, except that it begins with a supposition that there can be two fields, $\mathbf{E}_1$ and $\mathbf{E}_2$, which satisfy the basic laws: $\mathbf{\nabla} \times \mathbf{E}_1 = 0$, $\mathbf{\nabla} \times \mathbf{E}_2 = 0$, $\mathbf{D}_1 = \varepsilon_0 \mathbf{E}_1$, $\mathbf{D}_2 = \varepsilon_0 \mathbf{E}_2$, $\mathbf{\nabla} \cdot \mathbf{D}_1 = \rho$, and $\mathbf{\nabla} \cdot \mathbf{D}_2 = \rho$. Since both $\mathbf{E}_1$ and $\mathbf{E}_2$ have zero curl, they can be expressed as $\mathbf{E}_1 = -\mathbf{\nabla}\varphi_1$, and $\mathbf{E}_2 = -\mathbf{\nabla}\varphi_2$. From the divergence and displacement laws we then have $\nabla^2\varphi_1 = -\rho/\varepsilon_0$ and $\nabla^2\varphi_2 = -\rho/\varepsilon_0$. Therefore $\nabla^2(\varphi_1 - \varphi_2) = 0$. From here on, the proof continues just as for the electrostatic potential.

Each uniqueness theorem for **E** constitutes a criterion for the correctness of an expression for **E**, and if an expression has been

---

[1] This requirement is identical with the requirement that φ assumes prescribed values on the boundary, because

$$\varphi_{\text{boundary}} = \int_{\text{Boundary}} \mathbf{E} \cdot d\mathbf{l} + \varphi_c = \int_{\text{Boundary}} E_{\text{tangential}} dl + \varphi_c,$$

where φ_c is a reference potential at a point of the boundary.

obtained which satisfies the requirements stated in one of these theorems, the expression is definitely correct.

▼

Example 6-2.1   Prove that the electrostatic potential in a charge-free space bounded by a conducting enclosure is constant and equal to the potential of the enclosure.

Any constant potential satisfies Laplace's equation. The constant potential equal to the potential of the enclosure satisfies Laplace's equation and also the boundary conditions of the first kind. Hence, by the first uniqueness theorem, this potential is correct and is the only possible potential for the system under consideration.

Example 6-2.2   Prove that if in an electrostatic system of charged conductors the charge of each conductor is increased n times, the potential (with respect to infinity) at any point of space will also be increased n times.[1]

Suppose that the potential due to the original charges of the conductors is φ. Being the true potential compatible with the charges of the conductors, φ must satisfy Laplace's equation

$$\nabla^2 \varphi = 0,$$

and also the boundary conditions of the second kind, which for each conductor are

$$\varphi = \text{constant}, \qquad -\oint \varepsilon_0 \nabla \varphi \cdot d\mathbf{S} = q,$$

where the integral is extended over the surface of the conductor and q is the charge of the conductor. Suppose now that all charges are increased n times. The new potential φ' must satisfy Laplace's equation

$$\nabla^2 \varphi' = 0$$

and the new boundary conditions

$$\varphi' = \text{constant}, \qquad -\oint \varepsilon_0 \nabla \varphi' \cdot d\mathbf{S} = nq.$$

But since φ satisfies the first three equations above, $\varphi' = n\varphi$ satisfies the last three. Hence, by the second uniqueness theorem, $\varphi' = n\varphi$ is the correct and the only possible potential associated with the new charges of the system.

Example 6-2.3   Prove that the expression

$$\mathbf{E} = \frac{q}{4\pi\varepsilon_0 r^2} \mathbf{r}_u$$

---

[1] This means, incidentally, that the capacitance of an isolated conductor or capacitor does not depend on its charge or potential (voltage) and constitutes a constant characterizing each particular conductor or capacitor.

represents correctly the electric field in a concentric spherical capacitor whose inner sphere carries a charge q.

By inspection, we see that the expression in question satisfies the basic laws, (4-4.1a), (4-4.2b), (4-4.3), is compatible with total charge of the inner conductor ($\oint \varepsilon_0 \mathbf{E} \cdot d\mathbf{S} = q$), is perpendicular to its surface, and has no tangential component on the outer boundary (which is formed by the outer sphere of the capacitor). Therefore, by Uniqueness Theorems C and E, the field is correct. Note that the prescribed tangential component of $\mathbf{E}$ on the outer boundary is zero, as must be for any conducting surface under electrostatic conditions.

▲

6-3. Method of Harmonics

Functions that satisfy Laplace's equation are called *harmonic functions* or, simple, *harmonics*. Different harmonics are usually classified according to the system of coordinates in terms of which these harmonics are expressed. Thus one differentiates between rectangular harmonics, cylindrical harmonics, spherical harmonics, etc.

The method of harmonics consists in selecting a function compatible with the geometry of the system under consideration from the tables of

TABLE 6-I

Frequently Used Harmonic Functions[a]

Rectangular Harmonics
$\varphi = C_1 xyz + C_2 xy + C_3 yz + C_4 zx + C_5 x + C_6 y + C_7 z + C'.$ (H-1)
$\varphi = \sum_{n=1}^{\infty} (A_n \sin \alpha_n x + B_n \cos \alpha_n x)(C_n e^{\alpha_n y} + D_n e^{-\alpha_n y}) + C'.$ (H-2)
Cylindrical Harmonics
$\varphi = \sum_{n=1}^{\infty} (A_n r^n + B_n r^{-n})(C_n \cos n\theta + D_n \sin n\theta)$ $+ (F \ln r + G)(H\theta + C').$ (H-3)
Spherical Harmonics
$\varphi = \sum_{n=0}^{\infty} (A_n r^n + B_n r^{-n-1})[C_n P_n(\cos \theta) + D_n Q_n(\cos \theta)] + C'.$ (H-4)

[a] For derivation of these functions the reader is referred to text books on differential equations. $A_n, B_n, C_n, D_n, F, G, H, C'$ are arbitrary constants. Harmonics (H-1) and (H-4) are in three dimensions; (H-2) and (H-3) are in two dimensions. $P_n(\cos \theta)$ are Legendre polynomials of the first kind. Legendre polynomials of the second kind, $Q_n(\cos \theta)$, are infinite for $\cos \theta = \pm 1$, and thus are not allowed when the region under consideration includes the symmetry axis.

harmonic functions, and then adjusting the arbitrary constants appearing in the selected function to satisfy the boundary conditions of the first, second, or third kind. Once the selected harmonic function is made to satisfy the boundary conditions, it becomes, by the uniqueness theorems, the only possible and therefore the correct electrostatic potential for the charge-free regions of the system under consideration.

Several representative harmonic functions are given in Table 6-I. The fact that these functions are indeed solutions of Laplace's equation can be verified by direct substitution (see Problems 6.10 and 6.11).

▼

Example 6-3.1   A very thin conducting plate is placed in an initially uniform electric field **E** in such a manner that the plane of the plate is perpendicular to **E** (Fig. 6.3). Find how the presence of the plate alters the field.

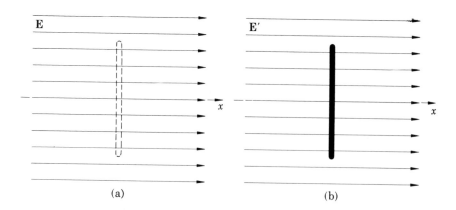

(a)   (b)

FIG. 6.3   (a) A thin conducting plate is placed normally in a uniform electric field. (b) The field remains the same.

Let the initial field **E** be in the direction of the x-axis. The initial potential is then $\varphi = -Ex + \varphi_0$, where φ_0 is a constant. Let the altered potential be φ'. It must satisfy the following boundary conditions:

(1) $\varphi' =$ constant on the surface of the plate

(2) $\displaystyle\oint_{\text{Plate}} \sigma \, dS = -\oint_{\text{Plate}} \varepsilon_0 \nabla\varphi' \cdot dS = 0$

(3) $\varphi' = \varphi = -Ex + \varphi_0$ at large distances from the plate

(these are the conditions of the second kind; the first condition reflects the fact that the plate is a conductor in an electrostatic system, the second condition reflects the fact that the plate has no net charge, the third condition reflects the fact that the effect of the plate can be felt only in the vicinity of the plate and thus establishes a reference potential for φ'). The geometry of the problem suggests that φ' may be represented by rectangular harmonics. We see by inspection that the first two boundary conditions are satisfied by the harmonic function (H-1) of Table 6-I with all constants except C_5 and C' set equal to zero,

$$\varphi' = C_5 x + C'.$$

The third boundary condition requires that for large x

$$C_5 x + C' = -Ex + \varphi_0.$$

The values of the two constants must then be $C_5 = -E$ and $C' = \varphi_0$. The potential φ' is therefore

$$\varphi' = -Ex + \varphi_0.$$

But this expression is identical with the expression for the initial potential φ. Thus the presence of the plate does not alter the initial potential (or field) at all. This, incidentally, justifies the use of small, thin test plates for measuring the displacement **D**; the plates measure the same **D** that would exist if the plates were not inserted in the field.

Example 6-3.2   A conducting sphere of radius a is placed in an initially uniform field **E** (Fig. 6.4). Find how the presence of the sphere alters the field.

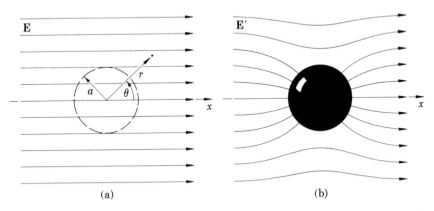

(a)   (b)

FIG. 6.4   (a) A conducting sphere is placed in a uniform electric field. (b) Resultant field.

The problem is essentially the same as the preceding one, except that now we have a conducting sphere instead of a conducting plate. The initial potential is again $\varphi = -Ex + \varphi_0$ and can be written as

$$\varphi = -Er \cos \theta + \varphi_0,$$

where θ is the polar angle of a spherical system of coordinates with the origin at the center of the sphere, as shown in Fig. 6.4. The boundary conditions for the final potential φ' are:

(1) $\varphi' = $ constant at $r = a$ (surface of the sphere)

(2) $- \oint_{\text{Sphere}} \varepsilon_0 \nabla\varphi' \cdot d\mathbf{S} = 0$

(3) $\varphi' = \varphi = -Er \cos\theta + \varphi_0$ for $r \to \infty$

(these are basically the same conditions as in the preceding example). The geometry of the problem indicates that φ' may be expressed in terms of spherical harmonics (H-4). Considering now the third boundary condition and consulting the table of Legendre polynomials (Table 5-I), we recognize that this condition will be satisfied by just a part of (H-4),

$$\varphi' = (A_1 r + B_1 r^{-2})C_1 P_1 (\cos\theta) + C' = (A_1 r + B_1 r^{-2})C_1 \cos\theta + C',$$

if we set $A_1 C_1 = -E$ and $C' = \varphi_0$. We then have

$$\varphi' = -E\left(1 + \frac{B_1}{A_1} r^{-3}\right) r \cos\theta + \varphi_0.$$

Turning now to the first boundary condition, we see that it will be satisfied if we set $B_1/A_1 = -a^3$. We then obtain

$$\varphi' = -E\left(1 - \frac{a^3}{r^3}\right) r \cos\theta + \varphi_0.$$

This expression does not contain any arbitrary constants that could be adjusted to satisfy the second boundary condition. Therefore, if correct, it must satisfy this condition automatically. To check this, we need to evaluate the integral $-\oint \varepsilon_0 \nabla\varphi' \cdot d\mathbf{S}$ over the surface of the sphere. Since $d\mathbf{S}$ for this surface is radial, the integral can be written as $-\oint \varepsilon_0 (\nabla\varphi')_r \, dS$, where $(\nabla\varphi')_r$ is the radial component of $\nabla\varphi'$. This component is (Table 2-I)

$$(\nabla\varphi')_r = \frac{\partial\varphi'}{\partial r} = -\frac{\partial}{\partial r} E\left(1 - \frac{a^3}{r^3}\right) r \cos\theta$$

$$= -E \cos\theta - E \frac{2a^3}{r^3} \cos\theta = -E\left(1 + \frac{2a^3}{r^3}\right) \cos\theta.$$

On the surface of the sphere, $r = a$, and therefore $(\nabla\varphi')_r = -3E \cos\theta$. But on this surface, to every positive value of $\cos\theta$ $(0 \leq \theta < \frac{1}{2}\pi)$ there corresponds a negative value of equal magnitude $(\frac{1}{2}\pi < \theta \leq \pi)$, so that the above surface integral vanishes.

Thus φ' that we have obtained satisfies all required boundary conditions and hence is the correct potential of the system under consideration. The corresponding field $\mathbf{E}'$ is obtained by taking the negative gradient of φ'. The result is

$$\mathbf{E}' = E\left(1 + \frac{2a^3}{r^3}\right)\cos\theta\,\mathbf{r}_u - E\left(1 - \frac{a^3}{r^3}\right)\sin\theta\,\boldsymbol{\theta}_u.$$

Example 6-3.3   A long conducting cylinder of radius a is placed in an initially uniform field $\mathbf{E}$ in such a manner that the axis of the cylinder is normal to $\mathbf{E}$ (Fig. 6.5). Neglecting end effects, find the field around the cylinder.[1]

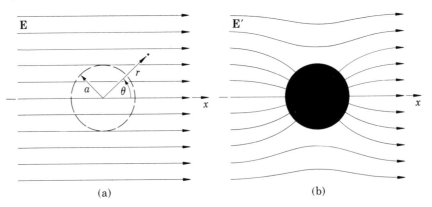

FIG. 6.5   (a) A conducting cylinder is placed in a uniform electric field. (b) Resultant field.

The problem is analogous to the preceding one. However, although we could solve it in exactly the same manner as the latter, we shall demonstrate now a slightly different method of solution.[2] Let the initial potential again be $\varphi = -Ex + \varphi_0$, which can be written as $\varphi = -Er\cos\theta + \varphi_0$, where θ is the azimuthal angle of the cylindrical system of coordinates shown in Fig. 6.5a. Let the altered potential be φ'. The symmetry of the system under consideration indicates that the potential of the cylinder is φ_0, because, as can be seen from Figs. 6.5a and 6.5b, the cylinder forms a part of the initial equipotential surface $\varphi = \varphi_0$, the position and the potential of which are not affected by the presence of the cylinder. We can write then for the boundary conditions of φ'

    (1) $\varphi' = \varphi_0$ at $r = a$ (surface of the cylinder)

    (2) $\varphi' = \varphi = -Er\cos\theta + \varphi_0$ for $r \to \infty$

(these are boundary conditions of the first kind). The geometry of the system suggests that φ' may be expressed in terms of cylindrical harmonics

---

    [1] To neglect end (edge) effects when using the method of harmonics means to neglect the boundary conditions at the corresponding surfaces.

    [2] This method can lead to a disaster if incorrectly applied to problems of the type 6.16 and 6.17.

(H-3). Considering the second boundary condition, we see that it can be satisfied by just a part of (H-3),

$$\varphi' = (A_1 r + B_1 r^{-1}) C_1 \cos\theta + C',$$

if we set $A_1 C_1 = -E$ and $C' = \varphi_0$. We then have

$$\varphi' = -E\left(1 + \frac{B_1}{A_1} r^{-2}\right) r \cos\theta + \varphi_0.$$

Considering now the first boundary condition, we see that it will be satisfied if we set $B_1/A_1 = -a^2$. The final expression for φ' is therefore

$$\varphi' = -E\left(1 - \frac{a^2}{r^2}\right) r \cos\theta + \varphi_0.$$

The corresponding field $\mathbf{E}'$ is

$$\mathbf{E}' = -\boldsymbol{\nabla}\varphi' = E\left(1 + \frac{a^2}{r^2}\right)\cos\theta\, \mathbf{r}_u - E\left(1 - \frac{a^2}{r^2}\right)\sin\theta\, \boldsymbol{\theta}_u.$$

Example 6-3.4   A voltage V is applied between two large rectangular conducting plates which form an angle θ_0 one with the other (Fig. 6.6). Neglecting edge effect, find the electric field in the space between the plates, and find the charge density on the plates.

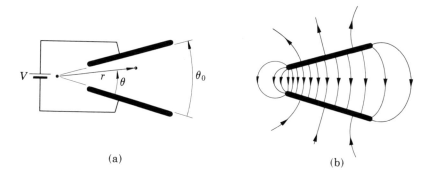

(a)   (b)

FIG. 6.6   (a) Geometrical relations for calculating electric field between two nonparallel conducting plates. (b) The map of the field.

If the edge effects are neglected, the boundary conditions are

$$(1)\ \varphi = \varphi_0 \qquad\qquad \text{at} \qquad \theta = 0$$
$$(2)\ \varphi = V + \varphi_0 \qquad \text{at} \qquad \theta = \theta_0,$$

where the potential of the negative plate is assumed to be φ_0. Consulting Table 6-I, we see that these boundary conditions can be satisfied by a part of the harmonics (H-3),

$$\varphi = H\theta + C',$$

if we set $H = V/\theta_0$ and $C' = \varphi_0$. The potential in the space between the plates is therefore

$$\varphi = \frac{V}{\theta_0} \theta + \varphi_0.$$

The corresponding field is

$$\mathbf{E} = -\nabla\varphi = -\frac{\partial\varphi}{r\partial\theta} \boldsymbol{\theta}_u,$$

or

$$\mathbf{E} = -\frac{V}{r\theta_0} \boldsymbol{\theta}_u.$$

The charge density on the plates, $\sigma = \pm\varepsilon_0 E$, is

$$\sigma = \pm\varepsilon_0 \frac{V}{r\theta_0}.$$

Example 6-3.5   A grounded conducting block has a very deep narrow slot covered by an insulated plate, as shown in Fig. 6.7, and a potential $\varphi = V_0 \sin \frac{\pi}{a} x$ is established in the plate. Find the potential in the slot.

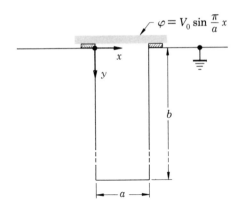

$$\varphi = V_0 \sin \frac{\pi}{a} x$$

Fig. 6.7 Method of harmonics can be used for finding electrostatic potential in a slot made in a conducting block.

The geometry of the problem suggests the use of rectangular coordinates. With the notations of Fig. 6.7, the boundary conditions are:

(1) $\varphi = 0$ at $x = 0$

(2) $\varphi = 0$ at $x = a$

(3) $\varphi = 0$ at $y = b$

(4) $\varphi = V_0 \sin \frac{\pi}{a} x$ at $y = 0$.

The first condition will be satisfied if we express φ in terms of rectangular harmonics (H-2) with $B_n = C' = 0$, so that

$$\varphi = \sum_{n=1}^{\infty} A_n \sin \alpha_n x \, (C_n e^{\alpha_n y} + D_n e^{-\alpha_n y}).$$

The second condition will be satisfied by this expression if we set $\alpha_n = \dfrac{n\pi}{a}$, so that

$$\varphi = \sum_{n=1}^{\infty} A_n \sin \frac{n\pi}{a} x \, (C_n e^{\frac{n\pi}{a} y} + D_n e^{-\frac{n\pi}{a} y}).$$

Since, by supposition, the slot is deep ($b \gg a$), so that $e^{-\frac{n\pi}{a} b} = 0$, the third condition will be satisfied if we set $C_n = 0$. We then obtain

$$\varphi = \sum_{n=1}^{\infty} A'_n \sin \frac{n\pi}{a} x \cdot e^{-\frac{n\pi}{a} y},$$

where A'_n is used as an abbreviation for the product $A_n D_n$. Finally, the fourth condition will be satisfied if we set A'_1 equal to V_0 and all other A'_n coefficients equal to zero. We then obtain

$$\varphi = V_0 \sin \frac{\pi}{a} x \cdot e^{-\frac{\pi}{a} y}.$$

Since this expression is a solution of Laplace's equation and satisfies all required boundary conditions, it is the correct solution of the problem.

An interesting result of this example is that the potential in a narrow grounded slot falls off exponentially with the distance from the top of the slot, so that the electrostatic field originating at the top of the slot is rapidly attenuated in the slot and does not penetrate the slot to any appreciable depth.

▲

6-4. Method of Axial Expansion

The method of axial expansion is used for determining the external electrostatic potential of axially symmetric charge distributions for points not on the symmetry axis when the potential on the axis is known.

If a charge distribution has no variation of charge density about an axis of symmetry, the external potential of the distribution can be represented by spherical harmonics (H-4) with $C_n = 1$ and $D_n = C' = 0$,

$$\varphi = \sum_{n=0}^{\infty} \left(A_n r^n + \frac{B_n}{r^{n+1}} \right) P_n(\cos \theta), \tag{6-4.1}$$

where θ is measured with respect to the symmetry axis. Since on the axis $\theta = 0$, so that $P_n = 1$ for all n (see Example 5-4.5), the potential reduces on the axis to

$$\varphi_{\text{axis}} = \sum_{n=0}^{\infty} \left(A_n r^n + \frac{B_n}{r^{n+1}} \right) = \sum_{n=0}^{\infty} \left(A_n z^n + \frac{B_n}{z^{n+1}} \right), \tag{6-4.2}$$

where z is the distance from the origin along the axis. Suppose now that the potential on the axis is already known and is expressed as a power series in z ("axial expansion")

$$\varphi_{\text{axis (known)}} = \sum_{n=0}^{\infty} \left(a_n z^n + \frac{b_n}{z^{n+1}} \right). \tag{6-4.3}$$

The coefficients a_n and b_n of this series must then be equal to the coefficients A_n and B_n of Eq. (6-4.2) and therefore to those of Eq. (6-4.1). Hence, a_n and b_n can be substituted in Eq. (6-4.1) and so, from the potential on the axis, the external potential of the charge distribution can be obtained for other points of space.

▼

Example 6-4.1   Find the potential of a thin, uniformly charged, circular ring of radius a and total charge q at all points for which $r > a$, where r is the distance from the center of the ring.

In Example 5-3.1 we have found that for $z > a$ the potential on the axis of the ring is

$$\varphi = \frac{q}{4\pi\varepsilon_0 z} - \frac{qa^2}{8\pi\varepsilon_0 z^3} + \cdots .$$

This gives for A_n and B_n of Eq. (6-4.1)

$$A_n = 0, \quad B_0 = \frac{q}{4\pi\varepsilon_0}, \quad B_1 = 0, \quad B_2 = -\frac{qa^2}{8\pi\varepsilon_0}, \quad \text{etc.}$$

The complete potential is therefore

$$\varphi = \frac{q}{4\pi\varepsilon_0 r} \left[1 - \frac{a^2}{2r^2} P_2(\cos\theta) + \cdots \right].$$

▲

Representation of an axially symmetric charge distribution in terms of axial multipoles. If in Eq. (6-4.1) all A_n's turn out to be zero, the potential becomes

$$\varphi = \sum_{n=0}^{\infty} \frac{B_n}{r^{n+1}} P_n(\cos\theta), \tag{6-4.4}$$

which can be written as

$$\varphi = \sum_{n=0}^{\infty} \frac{Q_n}{8\pi\varepsilon_0 r^{n+1}} P_n(\cos\theta), \tag{6-4.5}$$

where Q_n are new coefficients defined by

$$Q_n = 8\pi\varepsilon_0 B_n. \tag{6-4.6}$$

As one can see by comparing Eq. (6-4.5) with Eq. (5-4.8), Eq. (6-4.5) may be regarded as a series of multipole potentials associated with axial multipoles of moments $\frac{1}{2}Q_n$. This equation therefore constitutes an expansion formula for the potential of an axially symmetric charge distribution and shows that from the points for which Eq. (6-4.4) holds, the charge distribution may be regarded as a system of axial multipoles located on the symmetry axis. To differentiate between the multipole systems defined by Eq. (6-4.5) and those defined by the general expansion formula (5-5.1), one frequently refers to a Q_n coefficient given by Eq. (6-4.6) as the *multipole strength* and reserves the term *multipole moment* for the p coefficients given by Eqs. (5-5.2), (5-5.3), etc.

▼

Example 6-4.2   Construct the first two axial multipoles approximating the potential of a ring of radius a carrying a charge q for $r > a$ and compare this system with the corresponding system of general multipoles defined in Section 5-5.

Using the B_n coefficients found in Example 6-4.1, we have from Eq. (6-4.6)

$$\tfrac{1}{2}Q_0 = q, \qquad \tfrac{1}{2}Q_1 = 0, \qquad \tfrac{1}{2}Q_2 = -\tfrac{1}{2}qa^2$$

so that the axial multipoles that we are seeking are a monopole q and a quadrupole of moment $-\frac{1}{2}qa^2$ on the symmetry axis (z-axis).

The general multipoles, on the other hand, are, by Eqs. (5-5.1), (5-5.2), and (5-5.3), a monopole q and two quadrupoles of moments

$$p_{xx} = \tfrac{1}{2}qa^2, \qquad p_{yy} = \tfrac{1}{2}qa^2$$

on the x- and y-axis. As one can see, the axial multipole expansion and the general multipole expansion result here in entirely different multipole systems.

▲

6-5. Method of Images

As we already know, the potential of an arbitrary charge distribution satisfies Laplace's equation in a given region of space, provided that the charge distribution is outside this region. Hence, if one finds an arrangement of external charge distributions whose combined potential satisfies the boundary conditions of the first, second, or third kind on the boundaries of a charge-free region of space, then, by the

TABLE 6-II

Images in Conductors[a]

Actual System	Equivalent Image System

Charge distribution in front of an infinite
conducting plane:

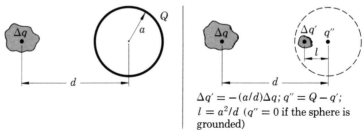

Charge distribution in front of two infinite
intersecting conducting planes:

Charge distribution in front of a conducting sphere
carrying a charge Q:

$\Delta q' = -(a/d)\Delta q; q'' = Q - q';$
$l = a^2/d$ $(q'' = 0$ if the sphere is
grounded)

Uniform line charge parallel to an equally long conducting
cylinder carrying a charge Q (end effects neglected):

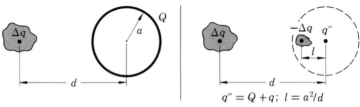

$q'' = Q + q; l = a^2/d$

[a] The relationships are given for a differential element Δq of each charge distribution.

uniqueness theorems, this combined potential will be the correct potential for this region, even if in reality the potential in the region is produced not by these charge distributions, but by an entirely different electrostatic system. For the purpose of calculating an electrostatic potential, one may therefore replace a real electrostatic system, or a part of it, by a set of fictitious charge distributions whose combined

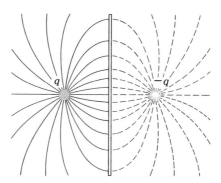

FIG. 6.8 Electric field between a charge q and a conducting plate is the same as the field between q and its "image" $-q$.

potential satisfies the boundary conditions of the real system. These fictitious charge distributions are called *image distributions*, or *electric images*, and the method of finding the potential of an electrostatic system by means of such fictitious charge distributions is called the method of images.

The images for several frequently encountered electrostatic systems are shown in Table 6-II. The correctness of these images can be easily verified by showing that they satisfy the required boundary conditions (to do so one needs to consider only a differential element of the original charge distribution and the corresponding differential element of the image distribution).

The simplest example of the method of images is given by a special case of the first system shown in Table 6-II: a point charge q placed at a distance a from a very large conducting plate. As one can see from Fig. 6.8, the field between q and the plate is exactly the same as the field that would exist in this region if the plate were replaced by the image charge $-q$ at a distance $2a$ from the charge q. The term "electric image" is derived from this particular example by analogy of the fictitious charge $-q$ with the optical mirror image of the real charge q.

There are no universal methods for obtaining images for arbitrary electrostatic systems. Electric images are therefore found mostly by inspection and trial and are verified by checking whether or not they satisfy the required boundary conditions (see Problems 6.23 and 6.24).

One can easily see that there is a reciprocal relation between real charges and their images: a real charge is the image of its own image. Therefore any part of an image system can be regarded as real; the rest of the system is then regarded as the image of the part assumed to be real.

▼

Example 6-5.1   A point charge q is placed at a distance a from a very large conducting plate. Find the electric field between the plate and the charge, and find the density of the surface charge induced on the plate.

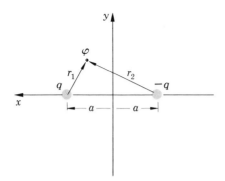

FIG. 6.9   Geometrical relations for calculating electric field between a point charge and a conducting plate by the method of images.

Using the first image system shown in Table 6-II, we replace the plate by the image charge $q' = -q$ as shown in Fig. 6.9. The potential at a point $P(x, y, z)$ is then (we abbreviate $y^2 + z^2$ as R^2)

$$\varphi = \frac{q}{4\pi\varepsilon_0 r_1} - \frac{q}{4\pi\varepsilon_0 r_2} = \frac{q}{4\pi\varepsilon_0}\left[\frac{1}{\sqrt{R^2 + (x-a)^2}} - \frac{1}{\sqrt{R^2 + (x+a)^2}}\right].$$

The field is $\mathbf{E} = -\nabla\varphi$, and its components are

$$E_x = -\frac{\partial\varphi}{\partial x} = \frac{q}{4\pi\varepsilon_0}\left\{\frac{x-a}{[R^2 + (x-a)^2]^{3/2}} - \frac{x+a}{[R^2 + (x+a)^2]^{3/2}}\right\},$$

$$E_y = -\frac{\partial\varphi}{\partial y} = \frac{q}{4\pi\varepsilon_0}\left\{\frac{y}{[R^2 + (x-a)^2]^{3/2}} - \frac{y}{[R^2 + (x+a)^2]^{3/2}}\right\},$$

$$E_z = -\frac{\partial\varphi}{\partial z} = \frac{q}{4\pi\varepsilon_0}\left\{\frac{z}{[R^2 + (x-a)^2]^{3/2}} - \frac{z}{[R^2 + (x+a)^2]^{3/2}}\right\}.$$

At the surface of the plate, $x = 0$, so that E_y and E_z vanish and only E_x remains (as it should, since the field must be normal at the surface of the plate). The field at the surface is then

$$\mathbf{E}_{\text{surface}} = \frac{q}{4\pi\varepsilon_0}\left[\frac{-a}{(R^2 + a^2)^{3/2}} - \frac{a}{(R^2 + a^2)^{3/2}}\right]\mathbf{i},$$

or

$$\mathbf{E}_{\text{surface}} = -\frac{qa}{2\pi\varepsilon_0(R^2 + a^2)^{3/2}}\,\mathbf{i}.$$

The induced surface charge density is $\sigma = D_{\text{surface}} = \varepsilon_0 E_{\text{surface}}$, or

$$\sigma = -\frac{qa}{2\pi(R^2 + a^2)^{3/2}}.$$

Example 6-5.2   A point charge q is placed at the distance d from the center of a grounded conducting sphere of radius $a < d$. Find the density of the induced surface charge on the sphere.

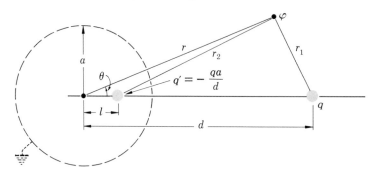

FIG. 6.10   Geometrical relations for calculating induced charges on a conducting sphere by the method of images.

Using the third image system shown in Table 6-II, we replace the sphere by the image charge $q' = -qa/d$, as shown in Fig. 6.10. The potential at any point $P(r_1, r_2)$ is then

$$\varphi = \frac{q}{4\pi\varepsilon_0 r_1} + \frac{q'}{4\pi\varepsilon_0 r_2} = \frac{q}{4\pi\varepsilon_0 r_1} - \frac{qa}{4\pi\varepsilon_0 r_2 d}.$$

Using the law of cosines, we now express r_1 and r_2 in terms of r and θ. This gives

$$\varphi = \frac{q}{4\pi\varepsilon_0}\left[\frac{1}{\sqrt{r^2 + d^2 - 2rd\cos\theta}} - \frac{a}{d\sqrt{r^2 + l^2 - 2lr\cos\theta}}\right].$$

The surface charge density is $\sigma = D_{\text{surface}} = \varepsilon_0 E_{\text{surface}}$, and since on the surface E must be radial,

$$\sigma = -\varepsilon_0 \frac{\partial\varphi}{\partial r}\bigg|_{\text{surface}} = -\varepsilon_0 \frac{\partial\varphi}{\partial r}\bigg|_{r=a}.$$

Differentiating and substituting $l = \dfrac{a^2}{d}$, we then have

$$\sigma = -\varepsilon_0 \frac{q}{4\pi\varepsilon_0} \left[-\frac{r - d\cos\theta}{(r^2 + d^2 - 2rd\cos\theta)^{3/2}} + \frac{a(r - l\cos\theta)}{d(r^2 + l^2 - 2lr\cos\theta)^{3/2}} \right]_{r=a}$$

$$= -\frac{q}{4\pi}\left[\frac{d\cos\theta - a}{(a^2 + d^2 - 2ad\cos\theta)^{3/2}} + \frac{\dfrac{a}{d}\left(a - \dfrac{a^2}{d}\cos\theta\right)}{\left(a^2 + \dfrac{a^4}{d^2} - \dfrac{2a^3}{d}\cos\theta\right)^{3/2}} \right]$$

$$= -\frac{q}{4\pi}\left[\frac{d\cos\theta - a}{(a^2 + d^2 - 2ad\cos\theta)^{3/2}} + \frac{\left(\dfrac{a}{d}\right)^3\left(\dfrac{d^2}{a} - d\cos\theta\right)}{\left(\dfrac{a}{d}\right)^3(a^2 + d^2 - 2ad\cos\theta)^{3/2}} \right]$$

or

$$\sigma = -\frac{q}{4\pi a}\frac{d^2 - a^2}{(a^2 + d^2 - 2ad\cos\theta)^{3/2}} \cdot$$

Example 6-5.3   An uncharged, insulated, conducting sphere of radius a is surrounded by a concentric, uniformly charged ring of radius b and total charge q (Fig. 6.11a). Find the potential at an external point P on the symmetry axis.

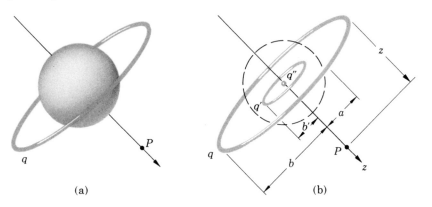

(a)   (b)

Fig. 6.11   (a) Conducting sphere surrounded by a charged ring q. (b) To find the electrostatic potential of the system, the sphere is replaced by an image ring q' and an image charge q''.

Using the third image system of Table 6-II, we replace the sphere by an image ring of charge $q' = -qa/b$ and radius $b' = a^2/b$ and an image point charge $q'' = qa/b$, as shown in Fig. 6.11b. The potential at P is then the sum of the potentials due to the original ring, image ring, and image point charge. Using the formula for the potential of a charged ring obtained in

Example 5-3.1, we have for the potential at P

$$\varphi = \frac{q}{4\pi\varepsilon_0\sqrt{b^2 + z^2}} + \frac{q'}{4\pi\varepsilon_0\sqrt{b'^2 + z^2}} + \frac{q''}{4\pi\varepsilon_0 z}$$

$$= \frac{q}{4\pi\varepsilon_0\sqrt{b^2 + z^2}} - \frac{qa}{4\pi\varepsilon_0 b\sqrt{\dfrac{a^4}{b^2} + z^2}} + \frac{qa}{4\pi\varepsilon_0 bz}$$

$$= \frac{q}{4\pi\varepsilon_0}\left(\frac{1}{\sqrt{b^2 + z^2}} - \frac{a}{\sqrt{a^4 + b^2 z^2}} + \frac{a}{bz}\right).$$

Example 6-5.4   A line charge of uniform density λ is placed radially inside a hollow conducting sphere of radius a, the two ends of the line charge being at the distance r_1 and r_2, respectively, from the center of the sphere (Fig. 6.12a). Find the image charge by which the sphere may be replaced for calculating the potential inside the sphere.

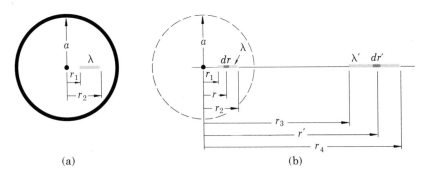

(a)   (b)

FIG. 6.12   (a) Line charge λ in a conducting sphere. (b) The sphere is replaced by an image line charge λ'.

According to the third image system of Table 6-II, the sphere may be replaced by a radial line charge whose ends are at the distance

$$r_3 = a^2/r_2 \quad \text{and} \quad r_4 = a^2/r_1$$

from the center of the sphere (Fig. 6.12b). The density of the image charge can be found as follows. Consider a differential length element dr of the original line charge. If this element is at a distance r from the center of the sphere, the corresponding element dr' of the image charge is at the distance $r' = a^2/r$ from the center. Differentiating, we obtain for the length of dr'

$$|dr'| = \left|-\frac{a^2}{r^2}\,dr\right| = \frac{a^2}{r^2}\,dr = \frac{r'^2}{a^2}\,dr.$$

Now, according to Table 6-II, if the charge contained in dr is dq, the charge contained in dr' is

$$dq' = -\frac{a}{r}\, dq = -\frac{r'}{a}\, dq.$$

The charge density of the image charge at the point r' is therefore

$$\lambda' = \frac{dq'}{dr'} = -\frac{r'}{a} \cdot \frac{a^2}{r'^2} \cdot \frac{dq}{dr} = -\frac{a}{r'} \cdot \frac{dq}{dr},$$

and since $\dfrac{dq}{dr} = \lambda$,

$$\lambda' = -\frac{a}{r'}\, \lambda.$$

▲

6-6. Method of Curvilinear Squares

The method of curvilinear squares is a graphical method for the analysis of two-dimensional fields (fields that vary in two linear dimensions only). It is based on representing these fields by so-called *curvilinear square maps*.

In this method, a drawing of the system under consideration in a cross-sectional plane normal to the direction along which the field of the system does not vary is first made. Then, field lines and equipotential lines are sketched by guess throughout the drawing to make a field map that forms a net of possibly accurate *curvilinear squares* (that is, curvilinear cells with 90° angles and length-to-width ratio equal to one). Next, a series of new maps is made where the curvilinear squares are gradually improved until the angles in all squares are sufficiently close to 90° and the length-to-width ratio of each square is sufficiently close to one. Special attention is paid to field lines and equipotential lines at conducting surfaces: the field lines must be normal to these surfaces, and the equipotential lines must be parallel to them. If a field model (lines-of-force picture) for the system under consideration is available, the model serves as the guide for making the maps (Fig. 6.13).

A finished field map prepared in the above manner has a number of special properties, of which the following ones are of special interest here.

(1) The potential difference $\Delta\varphi$ between adjacent equipotential lines is constant throughout the map.

(2) The voltage V between any two electrodes in the map is

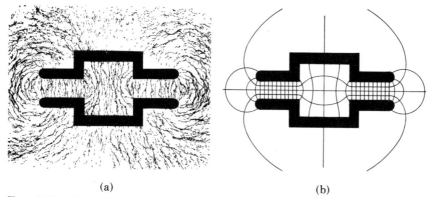

(a)   (b)

Fig. 6.13   (a) Lines-of-force picture for a two-plate transmission line with a central chamber. (b) Curvilinear square map of the same system.

divided by the equipotential lines into equal increments, each representing a potential difference

$$\Delta \varphi = \frac{V}{N_p}, \tag{6-6.1}$$

where N_p is the number of intervals made by the equipotential lines in the space between the electrodes.

(3) The electric field at the center of any curvilinear square in the map is

$$E \approx \frac{\Delta \varphi}{\Delta l}, \tag{6-6.2}$$

where $\Delta \varphi$ is the potential difference and Δl is the distance between the equipotential lines forming two sides of the square.

(4) The surface charge density at the surface of any conductor in the map is

$$\sigma \approx \varepsilon_0 \frac{\Delta \varphi}{\Delta l}, \tag{6-6.3}$$

where $\Delta \varphi$ is the potential difference and Δl is the distance from the point where σ is determined to the equipotential line adjacent to the conductor [Eqs. (6-6.2) and (6-6.3) become exact if the curvilinear squares in the map are sufficiently small].

(5) The electric flux $\Delta \Phi$ between adjacent field lines in a map representing a field of depth t is constant throughout the map and is

$$\Delta \Phi = \varepsilon_0 \Delta \varphi t, \tag{6-6.4}$$

where $\Delta \varphi$ is the potential difference between adjacent equipotential lines.

(6) If the map represents the field of a two-dimensional capacitor, the capacitance of the capacitor is

$$C = \varepsilon_0 \frac{N_f}{N_p} t, \qquad (6\text{-}6.5)$$

where N_f is the number of intervals made by the field lines in the map (number of "flux tubes"), N_p is the number of intervals made by the equipotential lines in the map, and t is the length (depth) of the capacitor.

The most important property of a finished curvilinear square map is, however, that the map yields a potential that automatically satisfies Laplace's equation and the boundary conditions of the first and the second kind. By the Uniqueness Theorems I and II, this means then that regardless of how the map was arrived at, the map represents correctly the field of the system under consideration.

Derivation of Curvilinear Square Map Properties. Let us consider a region of a two-dimensional electrostatic field between two cross-sectional planes separated by a distance Δt and oriented so that the field does not vary in the direction normal to them. On the front plane, let us draw a map of this field showing both the field lines and the equipotential lines, as in Fig. 6.14a. Using the vector identity

$$\nabla^2 \varphi = \lim_{\Delta v \to 0} \frac{\oint \nabla \varphi \cdot d\mathbf{S}}{\Delta v}, \qquad (V\text{-}39)$$

we shall now evaluate $\nabla^2 \varphi$ for the region represented by the map. Let the surface of integration in this formula be the surface of the curvilinear prism with the front surface $abb'a'$ shown in Figs. 6.14a and 6.14b. Since all "vertical" surfaces of this prism are parallel to the field lines, the integrand

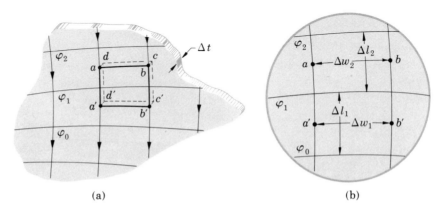

(a)   (b)

FIG. 6.14   Derivation of curvilinear map properties.

$\nabla \varphi \cdot d\mathbf{S} = -\mathbf{E} \cdot d\mathbf{S}$ is zero there, and the only contribution to the integral $\oint \nabla \varphi \cdot d\mathbf{S}$ comes from the two "horizontal" surfaces. If the prism is sufficiently small, and the map is sufficiently fine, $\nabla \varphi$ on the upper surface is $(\varphi_2 - \varphi_1)/\Delta l_2$ (see the enlargement of the region $abb'a'$ shown in Fig. 6.14b), and $\nabla \varphi$ on the lower surface is $(\varphi_1 - \varphi_0)/\Delta l_1$. The area of the upper surface is $\Delta w_2 \cdot \Delta t$, and the area of the lower surface is $\Delta w_1 \cdot \Delta t$. The integral is therefore

$$\oint \nabla \varphi \cdot d\mathbf{S} = \int_{abcd} \nabla \varphi \cdot d\mathbf{S} + \int_{a'b'c'd'} \nabla \varphi \cdot d\mathbf{S}$$

$$= \frac{\varphi_2 - \varphi_1}{\Delta l_2} \Delta w_2 \Delta t - \frac{\varphi_1 - \varphi_0}{\Delta l_1} \Delta w_1 \Delta t,$$

where the minus sign shows that $\nabla \varphi$ is opposite to $d\mathbf{S}$ on the lower surface. According to the above formula for $\nabla^2 \varphi$, this quantity must be zero if $\nabla^2 \varphi$ is to be zero. But $\nabla^2 \varphi$ must be zero in the region under consideration since the region is free from charge. Hence, the equation must hold

$$\frac{\varphi_2 - \varphi_1}{\Delta l_2} \Delta w_2 = \frac{\varphi_1 - \varphi_0}{\Delta l_1} \Delta w_1.$$

This equation will obviously be satisfied if $\varphi_2 - \varphi_1 = \varphi_1 - \varphi_0$ and $\Delta w_2/\Delta l_2 = \Delta w_1/\Delta l_1$. The first of these conditions is always fulfilled if the difference of potentials between adjacent equipotential lines, $\Delta \varphi = \varphi_{n+1} - \varphi_n$, is constant throughout the map. The second condition is always fulfilled if the map is constructed so that the curvilinear rectangles formed by adjacent equipotential lines and by adjacent field lines have the same width-to-length ratio $\Delta w_n/\Delta l_n$ throughout the map. In particular, this condition is fulfilled if the ratio is $1:1$—that is, if the entire map forms a net of curvilinear squares.

Thus, a curvilinear square map with equipotential lines marked in equal increments $\Delta \varphi$ yields a potential φ satisfying Laplace's equation. If $\Delta \varphi$ is made so that the conductors in the map obtain prescribed potentials, φ also satisfies the boundary conditions of the first kind. But the adjusting of $\Delta \varphi$ and the marking of the equipotential lines does not affect the structure of the map. Therefore a properly drawn curvilinear square map is automatically compatible with Laplace's equation and with the boundary conditions and hence is always a correct field map. The map properties 1 to 4 are then an obvious consequence of the above considerations.

Property 5 can be deduced as follows. The flux between two adjacent field lines in a square where the field lines are separated by a distance Δw_n and the equipotential lines are separated by a distance Δl_n is

$$\Delta \Phi = D \Delta w_n t = \varepsilon_0 E \Delta w_n t = \varepsilon_0 \frac{\Delta \varphi}{\Delta l_n} \Delta w_n t,$$

where $\Delta \varphi$ is the potential difference between the equipotential lines and t

is the depth of the field. But $\Delta w_n/\Delta l_n$ is the width-to-length ratio of the square and is one. Therefore $\Delta\Phi = \varepsilon_0\Delta\varphi t$, which is property 5.

Property 6 follows from properties 5 and 2. Since the charge on a conductor is equal to the total flux through a surface surrounding the conductor, the charge is given by

$$q = \Delta\Phi N_f = \varepsilon_0\Delta\varphi N_f t,$$

where N_f is the number of flux tubes ending on the conductor and t is the length of the conductor. Using property 2, we then obtain for the capacitance of a two-dimensional capacitor of length t

$$C = \frac{q}{V} = \varepsilon_0\frac{\Delta\varphi N_f}{\Delta\varphi N_p}t = \varepsilon_0\frac{N_f}{N_p}t,$$

where N_p is the number of intervals made by the equipotential lines between the two plates of the capacitor. This is property 6.

▼

Example 6-6.1   A long, charged conducting bar of over-all width $8a$ and thickness $2a$ has rounded edges of radius a. Find the ratio of the smallest and the largest surface charge density on any portion of the bar, neglecting end effects.

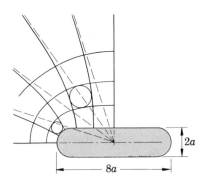

2a

8a

FIG. 6.15   The ratio of charge densities on a conducting bar can be found by the method of curvilinear squares.

Except near the ends, the electric field at the surface of the bar may be considered two-dimensional. The problem may be solved therefore by the method of curvilinear squares. The corresponding map is shown in Fig. 6.15 (the map needs to be determined for only one quadrant, since, by the symmetry of the bar, the field pattern is the same for all four quadrants).

A useful guide for constructing this particular map is the fact that from large distances the bar may be considered a line charge, and the field may be considered radial. In making this map, therefore, radial field lines were drawn first (dotted lines in Fig. 6.15). They were then appropriately curved near the surface of the bar to meet the surface at a right angle. The equi-potential lines were drawn next to produce curvilinear squares. The doubtful squares were then checked by inscribing in each of them a circle (two such circles are shown in Fig. 6.15). If a circle touched all four sides of a square, the square was good. If a circle touched only three sides, the "square" was actually an elongated rectangle and the map was corrected by altering the paths and spacings of field lines and equipotential lines until good squares were obtained everywhere on the map.

From this map and from Eq. (6-6.3) we see that the smallest surface charge density is on the flat portions of the bar, while the largest surface charge density is on the rounded portions. By Eq. (6-6.3), we can write $\sigma_{min}/\sigma_{max} = (\varepsilon_0 \Delta\varphi/\Delta l') \cdot (\Delta l''/\varepsilon_0 \Delta\varphi) = \Delta l''/\Delta l'$, where $\Delta l''$ and $\Delta l'$ rep-resent the spacing between the surface of the bar and the first equipotential line at the points under consideration. Measuring $\Delta l''$ and $\Delta l'$ we obtain $\Delta l' = 6$ mm, $\Delta l'' = 3$ mm, so that

$$\frac{\sigma_{min}}{\sigma_{max}} = \frac{1}{2} \, .$$

Example 6-6.2   A long, triangular conducting bar of length l is placed above a large conducting plate so that, neglecting end effects, the bar and the plate form a two-dimensional capacitor whose curvilinear square map is shown in Fig. 6.16. Find the capacitance.

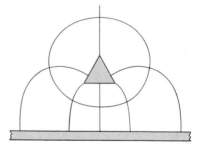

Fɪɢ. 6.16 The capacitance of a tri-angular bar placed above a conducting plate can be found by the method of curvilinear squares.

There are 6 flux tubes and 2 potential difference intervals in the map. By Eq. (6-6.5), the capacitance is therefore

$$C = 3\varepsilon_0 l.$$

▲

6-7. Method of Configuration Coefficients★

The method of configuration coefficients is a method of expressing correlations between charges and potentials in systems of conducting

★ This section may be omitted without loss of continuity.

bodies by means of certain quantities (configuration coefficients) which depend only on geometrical relations within the system.

The method is based on the fact that the potential produced by a system of n charged conductors can be expressed in terms of charges q_i residing on the conductors as

$$\varphi = \sum_{i=1}^{n} p_i q_i, \tag{6-7.1}$$

where p_i are quantities that depend only on the geometry of the system and on the location of the point of observation.

To prove Eq. (6-7.1), consider the general expression for the electrostatic potential of n conductors

$$\varphi = \sum_{i=1}^{n} \frac{1}{4\pi\varepsilon_0} \oint \frac{\sigma_i}{r_i} \, dS_i,$$

where $\sigma_i dS_i$ is the charge element of the i-th conductor, and r_i is the distance between this charge element and the point of observation. As one can see from this expression, the potential can be written as

$$\varphi = \sum_{i=1}^{n} \varphi_i,$$

where φ_i is the potential due to the charge residing on the i-th conductor. Therefore if we define the quantities (coefficients) p_i by the relation $p_i = \varphi_i/q_i$, we can write

$$\varphi = \sum_{i=1}^{n} p_i q_i.$$

We shall now prove that the coefficients p_i do not depend on charges of the conductors and thus are functions of geometrical relations only. To do this, let us replace the charges q_i on the conductors by the new charges q_i'. The new charges may be regarded as multiples of the old ones, so that $q_i' = \alpha_i q_i$. Let the potential due to the new charges be φ'. We then have

$$\varphi' = \sum_{i=1}^{n} \varphi_i'.$$

Each φ_i' must satisfy Laplace's equation and must be compatible with the charge q_i', so that these relations must hold:

$$\nabla^2 \varphi_i' = 0 \quad \text{and} \quad -\varepsilon_0 \oint \nabla\varphi_i' \cdot d\mathbf{S}_i = q_i' = \alpha_i q_i.$$

But these requirements are clearly satisfied if φ_i' is just $\alpha_i \varphi_i$, since φ_i, being a true potential, satisfies

$$\nabla^2 \varphi_i = 0 \quad \text{and} \quad -\varepsilon_0 \oint \nabla\varphi_i \cdot d\mathbf{S}_i = q_i.$$

By the Uniqueness Theorem II, the potential φ' must then be

$$\varphi' = \sum_{i=1}^{n} \alpha_i \varphi_i,$$

and since $\varphi_i = p_i q_i$, we must have

$$\varphi' = \sum_{i=1}^{n} \alpha_i p_i q_i = \sum_{i=1}^{n} p_i q_i',$$

where p_i are the coefficients which we had before the charges were changed. This proves Eq. (6-7.1).

From Eq. (6-7.1) it follows that the potential of any conductor in a system of charged conductors can be expressed as

$$\varphi_j = \sum_{i=1}^{n} p_{ji} q_i, \tag{6-7.2}$$

where φ_j is the potential of the j-th conductor, q_i is the charge of the i-th conductor and p_{ji} are configuration coefficients, which depend only on the geometrical relations within the system. These coefficients are usually called *coefficients of potential*.

If Eq. (6-7.2) is written for each conductor explicitly, it becomes a system of equations

$$\varphi_1 = p_{11} q_1 + p_{12} q_2 + \cdots + p_{1n} q_n$$
$$\varphi_2 = p_{21} q_1 + p_{22} q_2 + \cdots + p_{2n} q_n$$
$$\cdots$$
$$\varphi_n = p_{n1} q_1 + p_{n2} q_2 + \cdots + p_{nn} q_n. \tag{6-7.3}$$

These equations can be solved for the charges $q_1, q_2, \ldots q_n$, and give for the charge of the j-th conductor

$$q_j = \sum_{i=1}^{n} c_{ji} \varphi_i, \tag{6-7.4}$$

where c_{ji} depend only on various p_{ji} and hence themselves are configuration coefficients. They are called *coefficients of mutual capacitance*, or *induction coefficients* (if the system consists of one conductor only, there is only one coefficient of capacitance, which then is identical with the capacitance of the conductor).

The configuration coefficients p_{ji} and c_{ji} can be either calculated or measured, and once they are determined the potential of any conductor can be found from Eq. (6-7.2) if the charges of the conductors are known, and the charges can be found from Eq. (6-7.4) if the potentials are known.

To measure a coefficient p_{ji}, one usually measures the potential φ_{ji} of the j-th conductor when only the i-th conductor is charged, measures the charge q_i of the latter, and then determines p_{ji} from

$$p_{ji} = \frac{\varphi_{ji}}{q_i} \quad (q_j = 0 \quad \text{for} \quad j \neq i). \tag{6-7.5}$$

Similarly, to measure a coefficient c_{ji}, one measures the charge q_{ji} of the j-th conductor when all conductors except the i-th are at zero potential, measures the potential φ_i of the latter, and determines then c_{ji} from

$$c_{ji} = \frac{q_{ji}}{\varphi_i} \quad (\varphi_j = 0 \quad \text{for} \quad j \neq i). \tag{6-7.6}$$

If Eq. (6-7.4) is written for each conductor explicitly, it becomes a system of equations

$$\begin{aligned}
q_1 &= c_{11}\varphi_1 + c_{12}\varphi_2 + \cdots + c_{1n}\varphi_n \\
q_2 &= c_{21}\varphi_1 + c_{22}\varphi_2 + \cdots + c_{2n}\varphi_n \\
&\quad \cdots \\
q_n &= c_{n1}\varphi_1 + c_{n2}\varphi_2 + \cdots + c_{nn}\varphi_n.
\end{aligned} \tag{6-7.7}$$

Adding these equations, we obtain

$$\sum_{j=1}^{n} q_j = \left(\sum_{j=1}^{n} c_{j1} \right)\varphi_1 + \left(\sum_{j=1}^{n} c_{j2} \right)\varphi_2 + \cdots + \left(\sum_{j=1}^{n} c_{jn} \right)\varphi_n.$$

The left side of this equation represents the total charge Q of the system. The right side can be simplified by means of new coefficients, k_i, defined as $k_i = \sum_{j=1}^{n} c_{ji}$. We can write therefore

$$Q = k_1\varphi_1 + k_2\varphi_2 + \cdots + k_n\varphi_n. \tag{6-7.8}$$

Solving this equation for the potential of the j-th conductor, we obtain

$$\begin{aligned}
\varphi_j = &-k_j^{-1}(k_1\varphi_1 + k_2\varphi_2 + \cdots + k_{j-1}\varphi_{j-1} + k_{j+1}\varphi_{j+1} \\
&+ \cdots + k_n\varphi_n - Q).
\end{aligned}$$

Finally, introducing new coefficients, k_{ji}, defined as $k_{ji} = -k_j^{-1}k_i$, we obtain

$$\varphi_j = \sum_{i=1}^{n}{}' k_{ji}\varphi_i + k_j^{-1}Q, \tag{6-7.9}$$

where the prime on the summation sign is the "exclusion symbol" indicating that the term $k_{ii}\varphi_i$ (for which $j = i$) must be excluded from the sum. As one can see, the coefficients k_{ji} depend only on the configuration coefficients c_{ji}, and hence are themselves configuration coefficients. Therefore, once all the k's for a given system of conductors are known, the potential of any conductor can be calculated from Eq. (6-7.9) if the potentials of the remaining conductors and the total charge of the system are given.

The coefficients k_{ji} can be either calculated or measured. To measure a coefficient k_{ji} when $Q = 0$, all conductors except the j-th and the i-th are grounded, the potentials φ_j and φ_i are measured, and the value of the coefficient is then determined from

$$k_{ji} = \frac{\varphi_j}{\varphi_i} \quad \text{(All } \varphi\text{'s except } \varphi_i \text{ and } \varphi_j \text{ are zero).} \qquad (6\text{-}7.10)$$

▼

Example 6-7·1   Express the c coefficients in terms of the p coefficients for a system of two conductors.

For two conductors we have by Eq. (6-7.3)

$$\varphi_1 = p_{11}q_1 + p_{12}q_2$$
$$\varphi_2 = p_{21}q_1 + p_{22}q_2. \qquad (6\text{-}7.3a)$$

Solving these equations simultaneously for q's, we obtain

$$q_1 = \frac{p_{22}}{\Delta} \varphi_1 - \frac{p_{12}}{\Delta} \varphi_2$$

$$q_2 = -\frac{p_{21}}{\Delta} \varphi_1 + \frac{p_{11}}{\Delta} \varphi_2,$$

where

$$\Delta = p_{11}p_{22} - p_{21}p_{12}.$$

By Eq. (6-7.4), the expressions in front of φ's are the c coefficients. We thus have

$$c_{11} = \frac{p_{22}}{\Delta}, \qquad c_{12} = -\frac{p_{12}}{\Delta}, \qquad c_{21} = -\frac{p_{21}}{\Delta}, \qquad c_{22} = \frac{p_{11}}{\Delta}.$$

Example 6-7.2   Express the capacitance of a capacitor in terms of the c coefficients.

Let the charges of the capacitor plates be $q_1 = q$ and $q_2 = -q$. By Eq. (6-7.7), we then have

$$q = c_{11}\varphi_1 + c_{12}\varphi_2$$
$$-q = c_{21}\varphi_1 + c_{22}\varphi_2.$$

Solving these equations simultaneously for φ_1 and φ_2, we obtain

$$\varphi_1 = \frac{c_{22} + c_{12}}{c_{11}c_{22} - c_{12}c_{21}} q, \qquad \varphi_2 = -\frac{c_{11} + c_{21}}{c_{11}c_{22} - c_{12}c_{21}} q.$$

The voltage between the plates, $V_{12} = \varphi_1 - \varphi_2$, is then

$$V_{12} = \frac{c_{11} + c_{12} + c_{21} + c_{22}}{c_{11}c_{22} - c_{12}c_{21}} q.$$

The capacitance, $C = \dfrac{q}{V_{12}}$, is therefore

$$C = \frac{c_{11}c_{22} - c_{12}c_{21}}{c_{11} + c_{12} + c_{21} + c_{22}}.$$

Example 6-7.3   Calculate the configuration coefficients p_{ji}, c_{ji}, and k_{ji} for two concentric spheres shown in Fig. 6.17.

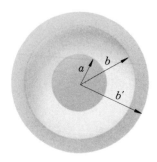

FIG. 6.17   Calculation of configuration coefficients for two concentric spheres.

By Eq. (6-7.3), the potentials of the spheres are

$$\varphi_1 = p_{11}q_1 + p_{12}q_2$$
$$\varphi_2 = p_{21}q_1 + p_{22}q_2.$$

Let the charge of the smaller sphere (sphere 1) be zero, and let the charge of the larger sphere (sphere 2) be q_2. By Examples 5-2.1 and 6-2.1, the potentials of the spheres are then $\varphi_1 = \varphi_2 = \dfrac{q_2}{4\pi\varepsilon_0 b'}$. Hence

$$p_{12} = \frac{1}{4\pi\varepsilon_0 b'}, \qquad p_{22} = \frac{1}{4\pi\varepsilon_0 b'}.$$

Now, let q_2 be zero, and let the charge of the smaller sphere be q_1. By Problem 5.26, the potentials are then

$$\varphi_1 = \frac{q_1}{4\pi\varepsilon_0 abb'}(bb' - ab' + ab), \qquad \varphi_2 = \frac{q_1}{4\pi\varepsilon_0 b'}.$$

Hence,

$$p_{11} = \frac{1}{4\pi\varepsilon_0 abb'}(bb' - ab' + ab), \qquad p_{21} = \frac{1}{4\pi\varepsilon_0 b'}.$$

The c coefficients can be obtained from the p coefficients with the aid of equations derived in Example 6-7.1. Substituting the above values of p's into these equations, we obtain

$$c_{11} = 4\pi\varepsilon_0 \frac{ab}{b-a}, \qquad c_{12} = -4\pi\varepsilon_0 \frac{ab}{b-a},$$

$$c_{21} = -4\pi\varepsilon_0 \frac{ab}{b-a}, \qquad c_{22} = 4\pi\varepsilon_0\left(\frac{ab}{b-a} + b'\right).$$

The k coefficients can now be obtained from the c coefficients. We have

$$k_1 = c_{11} + c_{21} = 0, \qquad k_2 = c_{12} + c_{22} = 4\pi\varepsilon_0 b',$$

$$k_{12} = -\frac{c_{12} + c_{22}}{c_{11} + c_{21}} = -\infty, \qquad k_{21} = -\frac{c_{11} + c_{21}}{c_{12} + c_{22}} = 0.$$

Example 6-7.4 The potential at a point P in the vicinity of two conductors located near the surface of the earth is being measured by means of a collector (probe) whose effect on the measured potential is negligible. When conductor 2 is grounded and voltage $V_1 = V_1'$ is applied to conductor 1, the voltmeter connected to the collector registers a voltage V_c'. When conductor 1 is grounded and voltage $V_2 = V_2'$ is applied to conductor 2, the voltmeter registers a voltage V_c''. What will be the potential at P for arbitrary values of V_1 and V_2?

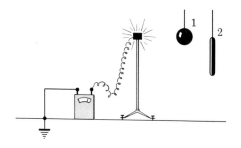

FIG. 6.18 Once the potential at a point near conductors 1 and 2 has been measured for two voltages applied to the conductors, the potential at this point for all other voltages applied to the conductors can be calculated from configuration coefficients.

In order to take into account the effect of the ground, we replace the ground by two image conductors as shown in Fig. 6.18. The potential φ_P at P, which is equal to the potential of the collector φ_c, can be then expressed, according to Eq. (6-7.9), as

$$\varphi_P = \varphi_c = k_{c1}V_1 + k_{c2}V_2 + k_{c3}V_3 + k_{c4}V_4,$$

where V_3 and V_4 are the potentials of the images. By the symmetry of the problem, we see that $V_3 = -V_1$ and $V_4 = -V_2$. We have therefore

$$\varphi_P = (k_{c1} - k_{c3}) V_1 + (k_{c2} - k_{c4}) V_2,$$

and replacing the expressions in parenthesis by K_1 and K_2, we obtain

$$\varphi_P = K_1 V_1 + K_2 V_2.$$

Substituting in this equation the values of φ_P, V_1, and V_2 given in the problem, we have

$$V_c' = K_1 V_1', \qquad V_c'' = K_2 V_2'',$$

so that

$$K_1 = \frac{V_c'}{V_1'}, \qquad K_2 = \frac{V_c''}{V_2''}.$$

For any values of V_1 and V_2, the potential at P is therefore

$$\varphi_P = \frac{V_c'}{V_1'} V_1 + \frac{V_c''}{V_2''} V_2.$$

▲

PROBLEMS

6.1. One plate of a thin parallel-plate capacitor of plate separation d is kept at the potential $\varphi = 0$, the other at $\varphi = V$. The capacitor contains a space charge of density $\rho = kx$, where k is a constant and x is the distance from the plate with $\varphi = 0$. Find the potential distribution in the capacitor, the electric field in the capacitor, and the surface charge density on the inner surfaces of the plates.

6.2. A spherical capacitor consists of two concentric spherical shells of radii a and b $(a < b)$. The inner shell is kept at the potential $\varphi = V$, the other at $\varphi = 0$. The space between the shells is filled with space charge of density $\rho = kr$ where k is a constant, and r is the distance from the center. Find the potential due to this system at all points of space and find the surface charge density on the spheres.

6.3. Consider two very long thin-walled coaxial cylinders of radii a and b $(a < b)$. The inner cylinder is kept at the potential $\varphi = V_a$, the outer at $\varphi = V_b$. The space between the cylinders contains a space charge of density $\rho = kr$, where k is a constant and r is the distance from the axis. Find the potential distribution between the cylinders and find the surface charge density on the cylinders.

6.4. Two long coaxial cylindrical shells of radii a and b are kept at the potentials V_a and V_b, respectively. Show that the potential at any point between the shells is

$$\varphi = V_a + (V_b - V_a) \frac{\ln (r/a)}{\ln (b/a)},$$

where r is the distance from the axis.

6.5. Prove that the electrostatic potential cannot be a maximum or a minimum in a charge-free region of space.

6.6. Prove that the Poisson integral

$$\varphi(x, y, z) = \frac{1}{4\pi\varepsilon_0} \int\limits_{\text{All space}} \frac{\rho(x', y', z')}{r} \, dv'$$

is a solution of Poisson's equation

$$\nabla^2\varphi = -\rho/\varepsilon_0.$$

[Hint: In the vector identity (V-25) substitute φ for U_1, $-\rho/\varepsilon_0$ for $\nabla^2 U_1$, and $1/r$ for U_2. Integrate (V-25) over all space excluding a small sphere of radius a centered at the point x, y, z. Express the surface integral of φ over the surface of the sphere as $\varphi_{\text{average}} \cdot 4\pi a^2$. Let a approach zero.]

6.7. Show that the average value of the electrostatic potential φ on any spherical surface is greater, equal to, or smaller than the value of φ at the center of the surface, depending on whether this surface encloses a charge distribution which is everywhere negative, zero, or positive. [Hint: The average value of φ on a surface S is $(\oint \varphi \, dS)/S$. Use the same procedure as in the preceding example, but integrate (V-25) over a sphere of radius R excluding a small sphere of radius a at its center.]

6.8. (a) Prove Uniqueness Theorem A. (b) Prove Uniqueness Theorem B. (c) Prove Uniqueness Theorem C.

6.9. Prove Uniqueness Theorem E.

6.10. Show that Rectangular Harmonics (H-1) and (H-2) given in Table 6-I are solutions of Laplace's equation.

6.11. Show that Cylindrical Harmonics (H-3) and Spherical Harmonics (H-4) given in Table 6-I are solutions of Laplace's equation.

6.12. A potential distribution on a spherical shell of radius a is given by

$$\varphi(\theta) = \left(\frac{k-1}{k+2}\right) E_0 a \cos \theta.$$

Prove that if all charge resides on this shell, the potential inside and outside the shell is, respectively,

$$\varphi(r, \theta) = \left(\frac{k-1}{k+2}\right) E_0 r \cos \theta$$

and

$$\varphi(r, \theta) = \left(\frac{k-1}{k+2}\right) E_0 \frac{a^3 \cos \theta}{r^2}.$$

In these formulas k and E_0 are constants, and r and θ are the spherical coordinates with the origin at the center of the shell.

6.13. A conducting cone of half-angle α is placed in a truncated, hollow, conducting cone of inside half-angle β. The cones are coaxial and their apexes are at the same point of the axis. Neglecting end effects, show that if a voltage V is established between the cones, the electric field in the space between them is (using the apex as the origin of coordinates)

$$\mathbf{E} = \frac{V}{r \sin \theta}\left[\ln\left(\tan\frac{\alpha}{2}\right) + \ln\left(\cot\frac{\beta}{2}\right)\right]^{-1}\boldsymbol{\theta}_u.$$

6.14. A conducting sphere carries a charge. A thin hemispherical conducting shell concentric with the sphere is placed near the sphere. Find how the presence of the shell alters the electric field of the sphere.

6.15. A small hemispherical bump of radius a is raised on the inner surface of one plate of a thin parallel-plate capacitor of plate separation d. (a) Find the potential distribution in the capacitor, if a voltage V is maintained between the plates. (b) Show that the total charge residing on the bump is

$$q = 3\pi\varepsilon_0 a^2 \frac{V}{d}.$$

6.16. A conducting sphere of radius a carrying a charge q is placed in an initially uniform field $\mathbf{E}$. Find how the presence of the sphere alters the field.

6.17. A long conducting cylinder of radius a carrying a charge of line density λ is placed in an initially uniform field $\mathbf{E}$ in such a manner that the axis of the cylinder is normal to $\mathbf{E}$. Neglecting end effects, find how the presence of the cylinder alters the field.

6.18. Rectangular plates of a capacitor have separation $d + a$ at one edge and $d - a$ at the other. The width of the plates (along parallel edges) is b, the length is l. Neglecting edge effects, show that the capacitance is

$$C = \varepsilon_0 \frac{b}{2\sin^{-1} a/l} \cdot \ln\frac{d+a}{d-a}$$

and show that for $a \ll d$ it approaches the capacitance of a parallel plate capacitor.

6.19. A spherical charge distribution of constant density ρ and radius a has a spherical cavity of radius $\frac{1}{2}a$. The center of the cavity is at a distance $\frac{1}{2}a$ from the center of the sphere. Using axial expansion, find the potential produced by this charge distribution at all points outside the sphere and compare the result with that obtained from a direct calculation of the potential.

6.20. Show that the potential of a thin, uniformly charged, circular disk of radius a and total charge q can be expressed for $r > a$ as

$$\varphi(r, \theta) = \frac{q}{4\pi\varepsilon_0 r}\left[1 - \frac{a^2}{4r^2}P_2(\cos\theta) + \cdots\right],$$

where r and θ are spherical coordinates with the origin at the center of the disk.

6.21. Show that the quadrupole strength of the disk described in the preceding problem is

$$Q = -\tfrac{1}{2}qa^2.$$

6.22. Show that the potential of a line charge of density λ and length $2a$ can be expressed for $r > a$ as

$$\varphi(r, \theta) = \frac{\lambda a}{2\pi\varepsilon_0 r}\left[P_0(\cos\theta) + \frac{a^2}{3r^2}P_2(\cos\theta) + \frac{a^4}{5r^4}P_4(\cos\theta) + \cdots\right],$$

where r and θ are spherical coordinates with origin in the middle of the line charge and having the line charge for the polar axis.

6.23. Prove that the images given in Table 6-II for the first two systems are correct.

6.24. Prove that the images given in Table 6-II for the last two systems are correct.

6.25. A point charge q is placed in front of a very large conducting plane. Show that the charge of any portion of the plane is proportional to the solid angle subtended by the area of this portion at the point where q is located.

6.26. A point charge q is placed at a distance d from the center of a grounded conducting sphere of radius a. Show that the ratio of the charge induced on the part of the sphere visible from q to that on the rest of the sphere is

$$\sqrt{\frac{d+a}{d-a}}.$$

6.27. A region of uniform field E is produced midway between two equal and opposite charges a great distance apart. Show by the method of images that when a conducting sphere of radius a is placed in this region, the potential around the sphere is

$$\varphi = -E\left(1 - \frac{a^3}{r^3}\right)r\cos\theta,$$

where r and θ are spherical coordinates about the center of the sphere.

6.28. A point charge $+q$ is placed at a distance d from the center of an uncharged conducting sphere of radius a. Show that the least positive charge which must be given to the sphere so that the surface charge of the sphere is everywhere positive is

$$q_{\min} = qa^2\frac{(3d-a)}{d(d-a)^2}.$$

6.29. A point charge q is placed inside a spherical conducting shell of radius a at a distance d from the center of the shell. Show that this charge induces on the inner surface of the shell a surface charge of density

$$\sigma = -\frac{q}{4\pi}\frac{a^2 - d^2}{(a^2 - 2ad\cos\theta + d^2)^{3/2}},$$

where θ is measured with respect to the symmetry axis of the system.

6.30. A quarter of a hollow conducting sphere is bounded by two semi-infinite perpendicular diametral planes. Find the images of a charge placed inside it.

6.31. A line charge of density λ is placed inside a hollow conducting circular tube of radius a at a distance l from the tube's axis. Find the voltage between the axis and the surface of the tube.

6.32. Neglecting end effects, show that the capacitance of a capacitor formed by two parallel cylinders of length l and radius a whose axes are separated by a distance $d(d \gg a)$ is

$$C = \frac{\pi \varepsilon_0 l}{\ln (d/a)}.$$

6.33. Neglecting end effects, show that the capacitance of a capacitor of length l formed by a cylindrical shell of radius a enclosed in a cylindrical shell of radius b is

$$C = 2\pi\varepsilon_0 l \left[\cosh^{-1} \frac{a^2 + b^2 - d^2}{2ab} \right]^{-1},$$

where d is the separation between the axes of the shells.

6.34. (a) Using the method of curvilinear squares, determine the capacitance per unit length of a transmission line formed by two equal parallel ribbons ("parallel ribbon capacitor") whose width is 10 times larger than the separation between them. (b) Compare the result with that obtained from an analytical calculation.

6.35. (a) Using the method of curvilinear squares, determine the capacitance per unit length of a cylindrical capacitor in which the radius of the inner cylinder is $\frac{1}{3}$ that of the outer one. (b) Check the result by means of the formula obtained in Example 5-2.3.

6.36. Using the method of curvilinear squares, determine the capacitance of the capacitor described in Problem 6.32 if $d/a = 8$; then check the result by using the formula given in Problem 6.32.

6.37. Using the method of curvilinear squares, find the capacitance of the capacitor described in Problem 6.33 if $a/d = 1$ and $b/d = 4$; then check the result by using the formula given in Problem 6.33.

6.38. Consider a two-dimensional system of conductors where the charge per unit length of each conductor is known, but the potentials of the conductors are not known. How should one mark the equipotential lines on a curvilinear square map of this system?

6.39.⋆ Show that the configuration coefficients for a thin parallel-plate capacitor of plate separation d and area S are

$$p_{12} = -\frac{d}{2\varepsilon_0 S} = p_{21}, \qquad p_{22} = 0 = p_{11},$$

$$c_{12} = -\frac{2\varepsilon_0 S}{d} = c_{21} \qquad c_{11} = 0 = c_{22},$$

and

$$k_{12} = -1 = k_{21}.^1$$

6.40.* Using the c coefficients given in the preceding problem, show that the capacitance of the capacitor described in that problem is

$$C = \varepsilon_0 \frac{S}{d}.$$

6.41.* Two charged conductors whose capacitances are C_1 and C_2, respectively, are separated by a distance d which is so large that each conductor may be regarded as a point charge from the location of the other. Show that the c coefficients are

$$c_{11} = \frac{(4\pi\varepsilon_0 d)^2 C_1}{(4\pi\varepsilon_0 d)^2 - C_1 C_2}$$

$$c_{22} = \frac{(4\pi\varepsilon_0 d)^2 C_2}{(4\pi\varepsilon_0 d)^2 - C_1 C_2},$$

$$c_{12} = -\frac{4\pi\varepsilon_0 d C_1 C_2}{(4\pi\varepsilon_0 d)^2 - C_1 C_2} = c_{21}.$$

6.42.* When the two conductors of the preceding problem carry the charges q and $-q$, respectively, the potential of conductor 1 is found to be $\varphi_1 = V_0$. Show that the potential of the second conductor is

$$\varphi_2 = -\frac{(4\pi\varepsilon_0 d - C_2)C_1}{(4\pi\varepsilon_0 d - C_1)C_2} V_0.$$

---

* This problem is based on the material presented in Section 6-7.
[1] We are using here $\varphi_\infty = 0$, as usual.

7

ENERGY AND FORCE
RELATIONS IN THE
ELECTROSTATIC FIELD
IN VACUUM

An electrostatic field is a carrier of *electrostatic energy*. Like any other form of energy, electrostatic energy satisfies the *principle of conservation*, according to which energy can be transformed from one form to another but can never be destroyed or created. In this chapter we shall study various energy relations in electrostatic fields, after which, using the principle of conservation of energy, we shall study force relations in electrostatic systems.

7-1. The Energy of an Electrostatic Field

Look at the lines-of-force picture of the electric field between a charged electric pendulum and a conducting plate (Fig. 7.1a). The picture is similar to that of a pendulum pulled to a plate by a set of elastic strings or springs (Fig. 7.1b). This analogy led Faraday and later Maxwell to the idea that an electric field could be regarded as an elastic medium in a state of stress.[1] But then an electric field should be a carrier of a definite amount of energy, just as a compressed or a stretched spring is. According to Maxwell's views, the energy stored in an electrostatic field should be

$$U = \frac{\varepsilon_0}{2} \int\limits_{\text{All space}} E^2 dv. \qquad (7\text{-}1.1a)$$

[1] Tension along the lines of force combined with pressure in perpendicular directions.

186

This equation has been found to be in complete agreement with all presently known phenomena involving energy and force relations in electrostatic fields. What is more, all such relations have been found to be derivable from this equation, and no equation for the energy of an electrostatic field (in vacuum) more general than this one has been discovered. Therefore Eq. (7-1.1a) is considered to represent the fundamental electrostatic energy law.

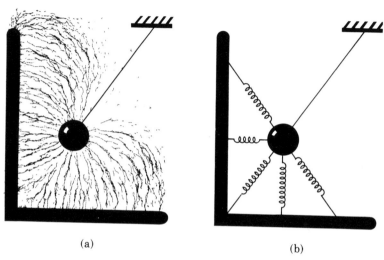

(a)   (b)

Fig. 7.1   (a) Lines-of-force picture for a charged electric pendulum near a conducting plate. The picture suggests that there is tension along the lines of force combined with pressure in perpendicular directions. (b) The effect of the electric field is similar to that of elastic springs.

Since in vacuum $\varepsilon_0 \mathbf{E} = \mathbf{D}$, this law is frequently written in the symmetrical form

$$U = \overset{\circ}{\frac{1}{2}} \int_{\text{All space}} \mathbf{E} \cdot \mathbf{D} \, dv. \qquad (7\text{-}1.1)$$

This law is sometimes written also in the differential form

$$U_v = \overset{\circ}{\frac{1}{2}} \mathbf{E} \cdot \mathbf{D}, \qquad (7\text{-}1.2)$$

where U_v is the *energy density* of the electrostatic field, defined as the ratio of the energy which may be associated with a differential element of the field to the volume of this element.

The symbol $^\circ$ in Eqs. (7-1.1a), (7-1.1), and (7-1.2) stands for a constant of proportionality, which we shall call the *energy constant*.

The value of this constant is

$$° = 1 \left[\frac{kg \cdot m^2 \cdot sec^{-3}}{volt \cdot amp} \right] = 1 \left[\frac{newton \cdot m}{volt \cdot amp \cdot sec} \right].$$

The size of the units of current and voltage in the *mksva* system has been defined by international agreement so that the magnitude of the energy constant is one.[1] Therefore this constant is usually omitted from the equations where it should normally occur. Since the energy constant is not dimensionless, however, the equations from which it is omitted become dimensionally inhomogeneous. To remedy the situation, the dimensions [force · length] are then regarded as being equivalent to the dimensions [voltage · current · time].

▼

Example 7-1.1   Find the electrostatic energy associated with a uniform spherical charge distribution of total charge q and radius a.

The electric field of this distribution is (see Example 4-4.1)

$$E = E_1 = \frac{qr}{4\pi\varepsilon_0 a^3} \qquad \text{for } r \leq a$$

$$E = E_2 = \frac{q}{4\pi\varepsilon_0 r^2} \qquad \text{for } r \geq a.$$

Since the field is radially symmetric, the volume element in Eq. (7-1.1a) may be expressed as $dv = 4\pi r^2 dr$, so that the energy is

$$U = \frac{°\varepsilon_0}{2} \int E^2 dv = \frac{°\varepsilon_0}{2} \int_0^a E_1^2 4\pi r^2 dr + \frac{°\varepsilon_0}{2} \int_a^\infty E_2^2 4\pi r^2 dr,$$

$$= \frac{°1}{2} \int_0^a \frac{q^2 r^2}{16\pi^2 \varepsilon_0 a^6} 4\pi r^2 dr + \frac{°1}{2} \int_a^\infty \frac{q^2}{16\pi^2 \varepsilon_0 r^4} 4\pi r^2 dr$$

$$= \frac{°q^2}{40\pi\varepsilon_0 a} + \frac{°q^2}{8\pi\varepsilon_0 a},$$

or

$$U = \frac{°3q^2}{20\pi\varepsilon_0 a}.$$

Example 7-1.2   Find the electrostatic energy of a uniformly charged spherical shell of total charge q and radius a.

---

[1] According to this agreement these relations must hold exactly:

$$° = 1 \,[kg \cdot m^2 \cdot sec^{-3}/volt \cdot amp] \quad \text{and} \quad \mu_0 = 4\pi \cdot 10^{-7} \,[volt \cdot sec/amp \cdot m],$$

where μ_0 is a constant defined in Section 10.4.

The electric field of the shell is

$$E = 0 \qquad \text{for } r \leq a,$$

$$E = \frac{q}{4\pi\varepsilon_0 r^2} \quad \text{for } r \geq a.$$

The energy is therefore

$$U = \frac{\overset{\circ}{\varepsilon_0}}{2} \int E^2 dv = \frac{\overset{\circ}{1}}{2} \int_a^\infty \frac{q^2}{16\pi^2\varepsilon_0 r^4} 4\pi r^2 dr,$$

or

$$U = \frac{\overset{\circ}{q^2}}{8\pi\varepsilon_0 a}.$$

▲

7-2. Energy in Terms of Charge Distribution

The fundamental energy law (7-1.1) can be transformed into various special forms which frequently are more convenient to use than the original expression itself. One of the most important special forms of the energy law is the equation representing the energy of the electrostatic field in terms of the charge distribution producing this field. It may be obtained as follows.

Substituting $\mathbf{E} = -\nabla\varphi$ into Eq. (7-1.1) and omitting for brevity the subscripts "all space" on the integrals, we have,

$$U = \frac{\overset{\circ}{1}}{2}\int \mathbf{E} \cdot \mathbf{D}\, dv = -\frac{\overset{\circ}{1}}{2}\int \nabla\varphi \cdot \mathbf{D}\, dv.$$

Using the vector identity (V-4), which may be written as

$$\nabla \cdot (\varphi\mathbf{D}) = \varphi\nabla \cdot \mathbf{D} + \nabla\varphi \cdot \mathbf{D},$$

or

$$\nabla\varphi \cdot \mathbf{D} = \nabla \cdot (\varphi\mathbf{D}) - \varphi\nabla \cdot \mathbf{D},$$

we obtain

$$U = -\frac{\overset{\circ}{1}}{2}\int \nabla \cdot (\varphi\mathbf{D})\, dv + \frac{\overset{\circ}{1}}{2}\int \varphi\nabla \cdot \mathbf{D}\, dv.$$

Changing the first integral in this expression into a surface integral by means of Gauss's theorem and substituting $\nabla \cdot \mathbf{D} = \rho$ in the second integral, we obtain

$$U = -\frac{\overset{\circ}{1}}{2}\oint \varphi\mathbf{D} \cdot d\mathbf{S} + \frac{\overset{\circ}{1}}{2}\int \varphi\rho\, dv,$$

where the surface integral is extended over the surface enclosing all space. However, since the charge distributions with which we deal in physics are confined to a finite region of space, this surface integral is zero, as can be seen from the following consideration. Suppose that the average distance from the charge-filled region to the surface of integration is R. The area of the surface is then proportional to R^2. Since R is much larger than the dimensions of the charge-filled region, this region may be regarded as a single point charge when viewed from this surface, so that φ and D may be regarded as point charge potential and point charge field. The integrand is then proportional to $1/R^3$ and the integral is proportional to $(1/R^3) \cdot R^2 = 1/R$. Since R may be assumed as large as one pleases, the integral can be made as small as one pleases and in the limit may be set equal to zero. Therefore we finally obtain

$$U = \overset{\circ}{\frac{1}{2}} \int \varphi \rho \, dv. \tag{7-2.1}$$

This equation can be written in an alternative form by expressing the potential φ in terms of the charge distribution ρ. Replacing φ in Eq. (7-2.1) by the Poisson integral (5-3.1) (with $\varphi_0 = 0$), we obtain

$$U = \overset{\circ}{\frac{1}{2}} \int \rho \left(\int \frac{\rho}{4\pi\varepsilon_0 r} \, dv' \right) dv = \overset{\circ}{\frac{1}{2}} \int \rho_1 \left(\int \frac{\rho_2}{4\pi\varepsilon_0 r_{12}} \, dv_2 \right) dv_1,$$

or

$$U = \overset{\circ}{\frac{1}{8\pi\varepsilon_0}} \iint \frac{\rho_1 \rho_2}{r_{12}} \, dv_1 dv_2, \tag{7-2.2}$$

where r_{12} is the distance between any two charge elements $dq_1 = \rho_1 dv_1$ and $dq_2 = \rho_2 dv_2$ of the charge distribution under consideration, and both integrals are extended over all space.

▼

Example 7-2.1   Find the electrostatic energy of a uniformly charged spherical shell of total charge q and radius a by using Eq. (7-2.1) and compare the result with that of Example 7-1.2.

The charge density in this distribution is $\sigma = q/4\pi a^2$ (surface charge). The potential at $r = a$ is $\varphi = q/4\pi\varepsilon_0 a$. Substituting these values into Eq. (7-2.1) and replacing dv by dS, we have

$$U = \overset{\circ}{\frac{1}{2}} \oint \sigma\varphi \, dS = \overset{\circ}{\frac{1}{2}} \oint \frac{q}{4\pi a^2} \frac{q}{4\pi\varepsilon_0 a} \, dS = \overset{\circ}{\frac{q^2}{32\pi^2\varepsilon_0 a^3}} \oint dS$$

or

$$U = \overset{\circ}{\frac{q^2}{8\pi\varepsilon_0 a}}.$$

The same result was obtained in Example 7-1.2.

▲

7-3. Energy of a System of Charge Distributions

Several special forms of the energy equation (7-1.1) can be obtained for the electrostatic energy associated with a system of discrete charge distributions.

Let us consider a system of charge distributions consisting of n separate charge-filled regions. Taking into account that the charge density outside the charge-filled regions is zero, we can write Eq. (7-2.1) for this system as

$$U = \overset{\circ}{\frac{1}{2}} \sum_i \int \varphi_i \rho_i dv_i, \tag{7-3.1}$$

where φ_i and ρ_i are the potential and the charge density within the i-th charge-filled region, and v_i is the volume of this region.

Each potential φ_i in Eq. (7-3.1) may be regarded as the sum of two potentials

$$\varphi_i = \varphi_i'' + \varphi_i',$$

where φ_i'' is the "internal" potential due to the charge contained in the i-th charge-filled region itself, while φ_i' is the "external" potential due to the charges contained in all other charge-filled regions of the system. Substituting these potentials into Eq. (7-3.1), we have

$$U = \overset{\circ}{\frac{1}{2}} \sum_i \int \varphi_i'' \rho_i dv_i + \overset{\circ}{\frac{1}{2}} \sum_i \int \varphi_i' \rho_i dv_i. \tag{7-3.2}$$

Since all φ_i'' and ρ_i depend only on the internal distribution of charge in the charge-filled regions, the first term on the right in Eq. (7-3.2) represents the *internal energy*, or the *self energy*, of the individual charge distributions comprising the system under consideration. This term is different from zero even if the system consists of only one single charge distribution, in which case it simply reduces to Eq. (7-2.1). On the other hand, since φ_i' depends on the mutual configuration of all charge distributions, the last term in Eq. (7-3.2) represents the *mutual energy*, or the *interaction energy*, of these distributions. This term is different from zero only if there are two or more discrete charge distributions in the system, since φ_i' by definition is zero otherwise.

Thus the energy of a system of discrete charge distributions can be expressed as the sum of the self energy, U_s, and the interaction energy, U', of these distributions.

Using the symbol U_s for the self energy, we can write Eq. (7-3.2) in the simpler form

$$U = \overset{\circ}{\frac{1}{2}} \sum_i \int \varphi_i' \rho_i dv_i + U_s. \tag{7-3.3}$$

The self energy of a charge distribution may change as a result of a rearrangement of charges within the distribution when the positions of neighboring charge distributions change. This must be taken into account when determining the *assembly work*—that is, the work required to set up a given system of charge distributions. If the self energy is independent of the configuration of the system, the assembly work is equal to the increment of interaction energy, but in general it is equal to the increment of the total electrostatic energy brought about in setting up the system.

Energy of a System of Point Charges. The last equation can be further simplified if the system of charge distributions under consideration can be regarded as a system of point charges—that is, if the linear dimensions of the charge-filled regions are much smaller than the distances between them. In this case the variation of the external potential inside the charge-filled regions is negligible. The external potential may then be considered constant throughout each of these regions, and φ_i' may be factored out from under the integral sign giving

$$\int \varphi_i' \rho_i dv_i = \varphi_i' \int \rho_i dv_i = \varphi_i' q_i,$$

where q_i is the total charge of the i-th region, or the i-th point charge.

Therefore for a system of point charges the energy equation (7-3.3) reduces to

$$U = \overset{\circ}{\frac{1}{2}} \sum_i \varphi_i' q_i + U_s. \tag{7-3.4}$$

This equation can be written in an alternative form by also expressing φ_i' in terms of the charges. Since φ_i' represents the sum of Coulomb's potentials produced at the position of the charge q_i by all other charges of the system, we have

$$\varphi_i' = \sum_k' \frac{q_k}{4\pi\varepsilon_0 r_{ik}},$$

where the prime on the summation sign indicates that the term in which the summation index k is equal to i is excluded from the sum. Substituting this expression into Eq. (7-3.4), we obtain

$$U = \overset{\circ}{\frac{1}{2}} \sum_i \sum_k' \frac{q_i q_k}{4\pi\varepsilon_0 r_{ik}} + U_s. \tag{7-3.5}$$

In the majority of problems in electrostatics, the self energy of a system of point charges may be considered unaffected by the phenomena taking place in or outside the system. For this reason U_s is usually left out of Eq. (7-3.5), and the interaction energy of a system of point charges is referred to as "the energy" of the system.

Example 7-3.1   Show that the self energy of discrete charge distributions is always larger than their interaction energy.

Let us consider a system of only two charge distributions. The total electrostatic energy of this system is, by the energy law (7-1.1a),

$$U = \frac{\overset{\circ}{\varepsilon_0}}{2} \int E^2 dv.$$

The field vector $\mathbf{E}$ in this equation can be expressed as the sum of two vectors

$$\mathbf{E} = \mathbf{E}_1 + \mathbf{E}_2,$$

where $\mathbf{E}_1$ represents the field due to the first charge distribution, and $\mathbf{E}_2$ represents the field due to the second charge distribution. Since

$$E^2 = (\mathbf{E}_1 + \mathbf{E}_2) \cdot (\mathbf{E}_1 + \mathbf{E}_2) = E_1^2 + E_2^2 + 2\mathbf{E}_1 \cdot \mathbf{E}_2,$$

we have

$$U = \frac{\overset{\circ}{\varepsilon_0}}{2} \int E_1^2 dv + \frac{\overset{\circ}{\varepsilon_0}}{2} \int E_2^2 dv + \frac{\overset{\circ}{\varepsilon_0}}{2} \int 2\mathbf{E}_1 \cdot \mathbf{E}_2 dv. \qquad (7\text{-}3.6)$$

The first term on the right in this equation depends only on the field produced by the first charge distribution, and the second term depends only on the field produced by the second charge distribution; these two terms represent therefore the self energy U_{s1} and U_{s2} of the two distributions. The last term, however, depends on both fields and, consequently, represents the mutual, or the interaction, energy U' of these charge distributions. Now, since the square of a real quantity cannot be smaller than zero, we have

$$(\mathbf{E}_1 - \mathbf{E}_2) \cdot (\mathbf{E}_1 - \mathbf{E}_2) \geq 0,$$

so that for any $\mathbf{E}_1$ and $\mathbf{E}_2$

$$E_1^2 + E_2^2 \geq 2\mathbf{E}_1 \cdot \mathbf{E}_2.$$

Substituting this correlation into the integrals of Eq. (7-3.6), we obtain

$$U_{s1} + U_{s2} \geq U',$$

where the equality sign applies only if $\mathbf{E}_1$ and $\mathbf{E}_2$ are everywhere equal to each other. This, however, is possible only if the two charge distributions overlap, and therefore the self energy of two discrete charge distributions is always larger than their interaction energy. By induction, the self energy of any number of discrete charge distributions is then always larger than their interaction energy.

Example 7-3.2   Find the interaction energy of two point charges q_1 and q_2 separated by a distance d.

Using the energy equation (7-3.5), we have

$$U' = \overset{\circ}{\frac{1}{2}} \sum_i \sum_k {}' \frac{q_i q_k}{4\pi\varepsilon_0 r_{ik}} = \overset{\circ}{\frac{1}{2}} \frac{q_1 q_2}{4\pi\varepsilon_0 r_{12}} + \overset{\circ}{\frac{1}{2}} \frac{q_2 q_1}{4\pi\varepsilon_0 r_{21}},$$

or

$$U' = \frac{\overset{\circ}{q_1 q_2}}{4\pi\varepsilon_0 d}.$$

Example 7-3.3   Find the total electrostatic energy of a point charge q and an infinitely large, conducting plane at a distance a from q, if the self energy of q is U_{sq}.

The total energy of this system may be expressed, according to Eq. (7-3.2), as

$$U = U_{sq} + \overset{\circ}{\frac{1}{2}} \int \varphi_1'' \sigma \, dS + \overset{\circ}{\frac{1}{2}} \int \varphi_1' \sigma \, dS + \overset{\circ}{\frac{1}{2}} \varphi_2' q,$$

where φ_1'' is the potential produced by the induced surface charge σ at the points of the surface of the conducting plane, φ_1' is the potential produced by the charge q at these points, and φ_2' is the potential produced by σ at the location of q. Since the plane is infinitely large and conducting, the total potential at any point of it must be zero, so that

$$\varphi_1'' + \varphi_1' = 0.$$

The sum of the two integrals in the above energy expression is therefore zero, and we obtain

$$U = U_{sq} + \overset{\circ}{\frac{1}{2}} \varphi_2' q.$$

The potential φ_2' can be found by replacing the conducting plane by the image charge $-q$ at the distance a behind the position of the plane (see Section 6-5). The final expression for the energy is then

$$U = - \frac{\overset{\circ}{q^2}}{16\pi\varepsilon_0 a} + U_{sq}.$$

Note that this energy is not equal to the energy of the point charge and its image.

▲

7-4. Energy of a Charge Distribution in an External Field

It is often necessary to know the energy associated with a single charge distribution due to the presence of an external electrostatic field at the location of this charge distribution. This energy can be found in the following manner.

Let ρ be some charge distribution and let ρ' be the charge distribution which produces the external field at the location of ρ. Let the field produced by ρ be $\mathbf{E}$, and that produced by ρ' be $\mathbf{E}'$.

The interaction energy of these charge distributions is, by Eq. (7-3.6),

$$U' = {}^{\circ}\varepsilon_0 \int \mathbf{E} \cdot \mathbf{E}' dv.$$

Substituting in this equation $\mathbf{E}' = -\nabla\varphi'$ and $\varepsilon_0 \mathbf{E} = \mathbf{D}$, and repeating the transformations employed in Section 7-2, we obtain for U'

$$U' = {}^{\circ}\int \rho\varphi' dv. \tag{7-4.1}$$

Since the integral in this equation depends only on the charge distribution ρ and external potential φ', the equation may be interpreted as representing the energy associated with the charge distribution due to the presence of the external field, or, as one usually says, the energy of the charge distribution *in* the external field. Note that, as it follows from the derivation, this energy is the same as the mutual, or interaction, energy of the charge distribution ρ and the charge distribution ρ' which produces the external field at the location of ρ.

If the charge distribution in Eq. (7-4.1) can be regarded as a point charge, φ' can be factored out from under the integral sign, and since $\int \rho \, dv = q$, the energy of a point charge in an external field is

$$U' = {}^{\circ}q\varphi'. \tag{7-4.2}$$

In conclusion, it may be added that if the charge distribution ρ and the potential φ' in Eq. (7-4.1) can be subdivided into partial charge distributions and partial potentials, then the energy U' can be expressed as the sum of partial energies, each corresponding to the product of one partial potential and one partial charge distribution (see Example 7-4.2).

▼

Example 7-4.1   Find the electrostatic interaction energy of two thin, interpenetrating spherical shells of radii a and b formed by the uniformly distributed charges q_a and q_b, respectively (Fig. 7.2).

The interaction energy of any two charge distributions is equal to the energy of one distribution in the field of the other and can be found therefore from Eq. (7-4.1). Furthermore, since the two shells are thin, we can replace in this equation the volume charge density ρ and the volume integral by the

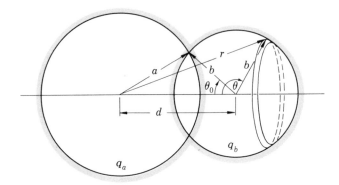

FIG. 7.2   Calculation of interaction energy for interpenetrating charged spherical shells.

surface charge density σ and the corresponding surface integral. Applying Eq. (7-4.1) to the shell b and using the relation $\rho_b dv_b = \sigma_b dS_b$, we then have

$$U' = {}^\circ\!\int \rho_b \varphi'_b dv_b = {}^\circ\!\oint \sigma_b \varphi'_b dS_b$$

and, substituting $\sigma_b = q_b/4\pi b^2$,

$$U' = \frac{{}^\circ q_b}{4\pi b^2} \oint \varphi'_b dS_b,$$

where φ'_b is the potential produced by the charge of the shell a at the points of the shell b, and S_b is the surface area of the shell b. The potential φ'_b is

$$\varphi'_b = \frac{q_a}{4\pi\varepsilon_0 a}, \qquad r \leq a,$$

$$\varphi'_b = \frac{q_a}{4\pi\varepsilon_0 r}, \qquad r \geq a.$$

Taking an infinitesimal ring as the surface element dS_b, we have, according to Fig. 7.2,

$$dS_b = 2\pi b^2 \sin\theta\, d\theta,$$

so that

$$U' = \frac{{}^\circ q_b}{4\pi b^2}\left(\int_0^{\theta_0} \frac{q_a}{4\pi\varepsilon_0 a} 2\pi b^2 \sin\theta\, d\theta + \int_{\theta_0}^{\pi} \frac{q_a}{4\pi\varepsilon_0 r} 2\pi b^2 \sin\theta\, d\theta\right),$$

and, since by the law of cosines

$$r = \sqrt{b^2 + d^2 - 2bd\cos\theta},$$

we obtain

$$U' = \frac{{}^{\circ}q_a q_b}{8\pi\varepsilon_0}\left(\frac{1}{a}\int_0^{\theta_0}\sin\theta\,d\theta + \int_{\theta_0}^{\pi}\frac{\sin\theta\,d\theta}{\sqrt{b^2 + d^2 - 2bd\cos\theta}}\right)$$

$$= \frac{{}^{\circ}q_a q_b}{8\pi\varepsilon_0}\left(-\frac{1}{a}\cos\theta\Big|_0^{\theta_0} + \frac{1}{bd}\sqrt{b^2 + d^2 - 2bd\cos\theta}\Big|_{\theta_0}^{\pi}\right).$$

Using the law of cosines once more, we have

$$\cos\theta_0 = \frac{d^2 + b^2 - a^2}{2bd},$$

and, substituting this expression into the last equation, we finally obtain after elementary simplifications (for $a + b \geq d \geq a - b$)

$$U' = \frac{{}^{\circ}q_a q_b}{16\pi\varepsilon_0 abd}[4ab - (a + b - d)^2].$$

Example 7-4.2   An idealized electrostatic model of an atom may be imagined as a point charge q (nucleus) located at the center of a thin spherical shell (electronic shell) formed by a uniformly distributed charge $-q$. Using this model, find the interaction energy of two identical atoms at different internuclear separations and estimate the upper limit of the dissociation energy for a diatomic molecule formed by these atoms.

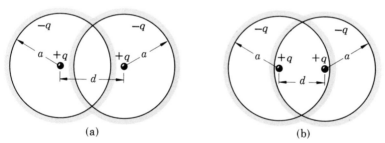

(a)   (b)

FIG. 7.3   Interaction between two atoms according to electrostatic model: (a) attraction, (b) repulsion.

Since outside the shell the field of each "atom" is zero, we have by Eq. (7-4.1) for $d > 2a$, with d and a as shown in Fig. 7.3,

$$U' = 0.$$

When the shells penetrate each other so that $a < d < 2a$, as shown in Fig. 7.3a, the interaction energy may be calculated by adding the following partial energies:

(1) The interaction energy of the two shells, which by the preceding example is

$$U'_1 = \frac{{}^{\circ}q^2}{16\pi\varepsilon_0 a^2 d}[4a^2 - (2a - d)^2].$$

(2) The interaction energy of the two nuclei, which by Example 7-3.2 is

$$U_2' = \frac{{}^{\circ}q^2}{4\pi\varepsilon_0 d}.$$

(3) and (4) The interaction energies of the nucleus of one atom and the shell of the other atom; since the potential produced by a uniformly charged spherical shell outside itself is the same as if the charge of the shell were concentrated at its center, these energies are

$$U_3' = -\frac{{}^{\circ}q^2}{4\pi\varepsilon_0 d}, \qquad U_4' = -\frac{{}^{\circ}q^2}{4\pi\varepsilon_0 d}.$$

The negative sign is here because of the negative charge on the shell.

The total interaction energy is therefore

$$U' = U_1' + U_2' + U_3' + U_4'$$

$$= \frac{{}^{\circ}q^2}{16\pi\varepsilon_0 a^2 d}[4a^2 - (2a - d)^2 + 4a^2 - 4a^2 - 4a^2],$$

or

$$U' = -\frac{{}^{\circ}q^2}{16\pi\varepsilon_0 a^2 d}(2a - d)^2.$$

When the penetration is such that $d < a$, as shown in Fig. 7.3b, the energy again may be calculated by adding partial energies. In this case the energies U_1' and U_2' are the same as for $a < d < 2a$, but the energies U_3' and U_4' are different; since the potential produced by each shell inside itself is $\varphi = -\dfrac{q}{4\pi\varepsilon_0 a}$, these energies, by Eq. (7-4.2), are

$$U_3' = -\frac{{}^{\circ}q^2}{4\pi\varepsilon_0 a}, \qquad U_4' = -\frac{{}^{\circ}q^2}{4\pi\varepsilon_0 a}.$$

The total interaction energy is then

$$U' = U_1' + U_2' + U_3' + U_4'$$

$$= \frac{{}^{\circ}q^2}{16\pi\varepsilon_0 a^2 d}[4a^2 - (2a - d)^2 + 4a^2 - 4ad - 4ad],$$

or

$$U' = \frac{{}^{\circ}q^2}{16\pi\varepsilon_0 a^2 d}[8a^2 - (2a + d)^2].$$

The dissociation energy is the energy that must be delivered to a molecule in order to completely separate the atoms comprising the molecule. The lowest interaction energy for the molecular model under consideration

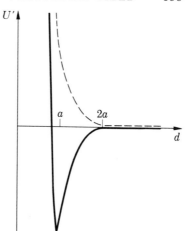

FIG. 7.4   Potential curve of a diatomic molecule according to electrostatic model (dashed curve represents an interaction between two atoms in a repulsive state, as explained in Problem 7.9).

is seen, by inspection, to occur when $d = a$ and, according to the last equation, is

$$U_{min} = - \frac{°q^2}{16\pi\varepsilon_0 a}.$$

Since the interaction energy of the two separated atoms is zero ($U' = 0$ for $d > 2a$), the upper limit of the dissociation energy is

$$U_d = 0 - U_{min} = \frac{°q^2}{16\pi\varepsilon_0 a}.$$

The potential curve (the plot of U' against the internuclear separation) for this molecular model is shown in Fig. 7.4.

▲

7-5. Energy of a Dipole in an External Field

Consider a dipole consisting of two point charges $+q$ and $-q$ separated by a small distance represented by the vector $\Delta\mathbf{l}$ directed from $-q$ to $+q$. Let this dipole be located in an external field $\mathbf{E}'$. The energies of the two charges in the field $\mathbf{E}'$ are, by Eq. (7-4.2),

$$U'_+ = °q\varphi'_+ \quad \text{and} \quad U'_- = -°q\varphi'_-,$$

where φ'_+ and φ'_- represent the potential of the external field at the location of the positive and negative charge, respectively. The energy of the dipole in the external field is the sum of the energies of the two charges in this field, or

$$U' = °q\varphi'_+ - °q\varphi'_- = °q(\varphi'_+ - \varphi'_-).$$

Now, the quantity in parentheses can be written as

$$\varphi'_+ - \varphi'_- = \Delta\varphi' = \Delta\mathbf{l} \cdot \nabla\varphi' = -\Delta\mathbf{l} \cdot \mathbf{E}',$$

so that

$$U' = -^\circ q\Delta\mathbf{l} \cdot \mathbf{E}'.$$

But $q\Delta\mathbf{l}$ is the dipole moment of the dipole, $\mathbf{p}$. Therefore we obtain for the energy of a dipole in an external field

$$U' = -^\circ\mathbf{p} \cdot \mathbf{E}'. \tag{7-5.1}$$

▼

Example 7-5.1   Show that the interaction energy of two dipoles $\mathbf{p}_1$ and $\mathbf{p}_2$ separated by a distance r can be expressed as

$$U' = ^\circ\left[\frac{\mathbf{p}_1 \cdot \mathbf{p}_2 - 3(\mathbf{r}_u \cdot \mathbf{p}_1)(\mathbf{r}_u \cdot \mathbf{p}_2)}{4\pi\varepsilon_0 r^3}\right].$$

According to Eq. (5-1.1), Eq. (5-4.10d), and vector identity (V-1), the field produced by the dipole $\mathbf{p}_2$ at the location of the dipole $\mathbf{p}_1$ is

$$\mathbf{E}' = -\nabla\left(\frac{\mathbf{p}_2 \cdot \mathbf{r}}{4\pi\varepsilon_0 r^3}\right) = \frac{3\mathbf{r}_u(\mathbf{p}_2 \cdot \mathbf{r})}{4\pi\varepsilon_0 r^4} - \frac{\nabla(\mathbf{p}_2 \cdot \mathbf{r})}{4\pi\varepsilon_0 r^3}$$

$$= \frac{3\mathbf{r}_u(\mathbf{p}_2 \cdot \mathbf{r}_u) - \nabla(\mathbf{p}_2 \cdot \mathbf{r})}{4\pi\varepsilon_0 r^3},$$

which, if vector identity (V-2) is applied to the last product,[1] and $(\mathbf{p}_2 \cdot \nabla)\mathbf{r}$ is replaced by $\mathbf{p}_2$ (see Problem 2.25), becomes

$$\mathbf{E}' = \frac{3\mathbf{r}_u(\mathbf{p}_2 \cdot \mathbf{r}_u) - \mathbf{p}_2}{4\pi\varepsilon_0 r^3}.$$

The substitution of this expression into Eq. (7-5.1) yields the above expression for the energy of the two dipoles after $\mathbf{p}$ is replaced by $\mathbf{p}_1$.

▲

7-6. Energy of a System of Charged Conductors

Special forms of the energy law (7-1.1) are also often used for the calculation of the electrostatic energy of a system of charged conductors.

Let us consider a system of n mutually external conductors in a charge-free space, and let us use the symbols S_i, φ_i, and q_i to designate the surface, the potential, and the total charge of the i-th conductor. Taking into account that under electrostatic conditions each conductor represents a region of constant potential, so that there is no electric

---

[1] Observe that $\mathbf{p}_2 \times \nabla \times \mathbf{r} = 0$ because $\nabla \times \mathbf{r} = 0$; $(\mathbf{r} \cdot \nabla)\mathbf{p}_2 = 0$ and $\mathbf{r} \times \nabla \times \mathbf{p}_2 = 0$ because $\mathbf{p}_2$ is a constant vector rather than a variable vector point function.

field inside conductors, we can write for the electrostatic energy of this system

$$U = \overset{\circ}{\frac{1}{2}} \int\limits_{\text{External space}} \mathbf{E} \cdot \mathbf{D} \, dv,$$

where the integration is extended only over the space surrounding the conductors. Substituting $\mathbf{E} = -\nabla\varphi$ and using the vector identity (V-4), we have, as in Section 7-2,

$$U = -\overset{\circ}{\frac{1}{2}} \int \nabla \cdot (\varphi\mathbf{D}) \, dv + \overset{\circ}{\frac{1}{2}} \int \varphi \nabla \cdot \mathbf{D} \, dv.$$

Since there is no charge in the space surrounding the conductors, $\nabla \cdot \mathbf{D} = 0$, and the last integral in this expression vanishes. The remaining integral can be transformed with the aid of Gauss's theorem into $n + 1$ surface integrals: one integral over the surface enclosing all space, and one integral over the surface of each conductor (all these surfaces form the boundaries of the volume of integration). As in Section 7-2, the surface integral over the surface enclosing all space vanishes, and we obtain

$$U = -\overset{\circ}{\frac{1}{2}} \sum_i \oint \varphi_i \mathbf{D} \cdot d\mathbf{S}'_i = \overset{\circ}{\frac{1}{2}} \sum_i \oint \varphi_i \mathbf{D} \cdot d\mathbf{S}_i,$$

where $d\mathbf{S}'_i$ is the surface element vector directed out of the volume of integration and therefore into the conductors, while $d\mathbf{S}_i$ is the surface element vector in the opposite direction—that is, out of the conductors. Since the potential is constant on the surface of each conductor, φ_i can be factored out from under the integral sign, so that

$$U = \overset{\circ}{\frac{1}{2}} \sum_i \varphi_i \oint \mathbf{D} \cdot d\mathbf{S}_i.$$

The surface integral in this expression is, according to Gauss's law (4-4.2a), equal to the total charge q_i of the i-th conductor. We obtain therefore for the energy of a system of charged conductors

$$U = \overset{\circ}{\frac{1}{2}} \sum_i \varphi_i q_i. \tag{7-6.1}$$

This formula represents the *total energy* of a system of charged conductors and should not be confused with the similar expression in Eq. (7-3.4) representing the *interaction energy* of a system of point charges.

    An important special case of systems of charged conductors is the system of two oppositely charged conductors, or a capacitor. Let us apply Eq. (7-6.1) to a capacitor formed by two arbitrarily shaped, mutually external conductors carrying charges q and $-q$ (Fig. 7.5). We obtain

$$U = \overset{\circ}{\frac{1}{2}} \varphi_1 q_1 + \overset{\circ}{\frac{1}{2}} \varphi_2 q_2 = \overset{\circ}{\frac{1}{2}} \varphi_1 q - \overset{\circ}{\frac{1}{2}} \varphi_2 q,$$

or

$$U = \overset{\circ}{\frac{1}{2}} q(\varphi_1 - \varphi_2).$$

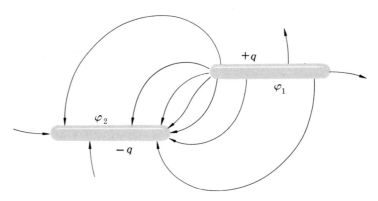

Fig. 7.5   Calculation of the energy of a capacitor.

Since the potential difference $\varphi_1 - \varphi_2$ is equal to the voltage V between the two conductors, the energy of the capacitor is simply

$$U = \overset{\circ}{\frac{1}{2}} qV. \tag{7-6.2}$$

This formula can be expressed in two alternative forms by using the capacitance C of the capacitor: since $C = q/V$, we have

$$U = \overset{\circ}{\frac{1}{2}} CV^2 \tag{7-6.3}$$

and

$$U = \overset{\circ}{\frac{1}{2}} \frac{q^2}{C}. \tag{7-6.4}$$

▼
Example 7-6.1   Two capacitors of capacitances C_1 and C_2 carrying charges q_1 and q_2, respectively, are connected in parallel. A spark appears when the connection is made. Find the energy dissipated by this spark if no other energy dissipation is taking place.

The total electrostatic energy of the two capacitors before connection is, by Eq. (7-6.4),

$$U_{before} = \frac{°1}{2} \frac{q_1^2}{C_1} + \frac{°1}{2} \frac{q_2^2}{C_2}.$$

Since the total capacitance of the two capacitors connected in parallel is equal to the sum of the individual capacitances and since the total charge after connection is equal to the sum of the original charges, the electrostatic energy after connection is

$$U_{after} = \frac{°1}{2} \frac{(q_1 + q_2)^2}{C_1 + C_2}.$$

By the principle of conservation of energy, the energy lost in the spark is then

$$U_{spark} = U_b - U_a = \frac{°1}{2} \frac{q_1^2}{C_1} + \frac{°1}{2} \frac{q_2^2}{C_2} - \frac{°1}{2} \frac{(q_1 + q_2)^2}{C_1 + C_2},$$

which after simplification becomes

$$U_{spark} = \frac{°(C_1 q_2 - C_2 q_1)^2}{2C_1 C_2 (C_1 + C_2)}.$$

▲

7-7. Correlation between Electrostatic Energy and Electrostatic Force

With the aid of Eq. (7-4.1) and the principle of conservation of energy we shall now determine the electric force which a charge distribution experiences in an electrostatic field.

Let us consider an arbitrary charge distribution ρ placed in an external electrostatic field produced by a charge distribution ρ'. The total energy of this system consists of the following components:

(1) The electrostatic energy U of the charge distributions.

(2) The energy W of the mechanical devices keeping the charge distributions in place (a charge distribution cannot be in a state of stable equilibrium under the action of electrostatic forces alone[1]).

The principle of conservation of energy requires that the total energy of this system always remains the same, so that

$$\frac{d}{dt}(U + W) = 0,$$

or

$$dU + dW = 0.$$

[1] This statement is known as the "Earnshaw theorem."

Suppose now that under the action of the electrostatic force **F**, the whole charge distribution ρ undergoes a small virtual displacement (translation) $d\mathbf{l}$ and that the density of ρ and of ρ' is not allowed to change during the displacement. In this case the self energies of the charge distributions will not change, so that $dU = dU'$, where U' is the mutual energy of the two charge distributions. We then have from the last equation for the increment in the mechanical energy

$$dW = -dU|_{\rho=\text{constant}} = -dU'|_{\rho=\text{constant}}$$

(for simplicity, we are writing $\rho = $ constant instead of $\rho = $ constant and $\rho' = $ constant). The increment in the mechanical energy is, however, equal to the work $\mathbf{F} \cdot d\mathbf{l}$ done by the electric force **F** in displacing the charge distribution along $d\mathbf{l}$, so that we obtain

$$\mathbf{F} \cdot d\mathbf{l} = -dU'|_{\rho=\text{constant}}.$$

Now, for constant ρ and ρ', constant orientation of ρ and ρ', and constant position of ρ', there corresponds a definite value of U' to every position of ρ. Therefore the energy increment dU' associated with the displacement $d\mathbf{l}$ can be expressed in terms of the gradient of the *energy field* determined by U':

$$dU' = \boldsymbol{\nabla} U' \cdot d\mathbf{l}\,|_{\rho=\text{constant}}.$$

We thus have

$$\mathbf{F} \cdot d\mathbf{l} = -\boldsymbol{\nabla} U' \cdot d\mathbf{l}\,|_{\rho=\text{constant}},$$

and since this correlation does not depend on the direction of $d\mathbf{l}$ (it holds for any $d\mathbf{l}$ whatsoever), we obtain

$$\mathbf{F} = -\boldsymbol{\nabla} U'\,|_{\rho=\text{constant}}. \tag{7-7.1}$$

From this formula the electrostatic force experienced by a charge distribution in an external field can be determined if the energy of this distribution at different points of the external field is known.

In the same manner the torque experienced by a charge distribution can be obtained by considering the work dW associated with an angular displacement $d\theta$ of a charge distribution. Since $dW = T_\theta d\theta = -dU = -(\partial U/\partial \theta)d\theta$, we have

$$T_\theta = -\frac{\partial U'}{\partial \theta}\bigg|_{\rho=\text{constant}}, \tag{7-7.2}$$

where T_θ is the torque with respect to an axis normal to the plane in which θ is measured.

Since $dU' = dU$ if ρ and ρ' are kept constant, Eqs. (7-7.1) and

(7-7.2) remain valid if instead of the interaction energy U' the total electrostatic energy U is used in them. We have therefore the alternative equations

$$\mathbf{F} = -\nabla U\big|_{\rho=\text{constant}} \tag{7-7.1a}$$

and

$$T_\theta = -\frac{\partial U}{\partial \theta}\bigg|_{\rho=\text{constant}}. \tag{7-7.2a}$$

For conductors, Eqs. (7-7.1) and (7-7.2) can be written in a somewhat different form. Suppose, for simplicity, that we have only two conductors carrying equal charges of opposite sign. Let one of the conductors undergo a small displacement (translation) $d\mathbf{l}$ under the action of the electrostatic force, and let the charges of the conductors remain constant. By Eq. (7-6.4), the energy of the system is $U = \frac{1}{2}\, q^2/C$. Since C is a function of geometrical relations only (see Sections 5-2 and 6-7), there corresponds a definite value of U to every position of the displaced conductor. Therefore, repeating the transformations which led to Eq. (7-7.1), we obtain for the force acting on the conductor

$$\mathbf{F} = -\nabla U\big|_{q=\text{constant}}. \tag{7-7.3}$$

By Eq. (7-6.3), however, U can be expressed also as $U = \frac{1}{2} CV^2$, where V is the voltage between the two conductors. Now,

$$d\left(\frac{1}{2}\frac{q^2}{C}\right)\bigg|_{q=\text{constant}} = -\frac{q^2}{2C^2}\, dC = -\frac{V^2}{2}\, dC = -d\left(\frac{1}{2}CV^2\right)\bigg|_{V=\text{constant}}.$$

Therefore Eq. (7-7.3) is equivalent to

$$\mathbf{F} = +\nabla U\big|_{V=\text{constant}}. \tag{7-7.4}$$

As can be shown with the aid of Section 6-7, Eqs. (7-7.3) and (7-7.4) remain valid even if there are more than two conductors in the system.

▼

Example 7-7.1   A voltage V is applied to a parallel plate capacitor of area A and plate separation x. Find the force between the plates by using Eq. (7-7.4) and Eq. (7-7.3).

Let us express the energy of the capacitor as a function of the voltage V. We have

$$U = \frac{1}{2}\int \mathbf{E}\cdot\mathbf{D}\,dv = \frac{\varepsilon_0}{2}\int E^2 dv = \frac{\varepsilon_0}{2}\left(\frac{V}{x}\right)^2 xA = \varepsilon_0 V^2\frac{A}{2x}.$$

By Eq. (7-7.4) the force is then

$$\mathbf{F} = +\nabla U\bigg|_V = -\frac{\overset{\circ}{\varepsilon_0}V^2 A}{2x^2}\,\mathbf{i}.$$

An alternative expression for the energy is

$$U = \overset{\circ}{\frac{1}{2}}\int \mathbf{E}\cdot\mathbf{D}\,dv = \overset{\circ}{\frac{1}{2\varepsilon_0}}\int D^2 dv = \overset{\circ}{\frac{1}{2\varepsilon_0}}\sigma^2 x A = \overset{\circ}{\frac{1}{2\varepsilon_0}}\left(\frac{q}{A}\right)^2 xA = \overset{\circ}{\frac{1}{2\varepsilon_0}}\left(\frac{q^2}{A}\right)x,$$

where q is the charge of the capacitor. By Eq. (7-7.3) the force is then

$$\mathbf{F} = -\nabla U\bigg|_q = -\frac{\overset{\circ}{q^2}}{2\varepsilon_0 A}\,\mathbf{i}.$$

But $q^2/\varepsilon_0 A = (q^2/\varepsilon_0 A^2)A = (\sigma^2/\varepsilon_0)A = [(\varepsilon_0 E)^2/\varepsilon_0]A = \varepsilon_0(V/x)^2 A$, and the two expressions for $\mathbf{F}$ are equal.

Example 7-7.2   Find the force between the two model atoms of Example 7-4.2 for different internuclear separations r.

For $r > 2a$ we have from Example 7-4.2 $U' = 0$, so that, by Eq. (7-7.1), $\mathbf{F} = 0$.

For $a < r < 2a$ we obtain, using the expression for U' found in Example 7-4.2 and substituting r for d,

$$\mathbf{F} = \nabla\left[\frac{\overset{\circ}{q^2}}{16\pi\varepsilon_0 a^2 r}\,(2a - r)^2\right]$$

$$= \frac{\partial}{\partial r}\left[\frac{\overset{\circ}{q^2}}{16\pi\varepsilon_0 a^2 r}\,(2a - r)^2\right]\mathbf{r}_u,$$

which upon differentiation becomes

$$\mathbf{F} = -\frac{\overset{\circ}{q^2}}{16\pi\varepsilon_0 a^2 r^2}\,(4a^2 - r^2)\mathbf{r}_u.$$

Since r in this case is always smaller than $2a$, this force is always directed toward the origin and thus represents an attraction.

For $r < a$ we similarly have

$$\mathbf{F} = -\nabla\left\{\frac{\overset{\circ}{q^2}}{16\pi\varepsilon_0 a^2 r}\,[8a^2 - (2a + r)^2]\right\}$$

$$= -\frac{\partial}{\partial r}\left\{\frac{\overset{\circ}{q^2}}{16\pi\varepsilon_0 a^2 r}\,[8a^2 - (2a + r)^2]\right\}\mathbf{r}_u,$$

which upon differentiation becomes

$$\mathbf{F} = +\frac{\overset{\circ}{q^2}}{16\pi\varepsilon_0 a^2 r^2}\,(4a^2 + r^2)\mathbf{r}_u.$$

This force is always directed from the origin and therefore represents a repulsion.

Example 7-7.3   Find the force between the two charged shells of Example 7-4.1.

Using Eq. (7-7.1) and the energy U' found in Example 7-4.1, we obtain, after substituting r for d,

$$\mathbf{F} = -\nabla \left\{ \frac{°q_a q_b}{16\pi\varepsilon_0 abr} [4ab - (a + b - r)^2] \right\}$$

$$= -\frac{\partial}{\partial r} \left\{ \frac{°q_a q_b}{16\pi\varepsilon_0 abr} [4ab - (a + b - r)^2] \right\} \mathbf{r}_u,$$

which after differentiation and simplification becomes

$$\mathbf{F} = \frac{°q_a q_b}{16\pi\varepsilon_0 abr^2} [r^2 - (a - b)^2] \mathbf{r}_u.$$

If both shells are of the same radius a, this expression reduces to

$$\mathbf{F} = \frac{°q_a q_b}{16\pi\varepsilon_0 a^2} \mathbf{r}_u.$$

Thus two equal, uniformly charged, interpenetrating shells repel each other with a force which is independent of the amount of interpenetration.

▲

7-8. Force Experienced by a Charge Distribution in an Electrostatic Field

Combining Eqs. (7-7.1) and (7-4.1), we can obtain an explicit equation for the force experienced by a charge distribution in an electrostatic field.

Let us express the energy U' of an arbitrary charge distribution in an external electrostatic field $\mathbf{E}'$ as a function of points in space. We can do this by using two systems of coordinates: ξ, η, ζ and x, y, z, shown in Fig. 7.6. The first system is "frozen" in the charge

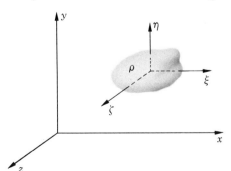

FIG. 7.6   Calculation of the force acting on a charge distribution in an external field.

distribution, and the origin of this system is located at the point x, y, z of the second system. We can then write Eq. (7-4.1) as

$$U'(x, y, z) = \int^{\circ} \rho(\xi, \eta, \zeta) \varphi'(x + \xi, y + \eta, z + \zeta) d\tau,$$

where $d\tau$ is a volume element in the system ξ, η, ζ. Applying Eq. (7-7.1) to this expression and taking into account that $\mathbf{V}$ in Eq. (7-7.1) operates upon the variables x, y, z only, we have

$$\mathbf{F} = -\mathbf{V}U'\big|_{\rho = \text{constant}} = -\int^{\circ} \rho(\xi, \eta, \zeta) \mathbf{V}[\varphi'(x + \xi, y + \eta, z + \zeta)] d\tau.$$

But

$$-\mathbf{V}[\varphi'(x + \xi, y + \eta, z + \zeta)] = \mathbf{E}'(x + \xi, y + \eta, z + \zeta)$$

and we obtain therefore

$$\mathbf{F} = \int^{\circ} \rho(\xi, \eta, \zeta) \mathbf{E}'(x + \xi, y + \eta, z + \zeta) d\tau.$$

Changing this expression back to a single system of coordinates, we finally obtain

$$\mathbf{F} = \int^{\circ} \rho \mathbf{E}'\, dv. \tag{7-8.1}$$

From this equation the force experienced by a charge distribution in an external electrostatic field can be found by direct integration.

Since the self energy $U_s = \int^{\circ} \frac{1}{2} \int \rho \varphi'' d\tau$ does not change if ρ is kept constant, φ' in the above expression for $\mathbf{V}U'$ can be replaced by $\varphi = \varphi' + \varphi''$. Then one obtains $\mathbf{E}$ rather than $\mathbf{E}'$ after taking the gradient. An alternative equation for the force acting on a charge distribution ρ is therefore

$$\mathbf{F} = \int^{\circ} \rho \mathbf{E}\, dv, \tag{7-8.2}$$

where $\mathbf{E}$ is the total field at the location of ρ.

In the case of a surface charge distribution or a line charge distribution, the charge element ρdv may be replaced by σdS or λdl, respectively, and the volume integration may be changed to a surface or line integration, accordingly.

If the charge distribution in Eq. (7-8.1) can be regarded as a point charge, $\mathbf{E}'$ may be factored out from under the integral sign, so that the force experienced by a point charge in an electrostatic field is

$$\mathbf{F} = {}^{\circ}q\, \mathbf{E}'. \tag{7-8.3}$$

If the field $\mathbf{E}'$ is itself produced by a point charge q', so that

$$\mathbf{E}' = \frac{q'}{4\pi\varepsilon_0 r^2} \mathbf{r}_u,$$

then

$$\mathbf{F} = \frac{{}^{\circ}qq'}{4\pi\varepsilon_0 r^2} \mathbf{r}_u, \qquad (7\text{-}8.4)$$

where r is the distance between the two charges. This equation is commonly known as *Coulomb's law*, and the force represented by this equation is known as *Coulomb's force*.

In earlier presentations of electromagnetic theory, based on mechanical basic measurables, Coulomb's law in the form

$$\mathbf{F} = \frac{qq'}{r^2} \mathbf{r}_u$$

was used for the definition of electric charge; Eq. (7-8.3) was then used for the definition of electrostatic field; and Eq. (7-4.2) was used for the definition of electrostatic potential.

▼

Example 7-8.1   Find the force experienced by a thin, uniformly charged rod of total charge q and length $2d$ lying along the axis of a thin,

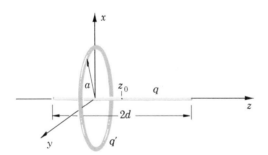

FIG. 7.7   Calculation of the electric force acting on a charged rod placed along the axis of a charged ring.

uniformly charged ring of radius a and total charge q' (Fig. 7.7) and then show that this force reduces to Coulomb's force if the rod is sufficiently far from the ring.

The field on the axis of the ring at a distance z from its center is, according to Example 4-5.2,

$$\mathbf{E}' = \frac{q'z}{4\pi\varepsilon_0(a^2 + z^2)^{3/2}} \mathbf{k},$$

so that, by Eq. (7-8.1), the force is

$$\mathbf{F} = {}^{\circ}\mathbf{k} \int \rho \, \frac{q'z}{4\pi\varepsilon_0(a^2 + z^2)^{3/2}} \, dv,$$

where ρ is the charge density of the rod. Since the rod is thin, we can replace $\rho \, dv$ by $\lambda \, dl = (q/2d) dz$. Denoting the distance between the center of the rod and the center of the ring by z_0, we then obtain

$$\mathbf{F} = {}^{\circ}\mathbf{k} \, \frac{qq'}{8\pi\varepsilon_0 d} \int_{z_0-d}^{z_0+d} \frac{z}{(a^2 + z^2)^{3/2}} \, dz = {}^{\circ}\mathbf{k} \, \frac{qq'}{8\pi\varepsilon_0 d} \, \frac{1}{\sqrt{a^2 + z^2}} \bigg|_{z_0+d}^{z_0-d},$$

or

$$\mathbf{F} = \frac{{}^{\circ}qq'}{8\pi\varepsilon_0 d} \left[\frac{1}{\sqrt{a^2 + (z_0 - d)^2}} - \frac{1}{\sqrt{a^2 + (z_0 + d)^2}} \right] \mathbf{k}.$$

If $z_0 - d \gg a$, we can neglect a in the radicals, so that in this case

$$\mathbf{F} = \frac{{}^{\circ}qq'}{8\pi\varepsilon_0 d} \left(\frac{1}{z_0 - d} - \frac{1}{z_0 + d} \right) \mathbf{k} = \frac{{}^{\circ}qq'}{8\pi\varepsilon_0 z_0 d} \left(\frac{1}{1 - \dfrac{d}{z_0}} - \frac{1}{1 + \dfrac{d}{z_0}} \right) \mathbf{k},$$

and if $z_0 \gg d$, we have

$$\mathbf{F} = \frac{{}^{\circ}qq'}{8\pi\varepsilon_0 z_0 d} \left(1 + \frac{d}{z_0} - 1 + \frac{d}{z_0} \right) \mathbf{k},$$

or

$$\mathbf{F} = \frac{{}^{\circ}qq'}{4\pi\varepsilon_0 z_0^2} \, \mathbf{k},$$

which is Coulomb's force.

▲

7-9. Calculation of Electrostatic Force from Charge Inhomogeneities

The force equation (7-8.1) can be written as

$$\mathbf{F} = {}^{\circ}\!\!\int_{\text{Boundary layer}} \rho \mathbf{E}' \, dv + {}^{\circ}\!\!\int_{\text{Interior}} \rho \mathbf{E}' \, dv,$$

where the first integral is extended over the boundary layer of the region occupied by ρ, and the second integral is extended over the interior part of the region. The volume of the boundary layer may be assumed as small as one pleases, so that, unless there is a surface charge at the boundary, the contribution of the first integral may be assumed equal to zero. We then have for the force

$$\mathbf{F} = {}^{\circ}\!\!\int_{\text{Interior}} \rho \mathbf{E}' \, dv. \tag{7-9.1}$$

Let us now replace in Eq. (7-9.1) $\mathbf{E}'$ by $-\nabla\varphi'$, and let us then transform the integrand by means of the vector identity (V-1). We have

$$\mathbf{F} = \overset{\circ}{\int_{\text{Interior}}} \rho\mathbf{E}'dv = -\overset{\circ}{\int_{\text{Interior}}} \rho\nabla\varphi'dv = \overset{\circ}{\int_{\text{Interior}}} \varphi'\nabla\rho\,dv - \overset{\circ}{\int_{\text{Interior}}} \nabla(\rho\varphi')dv.$$

If we now transform the last integral by means of the vector identity (V-20), we obtain

$$\mathbf{F} = \overset{\circ}{\int_{\text{Interior}}} \varphi'\nabla\rho\,dv - \overset{\circ}{\oint_{\text{Boundary}}} \rho\varphi'd\mathbf{S}. \tag{7-9.2}$$

The remarkable feature of this equation is that it correlates the force with the potential φ' rather than with the field vector $\mathbf{E}'$, and correlates the force with the *inhomogeneities* of the charge distribution.[1]

In the case of a charge distribution of constant density, Eq. (7-9.2) becomes especially simple. If $\rho = $ constant, $\nabla\rho = 0$, and we obtain, factoring out ρ from under the integral sign,

$$\mathbf{F} = -\overset{\circ}{\rho} \oint_{\text{Boundary}} \varphi'd\mathbf{S}. \tag{7-9.3}$$

Thus the electrostatic force acting on a constant charge distribution confined to a finite region of space is completely determined by the density of charge and the shape of the surface bounding this distribution. The direction of the force is then determined solely by the orientation of the surface elements, each surface element contributing to the force only in the direction of its normal (*inward* normal because of the minus in front of the integral).

▼

Example 7-9.1   Using Eq. (7-9.3), find the force on the charged rod described in Example 7-8.1.

Let the cross section area of the rod be S. By symmetry, only the end surfaces of the rod contribute to the force, and since the rod is thin, Eq. (7-9.3) reduces to

$$\mathbf{F} = -\overset{\circ}{\rho}(\varphi'_{z_0+d}S - \varphi'_{z_0-d}S)\mathbf{k},$$

where the subscripts indicate the location of the end surfaces. By Example 5-3.1, the potentials are

$$\varphi'_{z_0+d} = \frac{q'}{4\pi\varepsilon_0\sqrt{a^2 + (z_0 + d)^2}}, \qquad \varphi'_{z_0-d} = \frac{q'}{4\pi\varepsilon_0\sqrt{a^2 + (z_0 - d)^2}}.$$

---

[1] In this respect Eq. (7-9.2) is similar to Eq. (4-6.3). Note that Eq. (4-6.3) can be derived by the method used for deriving Eq. (7-9.2), and, conversely, Eq. (7-9.2) can be derived by the method used for deriving Eq. (4-6.3).

The charge density of the rod is $\rho = q/2Sd$. Substituting these values in the above equation for $\mathbf{F}$, we obtain

$$\mathbf{F} = \frac{°qq'}{8\pi\varepsilon_0 d}\left[\frac{1}{\sqrt{a^2 + (z_0 - d)^2}} - \frac{1}{\sqrt{a^2 + (z_0 + d)^2}}\right]\mathbf{k}.$$

The same expression was obtained in Example 7-8.1.

Example 7-9.2   A point charge q' is located at the center of a uniformly charged hemispherical shell of inner radius a, outer radius b, and charge density ρ (Fig. 7.8). Find the force exerted by the point charge on the shell.

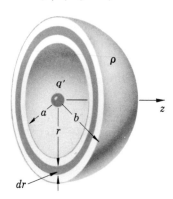

FIG. 7.8   Calculation of the electric force exerted by a point charge on a uniformly charged hemispherical shell.

Using Eq. (7-9.3) and the notations shown in Fig. 7.8, we have for the force acting on the shell

$$\mathbf{F} = -°\rho \underset{\text{Boundary}}{\oint} \varphi' d\mathbf{S}$$

$$= -°\rho \underset{\text{Flat surface}}{\int} \varphi' d\mathbf{S} - °\rho \underset{\text{Hemisphere } a}{\int} \varphi' d\mathbf{S} - °\rho \underset{\text{Hemisphere } b}{\int} \varphi' d\mathbf{S}$$

$$= °\mathbf{k}\rho \int_a^b \frac{q'}{4\pi\varepsilon_0 r} 2\pi r\, dr - °\rho \frac{q'}{4\pi\varepsilon_0 a} \underset{\text{Hemisphere } a}{\int} d\mathbf{S} - °\rho \frac{q'}{4\pi\varepsilon_0 b} \underset{\text{Hemisphere } b}{\int} d\mathbf{S}.$$

The last two integrals are $-\pi a^2\mathbf{k}$ and $\pi b^2\mathbf{k}$, respectively (because $\oint d\mathbf{S} = 0$ and $\int d\mathbf{S}$ over the plane bases of the hemispheres is $\pi a^2\mathbf{k}$ and $-\pi b^2\mathbf{k}$). Integrating the first integral and simplifying, we therefore obtain

$$\mathbf{F} = °\rho \frac{q'}{4\varepsilon_0}(b - a)\mathbf{k}.$$

▲

7-10. Force and Torque Experienced by a Dipole in an Electrostatic Field

Combining Eqs. (7-7.1) and (7-5.1), we obtain for the force acting upon a dipole of dipole moment $\mathbf{p}$ in an electrostatic field

$$\mathbf{F} = -\nabla U' \big|_{\rho=\text{constant}} = -\nabla U' \big|_{\mathbf{p}=\text{constant}}$$

or

$$\mathbf{F} = {}^{\circ}\nabla(\mathbf{p} \cdot \mathbf{E}')_{\mathbf{p}=\text{constant}}. \tag{7-10.1}$$

This equation can be expressed in an alternative form by using vector identity (V-2). Since $\nabla \times \mathbf{E}' = 0$ in an electrostatic field, and since $\mathbf{p} = \text{constant}$, we then obtain

$$\mathbf{F} = {}^{\circ}(\mathbf{p} \cdot \nabla)\mathbf{E}'. \tag{7-10.2}$$

Observe that the force acting on a dipole depends on the derivative (rate of change) of the external field rather than on the field itself. Therefore in a homogeneous field a dipole does not experience an electric force. Note also that the differential operations indicated in Eqs. (7-10.1) and (7-10.2) must be performed in a rectangular system of coordinates, because only then will the differentiation correspond to a pure translation of the charge distribution forming the dipole (see Section 7-7).

The torque acting on a dipole is, by Eqs. (7-7.2) and (7-5.1),

$$T_\theta = \frac{{}^{\circ}\partial}{\partial\theta}(\mathbf{p} \cdot \mathbf{E}')\bigg|_{p=\text{constant}} = \frac{{}^{\circ}\partial}{\partial\theta}(pE'\cos\theta) = -{}^{\circ}pE'\sin\theta, \tag{7-10.3}$$

where θ is the angle between $\mathbf{p}$ and $\mathbf{E}$. This equation can be written simply as

$$\mathbf{T} = {}^{\circ}\mathbf{p} \times \mathbf{E}'. \tag{7-10.4}$$

▼
Example 7-10.1   Express Eqs. (7-10.1) and (7-10.2) in scalar form.
Expanding Eq. (7-10.1), we obtain

$$F_x = {}^{\circ}p_x \frac{\partial E_x'}{\partial x} + {}^{\circ}p_y \frac{\partial E_y'}{\partial x} + {}^{\circ}p_z \frac{\partial E_z'}{\partial x}$$

$$F_y = {}^{\circ}p_x \frac{\partial E_x'}{\partial y} + {}^{\circ}p_y \frac{\partial E_y'}{\partial y} + {}^{\circ}p_z \frac{\partial E_z'}{\partial y}$$

$$F_z = {}^{\circ}p_x \frac{\partial E_x'}{\partial z} + {}^{\circ}p_y \frac{\partial E_y'}{\partial z} + {}^{\circ}p_z \frac{\partial E_z'}{\partial z}.$$

Expanding Eq. (7-10.2), we obtain

$$F_x = {}^\circ p_x \frac{\partial E_x'}{\partial x} + {}^\circ p_y \frac{\partial E_x'}{\partial y} + {}^\circ p_z \frac{\partial E_x'}{\partial z}$$

$$F_y = {}^\circ p_x \frac{\partial E_y'}{\partial x} + {}^\circ p_y \frac{\partial E_y'}{\partial y} + {}^\circ p_z \frac{\partial E_y'}{\partial z}$$

$$F_z = {}^\circ p_x \frac{\partial E_z'}{\partial x} + {}^\circ p_y \frac{\partial E_z'}{\partial y} + {}^\circ p_z \frac{\partial E_z'}{\partial z}.$$

Example 7-10.2   A dipole of moment **p** is placed at a distance x from a point charge q, so that **p** points directly toward q (Fig. 7.9). Find the force and the torque acting upon the dipole.

FIG. 7.9   Calculation of the electric force acting on a dipole placed near a point charge.

The electric field produced by the point charge is

$$\mathbf{E}' = \frac{q}{4\pi\varepsilon_0 r^2} \mathbf{r}_u = \frac{q(x\mathbf{i} + y\mathbf{j} + z\mathbf{k})}{4\pi\varepsilon_0 (x^2 + y^2 + z^2)^{3/2}}.$$

Differentiating, we have

$$\frac{\partial E_x'}{\partial y} = -\frac{3q}{4\pi\varepsilon_0} \frac{xy}{(x^2 + y^2 + z^2)^{5/2}},$$

$$\frac{\partial E_x'}{\partial z} = -\frac{3q}{4\pi\varepsilon_0} \frac{xz}{(x^2 + y^2 + z^2)^{5/2}},$$

$$\frac{\partial E_x'}{\partial x} = \frac{q}{4\pi\varepsilon_0} \left[\frac{1}{(x^2 + y^2 + z^2)^{3/2}} - \frac{3x^2}{(x^2 + y^2 + z^2)^{5/2}} \right].$$

For the point where the dipole is located, $y = z = 0$, so that

$$\frac{\partial E_x'}{\partial y} = \frac{\partial E_x'}{\partial z} = 0,$$

and

$$\frac{\partial E_x'}{\partial x} = -\frac{q}{2\pi\varepsilon_0 x^3}.$$

Since $\mathbf{p} = -p_x\mathbf{i}$, so that $p_y = p_z = 0$, the force acting upon the dipole is, by the preceding example,

$$\mathbf{F} = - \frac{q}{2\pi\varepsilon_0 x^3}\,\mathbf{p}.$$

Since $\mathbf{p} \parallel \mathbf{E}'$, the torque is zero.

▲

7-11. Maxwell's Stress Equation and Electrostatic Pressure

According to Section 7-8, the electric force experienced by a charge distribution depends only on this charge distribution and the external electrostatic field. But so does the *total* electrostatic field around a charge distribution. It also depends only on this charge distribution and the external field. It may be anticipated therefore that there should be a correlation between the force acting on a charge distribution and the total electric field in the surrounding space. Such a correlation indeed exists and may be derived as follows.

Using vector identity (V-22) and taking into account that the curl of an electrostatic field is always zero, we can write

$$\varepsilon_0 \int (\nabla \cdot \mathbf{E})\mathbf{E}\, dv = - \frac{\varepsilon_0}{2}\oint E^2 d\mathbf{S} + \varepsilon_0 \oint \mathbf{E}(\mathbf{E} \cdot d\mathbf{S}). \quad (7\text{-}11.1)$$

Since $\varepsilon_0 \nabla \cdot \mathbf{E} = \nabla \cdot \mathbf{D} = \rho$, we can rewrite this expression as

$$\int \rho\mathbf{E}\, dv = - \frac{\varepsilon_0}{2}\oint E^2 d\mathbf{S} + \varepsilon_0 \oint \mathbf{E}(\mathbf{E} \cdot d\mathbf{S}). \quad (7\text{-}11.2)$$

According to Eq. (7-8.2), however, the integral on the left represents the electric force acting upon ρ. Thus we obtain for the electric force acting upon a charge distribution in an electrostatic field

$$\mathbf{F} = - \frac{\varepsilon_0}{2}\oint E^2 d\mathbf{S} + \varepsilon_0 \oint \mathbf{E}(\mathbf{E} \cdot d\mathbf{S}), \quad (7\text{-}11.3)$$

where the integrals are extended over a surface enclosing the region occupied by the charge.

From Eq. (7-11.3) the force experienced by a charge distribution can be determined if the total electrostatic field at the points of an arbitrary surface enclosing the charge distribution is known. We shall call this equation *Maxwell's stress equation*, and we shall call the surface to which this equation is applied *Maxwellian surface*.

A remarkable aspect of Maxwell's stress equation is that it shows that the electric force acting on an electric charge may be attributed to the conditions (manifested as $\mathbf{E}$) in the space around the charge, rather than to the charge as such.

Although we obtained Maxwell's stress equation by considering a space charge distribution, the equation is also valid for a surface charge distribution, a line charge distribution, and a point charge distribution, which are merely the limiting cases of space charge distributions. This equation is valid also for a charge distribution carried by a conducting body, because, as it follows from Section 7-8, the electric force acting on a charge distribution does not depend on how this distribution is supported.

Equation (7-11.3) is often written in a symmetric form

$$\mathbf{F} = -\frac{1}{2} \oint \mathbf{E} \cdot \mathbf{D} \, dS + \oint \mathbf{E}(\mathbf{D} \cdot d\mathbf{S}). \qquad (7\text{-}11.3a)$$

For the case of the electric force acting on a charged conductor, Maxwell's stress equation can be considerably simplified. Applying this equation to the surface of the conductor and taking into account that $\mathbf{E}$ on this surface is normal to it, so that $\mathbf{E}(\mathbf{E} \cdot d\mathbf{S}) = \mathbf{E} \cdot \mathbf{E} \, d\mathbf{S} = E^2 d\mathbf{S}$, we have

$$\mathbf{F} = -\frac{\varepsilon_0}{2} \oint E^2 d\mathbf{S} + \varepsilon_0 \oint E^2 d\mathbf{S},$$

which gives

$$\mathbf{F} = \frac{\varepsilon_0}{2} \oint E^2 d\mathbf{S}, \qquad (7\text{-}11.4)$$

or

$$\mathbf{F} = \frac{1}{2} \oint \mathbf{E} \cdot \mathbf{D} \, d\mathbf{S}. \qquad (7\text{-}11.4a)$$

This equation suggests that the surface of a conductor in an electrostatic field is subjected to the *electrostatic pressure*

$$p = \frac{1}{2} \mathbf{E} \cdot \mathbf{D} \qquad (7\text{-}11.5)$$

producing a force on every element of the surface in the direction of the outward normal.

▼
Example 7-11.1   A conducting sphere of radius a consists of two separate hemispheres in contact with each other. Find the force with which one hemisphere is repelled from the other when the sphere is given a charge q (Fig. 7.10).

Applying Eq. (7-11.4) to the upper hemisphere, we have

$$\mathbf{F} = \frac{\overset{\circ}{\varepsilon_0}}{2}\oint E^2 d\mathbf{S},$$

where the integral needs to be extended only over the spherical surface of the hemisphere, because no electric field is present on the plane base of the hemisphere. Since on the spherical surface the field is constant and is

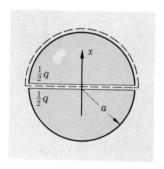

Fig. 7.10   Electric force between two charged hemispheres can be found from Maxwell's stress integral. For the purpose of calculation a small gap between the hemispheres is assumed and the integral is extended over the surface of the upper hemisphere.

equal to $E = q/4\pi\varepsilon_0 a^2$, we obtain after factoring E^2 out from under the integral sign

$$\mathbf{F} = \frac{\overset{\circ}{q^2}}{32\pi^2\varepsilon_0 a^4}\int d\mathbf{S}.$$

But $\int d\mathbf{S}$ over the spherical surface of the hemisphere is equal to $\pi a^2\mathbf{i}$ (because $\oint d\mathbf{S} = 0$ and $\int d\mathbf{S}$ over the plane base is $-\pi a^2\mathbf{i}$). Therefore the force with which this hemisphere is repelled from the other is

$$\mathbf{F} = \frac{\overset{\circ}{q^2}}{32\pi\varepsilon_0 a^2}\,\mathbf{i}.$$

Example 7-11.2   A large conducting plate of thickness t is partially inserted between the plates of a thin parallel-plate capacitor, as shown in Fig. 7.11. The capacitor's plates are of length a on a side and are separated by a distance d; a voltage V is applied between them. Find the electrostatic force acting on the conducting plate.

Let us construct a Maxwellian surface S as shown in Fig. 7.11; the front part and the rear part of S are outside the capacitor, and the vertical parts of S are in the regions where the electric field is homogeneous. Applying Maxwell's stress equation to this surface, we have

$$\mathbf{F} = -\frac{\overset{\circ}{\varepsilon_0}}{2}\oint E^2 d\mathbf{S} + \overset{\circ}{\varepsilon_0}\oint \mathbf{E}(\mathbf{E}\cdot d\mathbf{S}),$$

where the integrals need to be extended only over the parts de, fg, and bc of

S, because no appreciable field is present outside the capacitor, and the contribution of the parts ab, hf, cd, and fe is zero, by symmetry.

Since $\mathbf{E} \perp d\mathbf{S}$ on de, fg, and bc, the last integral in the above expression vanishes. On the surface de the electric field is $E = V/d$; on the surfaces fg

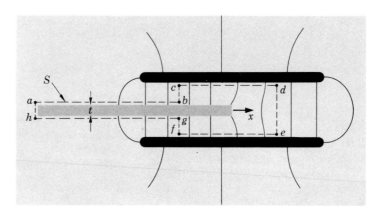

FIG. 7.11   Example of electric force calculation by means of Maxwell's stress integral.

and bc the electric field is $E = V/(d - t)$. We therefore have

$$\mathbf{F} = -\frac{°1}{2} \int \varepsilon_0 \frac{V^2}{d^2} \, d\mathbf{S}_{de} - \frac{°1}{2} \int \varepsilon_0 \frac{V^2}{(d-t)^2} \, d\mathbf{S}_{fg} - \frac{°1}{2} \int \varepsilon_0 \frac{V^2}{(d-t)^2} \, d\mathbf{S}_{bc}$$

$$= -\frac{°1}{2} \varepsilon_0 \frac{V^2}{d^2} \, \mathbf{i} \int dS_{de} + \frac{°1}{2} \varepsilon_0 \frac{V^2}{(d-t)^2} \, \mathbf{i} \int dS_{fg} + \frac{°1}{2} \varepsilon_0 \frac{V^2}{(d-t)^2} \, \mathbf{i} \int dS_{bc}$$

$$= -\frac{°1}{2} \varepsilon_0 \frac{V^2}{d^2} \, da\mathbf{i} + \frac{°1}{2} \varepsilon_0 \frac{V^2}{(d-t)^2} \, (d-t)a\mathbf{i}$$

$$= \frac{°1}{2} \varepsilon_0 V^2 \left(-\frac{a}{d} + \frac{a}{d-t} \right) \mathbf{i}.$$

Simplifying, we obtain

$$\mathbf{F} = \frac{°\varepsilon_0 at V^2}{2d(d-t)} \, \mathbf{i}.$$

▲

Problems

7.1. Assuming that the electrostatic energy of an electron is equal to its mass-energy, mc^2, where $m = 9.11 \cdot 10^{-31}$ kg is the electron mass and $c = 3 \cdot 10^8$ m/sec is the velocity of light, find the radius of an electron if the electron constitutes (a) a uniformly charged sphere of total charge $1.60 \cdot 10^{-19}$ amp $\cdot$ sec, (b) a uniformly charged spherical shell of the same charge.

7.2. An electrostatic system consists of two concentric spherical shells of radii a and b formed by uniformly distributed charges $+q$ and $-q$, respectively. Is the energy of the system equal to the sum of the energies of the two shells taken separately? Explain.

7.3. Find the electrostatic energy associated with a uniform spherical charge distribution of total charge q and radius a by using Eq. (7-2.1).

7.4. Show that a system of point charges cannot be in a state of stable equilibrium under the action of electrostatic forces alone (Earnshaw's theorem).

7.5. Show that the total electrostatic energy of two concentric spherical shells of radii a and b ($b > a$) formed by the uniformly distributed charges q_a and q_b, respectively, is

$$U = \frac{{}^{\circ}q_a^2}{8\pi\varepsilon_0 a} + \frac{{}^{\circ}q_b^2}{8\pi\varepsilon_0 b} + \frac{{}^{\circ}q_a q_b}{4\pi\varepsilon_0 b}.$$

7.6. Assuming that an atom may be regarded as a positive point charge nucleus in the center of a negative uniformly charged spherical shell, show that when the atom is excited so that the absolute value of its energy decreases n times, the radius of the shell increases n times (disregard the energy of the nucleus).

7.7. The ionization energy of a hydrogen atom (the work required to excite the atom to zero energy) is 13.6 eV. Using the atomic model described in the preceding problem, find the radius of the electron shell of a hydrogen atom.

7.8. Find the interaction energy of two different neutral atoms using the atomic model described in Problem 7.6 (see also Example 7-4.2), plot the potential curve for a diatomic molecule consisting of the two atoms, and show that the minimum of the interaction energy is

$$U' = -\frac{{}^{\circ}q_a q_b a}{16\pi\varepsilon_0 b^2},$$

where a and b are the radii of the electron shells ($b \geq a$), and q_a and q_b are the respective charges of the shells.

7.9. Suppose that the two atoms described in Example 7-4.2 have impenetrable shells (are in a "repulsive state"), so that after the atoms come in contact with each other, the shells must shift with respect to their nuclei to make a closer approach of the nuclei possible. Show that the interaction energy of the atoms is then

$$U' = 0 \qquad \text{for} \quad r \geq 2a,$$

and

$$U' = \frac{{}^{\circ}q^2 (2a - r)^2}{8\pi\varepsilon_0 ar(2a + r)} \qquad \text{for} \quad r \leq 2a,$$

where q is the charge of an electron shell, a is the radius of the shell, and r is the distance between the two nuclei. Plot the potential curve for U'.

7.10. Using the fundamental electrostatic energy law, find the energy of a thin parallel-plate capacitor and hence show that its capacitance is

$$C = \varepsilon_0 \frac{A}{d},$$

where A is the area of a plate and d is the separation between the plates.

7.11. Rectangular plates of a capacitor are separated by a distance $a + d$ at one edge and $d - a$ at the other. The width of the plates (along parallel edges) is b, the length is l. Neglecting edge effects and using the fundamental electrostatic energy law, find the energy of the capacitor and hence find its capacitance.

7.12. Conductor A is enclosed by conductor B. The two conductors carry electric charges q_A and q_B, and are kept at potentials φ_A and φ_B. Find the electrostatic energy of the system.

7.13. Starting from the fundamental energy law, show that the energy of a charged conductor in an external electrostatic field is

$$U = \oint^{\circ} \sigma \varphi' dS,$$

where S is the surface of the conductor, σ is the surface charge density on the conductor, and φ' is the external potential at the points of S.

7.14. Using the result of the preceding problem and the principle of conservation of energy, show that the electrostatic force experienced by a charged conductor in an external field $\mathbf{E}'$ is given by

$$\mathbf{F} = \oint^{\circ} \sigma \mathbf{E}' dS$$

and then show that this force can also be expressed in terms of the total field $\mathbf{E}$ on the surface of the conductor as

$$\mathbf{F} = \frac{1}{2} \oint^{\circ} \sigma \mathbf{E} \, dS.$$

7.15. An electrostatic voltmeter has two equal semicircular conducting plates, one stationary and one movable. The movable plate is suspended by an insulating fiber above the stationary plate and parallel to it so that the midpoints of the straight edges of the two plates are always on the same vertical line. The straight edges of the plates are initially at a right angle to each other. Neglecting edge effects, show that if a small voltage V is applied between the plates, the plates will be in equilibrium after the upper plate turns through the angle

$$\theta = \frac{\varepsilon_0 r^2 V^2}{4 \alpha d},$$

where r is the radius of curvature of the plates, d is their vertical separation and α is the torsion coefficient of the fiber (restoring torque per unit angular displacement).

7.16. By what factor does the electrostatic force between an electron and a proton exceed the gravitational force between them (the mass of a proton is 1836 times larger than the mass of an electron; the gravitational constant is $G = 6.67 \cdot 10^{-11}$ m³kg⁻¹sec⁻² ...) ?

7.17. What charge should be carried by a rain drop of 0.1 mm radius in order to counteract the force of gravity in a region where the earth's electric field is 130 volt/m? If the break-down field in air is $3 \cdot 10^6$ volt/m, can the drop support this charge?

7.18. Eight equal negative charges are placed at the corners of a cube. What positive charge should be placed at the center of the cube to keep the negative charges in equilibrium?

7.19. A point charge q is located at a distance d from an insulated conducting sphere carrying a charge Q. Find the work required to remove q to infinity.

7.20. Show that the force between two straight, parallel, uniformly charged fibers of length l and charge density λ_1 and λ_2 separated by a distance $d (d \ll l)$ is

$$F = \frac{°\lambda_1\lambda_2}{2\pi\varepsilon_0 d} \, l.$$

7.21. Using three methods other than those used in Example 7-7.1, show that the plates of a thin parallel-plate capacitor attract each other with the force

$$F = °\varepsilon_0 \frac{V^2 A}{2d^2},$$

where V is the voltage applied to the capacitor, A is the area of the plates, and d is the separation of the plates.

7.22. A point charge q is placed at a distance d from an infinite conducting plane. Find the force acting upon q.

7.23. Show that if a charge is placed within a spherical cavity made in a conducting material, the charge will be attracted to the inner surface of the cavity with a force

$$F = \frac{°q^2 ar}{4\pi\varepsilon_0 (a^2 - r^2)^2},$$

where q is the charge, a is the radius of the cavity, and r is the distance to the charge from the center of the cavity.

7.24. Show that the force experienced by a charge q placed at a distance r from the center of an uncharged, insulated, conducting sphere of radius a is

$$\mathbf{F} = -\frac{°q^2 a^3 (2r^2 - a^2)\mathbf{r}_u}{4\pi\varepsilon_0 r^3 (r^2 - a^2)^2}.$$

7.25. Show that a point charge q placed at a distance r from the surface of a conducting sphere of radius a carrying a charge $Q \gg q$ (Q and q have the same signs) will be in equilibrium if

$$r = r_0 \approx \frac{1}{2} a \sqrt{\frac{q}{Q}},$$

will be repelled from the sphere if $r > r_0$, and will be attracted to it if $r < r_0$.

7.26. Two long, straight fibers, carrying uniformly distributed, equal and opposite charges, are placed in a median plane inside a long circular conducting tube of inner radius a, symmetrically with respect to the axis of the tube. Show that no net electrostatic force will act on the fibers if their separation is

$$d = 2(\sqrt{5} - 2)^{1/2}a.$$

7.27. A point charge q is placed at a distance d from an infinite conducting plane having a hemispherical bump of radius a directly in front of q. Show that the point charge q is attracted toward the plane with the force

$$F = \frac{{}^{\circ}q^2}{16\pi\varepsilon_0 d^2}\left[1 + \frac{16a^3 d^5}{(d^4 - a^4)^2}\right].$$

7.28. According to Thomson's model, a hydrogen atom may be imagined as a sphere made of uniformly distributed positive charge q at the center of which a negative point charge $-q$ (the electron) is embedded. Show that if the electron is displaced from its equilibrium position, it will execute simple harmonic vibrations through the center of the "atom" with the frequency f given by

$$f^2 = \frac{{}^{\circ}q^2}{16\pi^3\varepsilon_0 a^3 m},$$

where a is the radius of the atom (positive sphere) and m is the mass of the electron.

7.29. Using Section 7-9, show that the electrostatic force between two interpenetrating, uniformly charged spheres of charge q and radius a, whose centers are separated by a distance d, is

$$F = -\frac{{}^{\circ}q^2 d}{128\pi\varepsilon_0 a^6}(d^3 - 18a^2 d + 32a^3).$$

7.30. Suppose that an atom may be imagined as a sphere of radius a made of uniformly distributed negative charge $-q$ (electron cloud) at the center of which a positive charge q (nucleus) is rigidly embedded. Show that if two such atoms approach each other so that the distance between their nuclei is d, the force between the atoms is

$$F = 0 \qquad\qquad\qquad\qquad\qquad\qquad\qquad \text{for} \quad d \geq 2a,$$

$$F = \frac{{}^{\circ}q^2}{128\pi\varepsilon_0 a^6 d^2}[32a^3(a^3 - d^3) + d^4(18a^2 - d^2)] \qquad \text{for} \quad 2a \geq d \geq a,$$

and

$$F = -\frac{{}^{\circ}q^2}{128\pi\varepsilon_0 a^6 d^2} [32a^3(a^3 - d^3) - d^4(18a^2 - d^2)] \quad \text{for} \quad a \ge d \ge 0.$$

7.31. Show that the arbitrariness of φ has no effect on the force calculated from Eqs. (7-9.2) or (7-9.3).

7.32. Show that the electrostatic interaction energy of two multipoles of orders n_1 and n_2 is proportional to $r^{-(n_1+n_2+1)}$, while the force is proportional to $r^{-(n_1+n_2+2)}$.

7.33. Two dipoles of moments p_1 and p_2 are placed at a distance r from each other. Show that if the moments of the dipoles are directed along the line joining them, the force exerted by one dipole upon the other is

$$F = \pm \frac{{}^{\circ}3p_1 p_2}{2\pi\varepsilon_0 r^4}.$$

7.34. Two dipoles of moments p_1 and p_2 are placed at a distance r from each other. The moment of the first dipole is directed along the line joining the dipoles, the moment of the second dipole is perpendicular to that line. Show that the forces experienced by the dipoles are

$$F_1 = \pm \frac{{}^{\circ}3p_1 p_2}{4\pi\varepsilon_0 r^4}, \qquad F_2 = \mp \frac{{}^{\circ}3p_1 p_2}{4\pi\varepsilon_0 r^4}$$

and are not colinear, while the torques are

$$T_1 = \pm \frac{{}^{\circ}p_1 p_2}{4\pi\varepsilon_0 r^3}, \qquad T_2 = \pm \frac{{}^{\circ}p_1 p_2}{2\pi\varepsilon_0 r^3}.$$

Is Newton's law of action and reaction satisfied in this case?

7.35. A small hemispherical cup of radius a is placed on the lower plate of a horizontal, thin, parallel-plate capacitor of plate separation $d(d \gg a)$, the spherical surface of the cup facing the upper plate. Show that if a voltage V is applied to the capacitor, the cup will rise if its weight is

$$W < {}^{\circ}\pi\varepsilon_0 \left(\frac{3aV}{2d}\right)^2.$$

7.36. An uncharged conducting sphere of radius a consisting of two separate hemispheres is placed in a homogeneous external field $\mathbf{E}$ so that $\mathbf{E}$ is perpendicular to the plane dividing the two hemispheres. Show that each hemisphere will be subjected to a force

$$F = {}^{\circ}\tfrac{9}{4}\pi\varepsilon_0 a^2 E^2$$

tending to separate it from the other hemisphere.

7.37. A soap bubble of radius a has a surface tension T. Show that if the bubble is given a charge q, the radius of the bubble will increase to r

given by

$$P(r^3 - a^3) + 4T(r^2 - a^2) - \frac{°q^2}{32\pi^2 \varepsilon_0 r} = 0,$$

where P is the atmospheric pressure.

7.38. A long cylinder of radius a is partially inserted into another long cylinder of radius b coaxial with the first. Show that if a voltage V is applied between the cylinders, the smaller cylinder will be pulled into the larger one with a force

$$F \approx \frac{°\pi\varepsilon_0 V^2}{\ln{(b/a)}}.$$

7.39. Show that the interaction energy of a system of spherically symmetric charge distributions is the same as if the total charge of each distribution were concentrated at its center.

7.40. Show that the force experienced by a spherically symmetric charge distribution in an arbitrary electrostatic field is the same as if the total charge of this distribution were concentrated at its center.

7.41. Consider a Maxwellian surface in the shape of a rectangular prism partially inserted between the plates of a parallel-plate capacitor. If the edge effects of the capacitor are neglected, and if Maxwell's stress integral is calculated for this surface, a force is found to be acting on the space enclosed by the surface. Explain this "capacitor paradox" and calculate the correction term that must be added to the stress integral in this particular case. (Hint: by neglecting edge effects in a parallel-plate capacitor, one creates $\nabla \times \mathbf{E}$ at the edges.)

7.42. Derive Maxwell's stress equation for the gravitational field.

8

ELECTROSTATIC FIELD
IN MATERIAL MEDIA

Thus far we have dealt with electrostatic fields in empty space, or vacuum. Electrostatic fields can also exist, however, in non-conducting material media, or dielectrics. The properties of electrostatic fields in these media will be discussed in the present chapter.

8-1. Cavity Definition of Electric Field Vectors

The measurement procedures by means of which we have defined the field vectors **E** and **D** in Sections 4-2 and 4-3 can be used directly for measurements in vacuum, gases, and liquids, but not in solids, since neither a test charge nor a test plate can move freely inside solid bodies. A more precise definition of **E** and **D** must therefore be made in order to make clear what we mean when we speak about electric fields inside material media and, in particular, inside solid bodies.

The only way to perform a field measurement in a solid body is to insert a measuring device (test charge or test plates) into a hole, or a cavity, made in the body. It has been found, however, that such a measurement is affected by the shape and orientation of the cavity. Therefore the shape and orientation of cavities to be used for field measurements must be specified in the definitions of **E** and **D** for material media. We shall define **E** and **D** for all media as follows.

*The electric field vector **E** at a point inside a material medium is defined as the vector **E** measured (by the method of Section 4-2) in a small, needle-shaped* *cavity made in this medium at that point and oriented so that the electric field in the cavity is in the direction of the axis of the cavity.* The essence of this definition is illustrated in Fig. 8.1. The requirement that the cavity be needle-shaped and oriented along the direction of the field is a result of investigations showing that the electric field measurements in liquids and gases by the direct method of Section 4-2 yield the same fields as the measurements inside small cavities of this type. The requirement that the cavity be small is needed in order to associate the electric field vector with a particular point of the medium (a "small" cavity is a

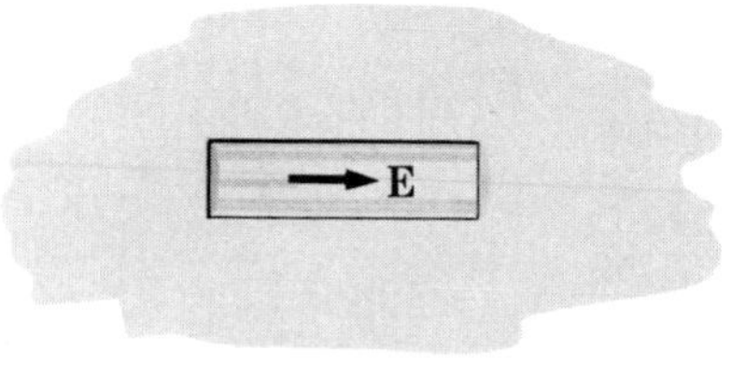

FIG. 8.1   To measure electric field in a material medium, a needle-shaped cavity or a long cylindrical cavity is used.

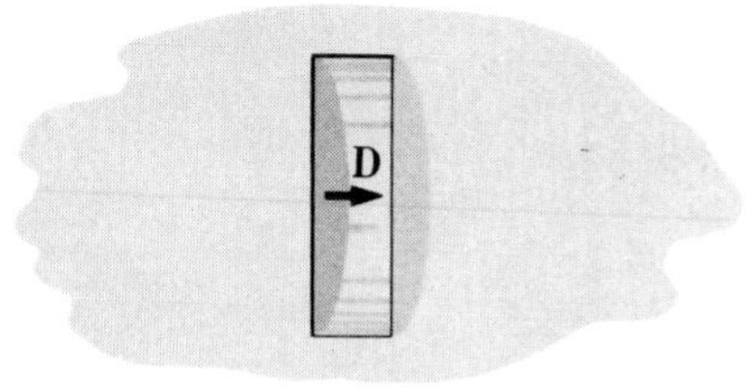

FIG. 8.2   To measure displacement field in a material medium, a coin-shaped cavity or a short cylindrical cavity is used.

cavity whose length is much smaller than the distance over which the field changes appreciably).

The displacement vector **D** *at a point inside a material medium is defined as the vector* **D** *measured (by the method of Section 4-3) in a small, coin-shaped cavity made in this medium at that point and oriented so that the displacement field in the cavity is in the direction of the axis of the cavity.* The essence of this definition is illustrated in Fig. 8.2. The requirement that the cavity be coin-shaped and oriented with its axis along the direction of the field is a result of investigations showing that the displacement field measurements in liquids and gases by the direct method of Section 4-3 yield the same fields as the measurements inside small cavities of this type. The requirement that the cavity be small is needed in order to associate the displacement field vector with a particular point of the medium.

The two definitions which we have just introduced are frequently expressed symbolically as

$$\mathbf{E}_{\text{medium}} = \mathbf{E}_{-} \quad \text{and} \quad \mathbf{D}_{\text{medium}} = \mathbf{D}_{|}. \qquad (8\text{-}1.1a, b)$$

8-2. Fundamental Laws of the Electrostatic Fields in Material Media

If we compare various lines-of-force patterns formed by small particles suspended in a dielectric liquid,[1] we find that these patterns have the same basic property as the lines-of-force pictures obtained in vacuum: there are no closed lines of force in any of them. We must suspect therefore that the curl and the circulation integral of the electrostatic fields in dielectrics, just as in vacuum, are zero:

$$\mathbf{\nabla} \times \mathbf{E} = 0, \qquad \oint \mathbf{E} \cdot d\mathbf{l} = 0. \qquad \text{(8-2.1a, b)}$$

If we perform Faraday's ice-pail experiment using a container (enclosure) filled with a dielectric liquid, we find that the result of the experiment is exactly the same as when the container is empty. We must suspect therefore that the divergence and flux density equations for displacement fields in dielectrics, just as in vacuum, are

$$\mathbf{\nabla} \cdot \mathbf{D} = \rho, \qquad \oint \mathbf{D} \cdot d\mathbf{S} = \int \rho \, dv. \qquad \text{(8-2.2a, b)}$$

The validity and generality of these four equations have been confirmed by all presently known phenomena involving static electric fields in dielectric media. Therefore, according to Section 3-2, these equations represent fundamental electrostatic field laws.

If we perform simultaneous $\mathbf{D}$ and $\mathbf{E}$ measurements in various dielectrics, we find that, in contrast to electrostatic fields in vacuum, there is no general law which correlates $\mathbf{D}$ and $\mathbf{E}$ in an arbitrary medium, although in the majority of common materials $\mathbf{D}$ and $\mathbf{E}$ are connected by the equation

$$\mathbf{D} = \varepsilon_0 \varepsilon \mathbf{E}. \qquad \text{(8-2.3)}$$

In this equation ε is a dimensionless factor of proportionality, different for different media, and frequently different for different points of the same medium. It is called the *permittivity*. If the permittivity is the same for all points of a medium, it is called the *dielectric constant*. The media for which Eq. (8-2.3) holds are called *electrically linear isotropic*

---

[1] See, for example, Physical Science Study Committee: *Physics*, D. C. Heath and Company, Boston (1960), p. 467; or J. Orear: *Fundamental Physics*, John Wiley and Sons, New York (1961), p. 136.

media. They are the media with which we shall be concerned in this book.

Frequently one expresses ε as

$$\varepsilon = \chi_e + 1. \tag{8-2.4}$$

The quantity χ_e defined by this equation is called *electric susceptibility.*

The displacement law $\mathbf{D} = \varepsilon_0\varepsilon\mathbf{E}$ reduces to the displacement law for vacuum, $\mathbf{D} = \varepsilon_0\mathbf{E}$, if $\varepsilon = 1$. Since the other two fundamental field laws for material media are identical with the corresponding laws for vacuum, a vacuum, as far as the electrostatic field is concerned, is merely a special case of a material medium—a medium of dielectric constant $\varepsilon = 1$.

In a general case, a medium is neither linear nor isotropic—that is, in general, $\mathbf{D}$ is not a linear function of $\mathbf{E}$, and the correlation between $\mathbf{D}$ and $\mathbf{E}$ depends on the direction of $\mathbf{E}$ relative to certain characteristic directions in the medium. An example of anisotropic media is a crystal. In a crystal, $\mathbf{D}$ and $\mathbf{E}$ are usually not even parallel to each other, each vector having a direction of its own.

Equations (8-2.1), (8-2.2), and (8-2.3) determine the circulation law and the divergence law for both the electric field $\mathbf{E}$ and the displacement field $\mathbf{D}$ and thus, by Helmholtz's theorem of vector analysis, constitute a complete set of equations uniquely specifying these fields.[1]

The similarity between Eqs. (8-2.1), (8-2.2), and (8-2.3) and the corresponding equations for the electrostatic fields in vacuum suggests that many of the formulas which we have learned from the preceding chapters remain valid for electrostatic fields in material media also. In particular, all formulas remain obviously valid for fields in infinite media of constant permittivity, provided that ε_0 in these formulas is replaced by the product $\varepsilon_0\varepsilon$.

8-3. Electrostatic Potential and Capacitance of Conductors and Capacitors in the Presence of Dielectric Media

Using the same argument as in Section 5-1 ($\nabla \times \mathbf{E} = 0$), we can again express $\mathbf{E}$ in terms of the electrostatic potential φ:

$$\mathbf{E} = -\nabla\varphi. \tag{8-3.1}$$

[1] See footnote 1 on page 87.

Taking the line integral of this equation, we obtain

$$\varphi_a - \varphi_b = \int_a^b \mathbf{E} \cdot d\mathbf{l} = V_{ab}, \tag{8-3.2}$$

where V_{ab} is the voltage between the points a and b. Thus the electrostatic potential φ can be used for describing electrostatic fields also in material media, and its correlation with the field vector $\mathbf{E}$ and with the voltage V_{ab} is the same as in vacuum.

The existence of the electrostatic potential in dielectric media allows one to define the capacitance of capacitors and isolated conductors in the presence of dielectric media. This definition is the same as for the conductors and capacitors in vacuum—that is,

$$C = \frac{q}{\varphi} \quad \text{and} \quad C = \frac{q}{V} \tag{8-3.3a, b}$$

for an isolated conductor and for a capacitor, respectively.

As it follows from Gauss's law (8-2.2b) and displacement law (8-2.3), the capacitance of a capacitor filled with a material of dielectric constant ε is ε times larger than the capacitance of the empty capacitor ($\varepsilon = 1$). This property is used for measuring ε of various dielectrics: one measures C_{filled} and C_{empty} and then calculates ε from

$$\varepsilon = \frac{C_{\text{filled}}}{C_{\text{empty}}}. \tag{8-3.4}$$

▼
Example 8-3.1   A parallel-plate capacitor of plate separation d and area A is filled with a material of dielectric constant ε. Neglecting edge effects, find the capacitance.

By symmetry, the field in the capacitor is homogeneous (except near the edges). The charge on the positive plate is then

$$q = \sigma A = DA = \varepsilon_0 \varepsilon E A = \varepsilon_0 \varepsilon \frac{V}{d} A,$$

so that the capacitance is, by Eq. (8-3.3b),

$$C = \varepsilon_0 \varepsilon \frac{A}{d}.$$

Example 8-3.2   A thin parallel-plate capacitor contains two dielectrics of dielectric constant ε_1 and ε_2, as shown in Fig. 8.3. Neglecting edge effects, find the capacitance.

Let the charge of the capacitor be q. By symmetry, the field in the capacitor is homogeneous (except near the edges). Constructing a Gaussian

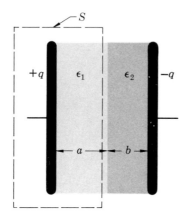

FIG. 8.3 First example of a capacitor with two dielectrics. The thickness of the capacitor is exaggerated.

surface S in the shape of a box enclosing the positive plate, and observing that if the edge effects are neglected the only contribution to the integral $\oint \mathbf{D} \cdot d\mathbf{S}$ comes from the portion of the Gaussian surface lying directly between the plates, we have from Gauss's law (8-2.2b)

$$\oint \mathbf{D} \cdot d\mathbf{S} = \int D \, dS = DA = q,$$

where A is the area of the enclosed plate. Hence, between the plates,

$$D = \frac{q}{A}.$$

The electric field is then, by the displacement law (8-2.3),

$$E_1 = \frac{q}{\varepsilon_0 \varepsilon_1 A} \quad \text{and} \quad E_2 = \frac{q}{\varepsilon_0 \varepsilon_2 A}$$

in dielectrics 1 and 2, respectively. The voltage between the plates is

$$V = \int \mathbf{E} \cdot d\mathbf{l} = \underset{\text{Dielectric 1}}{\int \mathbf{E_1} \cdot d\mathbf{l}} + \underset{\text{Dielectric 2}}{\int \mathbf{E_2} \cdot d\mathbf{l}}$$

$$= \frac{q}{\varepsilon_0 \varepsilon_1 A} \int_0^a dl + \frac{q}{\varepsilon_0 \varepsilon_2 A} \int_a^{a+b} dl,$$

or

$$V = \frac{q}{\varepsilon_0 A} \left(\frac{a}{\varepsilon_1} + \frac{b}{\varepsilon_2} \right).$$

The capacitance is therefore

$$C = \frac{q}{V} = \frac{\varepsilon_0 A}{(a/\varepsilon_1 + b/\varepsilon_2)}.$$

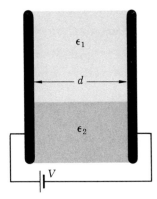

Fig. 8.4   Second example of a capacitor with
two dielectrics. The thickness of the capacitor
is exaggerated.

As a check, we note that this formula reduces to the expression for the
capacitance of an empty capacitor (Example 5-2.4) if $\varepsilon_1 = \varepsilon_2 = 1$.

Example 8-3.3   A thin parallel-plate capacitor of plate separation d
contains two dielectrics of dielectric constant ε_1 and ε_2, as shown in Fig.
8.4. Neglecting edge effects, find the capacitance.

Let the voltage between the plates be V. By symmetry, the electric
field between the plates is then $E = V/d$. The displacement is

$$D_1 = \varepsilon_0 \varepsilon_1 \frac{V}{d} \quad \text{and} \quad D_2 = \varepsilon_0 \varepsilon_2 \frac{V}{d}$$

in dielectrics 1 and 2, respectively. The charge on that part of the positive
plate which is in contact with dielectric 1 (area A_1) is then

$$q_1 = D_1 A_1 = \varepsilon_0 \varepsilon_1 \frac{V}{d} A_1.$$

The charge on that part of the positive plate which is in contact with dielectric
2 (area A_2) is

$$q_2 = D_2 A_2 = \varepsilon_0 \varepsilon_2 \frac{V}{d} A_2.$$

The total charge is $q = q_1 + q_2$, or

$$q = \varepsilon_0 \frac{V}{d} (\varepsilon_1 A_1 + \varepsilon_2 A_2).$$

The capacitance is therefore

$$C = \frac{q}{V} = \frac{\varepsilon_0 (\varepsilon_1 A_1 + \varepsilon_2 A_2)}{d}.$$

Again, if $\varepsilon_1 = \varepsilon_2 = 1$, the capacitance reduces to that of the empty capacitor (Example 5-2.4).

▲

8-4. Calculation of Electrostatic Field and Electrostatic Potential within Dielectric Media from Charge Distribution

One of the most important methods for calculating electrostatic fields in vacuum is the calculation of fields from the corresponding charge distributions by direct integration. As we shall now see, this method is also important for calculating fields in dielectric media, although the range of its applicability for fields in dielectric media is very limited.

By Poisson's theorem, the field vector $\mathbf{E}$ can be expressed as

$$\mathbf{E} = -\frac{1}{4\pi} \int_{\text{All space}} \frac{\mathbf{\nabla}'(\mathbf{\nabla}' \cdot \mathbf{E}) - \mathbf{\nabla}' \times (\mathbf{\nabla}' \times \mathbf{E})}{r} \, dv',$$

where primed operators are used in order to avoid ambiguity in the subsequent transformations. By the curl law (8-2.1a), $\mathbf{\nabla} \times \mathbf{E}$ is zero. By the divergence law (8-2.2a) and displacement law (8-2.3) (we are considering here only linear isotropic dielectrics),

$$\mathbf{\nabla}' \cdot \mathbf{E} = \mathbf{\nabla}' \cdot \frac{\mathbf{D}}{\varepsilon_0 \varepsilon} = \frac{1}{\varepsilon_0 \varepsilon} \mathbf{\nabla}' \cdot \mathbf{D} + \frac{\mathbf{D}}{\varepsilon_0} \cdot \mathbf{\nabla}' \frac{1}{\varepsilon} = \frac{1}{\varepsilon_0 \varepsilon} \rho + \frac{\mathbf{D}}{\varepsilon_0} \cdot \mathbf{\nabla}' \frac{1}{\varepsilon}.$$

The above Poisson integral for the electric field therefore reduces to

$$\mathbf{E} = -\frac{1}{4\pi\varepsilon_0} \int_{\text{All space}} \frac{\mathbf{\nabla}'(\rho/\varepsilon)}{r} \, dv' - \frac{1}{4\pi\varepsilon_0} \int_{\text{All space}} \frac{\mathbf{\nabla}'[\mathbf{D} \cdot \mathbf{\nabla}'(1/\varepsilon)]}{r} \, dv'. \quad (8\text{-}4.1)$$

This equation, in general, is not very useful for calculating $\mathbf{E}$, since in order to evaluate the last integral one needs to know $\mathbf{D}$, and if $\mathbf{D}$ is known then $\mathbf{E}$ is also known from Eq. (8-2.3). In the particular case of a dielectric of constant permittivity occupying all space, however, $\mathbf{\nabla}'(1/\varepsilon) = 0$, and Eq. (8-4.1) becomes

$$\mathbf{E} = -\frac{1}{4\pi\varepsilon_0\varepsilon} \int_{\text{All space}} \frac{\mathbf{\nabla}'\rho}{r} \, dv', \quad (8\text{-}4.2)$$

which is the same equation as Eq. (4-5.1) for $\mathbf{E}$ in vacuum except that the product $\varepsilon_0\varepsilon$ replaces now the single ε_0 standing in Eq. (4-5.1).

Transforming Eq. (8-4.2) in the same manner that we transformed Eq. (4-5.1) in Section 4-5, we obtain for the electric field associated with a charge distribution in a medium of constant permittivity ε occupying all space

$$\mathbf{E} = \frac{1}{4\pi\varepsilon_0\varepsilon} \int_{\text{All space}} \frac{\mathbf{r}_u}{r^2}\, dq. \qquad (8\text{-}4.3)$$

Similarly, using the corollary to Poisson's theorem and the transformations employed in Section 5-3, we obtain the corresponding equations for the electrostatic potential

$$\varphi = \frac{1}{4\pi\varepsilon_0} \int_{\text{All space}} \frac{\rho/\varepsilon}{r}\, dv' + \frac{1}{4\pi\varepsilon_0} \int_{\text{All space}} \frac{\mathbf{D}\cdot\mathbf{\nabla}'(1/\varepsilon)}{r}\, dv' \qquad (8\text{-}4.4)$$

and in a medium of constant ε occupying all space

$$\varphi = \frac{1}{4\pi\varepsilon_0\varepsilon} \int_{\text{All space}} \frac{dq}{r}. \qquad (8\text{-}4.5)$$

It is useful to note that Eqs. (8-4.3), (8-4.5) can be used even if the dielectric is limited in space, provided that the boundaries of the dielectric are so far from the regions where the charges are located and from the point of observation that the field at the boundaries may be neglected. This follows from Eq. (8-4.1), where in the case of constant ε, $\mathbf{\nabla}'(1/\varepsilon)$ is different from zero only on the boundaries, so that if $\mathbf{D} = 0$ on the boundaries, the last integral in Eq. (8-4.1) vanishes.

8-5. Boundary Conditions at a Dielectric Interface

If two different dielectric media are in contact with each other, there exists a thin transitional zone between them over which the values of the characteristic parameters of the media gradually change from the values which these parameters have in one medium to the values which they have in the other medium. It is frequently convenient to disregard the existence of this transitional zone and to assume that the characteristic parameters change abruptly over the "interface" between the media. From the basic laws (8-2.1), (8-2.2), and (8-2.3) one can derive then the correlations between the field vectors measured on the opposite sides of the interface. These correlations are called *boundary conditions at a dielectric interface.* They are useful for the solution of problems involving compound dielectrics.

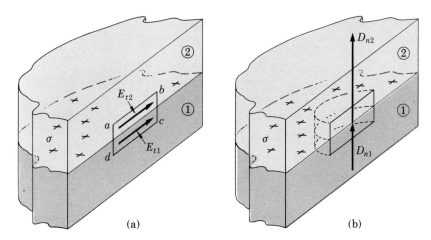

(a)   (b)

Fig. 8.5   (a) Boundary condition for **E** at a dielectric interface. The tangential component of **E** is the same on each side of the interface. (b) Boundary condition for **D** at a dielectric interface. The difference of the normal components of **D** on the two sides of the interface is equal to the density of the macroscopic surface charge residing on the interface.

To obtain the boundary condition for **E**, let us construct a small, very narrow rectangular loop crossing the interface between two dielectrics, 1 and 2, as shown in Fig. 8.5a, the long sides of the loop being tangent to the interface. Applying the circulation law (8-2.1b) to this loop, we have

$$\oint \mathbf{E} \cdot d\mathbf{l} = \int_a^b \mathbf{E}_2 \cdot d\mathbf{l} + \int_b^c \mathbf{E} \cdot d\mathbf{l} + \int_c^d \mathbf{E}_1 \cdot d\mathbf{l} + \int_d^a \mathbf{E} \cdot d\mathbf{l} = 0.$$

Since the loop is very narrow, we can neglect the integrals over the segments bc and da. Therefore

$$\int_a^b \mathbf{E}_2 \cdot d\mathbf{l} + \int_c^d \mathbf{E}_1 \cdot d\mathbf{l} = 0.$$

Since the segments ab and cd can be made as short as we please, we may regard the entire length of each segment as dl, in which case the last equation may be written as

$$\mathbf{E}_2 \cdot d\mathbf{l} + \mathbf{E}_1 \cdot (-d\mathbf{l}) = \mathbf{E}_2 \cdot d\mathbf{l} - \mathbf{E}_1 \cdot d\mathbf{l} = 0$$

or

$$(\mathbf{E}_2 - \mathbf{E}_1) \cdot d\mathbf{l} = 0,$$

where the minus sign is needed because the path from c to d is opposite to the path from a to b. Replacing in this equation $d\mathbf{l}$ by $\mathbf{t}_u dl$, where $\mathbf{t}_u$

is a unit vector in the direction of $d\mathbf{l}$ (and hence tangent to the interface) and cancelling dl, we finally obtain

$$(\mathbf{E}_2 - \mathbf{E}_1) \cdot \mathbf{t}_u = 0. \tag{8-5.1}$$

This equation can hold in a general case of an arbitrarily oriented $\mathbf{t}_u$ (arbitrarily oriented loop) only if vector $\mathbf{E}_2 - \mathbf{E}_1$ is normal to all $\mathbf{t}_u$. Therefore, since $\mathbf{t}_u$ is tangent to the interface, $\mathbf{E}_2 - \mathbf{E}_1$ must be normal to it. But then both $\mathbf{E}_2$ and $\mathbf{E}_1$ must be in a plane normal to the interface, and the components of $\mathbf{E}_2$ and $\mathbf{E}_1$ tangent to the interface and lying in this plane must be equal, or

$$E_{t1} = E_{t2}. \tag{8-5.2}$$

The two equations (8-5.1) and (8-5.2) represent, respectively, the vector and scalar boundary conditions for $\mathbf{E}$ at a dielectric interface. The essence of these conditions is that the tangential component of $\mathbf{E}$ is continuous across a dielectric interface.

To obtain the boundary condition for $\mathbf{D}$, let us construct a Gaussian surface in the shape of a small, very thin pillbox crossing the interface under consideration, as shown in Fig. 8.5b, the two bases of the box being tangent to the interface. Applying Gauss's law (8-2.2b) to this surface, we have

$$\oint \mathbf{D} \cdot d\mathbf{S} = \underbrace{\int \mathbf{D}_2 \cdot d\mathbf{S}}_{\text{Base 2}} + \underbrace{\int \mathbf{D} \cdot d\mathbf{S}}_{\text{Curved surface}} + \underbrace{\int \mathbf{D}_1 \cdot d\mathbf{S}}_{\text{Base 1}} = \int \rho \, dv.$$

Since the pillbox is very thin, we can neglect the integral over the curved surface. Since a very thin pillbox can enclose only the charge residing on the interface, we can replace the volume integral $\int \rho \, dv$ by the surface integral $\int \sigma \, dS$, where σ is the density of surface charge on the interface. We then have

$$\underbrace{\int \mathbf{D}_2 \cdot d\mathbf{S}}_{\text{Base 2}} + \underbrace{\int \mathbf{D}_1 \cdot d\mathbf{S}}_{\text{Base 1}} = \int \sigma \, dS.$$

Since both bases can be made as small as we please, we may regard the entire area of each base as dS, in which case the last equation may be written as

$$\mathbf{D}_2 \cdot d\mathbf{S} + \mathbf{D}_1 \cdot (-d\mathbf{S}) = (\mathbf{D}_2 - \mathbf{D}_1) \cdot d\mathbf{S} = \sigma \, dS$$

(we have assumed that the positive direction of $d\mathbf{S}$ is from dielectric 1 into dielectric 2, and since the surface element vectors in the above integrals are in the outward direction, $d\mathbf{S}$ for base 1 is negative).

Replacing $d\mathbf{S}$ in this equation by $\mathbf{n}_{12}dS$, where $\mathbf{n}_{12}$ is a unit vector in the direction of $d\mathbf{S}$, and cancelling dS, we finally obtain

$$(\mathbf{D}_2 - \mathbf{D}_1) \cdot \mathbf{n}_{12} = \sigma. \tag{8-5.3}$$

Since $\mathbf{n}_{12}$ is normal to the interface, $\mathbf{D}_2 \cdot \mathbf{n}_{12}$ and $\mathbf{D}_1 \cdot \mathbf{n}_{12}$ represent the components of $\mathbf{D}_2$ and $\mathbf{D}_1$ normal to the interface. Equation (8-5.3) can be written therefore also as

$$D_{n2} - D_{n1} = \sigma. \tag{8-5.4}$$

In the case when no charge resides on the interface, Eqs. (8-5.3) and (8-5.4) become

$$(\mathbf{D}_2 - \mathbf{D}_1) \cdot \mathbf{n}_{12} = 0 \tag{8-5.3a}$$

and

$$D_{n2} - D_{n1} = 0, \tag{8-5.4a}$$

so that if the interface carries no charge, the normal component of the displacement field is continuous across this interface.

The two equations (8-5.3) and (8-5.4) represent, respectively, the vector and scalar boundary conditions for $\mathbf{D}$ at a dielectric interface.

It is important to emphasize that the boundary conditions for $\mathbf{E}$ and $\mathbf{D}$ derived here are merely special forms of the basic laws (8-2.1) and (8-2.2) to which these laws reduce at a dielectric interface. For a dielectric interface these conditions have therefore the status of fundamental laws and must always be satisfied.

From the boundary conditions for $\mathbf{E}$ we can derive the boundary conditions for the electrostatic potential φ. Let us consider two points A and B located across from each other on the opposite sides of the interface shown in Fig. 8.6. The potential at A with respect to a reference point C at the edge of the interface is, by Eq. (8-3.2),

$$\varphi_A = \int_A^C \mathbf{E}_2 \cdot d\mathbf{l} + \varphi_C.$$

The potential at B is, similarly,

$$\varphi_B = \int_B^C \mathbf{E}_1 \cdot d\mathbf{l} + \varphi_C.$$

Let the path of integration in both integrals be adjacent to the interface. We can then write

$$\varphi_A = \int_A^C E_{t2}dl + \varphi_C \quad \text{and} \quad \varphi_B = \int_B^C E_{t1}dl + \varphi_C.$$

By the boundary condition (8-5.2), however, E_{t1} is everywhere equal

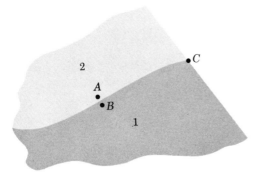

FIG. 8.6   The system of dielectrics used for proving that the electrostatic potential is the same on each side of a dielectric interface.

to E_{t2}. Hence the two integrals are equal, and therefore the two potentials φ_A and φ_B are also equal. Designating φ_B as φ_1 and φ_A as φ_2, we then obtain

$$\varphi_2 = \varphi_1. \tag{8-5.5}$$

Thus, the electrostatic potential is continuous across a dielectric interface.[1]

One should note that inasmuch as the boundary condition for φ is derived from the boundary condition for **E**, it is not independent of the latter but is, in fact, equivalent to it.

When dealing with linear isotropic dielectrics, it is frequently desirable to express the boundary condition for **D** (8-5.4) in terms of the potential φ. Since by Eqs. (8-2.3) and (8-3.1) $D_n = -\varepsilon_0\varepsilon\,\dfrac{\partial\varphi}{\partial n}$, this boundary condition can be written as

$$\varepsilon_0\varepsilon_1\frac{\partial\varphi_1}{\partial n_{12}} - \varepsilon_0\varepsilon_2\frac{\partial\varphi_2}{\partial n_{12}} = \sigma, \tag{8-5.6}$$

where n_{12} designates a direction along a normal to the boundary pointing from dielectric 1 into dielectric 2.

▼

Example 8-5.1   A thin dielectric disk of dielectric constant ε is placed in an initially uniform field **E**, the bases of the disk being normal to **E** (Fig. 8.7). Neglecting edge effects, find the final field outside and inside the disk.

---

[1] We assume that the interface does not carry a dipole-type charge distribution (see Problem 8.13).

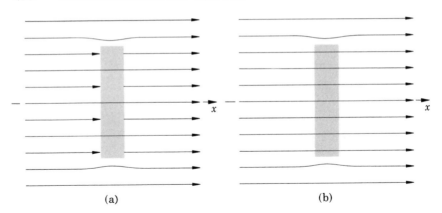

FIG. 8.7   A thin dielectric disk normal to an initially homogeneous electric field. (a) The map of the electric field **E**. (b) The map of the displacement field **D**.

The final field must satisfy the basic field laws (8-2.1), (8-2.2), and (8-2.3) inside and outside the disk, must satisfy Eqs. (8-5.2) and (8-5.4a) (boundary conditions) at the surface of the disk, and must be equal to the initial field at large distances from the disk. Once these requirements are satisfied, the problem is solved, since no other independent solution satisfying these requirements can exist. The geometry of the problem suggests that except at the edges of the disk the field outside the disk will remain undisturbed

$$\mathbf{E}_{\text{outside}} = \mathbf{E}, \tag{8-5.7}$$

and the field inside the disk will be uniform and normal to the disk. In this case, Eqs. (8-2.1), (8-2.2), and (8-2.3) will be satisfied both inside and outside the disk, and the requirement that the final field be equal to the initial field at large distances from the disk will be met. The boundary condition (8-5.2) at the bases of the disk will also be satisfied, since $E_{t\text{ outside}}$ and $E_{t\text{ inside}}$ will both be zero on the bases. As far as the boundary conditions at the side surface (curved surface) of the disk are concerned, we may disregard them altogether, since in a thin disk the side surface is responsible only for edge effects, which by the statement of the problem are to be neglected. All we need in order to complete the solution is, then, to satisfy the boundary condition (8-5.4a) at the bases of the disk, where we must have

$$D_{n\text{ outside}} = D_{n\text{ inside}},$$

or, since the field is normal to the disk,

$$D_{\text{outside}} = D_{\text{inside}}.$$

But $D_{\text{outside}} = \varepsilon_0 E_{\text{outside}}$, and $D_{\text{inside}} = \varepsilon_0 \varepsilon E_{\text{inside}}$. Therefore, by Eq. (8-5.7), the boundary condition (8-5.4a) will be satisfied if

$$\mathbf{E}_{\text{inside}} = \frac{1}{\varepsilon}\mathbf{E}. \tag{8-5.8}$$

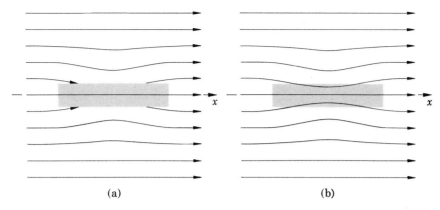

(a)   (b)

FIG. 8.8   A thin dielectric cylinder parallel to an initially homogeneous electric field. (a) **E** map. (b) **D** map. If $\varepsilon \gg 1$, the field is strongly distorted, and the solution given in the text is not valid.

Example 8-5.2   A thin dielectric cylinder of dielectric constant ε is placed in an initially uniform field **E**, the axis of the cylinder being parallel to **E** (Fig. 8.8). Neglecting end effects, find the final field inside and outside the cylinder.

By inspection we recognize that, except near the cylinder's ends, the field outside the cylinder is undisturbed

$$\mathbf{E}_{\text{outside}} = \mathbf{E}, \qquad (8\text{-}5.9)$$

and the field inside the cylinder is uniform and parallel to the axis. Since we neglect the end effects, the boundary conditions need be satisfied at the curved surface of the cylinder only, where, by Eqs. (8-5.2) and (8-5.4a), we must have

$$E_{t \text{ outside}} = E_{t \text{ inside}}$$

and

$$D_{n \text{ outside}} = D_{n \text{ inside}}.$$

Since we assume that the field is parallel to the cylinder's axis, the normal component of the field is zero, and the boundary condition for D is satisfied automatically. In the boundary condition for E we can drop the subscript "t." We then have $E_{\text{inside}} = E_{\text{outside}}$, and since $E_{\text{outside}} = E$, this condition will be satisfied if

$$\mathbf{E}_{\text{inside}} = \mathbf{E}. \qquad (8\text{-}5.10)$$

We have obtained Eqs. (8-5.9) and (8-5.10) largely by inspection, and therefore we may question their correctness. The equations satisfy, however, all required boundary conditions and the basic laws. Hence they are definitely correct provided that the end effects are indeed negligible.

Example 8-5.3   A conducting sphere of radius a carrying a charge q is submerged halfway into a nonconducting liquid of dielectric constant

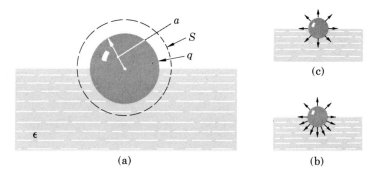

Fig. 8.9   (a) Charged conducting sphere floating in a nonconducting liquid. (b) Field lines of **D**. (c) Field lines of **E**.

ε (Fig. 8.9). Find the electric field outside the sphere and the charge density on the surface of the sphere.

Constructing a concentric spherical Gaussian surface S of radius r enclosing the sphere, and applying Gauss's law (8-2.2b) to this surface, we have

$$\oint \mathbf{D} \cdot d\mathbf{S} = \int_{S_1} \mathbf{D}_{\text{liquid}} \cdot d\mathbf{S} + \int_{S_2} \mathbf{D}_{\text{air}} \cdot d\mathbf{S} = q,$$

where S_1 and S_2 are the parts of the Gaussian surface passing through the liquid and through the air, respectively. The geometry of the problem suggests that the field is everywhere radial, so that $\mathbf{D} \cdot d\mathbf{S} = D \, dS$. It also suggests that D_{liquid} is constant at all points of S_1 and D_{air} is constant at all points of S_2, so that D can be factored out from under the integral signs. We can therefore write

$$D_{\text{liquid}} \int_{S_1} dS + D_{\text{air}} \int_{S_2} dS = q,$$

or

$$(D_{\text{liquid}} + D_{\text{air}}) 2\pi r^2 = q, \tag{8-5.11}$$

where $2\pi r^2$ is the area of S_1 and S_2. Now, by the displacement law (8-2.3), $D_{\text{liquid}} = \varepsilon_0 \varepsilon E_{\text{liquid}}$ and $D_{\text{air}} = \varepsilon_0 E_{\text{air}}$. Since the field is radial, it is tangent to the boundary between the liquid and the air, and hence, by the boundary conditions (8-5.2), $E_{\text{liquid}} = E_{\text{air}}$. The subscripts on E are then not needed, and we can write $D_{\text{liquid}} = \varepsilon_0 \varepsilon E$, $D_{\text{air}} = \varepsilon_0 E$. Substituting these expressions into Eq. (8-5.11), we obtain

$$(\varepsilon_0 \varepsilon E + \varepsilon_0 E) 2\pi r^2 = \varepsilon_0 (\varepsilon + 1) E 2\pi r^2 = q,$$

or

$$E = \frac{q}{2\pi \varepsilon_0 (\varepsilon + 1) r^2}, \tag{8-5.12}$$

which gives the electric field both in the liquid and in the air. The displacement is then

$$D_{liquid} = \frac{\varepsilon q}{2\pi(\varepsilon + 1)r^2} \quad \text{and} \quad D_{air} = \frac{q}{2\pi(\varepsilon + 1)r^2} . \quad (8\text{-}5.13a, b)$$

The surface charge density σ on the sphere is equal to the displacement at the surface of the sphere, so that

$$\sigma_1 = \frac{\varepsilon q}{2\pi(\varepsilon + 1)a^2} \quad \text{and} \quad \sigma_2 = \frac{q}{2\pi(\varepsilon + 1)a^2} \quad (8\text{-}5.14a, b)$$

on the submerged and the exposed half of the sphere, respectively.

In solving this problem we used symmetry considerations which may not appear entirely convincing. We may therefore want to verify the solution. This can be done in two ways. We can set $\varepsilon = 1$ and check whether the solution reduces to that valid for a sphere in vacuum. If it does, it probably is correct (it does). Or, we can check whether the field satisfies the basic laws (8-2.1), (8-2.2), (8-2.3) at all points outside the sphere, satisfies the boundary conditions (8-5.2), (8-5.4a) at the dielectric interface, is compatible with the charge residing on the sphere, and is regular at infinity, in which case the field is definitely correct by the uniqueness theorems for electrostatic fields (see Section 8-6). One can easily see that the field obtained here does satisfy these requirements. Therefore it is definitely correct.

▲

8-6. Special Methods for the Solution of Electrostatic Problems Involving Dielectrics of Constant ϵ

Combining Eqs. (8-2.2a), (8-2.3), and (8-3.1), we can write

$$\mathbf{\nabla} \cdot \mathbf{D} = \mathbf{\nabla} \cdot \varepsilon_0 \varepsilon \mathbf{E} = -\varepsilon_0 \mathbf{\nabla} \cdot (\varepsilon \mathbf{\nabla} \varphi) = \rho,$$

and, using vector identity (V-4), we obtain

$$\nabla^2 \varphi + \frac{1}{\varepsilon} \mathbf{\nabla} \varepsilon \cdot \mathbf{\nabla} \varphi = -\frac{\rho}{\varepsilon_0 \varepsilon} . \quad (8\text{-}6.1)$$

If ε is constant, $\mathbf{\nabla} \varepsilon = 0$, and we obtain

$$\nabla^2 \varphi = -\frac{\rho}{\varepsilon_0 \varepsilon} . \quad (8\text{-}6.2)$$

If $\rho = 0$, this equation reduces to

$$\nabla^2 \varphi = 0. \quad (8\text{-}6.3)$$

Thus, the electrostatic potential φ in media of constant ε, just as in vacuum, satisfies Poisson's equation (8-6.2) (charge-filled region) or

Laplace's equation (8-6.3) (charge-free region).[1] Therefore all special methods for the solution of electrostatic problems discussed in Chapter 6 can also be used for the solution of the corresponding problems of electrostatic fields in media of constant ε. As before, the criteria for the correctness of solutions are furnished by the uniqueness theorems stated in Section 6-2. These theorems are obviously valid for fields in dielectrics of constant permittivity occupying the entire region under consideration, because there is no essential difference between the basic electrostatic laws for vacuum and for dielectrics if ε is everywhere constant. They are valid, however, even if ε is different in different parts of the region, provided that the boundary conditions (8-5.5) and (8-5.6) are satisfied at all dielectric interfaces (see Problems 8.17 and 8.18).

The special methods discussed in Chapter 6 can be extended to problems involving dielectric interfaces. These latter problems are the only ones which are basically different from the problems discussed in Chapter 6. Therefore we shall limit the illustrative examples that follow to problems of this kind only.

▼

Example 8-6.1   A dielectric sphere of radius a and dielectric constant ε_1 is placed in a dielectric liquid of infinite extent and dielectric constant ε_2

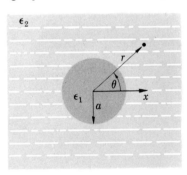

FIG. 8.10 Dielectric sphere in a dielectric liquid.

(Fig. 8.10). A uniform field **E** was originally present in the liquid. Find the resultant field inside and outside the sphere.

The problem can be solved by the method of harmonics (the corresponding problem with a conducting sphere was solved in Example 6-3.2). The initial potential can be written as $\varphi = -Ex + \varphi_0$, or

$$\varphi = -Er \cos \theta + \varphi_0.$$

----

[1] Note, however, that if ε is not constant, φ in dielectric media satisfies Eq. (8-6.1) rather than Poisson's or Laplace's equations.

Let the final potential inside the sphere be φ_1 and that outside the sphere be φ_2. By Eqs. (8-5.5) and (8-5.6), the boundary conditions are then

(1) $\varphi_1 = \varphi_2$ at $r = a$ (surface of the sphere)

(2) $\varepsilon_1 \dfrac{\partial \varphi_1}{\partial r} = \varepsilon_2 \dfrac{\partial \varphi_2}{\partial r}$ at $r = a$

(3) $\varphi_2 = \varphi = -Er \cos \theta + \varphi_0$ for $r \to \infty$.

The geometry of the problem suggests the use of spherical harmonics (see Table 6–I). The third boundary condition indicates that the potentials may be represented by just a part of the spherical harmonics (H-4)

$$\varphi_1 = (A_{11}r + B_{11}r^{-2}) \cos \theta + \varphi_0$$

and

$$\varphi_2 = (A_{21}r + B_{21}r^{-2}) \cos \theta + \varphi_0.$$

As we see no reason for the potential to be infinite anywhere within the sphere, we set $B_{11} = 0$ (otherwise $\varphi_1 \to \infty$ for $r \to 0$). By inspection we find that the boundary condition (3) is satisfied if $A_{21} = -E$. From boundary conditions (1) and (2), respectively, we then obtain the equations

$$A_{11}a = -Ea + B_{21}a^{-2}$$

and

$$\varepsilon_1 A_{11} = -\varepsilon_2(E + 2B_{21}a^{-3}).$$

Solving these two equations simultaneously, we obtain

$$A_{11} = -\frac{3\varepsilon_2}{\varepsilon_1 + 2\varepsilon_2} E, \qquad B_{21} = \frac{\varepsilon_1 - \varepsilon_2}{\varepsilon_1 + 2\varepsilon_2} Ea^3.$$

The potentials are therefore

$$\varphi_1 = -\frac{3\varepsilon_2}{\varepsilon_1 + 2\varepsilon_2} Er \cos \theta + \varphi_0,$$

$$\varphi_2 = -E\left(1 - \frac{\varepsilon_1 - \varepsilon_2}{\varepsilon_1 + 2\varepsilon_2} \frac{a^3}{r^3}\right) r \cos \theta + \varphi_0.$$

Since these potentials satisfy all three boundary conditions stated above, we are sure that they are correct.

Taking the gradient of these potentials, we obtain the corresponding equations for the electric field:

$$\mathbf{E}_1 = \frac{3\varepsilon_2}{\varepsilon_1 + 2\varepsilon_2} \mathbf{E}$$

and

$$\mathbf{E}_2 = E\left(1 + 2\frac{\varepsilon_1 - \varepsilon_2}{\varepsilon_1 + 2\varepsilon_2} \frac{a^3}{r^3}\right) \cos \theta\, \mathbf{r}_u - E\left(1 - \frac{\varepsilon_1 - \varepsilon_2}{\varepsilon_1 + 2\varepsilon_2} \frac{a^3}{r^3}\right) \sin \theta\, \boldsymbol{\theta}_u.$$

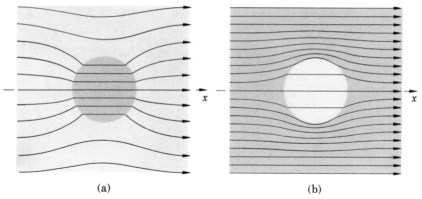

(a)   (b)

FIG. 8.11   Dielectric sphere of permittivity ε_1 is embedded in a dielectric medium of permittivity ε_2 in which a uniform electric field was present originally.   **D** maps of the resultant field are shown for (a) $\varepsilon_1 > \varepsilon_2$ and (b) $\varepsilon_1 < \varepsilon_2$.

It is interesting to note that these equations reduce to the equation obtained for the conducting sphere of Example 6-3.2 if $\varepsilon_1 = \infty$. Thus, as far as the electrostatic field is concerned, a conductor may be regarded as a dielectric of infinite permittivity. For $\varepsilon_1 = \varepsilon_2$, the above equations reduce to **E**; which simply means that if the dielectric constant of the sphere is the same as that of the surrounding medium the sphere has no effect on the initial field. For any ε_1 and ε_2, the field inside the sphere is homogeneous and in the same direction as the original field. If $\varepsilon_1 > \varepsilon_2$ (as for a dielectric sphere in vacuum), the field lines are "pulled" into the sphere, and in the sphere $E_1 < E$ while $D_1 > D$ (Fig. 8.11a). If $\varepsilon_1 < \varepsilon_2$ (as for a spherical cavity in a dielectric), the field lines are "pushed out" from the sphere, and in the sphere $E_1 > E$ while $D_1 < D$ (Fig. 8.11b).

Example 8-6.2   A point charge q in a medium of dielectric constant ε_1 is placed at a distance a from an infinite-plane boundary with another medium of dielectric constant ε_2. Prove that the field produced by the charge can be determined by means of the images shown in Fig. 8.12.

First of all we note that the potential due to the images shown in Fig. 8.12 automatically satisfies Laplace's equation because all point charge fields do so. Therefore, to prove that the images are correct, we need only to show that they are compatible with the boundary conditions at the dielectric interface. These conditions are

$$(1) \ \ \varphi_1 = \varphi_2 \qquad \text{at} \quad x = 0,$$

$$(2) \ \ \varepsilon_1 \frac{\partial \varphi_1}{\partial x} = \varepsilon_2 \frac{\partial \varphi_2}{\partial x} \quad \text{at} \quad x = 0.$$

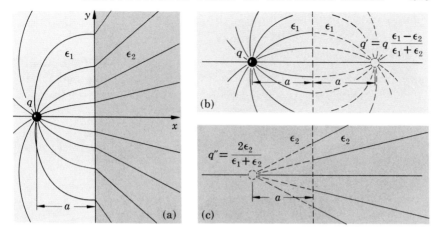

FIG. 8.12 (a) Point charge q in front of a plane dielectric interface. (b) To find the field in medium 1, the original charge together with the image charge q' is used, and the entire space is considered filled with medium 1. (c) To find the field in medium 2, the original charge is replaced by the image charge q'', and the entire space is considered filled with medium 2. (The field lines plotted in these figures are for $\varepsilon_2 \gg \varepsilon_1$).

The potential in medium 1 is, according to Fig. 8.12,

$$\varphi_1(x, y) = \frac{q}{4\pi\varepsilon_0\varepsilon_1} \left[\frac{1}{\sqrt{(x+a)^2 + y^2}} + \frac{\varepsilon_1 - \varepsilon_2}{\varepsilon_1 + \varepsilon_2} \frac{1}{\sqrt{(x-a)^2 + y^2}} \right],$$

and that in medium 2 is, similarly,

$$\varphi_2(x, y) = \frac{q}{4\pi\varepsilon_0\varepsilon_2} \frac{2\varepsilon_2}{\varepsilon_1 + \varepsilon_2} \frac{1}{\sqrt{(x+a)^2 + y^2}}.$$

We see by inspection that these potentials satisfy boundary condition (1). Substituting these potentials in boundary condition (2), we find that they satisfy this boundary condition also. Hence the images are correct. Observe that these images reduce to the ordinary image of a point charge in front of an infinite-plane conductor if $\varepsilon_2 = \infty$.

▲

8-7. Polarization

The theory of electric phenomena in material media becomes especially informative and concise if in addition to the two field vectors $\mathbf{E}$ and $\mathbf{D}$ the third field vector, the *polarization vector* $\mathbf{P}$, is used. The polarization vector is defined by the equation

$$\mathbf{P} = \mathbf{D} - \varepsilon_0 \mathbf{E}. \tag{8-7.1}$$

As we shall presently see, this vector allows a convenient description and analysis of electric phenomena in all nonconducting media, linear and nonlinear, isotropic and anisotropic, with no restriction upon the dielectric properties of the media at all.

Using the polarization vector $\mathbf{P}$, we shall now derive several important formulas for the electrostatic potential and electrostatic field in material media.

Let us take the divergence of Eq. (8-7.1). We have

$$\mathbf{\nabla} \cdot \mathbf{P} = \mathbf{\nabla} \cdot \mathbf{D} - \varepsilon_0 \mathbf{\nabla} \cdot \mathbf{E}.$$

This can be written as

$$\varepsilon_0 \mathbf{\nabla} \cdot \mathbf{E} = \mathbf{\nabla} \cdot \mathbf{D} - \mathbf{\nabla} \cdot \mathbf{P},$$

or

$$\mathbf{\nabla} \cdot \mathbf{E} = \frac{1}{\varepsilon_0} (\rho - \mathbf{\nabla} \cdot \mathbf{P}). \tag{8-7.2}$$

By the corollary to Poisson's theorem of vector analysis we obtain then for the electrostatic potential[1]

$$\varphi = \frac{1}{4\pi\varepsilon_0} \int_{\text{All space}} \frac{\rho - \mathbf{\nabla} \cdot \mathbf{P}}{r} \, dv', \tag{8-7.3}$$

where we have omitted the reference potential φ_0, as usual. Splitting this integral into two integrals and using $\mathbf{\nabla}'$ to avoid ambiguities in the transformations which follow, we have

$$\varphi = \frac{1}{4\pi\varepsilon_0} \int_{\text{All space}} \frac{\rho}{r} \, dv' - \frac{1}{4\pi\varepsilon_0} \int_{\text{All space}} \frac{\mathbf{\nabla}' \cdot \mathbf{P}}{r} \, dv'. \tag{8-7.4}$$

The last integral can be transformed with the aid of vector identity (V-4)

$$\mathbf{\nabla}' \cdot \frac{\mathbf{P}}{r} = \frac{\mathbf{\nabla}' \cdot \mathbf{P}}{r} + \mathbf{P} \cdot \mathbf{\nabla}' \frac{1}{r} \tag{8-7.5}$$

into

$$\frac{1}{4\pi\varepsilon_0} \int_{\text{All space}} \frac{\mathbf{\nabla}' \cdot \mathbf{P}}{r} \, dv' = \frac{1}{4\pi\varepsilon_0} \int_{\text{All space}} \mathbf{\nabla}' \cdot \frac{\mathbf{P}}{r} \, dv' - \frac{1}{4\pi\varepsilon_0} \int_{\text{All space}} \mathbf{P} \cdot \mathbf{\nabla}' \frac{1}{r} \, dv'.$$

By Gauss's theorem,

$$\frac{1}{4\pi\varepsilon_0} \int_{\text{All space}} \mathbf{\nabla}' \cdot \frac{\mathbf{P}}{r} \, dv' = \frac{1}{4\pi\varepsilon_0} \oint_{\text{All space}} \frac{\mathbf{P}}{r} \cdot d\mathbf{S}',$$

[1] Compare with Section 5-3.

and since $\mathbf{E}$ and $\mathbf{D}$, and therefore also $\mathbf{P}$, are regular at infinity, the surface integral vanishes. This means that the volume integral on the left vanishes also. Therefore Eq. (8-7.4) can be written in an alternative form as

$$\varphi = \frac{1}{4\pi\varepsilon_0} \int_{\text{All space}} \frac{\rho}{r} \, dv' + \frac{1}{4\pi\varepsilon_0} \int_{\text{All space}} \mathbf{P} \cdot \mathbf{\nabla}' \frac{1}{r} \, dv'. \qquad (8\text{-}7.6)$$

As can be seen from Eqs. (8-7.4) and (8-7.6), the electrostatic potential φ produced by a charge distribution ρ in the presence of a dielectric can be regarded as the sum of two partial potentials: the ordinary "vacuum" potential

$$\varphi_V = \frac{1}{4\pi\varepsilon_0} \int \frac{\rho}{r} \, dv'$$

identical with the potential associated with ρ (produced by ρ) in the absence of the dielectric, and the "polarization" potential φ_P, which can be expressed as either

$$\varphi_P = -\frac{1}{4\pi\varepsilon_0} \int \frac{\mathbf{\nabla}' \cdot \mathbf{P}}{r} \, dv' \quad \text{or} \quad \varphi_P = \frac{1}{4\pi\varepsilon_0} \int \mathbf{P} \cdot \mathbf{\nabla}' \frac{1}{r} \, dv', \qquad (8\text{-}7.7\text{a, b})$$

and which is associated with the dielectric. It is therefore clear that, as far as the calculation of φ (or any quantity derivable from φ) is concerned, a dielectric is equivalent to a certain charge distribution that would produce the potential φ_P if the dielectric were replaced by this charge distribution. This fictitious charge distribution[1] is called the *polarization charge distribution*. The concept of the polarization charge is very useful since it allows one to treat a dielectric as an equivalent charge distribution in vacuum, and thus allows one to apply the "vacuum" field theory developed in the preceding chapters to systems containing dielectrics.

The polarization charge distribution by which a particular dielectric may be replaced can be found either from Eq. (8-7.7a) or from Eq. (8-7.7b). Let us first consider Eq. (8-7.7a). In the case of a dielectric of finite extent, the integral of Eq. (8-7.7a) can be split into three integrals: an integral over the interior volume of the dielectric (Fig. 8.13), an integral over the volume of the boundary layer of the dielectric, and an integral over the space external to the dielectric, so

---

[1] As is explained below, this charge distribution is fictitious from the point of view of the macroscopic theory only.

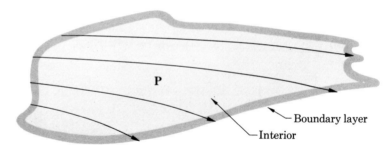

FIG. 8.13 Sometimes it is expedient to assume that a dielectric has an "interior part" and a "boundary layer."

that Eq. (8-7.7a) can be written as

$$\varphi_P = -\frac{1}{4\pi\varepsilon_0}\int_{\text{Interior}}\frac{\mathbf{\nabla}'\cdot\mathbf{P}}{r}\,dv' - \frac{1}{4\pi\varepsilon_0}\int_{\text{Boundary layer}}\frac{\mathbf{\nabla}'\cdot\mathbf{P}}{r}\,dv'$$
$$-\frac{1}{4\pi\varepsilon_0}\int_{\text{External space}}\frac{\mathbf{\nabla}'\cdot\mathbf{P}}{r}\,dv'.$$

Outside the dielectric, $\mathbf{P}=0$, and the last integral is therefore zero. The second integral can be written as two integrals by means of Eq. (8-7.5), so that

$$\varphi_P = -\frac{1}{4\pi\varepsilon_0}\int_{\text{Interior}}\frac{\mathbf{\nabla}'\cdot\mathbf{P}}{r}\,dv' - \frac{1}{4\pi\varepsilon_0}\int_{\text{Boundary layer}}\mathbf{\nabla}'\cdot\frac{\mathbf{P}}{r}\,dv'$$
$$+\frac{1}{4\pi\varepsilon_0}\int_{\text{Boundary layer}}\mathbf{P}\cdot\mathbf{\nabla}'\frac{1}{r}\,dv'.$$

The volume of the boundary layer may be assumed to be as small as one pleases, and since $\mathbf{P}$ is finite, the last integral in this equation vanishes. The second integral in this equation can be transformed into a surface integral by means of Gauss's theorem, and the potential then becomes

$$\varphi_P = -\frac{1}{4\pi\varepsilon_0}\int_{\text{Interior}}\frac{\mathbf{\nabla}'\cdot\mathbf{P}}{r}\,dv' - \frac{1}{4\pi\varepsilon_0}\oint_{\text{Boundary layer}}\frac{\mathbf{P}}{r}\cdot d\mathbf{S}'.$$

The surface of integration here consists of both the interior and exterior surfaces of the boundary layer, but since the exterior surface is outside the dielectric, $\mathbf{P}=0$ there, and the only contribution to the surface integral comes from the interior surface (observe that on this surface $d\mathbf{S}$ is pointing into the dielectric). Furthermore, since the boundary layer may be assumed to be as thin as one wishes, the surface of integration is just the surface of the dielectric. Substituting $\mathbf{n}_{\text{in}}dS'$ for $d\mathbf{S}'$, where $\mathbf{n}_{\text{in}}$ is a unit vector in the direction of an inward normal to the surface of the dielectric, we then obtain from the last equation

$$\varphi_P = -\frac{1}{4\pi\varepsilon_0} \int_{\text{Interior}} \frac{\nabla' \cdot \mathbf{P}}{r} \, dv' - \frac{1}{4\pi\varepsilon_0} \oint_{\text{Boundary surface}} \frac{\mathbf{P} \cdot \mathbf{n}_{\text{in}}}{r} \, dS'. \quad (8\text{-}7.8)$$

If we compare Eq. (8-7.8) with Eqs. (5-3.1) and (5-3.2), we immediately recognize that the potential φ_P can be attributed to a volume distribution of polarization charge

$$\rho_P = -\nabla \cdot \mathbf{P} \quad (8\text{-}7.9)$$

spread through the interior of the dielectric, and to a surface distribution of polarization charge

$$\sigma_P = -\mathbf{P} \cdot \mathbf{n}_{\text{in}} \quad (8\text{-}7.10)$$

spread over the surface of the dielectric. This means that for the purpose of the calculation of φ (or any quantity derivable from φ) the interior part of a dielectric may be replaced by the volume charge $\rho_P = -\nabla \cdot \mathbf{P}$, and the boundary layer of the dielectric may be replaced by the surface charge $\sigma_P = -\mathbf{P} \cdot \mathbf{n}_{\text{in}}$. Note that in this representation the real charges are regarded as contained in cavities made in the dielectric, so that σ_P is present on all interfaces between ρ and the dielectric.

The total electrostatic potential produced by a charge distribution ρ in the presence of a dielectric can then be expressed as

$$\varphi = \frac{1}{4\pi\varepsilon_0} \int \frac{\rho}{r} \, dv' + \frac{1}{4\pi\varepsilon_0} \int \frac{\rho_P}{r} \, dv' + \frac{1}{4\pi\varepsilon_0} \oint \frac{\sigma_P}{r} \, dS', \quad (8\text{-}7.11)$$

and the electric field $\mathbf{E}$ produced by ρ in the presence of a dielectric can therefore be expressed as

$$\mathbf{E} = \frac{1}{4\pi\varepsilon_0} \int \frac{\rho \mathbf{r}_u}{r^2} \, dv' + \frac{1}{4\pi\varepsilon_0} \int \frac{\rho_P \mathbf{r}_u}{r^2} \, dv' + \frac{1}{4\pi\varepsilon_0} \oint \frac{\sigma_P \mathbf{r}_u}{r^2} \, dS'. \quad (8\text{-}7.12)$$

On electrostatic field maps, the field lines begin and end on electric charges, which thus constitute the "sources" of the electrostatic fields. According to equation (8-7.12), the sources of the electrostatic field $\mathbf{E}$ in the presence of dielectrics are not only the real charges ρ, but also the fictitious, polarization charges ρ_P and σ_P. Therefore the field lines of $\mathbf{E}$ begin and end not only at the points where ρ is present, but also on dielectric surfaces (σ_P) as well as at points within the dielectrics (ρ_P). The field lines of $\mathbf{D}$, on the other hand, begin and end only on the real charges ρ. This follows from the divergence law $\nabla \cdot \mathbf{D} = \rho$, which shows that $\mathbf{D}$ is always associated with the real charges only, so that only the real charges are sources of $\mathbf{D}$. Therefore an $\mathbf{E}$ field and a $\mathbf{D}$

field may have entirely different structure when dielectrics are present. As a result, an **E** map and a **D** map of the same electrostatic system containing dielectrics may appear very different (see Figs. 8.7, 8.8, 8.9, and 8.16).

Let us now consider Eq. (8-7.7b). This equation can be written as

$$\varphi_P = \int_{\text{Dielectric}} \frac{\mathbf{P}}{4\pi\varepsilon_0} \cdot \nabla' \frac{1}{r} \, dv'. \tag{8-7.13}$$

If we compare this equation with Eq. (5-4.10a)

$$\varphi_{\text{dipole}} = \frac{\mathbf{P}}{4\pi\varepsilon_0} \cdot \nabla' \frac{1}{r} \tag{5-4.10a}$$

representing the potential of a dipole of moment **p**, we see that the integrand in Eq. (8-7.13) can be interpreted as the potential produced by a fictitious "polarization" dipole of moment $d\mathbf{p} = \mathbf{P}dv'$. The polarization vector **P** can be interpreted therefore as the dipole moment density (dipole moment per unit volume) of such polarization dipoles:

$$\mathbf{P} = \frac{d\mathbf{p}}{dv}. \tag{8-7.14}$$

The potential φ_P can then be regarded as the total potential produced by all these dipoles spread through the volume of the dielectric. This means that for the purpose of the calculation of φ (or any quantity derivable from φ) a dielectric may be replaced by a distribution of dipoles of dipole moment density $d\mathbf{p}/dv = \mathbf{P}$.

Thus a dielectric can be treated either as a space charge and surface charge distribution given by Eqs. (8-7.9) and (8-7.10) or as a dipole distribution given by Eq. (8-7.14). A choice between the two possibilities is arbitrary and is merely a question of expediency.

The representation of a dielectric as an equivalent charge distribution (ρ_P, σ_P, or $d\mathbf{p}/dv$) is especially useful for dealing with dielectrics possessing a permanent polarization **P**. Such permanently polarized dielectrics are called *electrets*.

Equation (8-7.14) constitutes an important link connecting the macroscopic theory of electric phenomena with the microscopic theory. In the microscopic theory, a polarized dielectric is regarded as an assemblage of atoms and molecules whose charges are displaced from their unperturbed positions under the influence of the applied field: molecules having permanent dipole moments are lined up so that the dipole moments are oriented predominantly in the direction of the applied field, and all atoms and molecules receive "induced" dipole moments as a result of a shift of the negative charges relative to the positive ones. The average dipole moment of these atomic and molecular dipoles per unit volume of a dielectric is defined as the polarization vector $\mathbf{P}$ in the microscopic theory. By setting $\mathbf{P}_{microscopic} = \mathbf{P}_{macroscopic}$, a transition between the two theories is achieved. The "fictitious" polarization charge of the macroscopic theory is, in the microscopic theory, the charge "bound" within atomic and molecular systems. The "real" charge of the macroscopic theory is, in the microscopic theory, the "free" charge accessible to macroscopic observations (such as the observations described in Section 4-1).

In concluding this section, let us note that the boundary conditions at a dielectric interface derived in Section 8-5 involve real (free) charges only.

▼

Example 8-7.1   A conducting sphere of radius a is embedded in an infinite dielectric of dielectric constant ε. The sphere carries a charge q. Compare the physical meaning of Eqs. (8-4.3) and (8-7.12) when they are used for calculating the electrostatic field of the sphere.

(a)   (b)

FIG. 8.14   Two methods of calculating the electric field of a charged body surrounded by a dielectric. (a) Direct calculation. (b) Dielectric is replaced by an equivalent charge distribution.

In Eq. (8-4.3) the effect of the dielectric is taken into account by using the product $\varepsilon_0 \varepsilon$ instead of ε_0, and only the real charge is used for the calculation. The physical system corresponding to this equation is shown in Fig. 8.14a. When Eq. (8-7.12) is used, however, the sphere is considered to be in a vacuum, and the dielectric is considered replaced by polarization charge distributions ρ_P and σ_P. By Eq. (8-4.3) (or by Gauss's and displacement laws), the field of the sphere is

$$\mathbf{E} = \frac{q}{4\pi\varepsilon_0 \varepsilon r^2}\,\mathbf{r}_u. \qquad (8\text{-}7.15)$$

Let us now see what this field is by Eq. (8-7.12). The polarization of the dielectric is, by Eqs. (8-7.1) and (8-7.15),

$$\mathbf{P} = \mathbf{D} - \varepsilon_0\mathbf{E} = \varepsilon_0\varepsilon\mathbf{E} - \varepsilon_0\mathbf{E} = (\varepsilon - 1)\frac{q}{4\pi\varepsilon r^2}\mathbf{r}_u.$$

The polarization space charge is then [using $\nabla\varepsilon = 0$ and $\nabla \cdot (\mathbf{r}_u/r^2) = 0$]

$$\rho_P = -\nabla \cdot \mathbf{P} = -\nabla \cdot \left[(\varepsilon - 1)\frac{q}{4\pi\varepsilon r^2}\mathbf{r}_u\right] = 0.$$

The polarization surface charge (representing the effect of the boundary of the cavity containing the sphere) is

$$\sigma_P = -\mathbf{P} \cdot \mathbf{n}_{in} = -(\varepsilon - 1)\frac{q}{4\pi\varepsilon a^2}.$$

The physical system corresponding to Eq. (8-7.12) is shown in Fig. 8.14b. Note that it is completely different from that shown in Fig. 8.14a. By Eq. (8-7.12), the field of the sphere is the sum of the field $\mathbf{E}_V$ produced by the real charge q and the field $\mathbf{E}_P$ produced by the polarization charge q_P, both charges thought to be located in a vacuum. The first field is

$$\mathbf{E}_V = \frac{q}{4\pi\varepsilon_0 r^2}\mathbf{r}_u. \tag{8-7.16}$$

The second field is, noting that $q_P = \sigma_P \cdot 4\pi a^2 = -(\varepsilon - 1)(q/\varepsilon)$,

$$\mathbf{E}_P = -\frac{(\varepsilon - 1)q}{4\pi\varepsilon_0\varepsilon r^2}\mathbf{r}_u. \tag{8-7.17}$$

Adding Eqs. (8-7.16) and (8-7.17) we again obtain Eq. (8-7.15).

Example 8-7.2   A cylindrical electret of length $2l$ and radius a has constant polarization $\mathbf{P}$ directed along the axis of the electret, as shown in

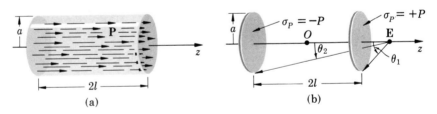

FIG. 8.15   (a) Cylindrical electret. (b) Equivalent charge distribution.

Fig. 8.15a. Find the electric field produced by the electret at an external point on the axis and then obtain the limiting values of the field for a very long and a very short electret.

The field of the electret can be calculated with the aid of Eq. (8-7.12). Since no real charge is present anywhere in the system under consideration, and since inside the electret $\mathbf{P}$ is constant so that $\rho_P = -\nabla \cdot \mathbf{P} = 0$, the field can be found from σ_P alone. On the cylindrical surface of the electret **P** is perpendicular to $\mathbf{n}_{in}$, so that $\sigma_P = -\mathbf{P} \cdot \mathbf{n}_{in} = 0$. The only contribution to the field comes therefore from σ_P on the flat bases of the electret, where **P** and $\mathbf{n}_{in}$ are parallel. On the left base, **P** and $\mathbf{n}_{in}$ have the same direction so that $\sigma_P = -\mathbf{P} \cdot \mathbf{n}_{in} = -P$. On the right base, **P** is opposite to $\mathbf{n}_{in}$ so that $\sigma_P = -\mathbf{P} \cdot \mathbf{n}_{in} = P$. By Eq. (8-7.12), the problem thus reduces to finding the field of two uniformly charged disks located at the ends of the electret and carrying surface charges $\pm P$ (Fig. 8.15b).

The field of a uniformly charged disk of charge density σ and radius a has been found in Example 4-5.3, and is

$$\mathbf{E} = \frac{\sigma}{2\varepsilon_0}\left(1 - \frac{z}{\sqrt{z^2 + a^2}}\right)\mathbf{k},$$

where z is the distance from the disk to the point of observation. The field of the electret under consideration can be obtained from this formula. Replacing σ by $\pm P$ and z by $z \mp l$ in it and adding the resulting expressions we obtain

$$\mathbf{E} = \frac{P}{2\varepsilon_0}\left[1 - \frac{z - l}{\sqrt{(z - l)^2 + a^2}}\right]\mathbf{k} - \frac{P}{2\varepsilon_0}\left[1 - \frac{z + l}{\sqrt{(z + l)^2 + a^2}}\right]\mathbf{k},$$

which after simplifications becomes

$$\mathbf{E} = \frac{\mathbf{P}}{2\varepsilon_0}\left[\frac{z + l}{\sqrt{(z + l)^2 + a^2}} - \frac{z - l}{\sqrt{(z - l)^2 + a^2}}\right]. \qquad (8\text{-}7.18)$$

This can also be written in terms of the angles subtended by the bases of the electret at the point of observation as

$$\mathbf{E} = \frac{\mathbf{P}}{2\varepsilon_0}(\cos\theta_2 - \cos\theta_1).$$

For a very long electret (rod electret), $\theta_2 \to 0$, and the field becomes

$$\mathbf{E}_{rod} = \frac{\mathbf{P}}{2\varepsilon_0}(1 - \cos\theta_1).$$

If, in addition, the point of observation is very close to the base, θ_1 is approximately $90°$, and the field becomes simply

$$\mathbf{E}_{rod} = \frac{\mathbf{P}}{2\varepsilon_0}.$$

For a very short electret (disk electret), $\theta_2 \to \theta_1$, and the field becomes

$$\mathbf{E}_{disk} = 0.$$

Example 8-7.3   Find the electric field **E** and the displacement field **D** at an internal axial point of the electret discussed in Example 8-7.2.

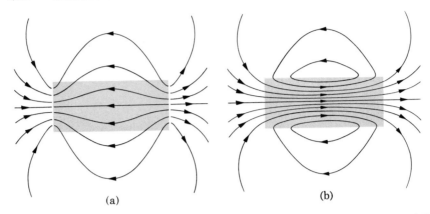

(a)   (b)

FIG. 8.16   (a) **E** map for a cylindrical electret. Note that the lines of **E** originate and terminate on the faces of the electret (surface charges σ_P). (b) **D** map for a cylindrical electret. Note that the lines of **D** have no beginning and no end, and that inside the electret **D** is opposite to **E**.

Replacing the electret by two uniformly charged disks as in Example 8-7.2, we have

$$\mathbf{E} = -\frac{P}{2\varepsilon_0}\left[1 - \frac{l-z}{\sqrt{(l-z)^2 + a^2}}\right]\mathbf{k} - \frac{P}{2\varepsilon_0}\left[1 - \frac{z+l}{\sqrt{(z+l)^2 + a^2}}\right]\mathbf{k},$$

or

$$\mathbf{E} = -\frac{\mathbf{P}}{2\varepsilon_0}(2 + \cos\theta_1 - \cos\theta_2),$$

where the notations are the same as in Fig. 8.15. For a very long electret (rod electret), $\theta_2 \to 0$, $\theta_1 \to \pi$, and the field becomes

$$\mathbf{E}_{\text{rod}} = 0.$$

For a very short electret (disk electret), $\theta_2 \to \frac{\pi}{2}$, $\theta_1 \to \frac{\pi}{2}$, and the field becomes

$$\mathbf{E}_{\text{disk}} = -\frac{\mathbf{P}}{\varepsilon_0}.$$

The displacement is found from $\mathbf{D} = \mathbf{P} + \varepsilon_0\mathbf{E}$ and is

$$\mathbf{D} = \frac{\mathbf{P}}{2}(\cos\theta_2 - \cos\theta_1).$$

Observe that the direction of **D** in the electret is opposite to that of **E** (the **E** and **D** maps for the electret are shown in Fig. 8.16a,b). For a very long electret the displacement becomes $\mathbf{D} = \mathbf{P}$. For a short electret (disk) it becomes $\mathbf{D} = 0$.

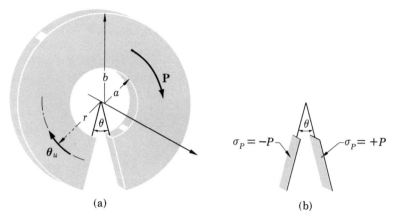

$\sigma_P = -P$ $-\sigma_P = +P$

(a)   (b)

FIG. 8.17   (a) Open ring electret. (b) Equivalent charge distribution.

Example 8-7.4   A ring electret has the polarization $\mathbf{P} = (A/r)\boldsymbol{\theta}_u$, where A is a constant, r is the distance from the axis of the electret, and $\boldsymbol{\theta}_u$ is a unit vector in the circular direction, as shown in Fig. 8.17. The electret has a narrow slot between two plane faces normal to $\boldsymbol{\theta}_u$, which form an angle θ with each other. Neglecting edge effects, find the electric field in the slot.

The field can be calculated from the polarization charges. The polarization space charge is (consult Table 2-I)

$$\rho_P = -\boldsymbol{\nabla} \cdot \mathbf{P} = -\frac{1}{r}\frac{\partial}{\partial \theta} P_\theta = -\frac{1}{r}\frac{\partial}{\partial \theta}\left(\frac{A}{r}\right) = 0.$$

The polarization surface charge is zero on the side surfaces of the ring because $\mathbf{P}$ is perpendicular to $\mathbf{n}_{in}$ there, but on the surfaces of the slot $\sigma_P = -\mathbf{P}\cdot\mathbf{n}_{in} = \pm P = \pm A/r$ ($\mathbf{P}$ is parallel to $\mathbf{n}_{in}$ there). The problem thus reduces to finding the field of two surface charge distributions $\sigma_P = \pm A/r$ located at the surfaces of the slot. This system of surface charges is similar to the system of two charged conducting plates discussed in Example 6-3.4. Therefore the field in the slot is, by Example 6-3.4,

$$\mathbf{E} = \frac{\sigma_P}{\varepsilon_0}\boldsymbol{\theta}_u = \frac{A}{\varepsilon_0 r}\boldsymbol{\theta}_u.$$

Example 8-7.5   A small spherical cavity of radius r is made in a large electret of constant polarization $\mathbf{P}$ (Fig. 8.18). Neglecting the effect of the outer boundaries of the electret, find the electric field at the center of the cavity.

Since the effect of the outer boundaries can be neglected, and since $\mathbf{P}$ is constant, the field can be calculated from the polarization surface charge

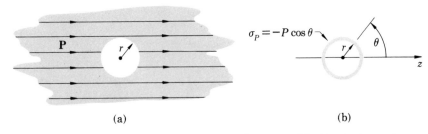

(a)   (b)

FIG. 8.18   (a) Spherical cavity in an electret.   (b) Equivalent charge distribution.

σ_P on the surface of the cavity. Referring to Fig. 8.18, we have

$$\sigma_P = -\mathbf{P} \cdot \mathbf{n}_{in} = -P \cos \theta.$$

The field is then, by Eq. (8-7.12),[1]

$$\mathbf{E} = -\frac{1}{4\pi\varepsilon_0} \oint \frac{\sigma_P \mathbf{r}_u}{r^2} dS' = \frac{1}{4\pi\varepsilon_0} \int_0^\pi \frac{P \cos \theta\, \mathbf{r}}{r^3} 2\pi r^2 \sin \theta\, d\theta,$$

where we have taken as dS' an elementary ring of area $2\pi r^2 \sin \theta\, d\theta$. By symmetry, the field is along the z-axis, so that only the z-component of $\mathbf{r}$, or $z\mathbf{k}$, needs to be considered when evaluating the above integral. But $z\mathbf{k} = \mathbf{k}r \cos \theta$, and hence

$$\mathbf{E} = \frac{\mathbf{k}}{4\pi\varepsilon_0} \int_0^\pi \frac{P \cos \theta\, r \cos \theta}{r^3} 2\pi r^2 \sin \theta\, d\theta = \frac{\mathbf{k}P}{2\varepsilon_0} \int_0^\pi \cos^2 \theta \sin \theta\, d\theta,$$

or

$$\mathbf{E} = \frac{\mathbf{P}}{3\varepsilon_0}.$$

Example 8-7.6   Find the electrostatic potential at a large distance from a small piece of electret of volume v and constant polarization $\mathbf{P}$ (Fig. 8.19).

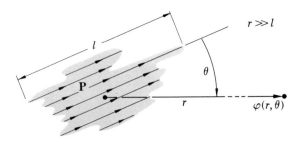

FIG. 8.19   Calculation of electric field at a large distance from a piece of electret.

[1] Note that $\mathbf{r}_u$ appearing in Eq. (8-7.12) is opposite to $\mathbf{r}$ shown in Fig. (8.18), the latter pointing *toward* the charge.

This problem can be solved most easily by regarding the electret as a single dipole. Since **P** is constant, the dipole moment of the electret is, according to Eq. (8-7.14),

$$\mathbf{p} = \mathbf{P}v.$$

The potential is then, by Eq. (5-4.9),

$$\varphi = \frac{Pv}{4\pi\varepsilon_0 r^2} \cos\theta. \tag{8-7.19}$$

Example 8-7.7   A thin disk electret of polarization **P** directed along the electret's axis is placed between two conducting plates which are in contact with each other ("shorted") as shown in Fig. 8.20. Find how the plates affect the internal and external fields, E_i and E_e, of the electret.

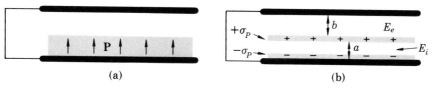

(a)   (b)

FIG. 8.20   (a) Disk electret between two shorted conducting plates.   (b) Equivalent charge distribution.

Let us replace the electret by the equivalent surface charges $\sigma_P = \pm P$, as shown. Since the plates are in contact with each other, the voltage between them is zero, and we have, by Eq. (8-3.2),

$$E_i a + E_e b = 0. \tag{8-7.20}$$

From the boundary condition for D, Eq. (8-5.4), we have

$$D_i - D_e = \sigma_{\text{real}} = 0 \tag{8-7.21}$$

(observe that this boundary condition involves only the real surface charge). Expressing D in terms of P and E, we have $D_i = P_i + \varepsilon_0 E_i = P + \varepsilon_0 E_i$ and $D_e = P_e + \varepsilon_0 E_e = \varepsilon_0 E_e$. Eq. (8-7.21) becomes then

$$P + \varepsilon_0 E_i - \varepsilon_0 E_e = 0. \tag{8-7.22}$$

Solving Eqs. (8-7.22) and (8-7.20) for E_e and E_i and taking into account the direction of **P**, we obtain

$$\mathbf{E}_i = -\frac{b}{\varepsilon_0(a+b)}\,\mathbf{P} \quad \text{and} \quad \mathbf{E}_e = \frac{a}{\varepsilon_0(a+b)}\,\mathbf{P}.$$

If $b \gg a$ (free electret) these solutions reduce to those obtained in Examples 8-7.2 and 8-7.3. If $b \to 0$, then $E_i \to 0$ (one stores electrets between shorted conducting plates; since $E_i = 0$ in this case, the electret does not lose its polarization).

▲

8-8. Energy and Force Relations for Electrostatic Fields with Dielectrics Present

The basic energy law for electrostatic systems containing dielectrics can be expressed as[1]

$$U = \frac{\varepsilon_0}{2} \int\limits_{\text{All space}} E^2 dv + \int\limits_{\text{All space}} \left(\int_0^{\mathbf{P}} \mathbf{E} \cdot d\mathbf{P} \right) dv. \qquad (8\text{-}8.1)$$

In this equation U is the total electric energy of an electrostatic system under consideration, the first term on the right is the so-called *field energy* U_f, and the second term on the right is the so-called *polarization energy* U_P.

The field energy

$$U_f = \frac{\varepsilon_0}{2} \int E^2 dv \qquad (8\text{-}8.2)$$

is attributed to the electric field as such and does not vanish even if there are no dielectrics in the field.

The polarization energy

$$U_P = \int \left(\int_0^{\mathbf{P}} \mathbf{E} \cdot d\mathbf{P} \right) dv \qquad (8\text{-}8.3)$$

is attributed to the polarization of dielectrics and vanishes if there are no polarized dielectrics in the field. The designation of U_P as the polarization energy is based upon the observation that an amount of energy given by Eq. (8-8.3) is absorbed by a dielectric when the polarization of the dielectric changes from zero to $\mathbf{P}$. Depending on the properties of the dielectric, the energy U_P may or may not be conserved (stored in the dielectric in a recoverable form). If $\mathbf{P}$ is a single-valued function of $\mathbf{E}$, the energy U_P is conserved, because then

$$\int_0^{\mathbf{P}} \mathbf{E} \cdot d\mathbf{P} = -\int_{\mathbf{P}}^0 \mathbf{E} \cdot d\mathbf{P}.$$

If the correlation between $\mathbf{P}$ and $\mathbf{E}$ is such that the curve representing $\mathbf{P}$ as a function of $\mathbf{E}$ (polarization curve) does not retrace itself when the field changes from $-\mathbf{E}$ to $+\mathbf{E}$ and back to $-\mathbf{E}$, as in Fig. 8.21, U_P is

---

[1] More than any other electric or magnetic law, this law and the corresponding law for magnetic fields are justified by their consequences rather than by their origin.

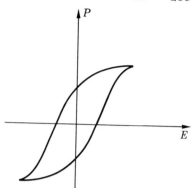

FIG. 8.21   Hysteresis loop for a dielectric.

not conserved, because then

$$\int_0^P \mathbf{E} \cdot d\mathbf{P} \neq -\int_P^0 \mathbf{E} \cdot d\mathbf{P}.$$

In this latter case the dielectric is said to exhibit a *hysteresis*. The loop formed by the polarization curve is called the *hysteresis loop*. As one can see from Fig. 8.21 and Eq. (8-8.3), the area enclosed by the hysteresis loop is proportional to the energy dissipated in the dielectric during each complete cycle in the change of **E**.

In a linear isotropic dielectric, $\mathbf{P} = \varepsilon_0(\varepsilon - 1)\mathbf{E}$, so that

$$\int_0^P \mathbf{E} \cdot d\mathbf{P} = \frac{\varepsilon_0(\varepsilon - 1)}{2} E^2,$$

and the polarization energy, according to Eq. (8-8.3), is

$$U_P = \frac{\varepsilon_0}{2} \int (\varepsilon - 1) \, E^2 dv. \qquad (8\text{-}8.4)$$

Therefore when all dielectrics contained in a system under consideration are linear and isotropic, the total energy of the system, according to Eq. (8-8.1), is

$$U = \frac{\varepsilon_0}{2} \int E^2 dv + \frac{\varepsilon_0}{2} \int (\varepsilon - 1) E^2 dv = \frac{\varepsilon_0}{2} \int \varepsilon E^2 dv, \qquad (8\text{-}8.5)$$

which is usually written in the symmetrical form

$$U = \frac{1}{2} \int \mathbf{E} \cdot \mathbf{D} \, dv. \qquad (8\text{-}8.6)$$

By inspecting the transformations used in Chapter 7 for obtaining the special forms and consequences of Eq. (7-1.1a), we find that the same transformations can be applied to Eq. (8-8.2), except that $\varepsilon_0 \mathbf{V} \cdot \mathbf{E}$, by Eqs. (8-7.2) and (8-7.9), is now equal to $\rho + \rho_P$ rather than to ρ. Therefore the equations obtained in Chapter 7 from Eq. (7-1.1a) apply also to the energy U_f of the electrostatic fields in the presence of dielectrics, provided that the charge density ρ appearing in these equations is replaced by the "effective" charge density $\rho + \rho_P$ (σ_P may be used instead of ρ_P on dielectric boundaries, in which case the volume integrals over the boundary layer must be replaced by the surface integrals over the boundary surface). In particular, we find that the force equation (7-7.1) can be rewritten for the electrostatic fields in the presence of dielectrics as

$$\mathbf{F} = -\mathbf{V}U_f'\big|_{\rho, \mathbf{P}=\text{constant}}, \qquad (8\text{-}8.7)$$

where U_f', in analogy with U' used in Chapter 7, is given by

$$U_f' = \overset{o}{\int}(\rho + \rho_P)\varphi' dv. \qquad (8\text{-}8.8)$$

The explicit equations for the force are then

$$\mathbf{F} = \overset{o}{\int}(\rho + \rho_P)\mathbf{E}' dv = \overset{o}{\int}(\rho + \rho_P)\mathbf{E}\, dv, \qquad (8\text{-}8.9a, b)$$

which follow from Eqs. (7-8.1) and (7-8.2). Note that Eqs. (8-8.9a, b) allow one to find not only the forces acting on charged bodies (real charge ρ) but also the forces acting on neutral dielectrics (polarization charge ρ_P).

Since the polarization $\mathbf{P}$ may be regarded as the dipole moment density associated with the polarization charges ρ_P, the force acting on a neutral dielectric can be expressed, by Eq. (7-10.2), also as

$$\mathbf{F} = \overset{o}{\int}(\mathbf{P} \cdot \mathbf{V})\, \mathbf{E}' dv. \qquad (8\text{-}8.10)$$

As we learned in Chapter 7, an especially important force relation for an electrostatic system in a vacuum is given by Maxwell's stress equation (7-11.3). By inspecting the transformations by means of which this equation was obtained, we find that it remains valid even if there are dielectrics in the system under consideration. The electrostatic force acting upon any object (charged body, dielectric, conductor, etc.) enclosed by a Maxwellian surface S passing through a vacuum is therefore always

$$\mathbf{F} = -\frac{\overset{o}{\varepsilon_0}}{2} \oint E^2 d\mathbf{S} + \overset{o}{\varepsilon_0} \oint \mathbf{E}(\mathbf{E} \cdot d\mathbf{S}). \qquad (8\text{-}8.11)$$

If S is the surface of a *free* conductor, the force becomes, by analogy with Eq. (7-11.4),

$$\mathbf{F} = \overset{\circ}{\frac{\varepsilon_0}{2}} \oint E^2 d\mathbf{S}, \tag{8-8.12}$$

so that a free conductor under electrostatic conditions can always be regarded as subjected to the electrostatic pressure

$$p = \overset{\circ}{\frac{\varepsilon_0}{2}} E^2. \tag{8-8.13}$$

It is important to remember, however, that all force equations given above may be used, in general, only for determining forces acting on a dielectric body (or bodies) as a whole rather than forces acting on a part of a body. This is because we have arrived at the concept of the polarization charge ρ_P by using Poisson's integral (8-7.3) extended over the entire volume of each dielectric.

In conclusion, let us mention once again that all equations which are valid for electrostatic systems contained in vacuum are also valid for similar systems contained in an infinite dielectric of constant ε, provided that ε_0 in these equations is replaced by the product $\varepsilon_0\varepsilon$.

▼

Example 8-8.1   A voltage V is applied to a parallel-plate capacitor consisting of square plates of length a separated by a distance d. A large dielectric slab of thickness d and dielectric constant ε is inserted between the plates, as shown in Fig. 8.22. Neglecting edge effects, find the force acting on the slab.

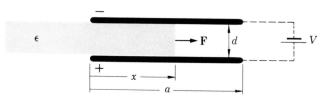

FIG. 8.22   Calculation of force acting on a dielectric slab in a parallel-plate capacitor.

We shall solve this problem by using the force-energy relation $F_x = -\partial U/\partial x$, valid for all isolated conservative systems. To make the capacitor an isolated system, we shall imagine that it is disconnected from the battery (observe that in this case the charge Q of the capacitor, rather than the voltage V, must be considered constant). The electric field in the capacitor is

$$E = \frac{V}{d}.$$

The displacement in the empty part of the capacitor and in the part occupied by the dielectric is, respectively,

$$D_1 = \varepsilon_0 \frac{V}{d} \quad \text{and} \quad D_2 = \varepsilon_0 \varepsilon \frac{V}{d}.$$

The charge of the capacitor (one plate) is then, by Gauss's law,

$$Q = \varepsilon_0 \frac{V}{d}(a - x)a + \varepsilon_0 \varepsilon \frac{V}{d} xa = \varepsilon_0 \frac{V}{d} a[a + (\varepsilon - 1)x],$$

and the voltage expressed in terms of the charge is therefore

$$V = \frac{Qd}{\varepsilon_0 a[a + (\varepsilon - 1)x]}.$$

The energy of the capacitor is, by Eq. (8-8.6),

$$U = {}^{\circ}\frac{1}{2} ED_1(a - x)ad + {}^{\circ}\frac{1}{2} ED_2 xad$$

$$= {}^{\circ}\varepsilon_0 \frac{V^2}{2d^2}(a - x)ad + {}^{\circ}\varepsilon_0 \varepsilon \frac{V^2}{2d^2} xad.$$

Simplifying and substituting V (which is a variable quantity if the capacitor is disconnected from the battery), we obtain

$$U = {}^{\circ}\varepsilon_0 \frac{V^2}{2d} a[a + (\varepsilon - 1)x] = \frac{{}^{\circ}Q^2 d}{2\varepsilon_0 a[a + (\varepsilon - 1)x]}.$$

The force on the dielectric is therefore

$$F_x = -\frac{\partial U}{\partial x} = \frac{{}^{\circ}Q^2 d(\varepsilon - 1)}{2\varepsilon_0 a[a + (\varepsilon - 1)x]^2} = \frac{{}^{\circ}\varepsilon_0 V^2 a(\varepsilon - 1)}{2d}.$$

Example 8-8.2   A small dielectric sphere of radius a and dielectric constant ε is placed at a distance $x \gg a$ from a point charge q (Fig. 8.23). Find the force on the dielectric sphere.

FIG. 8.23   Calculation of force acting on a small dielectric sphere in the electric field of a point charge.

This problem can be solved by using Eq. (7-10.2). The electric field produced by q at the location of the dielectric sphere is.

$$\mathbf{E}' = \frac{q}{4\pi\varepsilon_0 x^2} \mathbf{i}.$$

Since $x \gg a$, this field, in the first approximation, is uniform throughout the region occupied by the sphere. The electric field within the sphere is then, by Example 8-6.1,

$$\mathbf{E} = \frac{3}{\varepsilon + 2} \mathbf{E}',$$

and the polarization of the sphere is, by Eq. (8-7.1),

$$\mathbf{P} = \mathbf{D} - \varepsilon_0 \mathbf{E} = \varepsilon_0(\varepsilon - 1)\mathbf{E} = \frac{3\varepsilon_0(\varepsilon - 1)}{(\varepsilon + 2)} \mathbf{E}'.$$

Using Eq. (7-10.2) and taking into account that $a \ll x$, so that the sphere may be regarded as a single dipole of moment $\frac{4}{3}\pi a^3 \mathbf{P}$, we have therefore

$$\mathbf{F} = {}^\circ(\mathbf{p} \cdot \nabla)\mathbf{E}' = \frac{{}^\circ 4}{3}\pi a^3 P \frac{\partial}{\partial x}\mathbf{E}' = -\frac{{}^\circ 4}{3}\pi a^3 P \frac{q}{2\pi\varepsilon_0 x^3}\mathbf{i},$$

and substituting $\mathbf{P}$, we obtain

$$\mathbf{F} = -\frac{{}^\circ(\varepsilon - 1)q^2 a^3}{2\pi\varepsilon_0(\varepsilon + 2)x^5}\mathbf{i}.$$

Thus, the sphere is *attracted* to the point charge with a force proportional to x^{-5}.

Example 8-8.3   A point charge q is placed into a nonconducting liquid of dielectric constant ε. A spherical air bubble of radius a has formed at a distance $x \gg a$ from the point charge (Fig. 8.24). Find the electric force on the bubble, assuming that the liquid may be considered as extending to infinity in all directions.

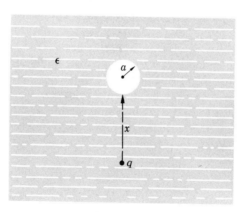

FIG. 8.24   Calculation of force acting on a spherical air bubble in a dielectric liquid under the influence of a point charge. It is assumed that $x \gg a$.

We note from Example 8-6.1 that if the original field at the location of the bubble is E', the effect of the bubble on the field outside it is to produce an additional field

$$\mathbf{E}'' = -2\frac{\varepsilon - 1}{2\varepsilon + 1}\frac{a^3}{r^3}E'\cos\theta\,\mathbf{r}_u - \frac{\varepsilon - 1}{2\varepsilon + 1}\frac{a^3}{r^3}E'\sin\theta\,\boldsymbol{\theta}_u.$$

Comparing this field with the field of a dipole embedded in a dielectric of dielectric constant ε, given by Eq. (5-4.13) with ε_0 replaced by $\varepsilon_0\varepsilon$,

$$\mathbf{E} = \frac{p}{2\pi\varepsilon_0\varepsilon} \frac{\cos\theta}{r^3} \mathbf{r}_u + \frac{p}{4\pi\varepsilon_0\varepsilon} \frac{\sin\theta}{r^3} \boldsymbol{\theta}_u,$$

we see that the bubble may be regarded as a dipole of moment

$$\mathbf{p} = -\frac{\varepsilon - 1}{2\varepsilon + 1} 4\pi\varepsilon_0\varepsilon a^3 \mathbf{E}'.$$

Since

$$\mathbf{E}' = \frac{q}{4\pi\varepsilon_0\varepsilon x^2} \mathbf{i},$$

$\mathbf{p}$ can be written as

$$\mathbf{p} = -\frac{\varepsilon - 1}{2\varepsilon + 1} \frac{qa^3}{x^2} \mathbf{i}.$$

The force on the bubble is then, by Eq. (7-10.2),

$$\mathbf{F} = {}^\circ(\mathbf{p} \cdot \nabla)\mathbf{E}' = -{}^\circ\left[\frac{\varepsilon - 1}{2\varepsilon + 1} \frac{qa^3}{x^2} \frac{\partial}{\partial x}\left(\frac{q}{4\pi\varepsilon_0\varepsilon x^2} \right) \right]\mathbf{i},$$

or

$$\mathbf{F} = \frac{{}^\circ(\varepsilon - 1)q^2 a^3}{2\pi\varepsilon_0\varepsilon(2\varepsilon + 1)x^5} \mathbf{i}.$$

Thus in contrast to the dielectric sphere of the preceding example, the bubble is *repelled* from the point charge with a force proportional to x^{-5}.

Example 8-8.4   A conducting sphere consisting of two separate hemispheres of radius a is placed in a nonconducting liquid of infinite extent and dielectric constant ε. Find the force with which one hemisphere is repelled from the other when the sphere is given a charge q.

This problem is the same as that discussed in Example 7-11.1, except that now the sphere is in a dielectric rather than in a vacuum. Therefore the solution can be obtained from that of Example 7-11.1 by replacing ε_0 by $\varepsilon_0\varepsilon$. This gives

$$\mathbf{F} = \frac{{}^\circ q^2}{32\pi\varepsilon_0\varepsilon a^2} \mathbf{i}.$$

Examples 8-8.5   A conducting sphere of radius a and density ρ floats in a nonconducting liquid of density $\rho' > 2\rho$ and dielectric constant ε. How much charge must be placed on the sphere in order to make the sphere half submerged in the liquid?

By Example 8-5.3, when the sphere is half submerged and carries a charge q, the electric field around it is

$$E = \frac{q}{2\pi\varepsilon_0(\varepsilon + 1)r^2}$$

and the displacement is

$$D_{\text{liquid}} = \frac{\varepsilon q}{2\pi(\varepsilon + 1)r^2}, \qquad D_{\text{air}} = \frac{q}{2\pi(\varepsilon + 1)r^2}.$$

Thus, the **E** and **D** fields in the liquid are the same as those that would be produced by the same sphere if the liquid occupied all space around the sphere and if the sphere carried a charge $q' = 2\varepsilon q/(\varepsilon + 1)$. Since electric fields are force fields, equal electric fields produce equal forces on charges located in these fields. By the preceding example, the electric force on the lower hemisphere is therefore

$$F_{\text{down}} = \frac{°\varepsilon q^2}{8\pi\varepsilon_0(\varepsilon + 1)^2 a^2}.$$

Similarly, the **E** and **D** fields in the air are the same as those that would be produced by the same sphere in a vacuum if the sphere carried a charge $q'' = 2q/(\varepsilon + 1)$. The electric force on the upper hemisphere is therefore, by Example 7-11.1,

$$F_{\text{up}} = \frac{°q^2}{8\pi\varepsilon_0(\varepsilon + 1)^2 a^2}.$$

The total force down is the sum of F_{down} and the weight of the sphere, or

$$F_{\text{down total}} = \frac{°\varepsilon q^2}{8\pi\varepsilon_0(\varepsilon + 1)^2 a^2} + \frac{4}{3}\pi a^3 \rho g.$$

The total force up is the sum of F_{up} and the bouyant force of the liquid, or

$$F_{\text{up total}} = \frac{°q^2}{8\pi\varepsilon_0(\varepsilon + 1)^2 a^2} + \frac{2}{3}\pi a^3 \rho' g.$$

Setting

$$F_{\text{total down}} = F_{\text{total up}}$$

and solving for q, we obtain

$$°q^2 = \frac{16\pi^2\varepsilon_0(\varepsilon + 1)^2(\rho' - 2\rho)a^5 g}{3(\varepsilon - 1)}.$$

Example 8-8.6 A thin disk electret of thickness a, face area A, and polarization P directed along the electret's axis is laid on a conducting plate. A second conducting plate, connected by a wire to the first, is placed above the electret at a distance b from its surface (Fig. 8.25). Find the force on this plate neglecting end effects.

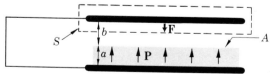

FIG. 8.25 Calculation of force acting on a metal plate placed above an electret. S is a Maxwellian surface enclosing the plate.

The force can be found from Eq. (8-8.12). The electric field above the plate is zero. The electric field below the plate is, by Example 8-7.7,

$$E = \frac{a}{\varepsilon_0 (a + b)} P.$$

The force is therefore, by Eq. (8-8.12),

$$F = \frac{^\circ \varepsilon_0}{2} \int_{\text{Plate}} \frac{a^2 P^2}{\varepsilon_0^2 (a + b)^2} \, dS = \frac{^\circ a^2 P^2 A}{2 \varepsilon_0 (a + b)^2}$$

directed towards the electret.

Example 8-8.7   Determine the change in electric energy which takes place when a linear isotropic dielectric is placed in the electric field of a capacitor carrying a constant charge.

Let the initial field be $\mathbf{E}_0$. The initial electric energy is then, by Eq. (7-1.1),

$$U_0 = \frac{^\circ 1}{2} \int \mathbf{E}_0 \cdot \mathbf{D}_0 dv.$$

When the dielectric is introduced into the field, the field changes to $\mathbf{E}$, and the energy becomes, by Eq. (8-8.6),

$$U = \frac{^\circ 1}{2} \int \mathbf{E} \cdot \mathbf{D} \, dv.$$

The change in energy is

$$\Delta U = \frac{^\circ 1}{2} \int (\mathbf{E} \cdot \mathbf{D} - \mathbf{E}_0 \cdot \mathbf{D}_0) dv,$$

which can be written as

$$\Delta U = \frac{^\circ 1}{2} \int (\mathbf{E} \cdot \mathbf{D}_0 - \mathbf{D} \cdot \mathbf{E}_0) dv + \frac{^\circ 1}{2} \int (\mathbf{E} + \mathbf{E}_0) \cdot (\mathbf{D} - \mathbf{D}_0) dv$$

$$= \frac{^\circ 1}{2} \int (\mathbf{E} \cdot \mathbf{D}_0 - \mathbf{D} \cdot \mathbf{E}_0) dv - \frac{^\circ 1}{2} \int \mathbf{\nabla}(\varphi + \varphi_0) \cdot (\mathbf{D} - \mathbf{D}_0) dv,$$

where φ and φ_0 are the potentials corresponding to $\mathbf{E}$ and $\mathbf{E}_0$. We shall show now that the last integral is zero. Since

$$\mathbf{\nabla}(\varphi + \varphi_0) \cdot (\mathbf{D} - \mathbf{D}_0) = \mathbf{\nabla} \cdot [(\varphi + \varphi_0)(\mathbf{D} - \mathbf{D}_0)]$$
$$- (\varphi + \varphi_0)\mathbf{\nabla} \cdot (\mathbf{D} - \mathbf{D}_0)$$

and since $\mathbf{\nabla} \cdot \mathbf{D} = \mathbf{\nabla} \cdot \mathbf{D}_0 = 0$ throughout the space under consideration, we can transform the last integral into a surface integral:

$$\frac{^\circ 1}{2} \int \mathbf{\nabla}(\varphi + \varphi_0) \cdot (\mathbf{D} - \mathbf{D}_0) dv = \frac{^\circ 1}{2} \oint (\varphi + \varphi_0)(\mathbf{D} - \mathbf{D}_0) \cdot d\mathbf{S}.$$

This surface integral is extended over a surface enclosing all space and over the surfaces of the capacitor plates. The surface enclosing all space makes no contribution to the integral because the field is regular at infinity. The surfaces of the capacitor plates also make no contribution to the integral. This is because φ and φ_0 are constant at all points of each plate, and the integrals

$$\oint \mathbf{D} \cdot d\mathbf{S} \quad \text{and} \quad \oint \mathbf{D}_0 \cdot d\mathbf{S}$$

are both equal to the charge residing on the plate over whose surface the integrals are taken. The surface integral under consideration is therefore zero, and so the last volume integral is zero. The change in the energy is then

$$\Delta U = \overset{\circ}{\frac{1}{2}} \int (\mathbf{E} \cdot \mathbf{D}_0 - \mathbf{D} \cdot \mathbf{E}_0) \, dv.$$

Now, outside the dielectric, $\mathbf{E} \cdot \mathbf{D}_0 - \mathbf{D} \cdot \mathbf{E}_0 = \mathbf{E} \cdot (\varepsilon_0 \mathbf{E}_0) - (\varepsilon_0 \mathbf{E}) \cdot \mathbf{E}_0 = 0$. Therefore the last integral needs to be extended only over the volume occupied by the dielectric. Thus we obtain

$$\Delta U = \overset{\circ}{\frac{1}{2}} \int_{\text{Dielectric}} (\mathbf{E} \cdot \mathbf{D}_0 - \mathbf{D} \cdot \mathbf{E}_0) \, dv$$

$$= \overset{\circ}{\frac{1}{2}} \int_{\text{Dielectric}} [\mathbf{E} \cdot (\varepsilon_0 \mathbf{E}_0) - \mathbf{D} \cdot \mathbf{E}_0] \, dv$$

$$= -\overset{\circ}{\frac{1}{2}} \int_{\text{Dielectric}} (\mathbf{D} - \varepsilon_0 \mathbf{E}) \cdot \mathbf{E}_0 \, dv,$$

or

$$\Delta U = -\overset{\circ}{\frac{1}{2}} \int \mathbf{P} \cdot \mathbf{E}_0 \, dv. \tag{8-8.14}$$

Example 8-8.9   A nonconducting liquid of dielectric constant ε and density ρ is contained in a U-tube of rectangular cross section. When the tube is inserted between the plates of a parallel-plate capacitor (Fig. 8.26)

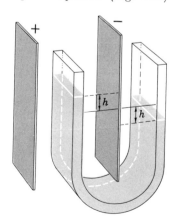

FIG. 8.26   Dielectric liquid is pulled in the electric field of a parallel-plate capacitor. This phenomenon can be used for determining ε of the liquid.

whose charges are kept constant, the liquid between the plates rises by an amount h. Neglecting all edge effects, find h if the initial field between the plates is $\mathbf{E}_0$, the dielectric constant of the tube is $\varepsilon' = 1$, and the inner dimensions of the tube's cross section are a (perpendicular to $\mathbf{E}_0$) and b (parallel to $\mathbf{E}_0$), with $a \gg b$.

By the preceding example, the final electric energy of the system is

$$U = U_0 - \overset{\circ}{\frac{1}{2}} \int \mathbf{P} \cdot \mathbf{E}_0 \, dv.$$

Since all edge effects are neglected, $\mathbf{P}$ may be assumed constant in the part of the tube located between the plates of the capacitor and zero elsewhere, and if the height of the liquid between the plates with respect to their lower edge is y, the energy can be written as

$$U = U_0 - \overset{\circ}{\frac{1}{2}} \mathbf{P} \cdot \mathbf{E}_0 aby.$$

The electric force on the liquid is then

$$F_y = -\frac{\partial U}{\partial y} = \overset{\circ}{\frac{1}{2}} \mathbf{P} \cdot \mathbf{E}_0 ab.$$

This force is kept in equilibrium by the weight of the liquid contained in the portion of the tube of length $2h$:

$$w = 2abh\rho g.$$

Combining the last two equations, we obtain

$$h = \frac{\overset{\circ}{}\,\mathbf{P} \cdot \mathbf{E}_0}{4\rho g}.$$

To complete the solution, we must find $\mathbf{P}$. Since the tube has a rectangular cross section with $a \gg b$, the field in the liquid contained in the tube is the same as in the thin disk discussed in Example 8-5.1. By Example 8-5.1, we then have in the liquid

$$\mathbf{D} = \varepsilon_0 \mathbf{E}_0 \quad \text{and} \quad \mathbf{E} = \frac{1}{\varepsilon} \mathbf{E}_0.$$

The polarization is therefore

$$\mathbf{P} = \mathbf{D} - \varepsilon_0 \mathbf{E} = \frac{\varepsilon_0(\varepsilon - 1)}{\varepsilon} \mathbf{E}_0,$$

and we finally obtain

$$h = \frac{\overset{\circ}{}\,\varepsilon_0(\varepsilon - 1)E_0^2}{4\varepsilon\rho g}.$$

▲

PROBLEMS

8.1. Prove that if a capacitor is filled with a material of dielectric constant ε, the capacitance of the capacitor will increase ε times.

8.2. A large dielectric slab of thickness t and dielectric constant ε is inserted between the plates of a thin parallel-plate capacitor of plate area A and plate separation d. The slab is parallel to the plates and its edges are outside the capacitor. Neglecting edge effects, show that the capacitance of the capacitor is

$$C = \varepsilon_0 \varepsilon A [\varepsilon d - (\varepsilon - 1)t]^{-1}.$$

8.3. The plates of a thin parallel-plate capacitor are separated by a distance d. The maximum voltage which can be applied to this capacitor before a spark occurs in the air inside the capacitor is V_0. A dielectric plate of dielectric constant ε and thickness $t < d$ is laid on the inner surface of one of the capacitor's plates. Show that the maximum voltage which can now be applied to the capacitor before a spark in the air inside the capacitor occurs is only

$$V = V_0[1 - (t/d)(1 - 1/\varepsilon)].$$

8.4. A parallel plate capacitor of plate area A and plate separation d is filled with a dielectric whose permittivity varies uniformly from ε_1 at one plate to ε_2 at the other. Neglecting edge effects, show that the capacitance of this capacitor is

$$C = \frac{\varepsilon_0 A}{d} \frac{\varepsilon_2 - \varepsilon_1}{\ln(\varepsilon_2/\varepsilon_1)}.$$

8.5. A cylindrical capacitor is filled with a dielectric of variable permittivity $\varepsilon = \alpha/r$, where α is a constant and r is the distance from the axis of the capacitor. The radius of the inner cylinder is a, that of the outer cylinder is b. Find the capacitance per unit length.

8.6. The radii of the two cylinders forming a cylindrical capacitor are a and b. The medium between the cylinders has a dielectric constant ε_1 from a to r and ε_2 from r to b. Show that the capacitance per unit length of this capacitor is

$$C_l = 2\pi\varepsilon_0 \left(\frac{1}{\varepsilon_1}\ln\frac{r}{a} - \frac{1}{\varepsilon_2}\ln\frac{r}{b}\right)^{-1}.$$

8.7. A conducting sphere of radius a receives a coat of material of uniform thickness t and dielectric constant ε. Show that the capacitance of the sphere increases by the factor

$$n = \frac{\varepsilon(a + t)}{\varepsilon a + t}.$$

8.8. A spherical capacitor is formed by two spheres whose radii are a and b, $a < b$. The inner sphere receives a uniform coat of material of thickness t and dielectric constant ε. Show that if $t \ll a$, the capacitance increases approximately by

$$\Delta C = 4\pi\varepsilon_0 t \frac{(\varepsilon - 1)b^2}{\varepsilon(b - a)^2}.$$

8.9. A spherical capacitor is filled with a dielectric of variable permittivity $\varepsilon = \alpha/r^2$, where α is a constant and r is the distance from the center. The radius of the inner sphere is a, that of the outer sphere is b. Find the capacitance.

8.10. The radii of the two spheres forming a spherical capacitor are a and b. The medium between the spheres has a dielectric constant ε_1 from a to r and ε_2 from r to b. Show that the capacitance of the capacitor is

$$C = 4\pi\varepsilon_0 \left[\frac{1}{\varepsilon_1}\left(\frac{1}{a} - \frac{1}{r}\right) - \frac{1}{\varepsilon_2}\left(\frac{1}{b} - \frac{1}{r}\right) \right]^{-1}.$$

8.11. A large dielectric slab of dielectric constant ε is placed in a uniform electric field $\mathbf{E}$ which makes an angle θ with the normal to the surface of the slab. Find the magnitude and direction of the electric field within the slab.

8.12. Consider an interface between two dielectrics, 1 and 2, of dielectric constant ε_1 and ε_2. At the interface, the electric field vector in the two dielectrics makes, respectively, angles α_1 and α_2 with the normal to the interface. Show that these angles satisfy the "law of refraction"

$$\varepsilon_1 \cot \alpha_1 = \varepsilon_2 \cot \alpha_2.$$

8.13. A dielectric interface carries a double layer of charge, whose dipole moment per unit area is $\tau\mathbf{n}_u$, where $\mathbf{n}_u$ is a unit vector normal to the interface. Show that the potentials on the two sides of the interface satisfy the condition

$$\varphi_1 - \varphi_2 = \tau/\varepsilon_0.$$

8.14. The lower half of a spherical capacitor is filled with a dielectric of dielectric constant ε. Show that the capacitance of the capacitor is the same as if the entire capacitor were filled with a material of dielectric constant

$$\varepsilon' = \tfrac{1}{2}(1 + \varepsilon).$$

8.15. Show that if the space between two equipotential surfaces of an electrostatic system is filled with a material of dielectric constant ε, the two surfaces will remain equipotential, but the potential difference between them will sink to $1/\varepsilon$ of its original value.

8.16. Show that if the space between two equipotential surfaces in the field of a capacitor is filled with a material of dielectric constant ε, the capacitance of the capacitor will increase by the factor

$$n = \frac{\varepsilon}{\varepsilon - f(\varepsilon - 1)},$$

where f is the ratio of the initial potential difference between the two surfaces to the voltage applied between the terminals of the capacitor.

8.17. Prove that in a linear isotropic dielectric the electrostatic potential satisfies Uniqueness Theorems I, II, and III of Section 6-2, provided that the boundary conditions discussed in Section 8-5 are satisfied at all dielectric interfaces.

8.18. Prove that in a linear isotropic dielectric the electric field satisfies Uniqueness Theorems A, B, C, and D of Section 6-2, provided that the boundary conditions discussed in Section 8-5 are satisfied at all dielectric interfaces.

8.19. If the charge of the capacitor described in Problem 8.9 is q, the potential in the capacitor is

$$\varphi = \frac{q}{4\pi\varepsilon_0 \alpha}(b - r).$$

Show that this potential does not satisfy Laplace's equation, but satisfies Eq. (8-6.1) instead.

8.20. A spherical capacitor is formed by two spheres of radii a and b. The capacitor is filled with a material of variable permittivity $\varepsilon = (\alpha + r)/r$, where α is a constant and r is the distance from the center. Using the basic laws, show that if $a < b$ the potential in the capacitor is

$$\varphi = \frac{q}{4\pi\varepsilon_0 \alpha}\ln\frac{b(\alpha + r)}{r(\alpha + b)},$$

where q is the charge of the capacitor. Then show that this potential satisfies Eq. (8-6.1).

8.21. An infinitely long circular dielectric cylinder of radius a and dielectric constant ε_1 is placed with its axis perpendicular to a uniform electric field $\mathbf{E}_0$ in an infinite dielectric liquid of dielectric constant ε_2. Show that the resultant field is

$$\mathbf{E} = \mathbf{E}_0 + E_0\frac{\varepsilon_1 - \varepsilon_2}{\varepsilon_1 + \varepsilon_2}\frac{a^2}{r^2}(\cos\theta\,\mathbf{r}_u + \sin\theta\,\boldsymbol{\theta}_u)$$

outside the cylinder and

$$\mathbf{E} = \frac{2\varepsilon_2}{\varepsilon_1 + \varepsilon_2}\mathbf{E}_0$$

inside the cylinder, where θ and r are cylindrical coordinates of the point of observation.

8.22. When a dielectric or conducting sphere is placed in a uniform electric field $\mathbf{E}_0$, the resultant field $\mathbf{E}$ outside the sphere becomes

$$\mathbf{E} = \mathbf{E}_0 + \mathbf{E}_d.$$

(a) Show that $\mathbf{E}_d$ can be attributed to a dipole-type charge distribution of moment $\mathbf{p}$ induced in the sphere by the field $\mathbf{E}$ and given by

$$\mathbf{p} = 4\pi\varepsilon_0\alpha\mathbf{E}_0,$$

where α is a constant of proportionality.

(b) The constant of proportionality α is called *polarizability*.[1] Show that in the case under consideration it is given by

$$\alpha = \frac{\varepsilon - 1}{\varepsilon + 2} a^3.$$

8.23. A dielectric sphere of dielectric constant ε and radius $2a$ contains a concentric conducting sphere of radius a. Show that if the spheres are placed in a uniform field $\mathbf{E}_0$, the total positive (or negative) charge induced on the metal sphere is

$$q = \frac{36\pi\varepsilon_0\varepsilon a^2}{5\varepsilon + 7} E_0.$$

8.24. A spherical shell of radii a and b ($b > a$) and dielectric constant ε is placed in an initially uniform field $\mathbf{E}_0$. Show that the final field inside the central cavity of the shell is

$$\mathbf{E} = \frac{9\varepsilon}{9\varepsilon - 2(\varepsilon - 1)^2(a^3/b^3 - 1)} \mathbf{E}_0.$$

8.25. Consider a line charge of density λ per unit length in a medium of dielectric constant ε_1 a distance a from an infinite plane boundary with another medium of dielectric constant ε_2. Show that the potential in medium 1 is the same as that due to the actual charge λ and an image line charge $\lambda' = [(\varepsilon_1 - \varepsilon_2)/(\varepsilon_1 + \varepsilon_2)]\lambda$ placed a distance a on the other side of the boundary (considering the entire space to be filled with medium 1). Show that the potential in medium 2 is the same as that due to an image line charge of density $\lambda'' = [2\varepsilon_2/(\varepsilon_1 + \varepsilon_2)]\lambda$ at the position actually occupied by λ (considering the entire space to be filled with medium 2).

8.26. Consider a line charge of density λ per unit length in a medium of dielectric constant ε_1 a distance d from the axis of an infinite circular cylinder of radius a and dielectric constant ε_2. Show that the potential outside the cylinder is the same as that due to the actual charge λ and two image charges $\lambda_1' = [(\varepsilon_1 - \varepsilon_2)/(\varepsilon_1 + \varepsilon_2)]\lambda$ and $\lambda_2' = -[(\varepsilon_1 - \varepsilon_2)/(\varepsilon_1 + \varepsilon_2)]\lambda$ located at distances $l = a^2/d$ and $l = 0$ from the axis of the cylinder, respectively (all charges lie in one plane and the entire space is considered to be filled with medium 1). Show that the potential in the cylinder is the same as that due to an image line charge of density $\lambda'' = [2\varepsilon_2/(\varepsilon_1 + \varepsilon_2)]\lambda$ at the position actually occupied by λ (considering the entire space to be filled with medium 2).

---

[1] Polarizability is frequently defined as $\mathbf{p} = \alpha\mathbf{E}$, where α incorporates the factor $4\pi\varepsilon_0$.

8.27. Show that the electrostatic potential measured at the center of a spherical cavity made in a uniformly polarized dielectric is independent of the size of the cavity.

8.28. Assuming that the electret described in Example 8-7.2 is such that $l \gg a$, and using the method of axial expansion, find the potential at all points near one end of the electret.

8.29. A spherical electret of radius a is made from a permanently polarized material of uniform polarization **P**. Show that the potential of the electret at a distance $r > a$ from the center is

$$\varphi = \frac{\mathbf{P} \cdot \mathbf{r}}{3\varepsilon_0} \left(\frac{a}{r}\right)^3.$$

8.30. A spherical electret of diameter $2a$ and a cubical electret of length $2a$ on a side both have the same uniform polarization **P**. Show that at large distances from the electrets the maximum field produced by the cubical electret exceeds that produced by the spherical electret $6/\pi$ times.

8.31. Two electrets of different shape are made from equal amounts of the same material of the same uniform polarization **P**. Show that at large distances from the electrets the maximum fields which the two electrets can produce are equal.

8.32. A disk electret of radius a and uniform polarization **P** directed along the symmetry axis is placed between two conducting plates connected by a wire. The wire is then removed from the plates and the plates are removed from the electret. Show that opposite charges, not exceeding $q = \pi a^2 P$, will appear on the plates.

8.33. Show that the force between two point charges q_1 and q_2 embedded in an infinite liquid of dielectric constant ε a distance r apart is

$$\mathbf{F} = \frac{\overset{\circ}{q_1 q_2}}{4\pi\varepsilon_0 \varepsilon r^2} \mathbf{r}_u.$$

8.34. Two point charges q_1 and q_2 are placed at the respective centers of two small spherical cavities located a distance r apart in an infinite solid body of dielectric constant ε. Show that each charge is subjected to the force

$$\mathbf{F} = \frac{\overset{\circ}{3 q_1 q_2}}{4\pi\varepsilon_0 (2\varepsilon + 1) r^2} \mathbf{r}_u.$$

8.35. The space between the plates of a thin parallel-plate capacitor of plate separation d is filled with a dielectric of dielectric constant ε. A voltage V is applied to the capacitor. Find the force acting on a point charge q when this charge is placed in (a) a very small needle-shaped cavity made in the dielectric with the axis normal to the plates, and (b) a very small coin-shaped cavity made in the dielectric with the axis normal to the plates.

8.36. A small, slender dielectric cylinder of dielectric constant ε and volume v is placed at a large distance r from a small conducting sphere of radius a kept at a potential V. The axis of the cylinder is along the line joining the sphere with the cylinder. Neglecting the end effects of the cylinder, show that the cylinder is attracted to the sphere with a force

$$F = \frac{°2\varepsilon_0(\varepsilon - 1) V^2 a^2 v}{r^5}.$$

8.37. A small piece of electret of uniform polarization P and volume v_1 is placed at a large distance r from a small, thin dielectric disk of dielectric constant ε and volume v_2. The polarization of the electret is in the direction of the line joining the electret with the disk. The flat surfaces of the disk are normal to this line. Neglecting the edge effects of the disk, show that the disk is attracted to the electret with a force

$$F = \frac{°3(\varepsilon - 1) P^2 v_1^2 v_2}{4\pi^2 \varepsilon_0 \varepsilon r^7}.$$

8.38. A large container made of dielectric material is covered with two conducting plates separated from each other by a straight narrow gap. The container is filled with a dielectric liquid of dielectric constant ε and density ρ, and a voltage V is applied between the plates. A small spherical air bubble has formed in the liquid at a depth h directly below the gap separating the plates. Neglecting all edge and end effects, show that the bubble will not rise if

$$°V^2 \geq \frac{(2\varepsilon + 1)\pi^2 \rho g h^3}{3\varepsilon_0 \varepsilon(\varepsilon - 1)}.$$

8.39. A cylindrical capacitor consisting of two coaxial cylinders of radii a and b and length l is used as an electrostatic dust percipitator (dust particles in the inhomogeneous field of the capacitor experience an attraction to the inner cylinder). The air to be filtered contains spherical dust particles of density ρ and dielectric constant ε. Show that when a voltage V is applied to the capacitor, the velocity v with which the air must be blown through the capacitor in order to be made completely free of dust must be

$$v \leq \frac{\sqrt{°3\varepsilon_0(\varepsilon - 1)l} \, lV}{b \ln (b/a)\sqrt{\rho(\varepsilon + 2)(b^2 - a^2)}}.$$

8.40. A parallel-plate capacitor of plate separation t and area A has a dielectric slab also of area A and thickness t between the plates. The plates and the dielectric are not fastened to each other. Show that when a voltage V is applied to the capacitor and the capacitor is kept in a horizontal position, the entire capacitor can be lifted by its upper plate without coming apart if the combined weight w of the lower plate and dielectric satisfies the relation

$$w \leq \frac{°\varepsilon_0 \varepsilon^2 V^2 A}{2t^2}.$$

8.41. A long, horizontal, hollow dielectric cylinder of dielectric constant ε, inner radius a, outer radius b, and length l has its upper half replaced by two semi-infinite horizontal metal plates which almost touch each other along the axis of the cylinder. Show that if a voltage V is applied between the plates, the dielectric will stay in place without being fastened to the plates provided that its weight w satisfies the relation

$$w \leq \frac{°\varepsilon_0(\varepsilon^2 - 1)V^2l}{\pi^2}\left(\frac{1}{a} - \frac{1}{b}\right).$$

8.42. The upper half of a hollow conducting sphere of radius b is filled with a solid dielectric of dielectric constant ε. The dielectric has a hemispherical depression of radius a concentric with the hollow sphere. A conducting sphere of radius a is placed into this depression, and a voltage V is applied between the two spheres. Show that the smaller sphere will stay in place without being fastened to the dielectric if the weight of the smaller sphere w satisfies the relation

$$w \leq °\tfrac{1}{2}\pi\varepsilon_0(\varepsilon^2 - 1)\frac{V^2b^2}{(b - a)^2}.$$

8.43. A line charge of density λ is placed in a dielectric liquid of dielectric constant ε_1 parallel to, and at a distance a from, the infinite-plane boundary with a solid dielectric ε_2. Show that the force per unit length of the line charge is

$$f_l = \frac{°\lambda^2(\varepsilon_1 - \varepsilon_2)}{4\pi\varepsilon_0\varepsilon_1 a(\varepsilon_1 + \varepsilon_2)}.$$

8.44. Two coaxial cylinders of radii a and b are lowered vertically into a dielectric liquid of density ρ. Show that if the liquid in the space between the cylinders rises a distance h when a voltage V is applied between them, the dielectric constant of the liquid is

$$\varepsilon = \frac{\rho g h(b^2 - a^2)\ln(b/a)}{°\varepsilon_0 V^2} + 1.$$

8.45. A nonconducting liquid of dielectric constant ε and density ρ is contained in a U-tube of circular cross section. The inner radius of the tube is a, and the dielectric constant of the tube is $\varepsilon' = 1$. One half of the tube is located between the plates of a thin parallel-plate capacitor, the other half is outside the capacitor. The separation between the plates is d, $(d > a)$, and the voltage between the plates is V. Show that difference of liquid levels in the two halves of the tube is

$$\Delta h \approx \frac{°\varepsilon_0(\varepsilon - 1)V^2}{(\varepsilon + 1)\rho g d^2}.$$

8.46. Show that the electrostatic energy of a system consisting of a small dielectric or conducting sphere located at a distance r from a point charge q can be expressed as

$$U = -\frac{°\alpha q^2}{8\pi\varepsilon_0 r^4} + U_{sq},$$

where α is the polarizability of the sphere (see Problem 8.22) and U_{sq} is the self energy of the point charge.

9

STATIONARY ELECTRIC
FIELD IN CONDUCTING
MEDIA

The sphere of existence of electric fields is not limited to vacuum and dielectrics. Electric fields can exist in all media, including conductors. In this chapter we shall study the time-independent electric fields in conducting media. We shall call these fields the *stationary* fields.

9-1. Electric Fields in Conductors. Current Density Field

The electric field in a conductor is defined in the same manner as the electric field in any other medium—that is, as the electric field $\mathbf{E}$ measured in a needle-shaped cavity drilled along the direction of the field.

Electric fields in conductors are always accompanied by electric currents (electrostatic fields cannot exist in conductors). It is convenient to describe these currents in terms of the *electric current density* $\mathbf{J}$. The current density is a vector defined by the formula

$$I = \int \mathbf{J} \cdot d\mathbf{S}, \tag{9-1.1}$$

where I is the current through the surface of integration S. The current density may also be defined in the equivalent differential form as

$$J_a = \frac{dI}{dS_a}, \tag{9-1.2}$$

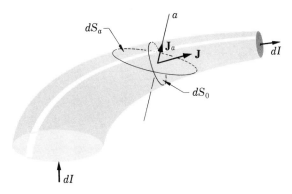

FIG. 9.1   Definition of electric current density.

where J_a is the component of $\mathbf{J}$ along some direction a, dS_a is an element of area normal to this direction, and dI is the current through this element of area (Fig. 9.1). From this definition it follows that $J = dI/dS_0$, where dS_0 is an element of area so oriented that the ratio dI/dS is a maximum (compare with the definition of the displacement vector $\mathbf{D}$, p. 81). The sense of the direction of $\mathbf{J}$ is defined to be the same as that of the current I at the point under consideration; the general orientation of $\mathbf{J}$ is therefore from the positive to the negative terminal of the current source. The units of current density are amp/m².

The space distribution of the electric current density constitutes a vector field. This field is intimately related to the electric field $\mathbf{E}$.

9-2. Fundamental Laws of the Stationary Electric Fields in Conducting Media

Just like electrostatic fields, electric fields of current-carrying conductors can be made "visible" by means of lines-of-force pictures formed by grass seeds (Plates 6–9).[1]   The study of these fields has shown that the curl and circulation laws for them are the same as for the electrostatic fields:

$$\nabla \times \mathbf{E} = 0, \qquad \oint \mathbf{E} \cdot d\mathbf{l} = 0. \qquad (9\text{-}2.1a, b)$$

[1] The method for obtaining such pictures is described in Oleg Jefimenko "Demonstration of the Electric Fields of Current-Carrying Conductors," *American Journal of Physics* **30,** 19 (1962).

The study of the stationary current density fields has shown that the divergence and flux laws for them are

$$\nabla \cdot \mathbf{J} = 0, \qquad \oint \mathbf{J} \cdot d\mathbf{S} = 0. \qquad \text{(9-2.2a, b)}$$

Furthermore, it has been established that in the majority of common conducting media the current density field $\mathbf{J}$ is connected with the electric field $\mathbf{E}$ by the equation

$$\mathbf{J} = \sigma\mathbf{E}, \qquad \text{(9-2.3)}$$

where σ is a factor of proportionality called the *conductivity*. The conductivity has different values for different substances and usually depends on temperature and other parameters characterizing the state of the substance under consideration. The units of conductivity are amp/volt $\cdot$ m. The reciprocal of the conductivity is called the *resistivity* ρ,

$$\rho = \frac{1}{\sigma}; \qquad \text{(9-2.4)}$$

its units are volt $\cdot$ m/amp. Equation (9-2.3) is usually called *Ohm's law*, and the media for which this law holds are called *ohmic conductors*, or *linear isotropic conductors*.

Equations (9-2.1), (9-2.2), and (9-2.3) completely determine the curl and divergence laws for both the stationary $\mathbf{E}$ field and the stationary $\mathbf{J}$ field and thus, by Helmholtz's theorem of vector analysis, constitute a complete set of equations uniquely specifying these fields.

As one can see, the basic field laws for the stationary fields are analogous to the basic laws for the electrostatic fields in charge-free dielectrics. In fact, they can be formally obtained from the corresponding electrostatic laws by merely substituting $\mathbf{J}$ for $\mathbf{D}$ (I for Q), and σ for $\varepsilon_0\varepsilon$. Similarly, the dimensions of the stationary field quantities can be formally obtained from the dimensions of the corresponding electrostatic quantities by merely changing amp $\cdot$ sec to amp. This is a very useful analogy, since it allows one to write down immediately various consequences of the stationary field laws by using the consequences derived previously from the electrostatic field laws, and also allows one to extend the techniques and methods used for the solution of electrostatic problems to the solution of the stationary field problems.

Ohm's law (9-2.3) constitutes an important link connecting the macroscopic theory of currents in metallic conductors with the microscopic theory. In the microscopic theory, electric current in metals is attributed to a drift of free electrons under the action of the applied electric field, and the current density is given by (compare with Example 1-3.3)

$$\mathbf{J} = en\mathbf{v}_d,$$

where e is the charge of an electron, n is the number of free electrons per unit volume, and $\mathbf{v}_d$ is the drift velocity of the electrons. The drift velocity is

$$\mathbf{v}_d = \frac{1}{2}\frac{e\mathbf{E}}{m}t,$$

where m is the mass of an electron, $\mathbf{E}$ is the applied electric field, and t is the average time between collisions of an electron with the atoms (ions) that make up the metal. This time is given by

$$t = \frac{l}{v_t},$$

where l is the mean free path of the electrons, and v_t is their thermal velocity (which usually is much larger than v_d). Combining these equations, one obtains

$$\mathbf{J} = \frac{1}{2}n\frac{e^2l}{mv_t}\mathbf{E},$$

and if one sets

$$\frac{1}{2}n\frac{e^2l}{mv_t} = \sigma,$$

where σ is the conductivity of the metal, a transition between the macroscopic and the microscopic theory is achieved.

9-3. Some Consequences of the Fundamental Laws. Conductance and Resistance

We shall now derive the most important consequences of the stationary field laws.

According to the curl law (9-2.1a) and corollary to Poisson's theorem of vector analysis, a stationary electric field in a conductor can be expressed in terms of the scalar potential φ defined (just as for the electrostatic field) by the equation

$$\mathbf{E} = -\nabla\varphi. \tag{9-3.1}$$

Taking the line integral of this equation, we obtain the familiar integral formula for the potential

$$\varphi_a - \varphi_b = \int_a^b \mathbf{E} \cdot d\mathbf{l} = V_{ab}, \qquad (9\text{-}3.2)$$

where V_{ab} is the voltage between the points a and b.

Applying the circulation law (9-2.1b) to an infinitesimal loop enclosing the interface between two different conductors, we obtain the boundary condition for $\mathbf{E}$ (compare with the derivation of the boundary conditions at a dielectric interface, Section 8-5)

$$E_{t1} = E_{t2}, \qquad (9\text{-}3.3)$$

and hence the boundary condition for φ

$$\varphi_1 = \varphi_2. \qquad (9\text{-}3.4)$$

Applying the flux law (9-2.2b) to an infinitesimal "pill box" enclosing the interface between two different conductors, we similarly obtain the boundary condition for $\mathbf{J}$ (compare with the derivation of the boundary conditions for $\mathbf{D}$ in Section 8-5)

$$J_{n1} = J_{n2}, \qquad (9\text{-}3.5)$$

and combining this equation with Eqs. (9-2.3) and (9-3.1), we obtain

$$\sigma_1 \frac{\partial \varphi_1}{\partial n} = \sigma_2 \frac{\partial \varphi_2}{\partial n}, \qquad (9\text{-}3.6)$$

where n designates a direction normal to the interface. Observe that because no current can be present in a dielectric, Eq. (9-3.5) implies that J_n, and hence E_n, is zero on a conductor-dielectric interface, so that only J_t and E_t may exist on such an interface under stationary conditions.

Finally, combining Eqs. (9-2.2a), (9-2.3), and (9-3.1), we can write

$$\mathbf{\nabla} \cdot \mathbf{J} = \mathbf{\nabla} \cdot \sigma\mathbf{E} = \mathbf{\nabla}\sigma \cdot \mathbf{E} + \sigma\mathbf{\nabla} \cdot \mathbf{E} = -\mathbf{\nabla}\sigma \cdot \mathbf{\nabla}\varphi - \sigma\nabla^2\varphi = 0,$$

or

$$\nabla^2\varphi + \frac{1}{\sigma}\mathbf{\nabla}\sigma \cdot \mathbf{\nabla}\varphi = 0, \qquad (9\text{-}3.7)$$

which in the case of constant σ reduces to Laplace's equation

$$\nabla^2\varphi = 0. \qquad (9\text{-}3.8)$$

To complete this set of equations, we shall now introduce two important quantities correlating current and voltage in a conductor.

The first of these quantities is the *conductance G*. It is defined by the equation

$$G = \frac{I}{V},\tag{9-3.9}$$

where V is the voltage applied to the conductor, and I is the current in it. As one can see from this formula, G constitutes the stationary field counterpart of the capacitance C. The other quantity is the reciprocal of the conductance, called the *resistance R*. The resistance is thus defined by

$$R = \frac{1}{G},\tag{9-3.10}$$

or

$$R = \frac{V}{I}\tag{9-3.11}$$

(this formula is often mistaken for a law and is sometimes referred to as "Ohm's law"). The units of resistance are volt/amp, commonly called "ohm"; the units of conductance are amp/volt, sometimes called "mho". The procedure for the calculation of the conductance or resistance is analogous to that for the calculation of capacitance.

In any conducting system in which a steady current is maintained by external sources, there are at least two conducting bodies by means of which the electric field is established in the system and through which the current enters and leaves this system. They are called *electrodes* and correspond to the capacitor plates of an electrostatic system. In order to minimize heat losses (see Section 9-7), electrodes are usually made of materials having very high conductivity σ, so that for a finite current the electric field inside an electrode is practically zero, and hence the potential at all points of an electrode is practically constant. It is therefore customary to consider electrodes as equipotential bodies whenever no explicit statement to the contrary is made.

▼

Example 9-3.1   Determine the conductance and the resistance of a straight cylindrical rod of conductivity σ, cross-section area S, and length l, between two plane electrodes normal to the axis of the rod (Fig. 9.2).

The electric field in the rod is homogeneous (a straight rod is the stationary field counterpart of a parallel-plate capacitor of electrostatics) and is given by

$$E = \frac{V}{l},$$

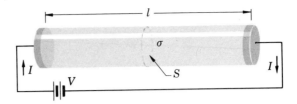

FIG. 9.2   Calculation of the conductance and resistance of a cylindrical rod.

where V is the voltage applied to the rod. Substituting this expression into Ohm's law (9-2.3), we have

$$J = \sigma \frac{V}{l} .$$

The current in the rod is then

$$I = \int \mathbf{J} \cdot d\mathbf{S} = \sigma \frac{VS}{l} ,$$

and the conductance, $G = I/V$, is therefore

$$G = \sigma \frac{S}{l}$$

(in analogy with the capacitance of a parallel plate capacitor). The resistance, $R = V/I$, is

$$R = \frac{l}{\sigma S} = \rho \frac{l}{S} .$$

Example 9-3.2   A spherical electrode of radius a is lowered centrally into a perfectly conducting hemispherical bowl of inner radius b, which is then filled with a conducting liquid of conductivity σ (Fig. 9.3). Find the resistance of the liquid between the bowl and the sphere.

Describing a concentric spherical Gaussian surface S of radius r around the spherical electrode and applying the flux law (9-2.2b) to this surface, we have

$$\oint \mathbf{J} \cdot d\mathbf{S} = 0.$$

Let us now split this integral into three integrals: the integral over the part of the Gaussian surface submerged in the liquid, S_1; the integral over the part of the Gaussian surface crossing the lead wire, S_2; and the integral over the part of the Gaussian surface external to the liquid and to the lead wire, S_3. We then obtain

$$\oint \mathbf{J} \cdot d\mathbf{S} = \int \mathbf{J}_1 \cdot d\mathbf{S}_1 + \int \mathbf{J}_2 \cdot d\mathbf{S}_2 + \int \mathbf{J}_3 \cdot d\mathbf{S}_3 = 0.$$

By symmetry, the current density J on the surface S_1 is radial and constant,

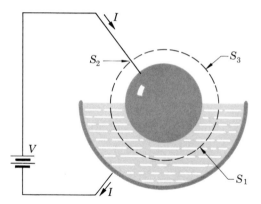

FIG. 9.3   Calculation of the resistance of a liquid contained in a hemi-spherical bowl.

so that the first integral is

$$\int \mathbf{J}_1 \cdot d\mathbf{S}_1 = J \int dS_1 = J 2\pi r^2.$$

By the definition of current density, the second integral represents the current carried by the lead wire in the outward direction, or

$$\int \mathbf{J}_2 \cdot d\mathbf{S}_2 = -I,$$

where I is the current entering the Gaussian surface through this wire. Since no current is present outside the liquid and the lead wire, the third integral is zero. We thus have

$$J 2\pi r^2 - I = 0,$$

or, solving for J and taking into account the radial direction of the current,

$$\mathbf{J} = \frac{I}{2\pi r^2} \mathbf{r}_u.$$

The field is then, by Ohm's law (9-2.3),

$$\mathbf{E} = \frac{I}{2\pi \sigma r^2} \mathbf{r}_u.$$

Taking the line integral of $\mathbf{E}$, we obtain for the voltage V_{ab} between the two electrodes

$$V_{ab} = \int_a^b \mathbf{E} \cdot d\mathbf{r} = \int_a^b \frac{I}{2\pi \sigma r^2} \mathbf{r}_u \cdot d\mathbf{r} = \frac{I}{2\pi \sigma} \left(\frac{1}{a} - \frac{1}{b} \right),$$

which, by Eq. (9-3.11), gives for the resistance

$$R = \frac{1}{2\pi \sigma} \left(\frac{1}{a} - \frac{1}{b} \right).$$

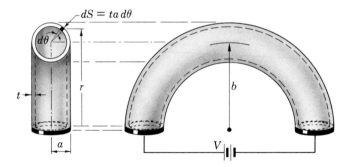

FIG. 9.4   Calculation of the resistance of a circular tube.

Example 9-3.3   A thin-walled tube of circular cross-section, radius a, wall thickness $t \ll a$, and resistivity ρ is bent to form a "half-ring" of median radius b (Fig. 9.4). Two flat electrodes are attached to the ends of the tube. Find the resistance of the tube between the two electrodes, and determine the limiting value of this resistance for a very narrow tube ($a \ll b$).

By inspection we see that the field lines are coaxial circular arcs parallel to the axis of the tube. The field is therefore

$$E = \frac{V}{\pi r},$$

where V is the voltage applied to the tube and πr is the length of the arc of radius r joining the two electrodes. The current density is then

$$J = \frac{V}{\rho \pi r}.$$

The current in the tube can be found by integrating J over the cross-sectional area of the tube. The element of area for this integration is $dS = ta\, d\theta$, where θ is the angle between the vertical plane and the radius vector joining dS with the axis of the tube. The radius r expressed in terms of θ is $r = b + a \cos \theta$. The current is therefore

$$I = \int \mathbf{J} \cdot d\mathbf{S} = \int_0^{2\pi} \frac{Vta\, d\theta}{\rho \pi (b + a \cos \theta)}$$

$$= \frac{Vta}{\rho \pi} \cdot \frac{4}{\sqrt{b^2 - a^2}} \tan^{-1} \left[\frac{(b - a) \tan \theta/2}{\sqrt{b^2 - a^2}} \right] \Bigg|_0^{\pi}$$

$$= \frac{Vta}{\rho \pi} \cdot \frac{4}{\sqrt{b^2 - a^2}} \cdot \frac{\pi}{2} = \frac{2Vta}{\rho \sqrt{b^2 - a^2}},$$

and the resistance, $R = V/I$, is

$$R = \rho \frac{\sqrt{b^2 - a^2}}{2ta}.$$

If $a \ll b$, we can write

$$R = \rho \frac{b}{2ta},$$

which upon multiplication and division by π and substitution of S for $2\pi at$ (cross-sectional area of the tube wall) and l for πb (length of the tube) gives

$$R = \rho\,\frac{\pi b}{2\pi at} = \rho\,\frac{l}{S}\,.$$

Thus in this limiting case the resistance approaches the value that it would have if the tube were straight (see Example 9-3.1).

Example 9-3.4   A coaxial cable has two layers of different insulating materials between the core and the sheath. The length of the cable is l; the radius of the core is a, that of the sheath is b, the radius of the boundary between the two insulating layers is c, the resistivity of the inner layer is ρ_1, that of the outer is ρ_2 (Fig. 9.5). Find the leakage resistance of the cable.

The leakage current density is, by the flux law (9-2.2b),

$$J = \frac{I}{2\pi rl}\,.$$

The electric field associated with this current is

$$E_1 = \frac{\rho_1 I}{2\pi rl} \quad \text{and} \quad E_2 = \frac{\rho_2 I}{2\pi rl}$$

for the inner and the outer insulating layers, respectively. The voltage between the core and the sheath is

$$\begin{aligned}
V_{ab} &= \int_a^b \mathbf{E}\cdot d\mathbf{r} = \int_a^c E_1 dr + \int_c^b E_2 dr \\
&= \int_a^c \frac{\rho_1 I}{2\pi rl}\,dr + \int_c^b \frac{\rho_2 I}{2\pi rl}\,dr \\
&= \frac{I}{2\pi l}\,(\rho_1 \ln c/a + \rho_2 \ln b/c).
\end{aligned}$$

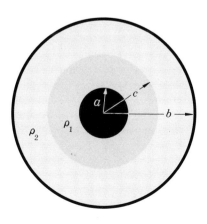

FIG. 9.5   Calculation of the leakage resistance of a coaxial cable with two layers of insulating material.

The resistance is therefore

$$R = \frac{1}{2\pi l} (\rho_1 \ln c/a + \rho_2 \ln b/c).$$

▲

9-4. Special Methods for the Solution of Stationary Electric Field Problems

Just as in the case of the electrostatic field problems involving linear isotropic dielectrics, most special methods for the solution of the stationary field problems involving ohmic conductors are based on the uniqueness theorems for the potential φ representing the fields under consideration.

The potential for the stationary fields in ohmic conductors of constant conductivity satisfies Laplace's equations, is constant on the surfaces of electrodes, and satisfies the boundary conditions at conductor-conductor interfaces analogous to the boundary conditions which are satisfied by the electrostatic potential at dielectric-dielectric interfaces. Therefore the potential φ for the stationary fields in ohmic conductors[1] is subject to essentially the same uniqueness theorems that apply to the electrostatic φ except that the theorems are now formulated in reference to electrodes and currents instead of conductors and charges. Consequently, all those special methods for the solution of the *electrostatic* problems that are based on the uniqueness theorems for φ are applicable for the solution of the *stationary field* problems as well.

Moreover, it is clear that the electrostatic and the stationary field problems of identical geometry have identical solutions, except that in the formulas representing the electrostatic solutions the symbols $\mathbf{D}$, Q, C, and $\varepsilon_0 \varepsilon$ appear in places where the symbols $\mathbf{J}$, I, G, and σ appear in the formulas representing the stationary field solutions. Hence, one can "borrow" solutions for the stationary field problems from electrostatic problems.

It must be pointed out, however, that there are certain limitations in the applicability of such borrowed solutions. In particular, the lead wires necessary for maintaining the current in conductors may introduce field distortions that do not have a counterpart in the electrostatic fields, and thus may impair the accuracy of the results obtained from the borrowed solutions. Furthermore, since in the free space $\varepsilon = 1$,

---

[1] We assume that σ is a constant.

while $\sigma = 0$, the electrostatic systems may have fringing fields (edge effects) that do not have a counterpart in the geometrically similar stationary field systems (see Example 9-4.5). This also imposes limitations on the use of the borrowed solutions.

Another important exception to the analogy between the electrostatic and the stationary field problems is that whereas there are only two types of electrostatic images (one due to the dielectric-conductor interface, the other due to the dielectric-dielectric interface), there are three types of images for stationary fields. The first type is due to the conductor-electrode interface (Table 9-I), the second due to the conductor-conductor interface,[1] and the third due to the conductor-dielectric interface (Table 9-II); the latter has no counterpart in electrostatics.[2]

▼

Example 9-4.1   A spherical shell of resistivity ρ contains two conical electrodes as shown in Fig. 9.6. Find the resistance of the shell between the two electrodes and check the result by investigating the limiting case of $\alpha = \pi/2 - \beta$, where $\beta \ll 1$ (in this limiting case the shell becomes a thin flat ring).

This problem can be solved by using the method of harmonics. By

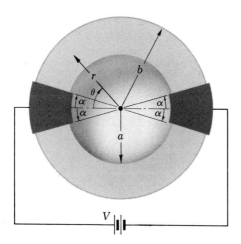

FIG. 9.6   Calculation of the resistance of a spherical shell.

[1] These images are analogous to the ones described in Example 8-6.2 and Problems 8.25 and 8.26.

[2] The correctness of the images given in Tables 9-I and 9-II is verified, as usual, by checking whether the images satisfy the required boundary conditions.

the symmetry of the problem, the potential must be constant on conical surfaces coaxial with the electrodes and having the common apex in the center of the shell. A suitable function found from Tables 6-I and 5-I is

$$\varphi = A_0 Q_0 (\cos \theta) = A \ln \frac{1 + \cos \theta}{1 - \cos \theta}.$$

The constant A can be determined from the boundary conditions

$$(1) \text{ at } \theta = \alpha, \qquad \varphi = \frac{V}{2},$$

$$(2) \text{ at } \theta = \pi - \alpha, \qquad \varphi = -\frac{V}{2},$$

which require that

$$A = \frac{V}{2} \left(\ln \frac{1 + \cos \alpha}{1 - \cos \alpha} \right)^{-1}.$$

The electric field is then

$$\mathbf{E} = -\nabla \varphi = -\frac{\partial \varphi}{r \partial \theta} \, \boldsymbol{\theta}_u = -\frac{\partial}{r \partial \theta} \left(A \ln \frac{1 + \cos \theta}{1 - \cos \theta} \right) \boldsymbol{\theta}_u$$

$$= \frac{2A}{r \sin \theta} \, \boldsymbol{\theta}_u.$$

The current density is therefore

$$\mathbf{J} = \frac{1}{\rho} \mathbf{E} = \frac{2A}{\rho r \sin \theta} \, \boldsymbol{\theta}_u.$$

The current in the shell may now be found by integrating $\mathbf{J}$ over the cross section of the shell. Taking the equatorial cross section (simplest integration, $\theta = \pi/2$, $\sin \theta = 1$), we have

$$I = \int \mathbf{J} \cdot d\mathbf{S} = \int_a^b \frac{2A}{\rho r} \, 2\pi r \, dr = \frac{1}{\rho} \, 4\pi A (b - a),$$

and substituting A,

$$I = \frac{1}{\rho} \, 2\pi V (b - a) \left(\ln \frac{1 + \cos \alpha}{1 - \cos \alpha} \right)^{-1}.$$

The resistance, $R = V/I$, is then

$$R = \frac{\rho}{2\pi (b - a)} \ln \frac{1 + \cos \alpha}{1 - \cos \alpha}.$$

If $\alpha = \pi/2 - \beta$, where $\beta \ll 1$, we can write

$$\ln \frac{1 + \cos \alpha}{1 - \cos \alpha} = \ln \frac{1 + \cos (\pi/2 - \beta)}{1 - \cos (\pi/2 - \beta)} = \ln \frac{1 + \sin \beta}{1 - \sin \beta} \approx \ln \frac{1 + \beta}{1 - \beta} \approx 2\beta.$$

The resistance becomes in this case

$$R \approx \frac{\rho}{2\pi(b-a)} 2\beta.$$

Multiplying and dividing this expression by $(b+a)/2$, we obtain

$$R \approx \rho 2\beta \frac{b+a}{2} \cdot \frac{1}{2\pi(b-a)} \cdot \frac{2}{b+a}.$$

If we now observe that for $\beta \ll 1$ the conducting shell degenerates into a flat circular ring of average thickness $t = 2\beta \cdot (b+a)/2$ and area $S = \pi(b^2 - a^2)$, we can write

$$R \approx \rho \frac{t}{S},$$

which was to be expected by analogy with the parallel-plate capacitor or by Example 9-3.1.

Example 9-4.2   To measure the conductivity of sea water, two spherical electrodes (Fig. 9.7a) of radius a are lowered in the sea to a depth h at a distance d from each other (both h and d are large compared to a). Find the conductivity of the water if a voltage V applied to the electrodes produces a current I between them, and estimate the accuracy of the obtained expression.

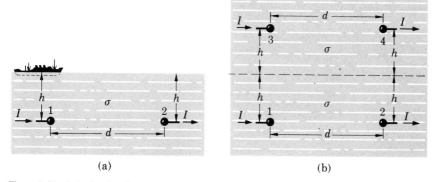

(a)   (b)

FIG. 9.7   Method of images for current carrying conductors. (a) Two spherical electrodes in water. (b) Equivalent image system.

We shall solve this problem by the method of images. The appropriate image system is shown in Fig. 9.7b. By analogy with electrostatics or by the flux law (9-2.3), the potential due to a positive spherical electrode delivering a current I to an ohmic conductor is $\varphi = I/4\pi\sigma r$, where r is the distance from the center of the electrode to the point of observation (we assume that the electrode is so small compared to other characteristic dimensions of the system, that the field around the electrode may be considered spherically

TABLE 9-I

Images in Conductor-Electrode Interfaces[a]

Actual System	Equivalent Image System

Point or line electrode in front of an
infinite plane electrode:

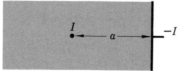 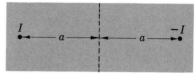

Point or line electrode in front of two intersecting,
infinite plane electrodes:

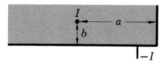 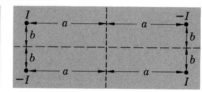

Point electrode in front of a spherical electrode:

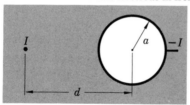 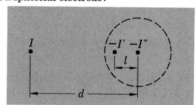

$$I' = (a/d)\,I; \quad I'' = I - I'; \quad l = a^2/d$$

Line electrode in front of a cylindrical electrode:

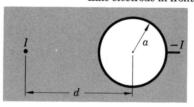 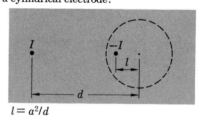

$$l = a^2/d$$

[a] Except for the third system, all images in this table are valid also for thin conducting
sheets.

TABLE 9-II
Images in Conductor-Dielectric Interfaces[a]

Actual System	Equivalent Image System
Point or line electrode in front of an infinite plane conductor-dielectric boundary:	

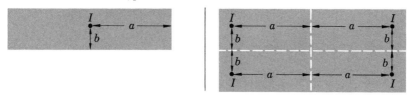

| Point or line electrode in front of two intersecting, infinite, plane conductor-dielectric boundaries: | |

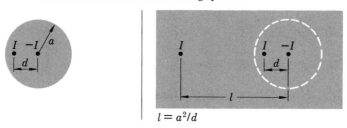

| Two line electrodes in a conducting cylinder: | |

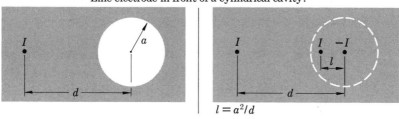

$$l = a^2/d$$

Line electrode in front of a cylindrical cavity:

$$l = a^2/d$$

[a] All images in this table are valid also for thin conducting sheets.

symmetric). The potential on the surface of the electrode 1, being the sum of the potentials due to the two electrodes and their images, is then

$$\varphi_1' = \frac{I}{4\pi\sigma a} - \frac{I}{4\pi\sigma d} - \frac{I}{4\pi\sigma\sqrt{d^2 + 4h^2}} + \frac{I}{4\pi\sigma 2h}$$

$$= \frac{I}{4\pi\sigma a}\left[1 - \frac{a}{d} - \frac{a}{\sqrt{d^2 + 4h^2}} + \frac{a}{2h}\right].$$

The potential on the surface of the electrode 2 is similarly

$$\varphi_2 = \frac{I}{4\pi\sigma a}\left[-1 + \frac{a}{d} + \frac{a}{\sqrt{d^2 + 4h^2}} - \frac{a}{2h}\right].$$

The voltage between the two electrodes is therefore

$$V = \varphi_1 - \varphi_2 = \frac{I}{2\pi\sigma a}\left[1 - \frac{a}{d} - \frac{a}{\sqrt{d^2 + 4h^2}} + \frac{a}{2h}\right].$$

This gives for the conductivity

$$\sigma = \frac{I}{2\pi a V}\left[1 - \frac{a}{d} - \frac{a}{\sqrt{d^2 + 4h^2}} + \frac{a}{2h}\right].$$

To estimate the accuracy of this expression, we first note that the method of images as we have used it in this problem applies only to point charges or point electrodes. Also, the method for the calculation of potentials that we have used here is justifiable only if all electrodes may be regarded as point sources from the location of other electrodes. As it follows from Problem 4.12 and Eq. (5-3.4), any electrode may be regarded as a point source from a distance $l \geq na$, provided that the maximum admissible error in the potential does not exceed $(100/n)\%$. Hence, neglecting the effect of the lead wires, the accuracy of our expression for σ may be expected to be at least $(a/d)100\%$ or $(a/2h)100\%$, whichever is larger.

Example 9-4.3   Under the action of mechanical stress, a conducting bar of conductivity σ is deformed from the initial shape shown in Fig. 9.8a to the final shape shown in Fig. 9.8b. Find the relative change in the resistance of the bar between the faces A and B if the thickness of the bar does not change.

This problem can be solved by the method of curvilinear squares. By analogy with the capacitance, the conductance of a plane conductor of uniform thickness t and conductivity σ is given by [see Eq. (6-6.5)]

$$G = \frac{N_f}{N_p}\sigma t,$$

where N_f is the number of flux tubes (current tubes), and N_p is the number of potential division (voltage steps) on the conductor's field map. Using

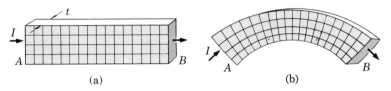

FIG. 9.8 Method of curvilinear squares for current-carrying conductors. (a) Curvilinear-square map of a conducting bar. (b) Curvilinear-square map of the bar after it has deformed.

the maps drawn in Figs. 9.8a and 9.8b, we then have for the original and the deformed bar, respectively,

$$G_o = \frac{4}{16} \sigma t \quad \text{and} \quad G_d = \frac{4}{18} \sigma t.$$

The relative change in resistance (the reciprocal of the relative change in conductance) is therefore

$$\frac{R_d}{R_o} = \frac{G_o}{G_d} = 1.125.$$

Example 9-4.4   Electric current enters an infinite plane conducting sheet at a point P and leaves at infinity. A circular hole, exclusive of P, is cut in the sheet, and the point G nearest to P on the edge of the hole is grounded (Fig. 9.9). Show that the potential at any point on the edge of the hole with respect to the ground is twice that which was present before the hole was cut.

Before the hole was cut, the electric field $\mathbf{E}_0$ in the sheet was radial, so that if the thickness of the sheet is t we have from the flux law (9-2.2b) and Ohm's law (9-2.3)

$$\mathbf{E}_0 = \frac{I}{2\pi\sigma t r} \mathbf{r}_u.$$

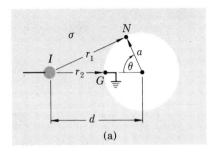

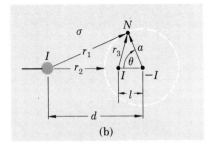

FIG. 9.9 Method of images for current-carrying conductors. (a) Actual system. (b) Equivalent image system.

The corresponding potential at any point N of the circle forming the edge of the hole was then

$$\varphi_0(a, \theta) = \int_{a,\theta}^{G} \mathbf{E}_0 \cdot d\mathbf{r} = -\frac{I}{2\pi\sigma t} \ln \frac{r_1}{r_2} = -\frac{I}{2\pi\sigma t} \ln \frac{\sqrt{d^2 + a^2 - 2ad \cos \theta}}{d - a},$$

where the symbols are the same as in Fig. 9.9a. The potential at the same point after the hole was cut is obtained by the method of images (Table 9-II) and is, accordingly, the sum of the three partial potentials

$$\varphi(a, \theta) = -\frac{I}{2\pi\sigma t} \ln \frac{\sqrt{d^2 + a^2 - 2ad \cos \theta}}{d - a} - \frac{I}{2\pi\sigma t} \ln \frac{\sqrt{l^2 + a^2 - 2al \cos \theta}}{a - l}$$
$$+ \frac{I}{2\pi\sigma t} \ln \frac{a}{a},$$

where the symbols are the same as in Fig. 9.9b. Substituting $l = a^2/d$, we obtain after simplifications

$$\varphi(a, \theta) = -\frac{I}{2\pi\sigma t} \ln \frac{(d^2 + a^2 - 2ad \cos \theta)}{(d - a)^2} = 2\varphi_0(a, \theta).$$

Example 9-4.5   As it has been stated above, one can find the conductance of a conductor by replacing $\varepsilon_0 \varepsilon$ by σ in the expression for the capacitance of the geometrically similar capacitor. Investigate the limitations of this method by considering the system of two electrodes (Fig. 9.10), the space between which is partially filled with a material of conductivity σ and dielectric constant ε.

The ratio of the capacitance to the conductance of this system is

$$\frac{C}{G} = \frac{QV}{VI} = \frac{Q}{I},$$

where Q is the charge of one electrode and I is the current carried by the intervening medium from one electrode to the other. The charge Q can be expressed as the surface integral $\oint \mathbf{D} \cdot d\mathbf{S}$ evaluated over a surface enclosing the electrode carrying Q, so that

$$\frac{C}{G} = \frac{1}{I} \oint \mathbf{D} \cdot d\mathbf{S}.$$

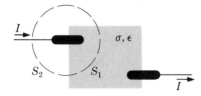

FIG. 9.10   Correlation between capacitance and conductance.

The surface integral can be expressed as the sum of two integrals taken over the surface S_1 (lying inside the material between the two electrodes) and S_2 (external to the material). This gives with $\mathbf{D}_1$ replaced by $\varepsilon\varepsilon_0\mathbf{E}_1$,

$$\frac{C}{G} = \frac{1}{I}\left(\int \varepsilon_0\varepsilon\mathbf{E}_1 \cdot d\mathbf{S}_1 + \int \mathbf{D}_2 \cdot d\mathbf{S}_2\right).$$

Replacing $\mathbf{E}_1$ by $\mathbf{J}/\sigma$, we now obtain

$$\frac{C}{G} = \frac{1}{I}\left(\int \varepsilon_0\varepsilon\frac{\mathbf{J}}{\sigma} \cdot d\mathbf{S}_1 + \int \mathbf{D}_2 \cdot d\mathbf{S}_2\right)$$

$$= \frac{1}{I}\left(\varepsilon_0\varepsilon\frac{I}{\sigma} + \int \mathbf{D}_2 \cdot d\mathbf{S}_2\right)$$

$$= \frac{\varepsilon_0\varepsilon}{\sigma} + \frac{1}{I}\int \mathbf{D}_2 \cdot d\mathbf{S}_2 = \frac{\varepsilon_0\varepsilon}{\sigma} + \frac{Q'}{I},$$

where Q' is the charge that is responsible for the flux through the surface S_2. If this charge is very small it may be disregarded as the "edge effect." In this case one can write

$$\frac{C}{G} = \frac{\varepsilon_0\varepsilon}{\sigma}, \quad \text{or} \quad G = \frac{\sigma C}{\varepsilon_0\varepsilon},$$

so that the conductance may be obtained from the capacitance by merely replacing $\varepsilon_0\varepsilon$ by σ. This formula is accurate, however, only to the extent that one can neglect the edge effects in the calculation of C.

▲

9-5. Displacement Field and Static Charge in Current-Carrying Conductors

As in any material medium, the displacement field in a current-carrying conductor is defined in terms of the displacement vector $\mathbf{D}$ measured in a coin-shaped cavity whose axis lies in the direction of this vector. It has been found that $\mathbf{D}$ in conductors carrying a steady current is subject to the same basic laws as in the dielectric media. In particular, for the majority of common conductors

$$\mathbf{D} = \varepsilon_0\varepsilon\mathbf{E}, \tag{9-5.1}$$

and for all conductors

$$\nabla \cdot \mathbf{D} = \rho \quad \text{and} \quad \oint \mathbf{D} \cdot d\mathbf{S} = \int \rho\, dv. \tag{9-5.2a, b}$$

An important consequence of these equations is that currents are associated with accumulations of static space and surface charge in the conductors that carry these currents.

A static space charge accumulates in electrically inhomogeneous current-carrying conductors at the points where either ε or σ, or both ε and σ, are such functions of position that $\nabla(\varepsilon/\sigma)$ does not vanish. This can be shown by combining Eqs. (9-5.2a), (9-5.1), and (9-2.3), which give for a space charge distribution[1]

$$\rho_{\text{charge}} = \nabla \cdot \mathbf{D} = \nabla \cdot \varepsilon_0\varepsilon\mathbf{E} = \nabla \cdot \varepsilon_0\varepsilon \frac{\mathbf{J}}{\sigma}$$

$$= \varepsilon_0 \mathbf{J} \cdot \nabla \frac{\varepsilon}{\sigma} + \varepsilon_0 \frac{\varepsilon}{\sigma} \nabla \cdot \mathbf{J}.$$

Since $\nabla \cdot \mathbf{J} = 0$ by Eq. (9-2.2a), we obtain

$$\rho_{\text{charge}} = \varepsilon_0\mathbf{J} \cdot \nabla \frac{\varepsilon}{\sigma}. \tag{9-5.3}$$

A static surface charge accumulates on the interface between two different conductors at the points where the currents traverse this interface. This can be shown as follows. According to Eq. (8-5.4) (which, being a consequence of $\nabla \cdot \mathbf{D} = \rho$, is valid for conductors as well as for dielectrics) the surface charge on an interface is

$$\sigma_{\text{charge}} = D_{n2} - D_{n1}.$$

Since

$$D = \varepsilon_0\varepsilon E = \varepsilon_0 \frac{\varepsilon}{\sigma} J,$$

we can write

$$\sigma_{\text{charge}} = \varepsilon_0 \frac{\varepsilon_2}{\sigma_2} J_{n2} - \varepsilon_0 \frac{\varepsilon_1}{\sigma_1} J_{n1}.$$

But, by Eq. (9-3.5),

$$J_{n1} = J_{n2},$$

and hence we obtain

$$\sigma_{\text{charge}} = \varepsilon_0 J_n \left(\frac{\varepsilon_2}{\sigma_2} - \frac{\varepsilon_1}{\sigma_1} \right). \tag{9-5.4}$$

Since all complete conducting systems contain interfaces traversed by currents (conductor-electrode interfaces, for example) and many systems contain inhomogeneous conductors, electric currents in conductors are always associated with stationary charge accumulations.[2] Therefore, according to Eqs. (9-5.1) and (9-5.2), the stationary electric field (or potential) in a current-carrying conductor can be determined

---

[1] We shall use subscripts "charge" to differentiate the charge densities ρ and σ from the resistivity ρ and conductivity σ whenever a confusion of symbols could result if the subscripts were not used.

[2] Charges accumulate also on conductor-dielectric interfaces (see Section 9-6).

by the ordinary electrostatic methods from these charge accumulations once the location and density of all these accumulations are known. That is to say, as far as the calculation of the stationary electric field inside (or outside, see Section 9-6) a current-carrying conductor is concerned, the current as such may be completely ignored, and only the charge distribution on the surface and in the interior of the conductor needs to be taken into account. Thus the stationary fields of current-carrying conductors, just like the electrostatic fields, have electric charges as their sources.[1]

The phenomenon of the formation of space and surface charge accumulations associated with leakage currents in dielectrics is called *dielectric absorption*. The dielectric absorption is, among other things, responsible for the residual charge appearing on the plates of a capacitor shortly after the capacitor has been disconnected from the voltage source and has been discharged by a spark. It may also be responsible for certain properties of wax electrets (see Example 9-5.2).

▼

Example 9-5.1   Find the surface charge accumulating on the surfaces of electrodes and on the dielectric interface of the coaxial cable of Example 9-3.4 when a voltage V is applied between the core and the sheath.

The current density at the interface is

$$J = \frac{I}{2\pi cl} = \frac{V}{2\pi clR},$$

where R is the leakage resistance of the cable. Using the value for R found in Example 9-3.4, we have

$$J = \frac{V}{c(\rho_1 \ln c/a + \rho_2 \ln b/c)}.$$

The surface charge density on the interface is then, by Eqs. (9-5.4) and (9-2.4),

$$\sigma_{\text{charge}} = \frac{\varepsilon_0 V}{c(\rho_1 \ln c/a + \rho_2 \ln b/c)} (\rho_2\varepsilon_2 - \rho_1\varepsilon_1),$$

where ε_1 and ε_2 are the dielectric constants of the inner and outer insulator, respectively. The surface charge density on the electrodes is, similarly, (taking into account that the resistivity of electrodes is zero by definition)

$$\sigma_{\text{charge}} = + \frac{\varepsilon_0 V}{a(\rho_1 \ln c/a + \rho_2 \ln b/c)} \rho_1\varepsilon_1$$

---

[1] It must be emphasized that the charge accumulations described above are associated with stationary currents and are different from the charge distributions that appear in conductors carrying time-dependent currents.

and

$$\sigma_{\text{charge}} = -\frac{\varepsilon_0 V}{b(\rho_1 \ln c/a + \rho_2 \ln b/c)} \rho_2 \varepsilon_2$$

for the inner and outer electrode, respectively.

Example 9-5.2   A heated wax slab of thickness d and area S is placed between two parallel plate electrodes, and a voltage V is applied to them. Because of the irregular cooling of the slab, its permittivity becomes smaller near the surfaces than well inside, and will be assumed to be given by $\varepsilon = k_1\left(1 + k_2 \sin \dfrac{\pi x}{d}\right)$, where k_1 and k_2 are constants, and x is the distance from the positive electrode toward the negative one. The conductivity σ of the slab will be assumed constant. Find the space charge accumulating in the slab as a result of the current in it (such charge accumulations may be formed during the making of wax electrets).

By Eq. (9-5.3) the space charge is

$$\rho = \varepsilon_0 \mathbf{J} \cdot \nabla\left(\frac{\varepsilon}{\sigma}\right) = \varepsilon_0 \frac{\mathbf{J}}{\sigma} \cdot \nabla\left[k_1\left(1 + k_2 \sin \frac{\pi x}{d}\right)\right]$$

$$= \varepsilon_0 \mathbf{E} \cdot \left(k_1 k_2 \frac{\pi}{d} \cos \frac{\pi x}{d} \mathbf{i}\right)$$

$$= \varepsilon_0 k_1 k_2 \frac{\pi}{d} \mathbf{E} \cdot \cos \frac{\pi x}{d} \mathbf{i}.$$

Since $\mathbf{J}$ and σ are constant everywhere in the slab, $\mathbf{E} = \mathbf{J}/\sigma$ is also constant, and hence $E = V/d$. The space charge is therefore

$$\rho_{\text{charge}} = \pi \varepsilon_0 k_1 k_2 \frac{V}{d^2} \cos \frac{\pi x}{d}.$$

Example 9-5.3   Show that the potential

$$\varphi = \frac{I}{4\pi \sigma r}$$

due to a single spherical electrode delivering a current I to an infinite conductor of conductivity σ is the same as that given by the electrostatic formula

$$\varphi = \frac{q}{4\pi \varepsilon_0 \varepsilon r},$$

where q is the charge on the electrode-conductor interface and ε is the permittivity of the conductor.

Let the quantities pertaining to the conductor be designated by subscript 2 and those pertaining to the electrode by subscript 1. According to Eq. (9-5.4), the surface charge density on the electrode-conductor interface is then

$$\sigma_{\text{charge}} = \varepsilon_0 J_n \left(\frac{\varepsilon_2}{\sigma_2} - \frac{\varepsilon_1}{\sigma_1} \right).$$

The conductivity of the electrode, σ_1, is infinite by definition. The current density at the interface is, by symmetry,

$$J_n = \frac{I}{4\pi a^2},$$

where a is the radius of the electrode. We have therefore

$$\sigma_{\text{charge}} = \varepsilon_0 \frac{I}{4\pi a^2} \frac{\varepsilon_2}{\sigma_2}.$$

Multiplying this expression by the surface area of the electrode, we obtain for the total charge residing on the electrode $q = \varepsilon_0 \varepsilon_2 I / \sigma_2$. The potential due to this charge is, by symmetry,

$$\varphi = \frac{q}{4\pi\varepsilon_0\varepsilon_2 r}.$$

Substituting q in this expression and dropping the subscripts, we therefore obtain for the potential due to the electrode under consideration

$$\varphi = \frac{1}{4\pi\varepsilon_0\varepsilon r} \cdot \frac{\varepsilon_0\varepsilon I}{\sigma} = \frac{I}{4\pi\sigma r},$$

which was to be proved.

▲

9-6. Electric Field Outside a Current-Carrying Conductor

In contrast to the electrostatic field outside a conductor in the state of electrostatic equilibrium, the electric field outside a conductor carrying a current has a nonvanishing tangential component at the surface of the conductor. Indeed, as it has been shown in Sections 8-5 and 9-3, the tangential component of **E** must be continuous across a dielectric-dielectric and a conductor-conductor interface. Since there is no demarcation line between substances which we call conductors and substances which we call dielectrics, however, the tangential component of **E** must also be continuous across a conductor-dielectric interface and, thus, across any interface whatsoever. Therefore at the surface of any body, **E** satisfies the relation

$$E_{t\,\text{outside}} = E_{t\,\text{inside}}. \tag{9-6.1}$$

Hence, since at the surface of a current-carrying conductor there is a nonvanishing tangential component of **E** inside the conductor, there also must be an equal nonvanishing component of **E** outside the conductor.

On the other hand, the normal component of the electric field outside a current-carrying conductor is exactly the same as it would be if the conductor were in electrostatic equilibrium:

$$E_{n \text{ outside}} = \frac{\sigma}{\varepsilon_0 \varepsilon}, \tag{9-6.2}$$

where σ is the surface charge density on the conductor and ε is the dielectric constant of the medium outside the conductor. Indeed, the boundary conditions for D_n obtained in Section 8-5 require that at the surface of any body

$$D_{n \text{ outside}} - D_{n \text{ inside}} = \sigma,$$

and, since E_n, and hence also D_n, is zero inside a conductor at a conductor-dielectric interface, Eq. (9-6.2) results.

One should note that Eq. (9-6.1) implies the continuity of the potential φ across the surface of a current-carrying conductor (see Sections 8-5 and 9-3)

$$\varphi_{\text{outside}} = \varphi_{\text{inside}}. \tag{9-6.3}$$

These properties of the electric field outside a current-carrying conductor have a remarkable consequence: a time-independent electric field can exist in a charge-free space completely enclosed by conducting walls, provided that there is an electric current in these walls. What is more, one can confine and shape time-independent electric fields in chambers with current-carrying walls. The structure of such fields is determined by the geometry of the chamber and is not affected by stationary charges or steady currents outside the chamber. Figure 9.11 presents a simple example of such confinement and shaping of electric fields.

It is interesting to note that the structure of the field inside a chamber with current-carrying walls does not depend on the conductivity of the walls. Therefore the poorer the conductor used for the chamber walls, the better, because with poorer conductors less energy is needed to maintain the field (see Section 9-7). The poorer the conductor, however, the longer the time required for the field to establish itself in equilibrium (see Chapter 15). Thus, if rapidly varying fields are present either outside or inside the chamber, walls made of good conductors are needed.

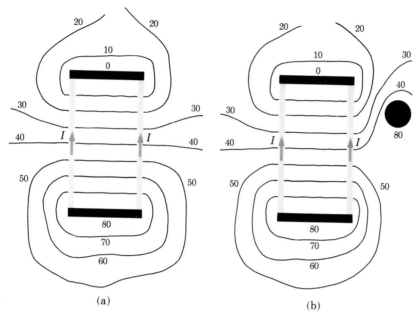

FIG. 9.11   (a) Map of the electric field inside and outside a chamber with semiconducting current-carrying walls.   The map shows equipotential lines (marked in volts) determined with a radioactive probe.   The current in the walls is 0.5×10^{-6} amp.   (b) Map of the electric field of the same system but with a conducting disk at 80 volts potential placed outside the chamber.   Although the field outside the chamber has changed, the field inside remains the same as before.

There are numerous examples when a field produced by current-carrying conductors is more convenient to use than the ordinary electrostatic field.   For instance, a uniform electrostatic field 10 m long is impractical with a parallel-plate capacitor; the plates would have to be as wide as the front of a house.   However, one can easily produce a uniform field 10 m long in a tube, say 1 cm in diameter, simply by coating the inside of this tube with a uniform semi-conducting film and by establishing a current in this film.

The surest way to determine the electric field in the space external to a current-carrying conductor is to find the potential φ in this space and then take the gradient of this potential.   It must be kept in mind, however, that the surface of a current-carrying conductor is, in general, not an equipotential one, and therefore the potential distribution on this surface must be determined before the potential in the surrounding space can be found.

▼

Example 9-6.1   A straight conducting tube of uniform conductivity and length l is sealed off at its ends by two plane electrodes normal to the axis of the tube. What is the electric field inside the tube when a voltage V is applied between these electrodes?

By symmetry of the system, we immediately recognize that the field inside the tube is homogeneous, so that

$$E = \frac{V}{l}.$$

Example 9-6.2   Two very large, thin, rectangular, uniform, conducting plates of length l meet along one of their edges. Their opposite edges are separated by a distance d from each other. A battery of terminal voltage V is connected to these edges, thus producing a current in the plates (Fig. 9.12a). Neglecting edge effects, find the electric field in the space between the plates.

The electric field within the plates is

$$E_{\text{plates}} = \frac{V}{2l}$$

and tangent to the surface of the plates. By inspection, we recognize that the field between the plates is then simply

$$E = \frac{V}{d}$$

directed at a right angle to the symmetry plane of the system. Indeed, at the surface of the plates the tangential component of this field is

$$E_t = \frac{V}{d} \sin \alpha = \frac{V}{d} \cdot \frac{d}{2l} = \frac{V}{2l},$$

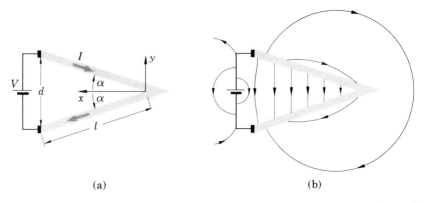

(a)   (b)

FIG. 9.12   (a) Two intersecting plates carrying a current. (b) Schematic map of the electric field between and outside the plates.

so that the boundary condition for E_t is satisfied. Since this is the only condition imposed by the statement of the problem upon the field between the plates, however, the field that we have found is the correct one. The charge density on the inner surfaces of the plates is then

$$\sigma = \pm \varepsilon_0 E_n = \pm \varepsilon_0 E \cos \alpha,$$

or

$$\sigma = \pm \varepsilon_0 \frac{V}{d} \sqrt{1 - \frac{d^2}{4l^2}},$$

where the plus sign indicates the plate connected to the positive terminal of the battery and the minus sign indicates the plate connected to the negative terminal. A schematic map of this field is shown in Fig. 9.12b and is to be compared with the lines-of-force picture for this system shown in Plate 7.

Example 9-6.3   Two moderately-conducting plates form a thin parallel-plate capacitor of length l and plate separation d. The capacitor is shorted and grounded along one of its edges and a voltage V is applied to it at the opposite edge, thus producing a stationary current in the plates (Fig. 9.13a). Neglecting edge effects, find the electric field in the space between the plates and the surface charge density on the plates and on the shorting bar.

We shall find the electric field in the space between the plates by finding first the corresponding potential function φ. The electric field inside the plates is, by inspection, $\mathbf{E} = -(V/2l)\mathbf{i}$ and $\mathbf{E} = (V/2l)\mathbf{i}$ for the upper and the lower plates, respectively. The potential (with respect to the ground) at any point of the upper plate $(y = d/2)$ is therefore

$$\varphi(x)_{\text{upper plate}} = \int_x^0 \mathbf{E} \cdot d\mathbf{l} + \varphi_0 = \frac{Vx}{2l} + 0 = \frac{Vx}{2l}.$$

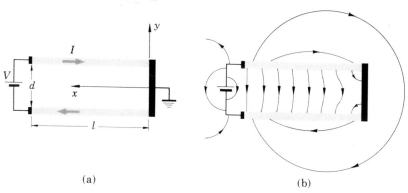

(a)   (b)

FIG. 9.13   (a) A shorted parallel-plate capacitor carrying a current. (b) Schematic map of the electric field between and outside the plates.

Similarly, the potential at any point of the lower plate ($y = -d/2$) is

$$\varphi(x)_{\text{lower plate}} = \int_x^0 \mathbf{E} \cdot d\mathbf{l} + \varphi_0 = -\frac{Vx}{2l} + 0 = -\frac{Vx}{2l}.$$

These expressions constitute the boundary conditions which must be satisfied by the potential function φ in the space between the plates. The potential function compatible with the geometry of the problem and capable of satisfying these boundary conditions is

$$\varphi = Axy$$

[this is function (H-1) of Table 6-I with all constants other than C_2 set equal to zero and $C_2 = A$]. Since at $y = \pm d/2$ the potential must reduce to $\varphi = \pm Vx/2l$, we have

$$Ax\frac{d}{2} = \frac{Vx}{2l}$$

or

$$A = \frac{V}{ld}.$$

The potential in the space between the plates is then

$$\varphi = \frac{V}{ld}xy.$$

Taking the gradient of this expression, we now obtain for the electric field between the plates

$$E_x = -\frac{\partial\varphi}{\partial x} = -\frac{Vy}{ld}$$

and

$$E_y = -\frac{\partial\varphi}{\partial y} = -\frac{Vx}{ld}.$$

The surface charge on the plates is, by Eq. (9-6.2),

$$\sigma = \varepsilon_0 E_{n \text{ outside}} = \mp\varepsilon_0 E_y$$

or

$$\sigma = \pm\varepsilon_0 \frac{Vx}{ld},$$

where $+$ and $-$ correspond to the upper and the lower plate, respectively. The surface charge on the shorting bar is similarly

$$\sigma = -\varepsilon_0 \frac{Vy}{ld}.$$

A schematic map of this field is shown in Fig. 9.13b. This map is to be compared with the lines-of-force picture for this system shown in Plate 6.

Example 9-6.4   A small spherical cavity has formed inside a large conducting slab that was carrying a uniform current of density $\mathbf{J}_0 = J_0\mathbf{k}$ prior to the formation of the cavity. Prove that the potentials after the formation of the cavity are

$$\varphi_{\text{slab}} = -\rho J_0\left(1 + \frac{a^3}{2r^3}\right) r \cos \theta$$

and

$$\varphi_{\text{cavity}} = -\tfrac{3}{2}\rho J_0 r \cos \theta,$$

where ρ is the resistivity of the slab, a is the radius of the cavity, r is the distance from the center of the cavity, and θ is the polar angle with respect to the z-axis. Also find the charge on the surface of the cavity.

By the uniqueness theorems for potential functions, the above expressions are correct if they constitute solutions of Laplace's equation $\nabla^2\varphi = 0$ and satisfy the boundary conditions characterizing the system under consideration. As can be easily verified by direct differentiation or by consulting Table 6-I, these expressions do constitute solutions of Laplace's equation. The boundary conditions characterizing the system under consideration are as follows:

(1) Since the cavity is small, the potential at large distances from the cavity must be the same as it was before the formation of the cavity,

$$\varphi_{r \gg a} = \int_r^0 \mathbf{E}_{\text{initial}} \cdot d\mathbf{r} = \int_r^0 \rho\mathbf{J}_0 \cdot d\mathbf{r} = -\rho J_0 r \cos \theta.$$

(2) Since the potential must be continuous across the surface of the conductor,

$$\varphi_{\text{cavity}} = \varphi_{\text{slab}} \quad \text{at} \quad r = a.$$

(3) Since there may be no normal component of the electric field in the slab at the surface of the cavity,

$$\frac{\partial\varphi_{\text{slab}}}{\partial r} = 0 \quad \text{at} \quad r = a.$$

The potentials φ_{slab} and φ_{cavity} given in the problem clearly satisfy all these conditions and hence are the only possible and thus the correct potentials. The charge on the wall of the cavity is, according to Eq. (9-6.2),

$$\sigma = \varepsilon_0 E_{n\,\text{cavity}} = -\varepsilon_0 E_{r\,\text{cavity}} = \varepsilon_0 \frac{\partial\varphi_{\text{cavity}}}{\partial r},$$

or

$$\sigma = -\tfrac{3}{2}\varepsilon_0\rho J_0 \cos \theta.$$

▲

9-7. Dissipation of Energy in Current-Carrying Conductors

An electric current generates heat in the conductor which carries this current. Thus energy is continuously dissipated in a current-carrying conductor, and a continuous supply of energy compensating for this dissipation is necessary in order to maintain the current and hence the electric field in the conductor. This energy dissipation is the most important characteristic differentiating the electric field in a current-carrying conductor from the electric field in a dielectric, where no energy is consumed once the field has been established and therefore no energy is needed to maintain the field.

The generation of heat caused by an electric current in a conductor can be attributed mainly to the effect known as *Joule's heating*.

The basic law representing the dissipation of energy in the process of Joule's heating is, according to calorimetric measurements,

$$P = \overset{\circ}{\int_{\text{All conductor}}} \mathbf{J} \cdot \mathbf{E} \, dv, \qquad (9\text{-}7.1)$$

where P is the rate of energy dissipation, $P = dU/dt$, or, which is the same, the power consumed in the process of Joule's heating. The rate of the energy dissipation per unit volume of a conductor, $P_v = dP/dv$, is accordingly

$$P_v = {}^{\circ}\mathbf{J} \cdot \mathbf{E}. \qquad (9\text{-}7.2)$$

These two equations are frequently referred to as *Joule's law* in its integral and differential form, respectively. Joule's law constitutes the stationary field counterpart of the basic electrostatic energy law (7-1.1) and (7-1.2) [observe, however, that unlike Eqs. (7-1.1) and (7-1.2), Eqs. (9-7.1) and (9-7.2) do not contain the factor $\frac{1}{2}$].

Joule's law (9-7.1) can be transformed into various special forms which in many instances are more convenient to use than the original expression itself.

One of the most important special forms of Joule's law is the equation representing the rate of energy dissipation due to Joule's heating in terms of the currents entering a conductor through individual electrodes. It may be obtained as follows. Substituting $\mathbf{E} = -\boldsymbol{\nabla}\varphi$ into

Eq. (9-7.1), and using vector identity (V-4), we have

$$P = \overset{\circ}{\int} \mathbf{J} \cdot \mathbf{E} \, dv = - \overset{\circ}{\int} \mathbf{J} \cdot \nabla \varphi \, dv$$

$$= - \overset{\circ}{\int} \nabla \cdot (\varphi \mathbf{J}) \, dv + \overset{\circ}{\int} \varphi \nabla \cdot \mathbf{J} \, dv.$$

Since for a stationary current $\nabla \cdot \mathbf{J} = 0$, the last integral vanishes. Changing the remaining integral into a surface integral by means of Gauss's theorem, we then have

$$P = - \overset{\circ}{\oint} \varphi \mathbf{J} \cdot d\mathbf{S},$$

where the integration is extended over the surface of the conductor under consideration. This integral can be expressed as the sum of $n + 1$ integrals

$$P = - \overset{\circ}{\sum_{n=1}^{n+1}} \int \varphi_n \mathbf{J}_n \cdot d\mathbf{S}_n,$$

where the first n integrals are taken over the electrode-conductor interfaces, while the last, $n + 1$-st, integral is taken over the remaining portion of the conductor's surface (free surface). Since the current density has no normal component at the free surface of the conductor, $\mathbf{J}_{n+1} \cdot d\mathbf{S}_{n+1}$ is zero, and this last integral vanishes. Furthermore, since an electrode-conductor interface constitutes an equipotential surface, φ_n is constant in each of the remaining n integrals and may be factored out from under the integral signs, so that

$$P = - \overset{\circ}{\sum_{n=1}^{n}} \varphi_n \int \mathbf{J}_n \cdot d\mathbf{S}_n.$$

But each integral $\int \mathbf{J}_n \cdot d\mathbf{S}_n$ represents the current *leaving* the conductor through the n-th electrode. Therefore, substituting

$$\int \mathbf{J}_n \cdot d\mathbf{S}_n = -I_n,$$

we finally obtain

$$P = \overset{\circ}{\sum_{n=1}^{n}} \varphi_n I_n, \tag{9-7.3}$$

where φ_n is the potential of the n-th electrode, and I_n is the current *entering* the conductor through this electrode.

The most common conducting system consists of a conductor with only two electrodes. For this system Eq. (9-7.3) reduces to a much simpler form. Indeed, by the flux law (9-2.3), in a two-electrode system one electrode delivers the current to the conductor, while the other carries this current away from it, so that we can write $I_1 = I$ and $I_2 = -I$, where I is the current in the conductor. We then have from Eq. (9-7.3)

$$P = {}^\circ(\varphi_1 I_1 + \varphi_2 I_2) = {}^\circ(\varphi_1 I - \varphi_2 I) = {}^\circ I(\varphi_1 - \varphi_2).$$

But $\varphi_1 - \varphi_2$ represents the voltage V between the two electrodes, and hence we obtain

$$P = {}^\circ IV. \tag{9-7.4}$$

This formula can be expressed in two alternative forms by using the resistance of the conductor, R. Since $R = V/I$, we have by substitution

$$P = {}^\circ I^2 R, \tag{9-7.5}$$

and

$$P = {}^\circ \frac{V^2}{R}. \tag{9-7.6}$$

▼

Example 9-7.1   At what points is the conductor of the two-dimensional conducting system shown in Fig. 9.14 most likely to start melting in consequence of Joule's heating?

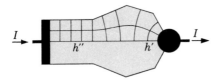

Fɪɢ. 9.14   A two-dimensional conductor between a plane electrode and a cylindrical electrode.

The melting is most likely to begin at the points of the largest P_v, which, according to Joule's law (9-7.2), occurs at the points of the largest **E**. By using the method of curvilinear squares, we find that in this system there are two regions where **E** is especially large: one is at the cylindrical electrode (h'), the other is in the straight part of the conductor (h''). The melting is therefore most likely to start somewhere within these regions.

Example 9-7.2   Show that when a capacitor is charged by a battery, the amount of Joule's heat developed in the circuit is equal to the final electrostatic energy of the capacitor, so that not more than one half of the energy released by the battery is stored in the capacitor (assume that the charging occurs so slowly that the current can be treated as being essentially stationary).

Let the potentials of the capacitor plates and the potentials of the battery terminals be φ_c', φ_c'', φ_b' and φ_b'', as shown in Fig. 9.15. Using

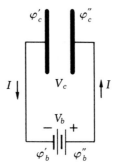

FIG. 9.15   Dissipation of energy during the charging of a capacitor.

Eq. (9-7.4), we then have for the rate of Joule's heating in the two lead wires

$$P = {}^{\circ}I(\varphi'_c - \varphi'_b) + {}^{\circ}I(\varphi''_b - \varphi''_c)$$
$$= {}^{\circ}I(\varphi''_b - \varphi'_b) - {}^{\circ}I(\varphi''_c - \varphi'_c).$$

But $\varphi''_b - \varphi'_b$ represents the terminal voltage V_b of the battery (constant), while $\varphi''_c - \varphi'_c$ represents the voltage V_c across the capacitor (increasing). The rate of the energy dissipation due to heating is therefore

$$\frac{dU}{dt} = P = {}^{\circ}IV_b - {}^{\circ}IV_c.$$

The energy dissipated in the lead wires during charging (duration T) is

$$U = {}^{\circ}\int_0^T I(V_b - V_c)\,dt$$
$$= {}^{\circ}\int_0^T IV_b\,dt - {}^{\circ}\int_0^T IV_c\,dt$$
$$= {}^{\circ}V_b\int_0^T I\,dt - {}^{\circ}\int_0^T IV_c\,dt.$$

Since $I\,dt = dq$ (dq is the charge delivered to the capacitor during the time interval dt), we have, using the final charge on the capacitor Q and the capacitance of the capacitor $C = q/V_c$,

$$U = {}^{\circ}V_bQ - {}^{\circ}\int_0^Q V_c\,dq = {}^{\circ}V_bQ - {}^{\circ}\int_0^Q \frac{q}{C}\,dq$$
$$= {}^{\circ}V_bQ - {}^{\circ}\frac{Q^2}{2C}.$$

After the charging is completed, $V_b = V_c = CQ$, so that

$$U = {}^{\circ}\frac{1}{2}\frac{Q^2}{C},$$

which according to Eq. (7-6.4) is equal to the energy stored in the capacitor in the process of charging.

▲

9-8. Stored Energy and Forces Associated with the Electric Field of Current-Carrying Conductors

Like all electric fields, the electric field of a current-carrying conductor possesses energy given by the basic law (assuming linear isotropic media)

$$U = \frac{\overset{\circ}{1}}{2} \int_{\text{All space}} \mathbf{E} \cdot \mathbf{D} \, dv. \tag{9-8.1}$$

This energy is associated with both the internal and the external fields of the conductor.

Like all electric fields, the field of a current-carrying conductor exerts forces upon charges located in this field. These forces can be found from the usual force equations[1]

$$\mathbf{F} = \overset{\circ}{\int} \rho \mathbf{E}' dv \quad \text{or} \quad \mathbf{F} = \overset{\circ}{\int} \rho \mathbf{E} \, dv. \tag{9-8.2a, b}$$

Since a current-carrying conductor always has a surface charge and may also have interface and space charges (see Section 9-5), a current-carrying conductor always experiences *electric* forces due to its own field or due to external fields.

Like all conductors, the current-carrying conductors also exert the image forces on the charged bodies placed near these conductors. These forces are identical with the image forces appearing in electrostatics and are found from the image systems given in Table 6-II (the presence of a current in the conductor has no effect upon the image field, as can be easily deduced from the uniqueness theorems for $\mathbf{E}$ or φ). The total force on a charged body placed in the vicinity of a current-carrying conductor is, of course, the sum of the force due to the image field and the force due to the conductor's field proper.

▼

Example 9.8.1   A current I is maintained between two small spherical electrodes placed at a large distance r from each other in an infinite liquid of conductivity σ and permittivity ε. Neglecting the effect of the lead wires, find the force between the electrodes.

---

[1] These equations are valid for all electric fields regardless of their origin because they are valid for electrostatic fields and because all electric fields are force fields by definition.

By Example 9-5.3, the electric field produced by one electrode at the location of the other is $E = I/4\pi\sigma r^2$, and the charge of the electrodes is $q = \varepsilon_0 \varepsilon I/\sigma$. Taking into account that the electrodes are small compared to r so that each electrode may be regarded as a point charge from the location of the other, we then have by Eq. (9-8.2a)

$$F = \frac{{}^\circ\varepsilon_0\varepsilon I^2}{4\pi\sigma^2 r^2} = \frac{{}^\circ q^2}{4\pi\varepsilon_0\varepsilon r^2}.$$

Example 9-8.2   Neglecting the outside field and the edge effects, find the electric force with which the plates of the shorted capacitor of Example 9-6.3 attract each other (the width of the plates is b).

For the normal component of the force acting upon the upper plate we have

$$F_n = {}^\circ\!\!\int \sigma E_n' \, dS,$$

where σ is the surface charge density on the plate and E_n' is the normal component of the external electric field at the location of σ. This component is equal to the normal component of the total field E_n just outside the plate minus the contribution of the surface charge σ to this component. By Examples 4-5.3 and 9-6.3, this contribution is $\sigma/2\varepsilon_0 = \frac{1}{2}E_n$, and hence $E_n' = \frac{1}{2}E_n$. Using the expressions obtained for σ and E_y in Example 9-6.3 and observing that $E_n = E_y$, we then have (disregarding the minus sign)

$$F_n = {}^\circ\!\!\int_0^l \varepsilon_0 \frac{Vx}{ld} \cdot \frac{1}{2}\frac{Vx}{ld} \cdot b \, dx = \frac{{}^\circ\varepsilon_0}{2}\frac{V^2 b}{l^2 d^2}\int_0^l x^2 \, dx$$

or

$$F_n = \frac{{}^\circ\varepsilon_0}{6}\frac{V^2}{d^2} bl.$$

Example 9-8.3   A point charge q is placed midway between the current-carrying plates shown in Fig. 9.16. The plates are very wide, and the angle between them is $\pi/2$. Find the force acting on the charge.

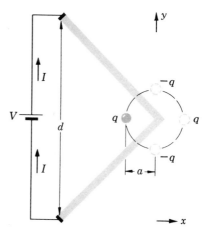

FIG. 9.16   Calculation of the force on a point charge placed near two intersecting current-carrying plates.

The force acting on the charge is the sum of the force due to the field of the plates and the force due to the image field. The field of the plates is, by Example 9-6.2, $\mathbf{E} = -\mathbf{j}V/d$. The image field is formed by three image charges as shown in Fig. 9.16. This field is

$$
\mathbf{E}_i = \mathbf{i}\left(-\frac{q}{4\pi\varepsilon_0 2a^2}\cdot\frac{\sqrt{2}}{2} - \frac{q}{4\pi\varepsilon_0 2a^2}\cdot\frac{\sqrt{2}}{2} + \frac{q}{4\pi\varepsilon_0 4a^2}\right)
$$

$$
= \mathbf{i}\frac{q}{16\pi\varepsilon_0}(1 - 2\sqrt{2}).
$$

The force is therefore

$$
\mathbf{F} = \mathbf{i}\frac{\overset{\circ}{q}^2}{16\pi\varepsilon_0}(1 - 2\sqrt{2}) - \mathbf{j}\frac{\overset{\circ}{q}V}{d}.
$$

▲

PROBLEMS

9.1. Using Section 6-2 as a guide, state and prove three uniqueness theorems for the potential and four uniqueness theorems for the stationary electric field in current-carrying conductors.

9.2. A metal bar of conductivity σ is bent to form a flat 90° sector (quarter-ring) of inner radius a, outer radius b, and thickness t (Fig. 9.17).

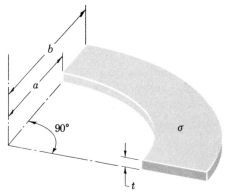

FIG. 9.17   Find the resistance of this 90° sector.

Show that the resistance of this sector between the two horizontal surfaces is

$$
R = \frac{4t}{\sigma\pi(b^2 - a^2)}.
$$

9.3. Show that the resistance of the conducting sector, described in Problem 9.2, between the two end surfaces (vertical areas) of the sector is

$$
R = \frac{\pi}{2\sigma t \ln(b/a)}.
$$

9.4. Show that the resistance of the conducting sector, described in Problem 9.2, between the two curved surfaces is

$$R = \frac{2}{\sigma \pi t} \ln \frac{b}{a}.$$

9.5. A conducting circular cylinder of resistivity ρ, inner radius a, outer radius b, and length L is cut in half along its length. The cylinder is then reassembled with two thin sheet electrodes inserted between the halves, each side of both electrodes being in contact with the entire area of the wall exposed in cutting the cylinder. Show that the resistance of the cylinder between these electrodes is

$$R = \frac{\pi \rho}{2L \ln (b/a)}.$$

9.6. Two small circular electrodes of radius b are attached at two antipodal points to a thin spherical shell of thickness t, radius a, and conductivity σ. Show that the resistance of the shell between these electrodes is

$$R \approx \frac{1}{\pi \sigma t} \ln \frac{2a}{b}.$$

9.7. A conductor of conductivity σ is made in the shape of a truncated cone of half angle α with the two bases formed by concentric spherical surfaces of radii a and $b > a$, respectively; the spherical surfaces have their center at the apex of the conical surface of the cone. Show that the resistance of this conductor between the two bases is

$$R = \frac{1}{2\pi\sigma(1 - \cos \alpha)} \left(\frac{1}{a} - \frac{1}{b} \right).$$

9.8. A spherical electrode of radius a has two thin-walled, cone-shaped conductors attached to it opposite each other, each conductor having a ring electrode attached to its free end. The wall thickness of the conducting cones is t, the conductivity is σ, the distance from the edge of each cone to the center of the spherical electrode is d, and the half-angle of each cone is α. Show that the resistance between the spherical electrode and the two ring electrodes is

$$R = \frac{1}{4\pi\sigma t \sin \alpha} \ln \frac{d}{a}.$$

9.9. A spherical grounding terminal of an antenna tower is sunk halfway into the ground and carries a current I to the ground. Show that this current produces a voltage between the feet of a man directly approaching the tower ("step voltage"), the magnitude of the voltage being

$$V = \frac{I}{2\pi\sigma r} \cdot \frac{l}{r + l},$$

where l is the length of the man's step, r is his distance from the tower, and σ is the conductivity of the ground.

9.10. Two spherical grounding electrodes, each of radius a, are sunk halfway into the surface of the ground at a distance $d \gg a$ from each other. A second pair of electrodes, identical with the first, is sunk into the surface of the ground at a distance $h \gg a$ from the first, so that the four electrodes form a rectangle of length d and width h. Show that when a voltage V is applied to the first pair of electrodes, an "interference voltage"

$$V_i = Va\left(\frac{1}{h} - \frac{1}{\sqrt{h^2 + d^2}}\right)$$

will appear between the second pair.

9.11. A coaxial cable contains an insulating material of conductivity σ_1 in its lower half and of conductivity σ_2 in its upper half. The radius of the central wire is a, that of the sheath is b, the length of the cable is l. Show that the leakage resistance of the cable is

$$R = \frac{1}{\pi l(\sigma_1 + \sigma_2)} \ln \frac{b}{a}.$$

9.12. Show that, disregarding the temperature- and pressure-induced variations, the resistance of any conducting system consisting of ohmic conductors does not depend on the voltage applied to the system.

9.13. The capacitance of a capacitor is C, the dielectric constant and the leakage conductivity of its dielectric are ε and σ, respectively. Show that if a voltage V is applied to the capacitor, the leakage current in it is

$$I \approx \frac{\sigma C}{\varepsilon_0 \varepsilon} V.$$

9.14. A small circular hole of radius a is made near the center of a large conducting sheet of resistivity ρ initially carrying a current of uniform density $\mathbf{J}_0$. (a) Show that after the hole is made, the potential distribution in the sheet and in the hole is, respectively,

$$\varphi_{\text{sheet}} = -\rho J_0 r \left(1 + \frac{a^2}{r^2}\right) \cos \theta,$$

$$\varphi_{\text{hole}} = -2\rho J_0 r \cos \theta,$$

where r and θ are polar coordinates about the center of the hole, and θ is measured with respect to the original direction of the current. (b) Show that the electric field in the hole is

$$\mathbf{E}_{\text{hole}} = 2\mathbf{E}_0,$$

where $\mathbf{E}_0$ is the original electric field in the sheet.

9.15. A stationary current of uniform density $\mathbf{J}_0$ is carried by a large conducting sheet of conductivity σ. Show that if a small circular portion of radius a in the central part of this sheet is replaced by one having the conductivity σ', the current in this portion will be

$$J = J_0 \frac{2\sigma'}{\sigma + \sigma'}.$$

9.16. A sphere of conductivity σ' is embedded in a large conducting block of conductivity σ and a current is established in the block. The sphere itself is not accessible for current measurements, but the current has been measured near the surface of the block and has been found to be everywhere of the same density J_0. Show that the current density in the sphere must then be

$$J_{sphere} = J_0 \frac{3\sigma'}{2\sigma + \sigma'}.$$

9.17. A spherical electrode of radius a is placed in a medium of conductivity σ at a distance $d > a$ from a large perfectly conducting plate. Show that the resistance between the sphere and the plate is in the first approximation

$$R = \frac{1}{4\pi\sigma a}\left(1 - \frac{a}{2d}\right).$$

9.18. Two small circular electrodes are placed on a large, thin, conducting sheet so that the line joining their centers is perpendicular to the edge of the sheet. Show that the resistance between the electrodes is in the first approximation

$$R = \frac{1}{2\pi\sigma t}\ln\frac{(d_2^2 - d_1^2)^2}{4d_1 d_2 a_1 a_2},$$

where a_1, a_2 are the radii of the electrodes, d_1, d_2 are the distances of their centers from the edge of the sheet, σ is the conductivity of the sheet, and t is its thickness.

9.19. Show that the resistance of a long conducting strip of conductivity σ, thickness t, and width b between two small circular electrodes of radius a with their centers distance d apart on the middle line of the strip is in the first approximation

$$R = \frac{1}{\pi\sigma t}\ln\left(\frac{b}{\pi a}\sinh\frac{\pi d}{b}\right).$$

9.20. A current is carried by a medium of conductivity σ from a large hollow spherical electrode of radius a to a point electrode located inside the first one at a distance d from its center. Find the distribution of current density at the inner surface of the outer electrode.

9.21. The radii of the core and the sheath of a coaxial cable are a and $3a$, respectively. The conductivity of the medium between the core and the sheath is σ. Using the method of curvilinear squares, find leakage resistance per unit length of the cable and compare the result numerically with that obtained from analytical calculation.

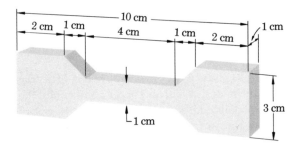

FIG. 9.18   Find the resistance of this bar.

9.22. Using the method of curvilinear squares, find the resistance between the end surfaces of the conducting bar shown in Fig. 9.18.

9.23. Find the resistance of the medium of conductivity σ and thickness t between the hollow cylindrical electrode and the long rectangular electrode shown in Fig. 9.19.

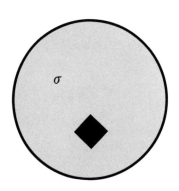

FIG. 9.19   Find the resistance of the medium between the inner bar and the outer cylinder.

9.24. Two circular electrodes of radius $a = 2$ cm are laid on the edge of a thin circular disk of conductivity σ, thickness t, and radius $r = 10$ cm, so that the centers of the two electrodes are on the periphery of the disk and 10 cm apart. Using the method of curvilinear squares, or otherwise, find the resistance of the disk between the two electrodes.

9.25. Using dimensional analysis, show that the ratio of resistances of any two ohmic conductors of identical shapes but of different linear dimensions is

$$\frac{R_1}{R_2} = \frac{\sigma_2 l_2}{\sigma_1 l_1},$$

where l_1 and l_2 are the distances between any two corresponding points on the two conductors ("characteristic lengths"), and σ_1 and σ_2 are the conductivities.

9.26. Show that the distribution of the surface charge in the hole of the conductor described in Problem 9.14 is $\sigma = -2\varepsilon_0 E_0 \cos \theta$.

9.27. What is the total charge accumulating in the upper half of the wax electret described in Example 9-5.2?

9.28. The dielectric of a thin parallel-plate capacitor of plate area A consists of two plane slabs of thicknesses a and b, dielectric constants ε_a and ε_b, and conductivities σ_a and σ_b, respectively. (a) Show that the leakage resistance of this capacitor is

$$R = \frac{a\sigma_b + b\sigma_a}{A\sigma_a\sigma_b}.$$

(b) Show that when a voltage V is applied to the capacitor, the potential of the dielectric interface with respect to the plate adjacent to the slab of thickness a is

$$\varphi = \pm \frac{Va\sigma_b}{a\sigma_b + b\sigma_a}.$$

(c) Show that the surface charge appearing on the interface when a voltage V is applied to the capacitor is

$$\sigma_{\text{charge}} = \pm\varepsilon_0 \frac{V(\varepsilon_a\sigma_b - \varepsilon_b\sigma_a)}{a\sigma_b + b\sigma_a}.$$

9.29. A parallel-plate capacitor of plate separation d is filled with a laminated material so composed that its permittivity is

$$\varepsilon = k_1\left(1 + k_2\cos\frac{\pi x}{d}\right),$$

and its conductivity is

$$\sigma = k_3\left(1 + k_4\sin\frac{\pi x}{d}\right),$$

where k_1, k_2, k_3, and k_4 are constants and x is the distance from the positive plate toward the negative one. (a) Find the capacitance and the leakage resistance of this capacitor. (b) Find the density of space charge accumulating in the laminated material when a voltage V is applied to the capacitor.

9.30. Show that the stationary electric field of an infinite current-carrying ohmic conductor of conductivity σ satisfies the relation

$$\mathbf{E} = -\frac{1}{4\pi} \int_{\text{All space}} \frac{(\mathbf{J} \cdot \nabla\sigma)\mathbf{r}_u}{\sigma^2 r^2} dv'$$

if the field is regular at infinity.

9.31. Find the electric field between the plates described in Example 9-6.2 by first determining the potential and then taking the gradient of this potential.

9.32. Two large, thin, rectangular, conducting plates of length l meet at an angle 2α along one of their edges, while their opposite edges are shorted by means of a perfectly conducting plate extending over the entire length of these edges. Show that if a voltage V is applied between the common edge of the two plates (negative terminal) and the shorting plate (positive terminal) the electric field in the space between the plates is

$$\mathbf{E} = \frac{V}{l \cos \alpha}\, \mathbf{i} = \frac{V}{L}\, \mathbf{i},$$

where $\mathbf{i}$ is a unit vector normal to the shorting plate and pointing toward the common edge, and L is the distance between this plate and the edge.

9.33. A long cylindrical conducting tube of uniform conductivity has a narrow slot along its entire length. Two electrodes are attached to the exposed surfaces of the tube's wall in the slot, both electrodes extending over the entire length of the tube. (a) Show that if a voltage V is applied between the electrodes, the electric field in the space inside the tube is

$$\mathbf{E} = \frac{V}{\pi r}\, \mathbf{\theta}_u,$$

where r and θ are polar coordinates about the slot as the z-axis. (b) Find the surface charge on the inner surface of the tube.

9.34. A cylindrical coaxial cable carries a current from a battery of voltage V located at $z = 0$ to a load resistance R and back. (a) Show that the potential in the space between the central wire and the sheath is

$$\varphi = \frac{V}{\ln b/a}\left\{\left[1 - \frac{R_a z}{l(R_a + R_b + R)}\right]\ln b/r + \frac{R_b z}{l(R_a + R_b + R)}\,\ln r/a\right\},$$

where l is the length of the cable, R_a is the resistance of the central wire, a is the radius of this wire, R_b is the resistance of the sheath, and b is the radius of the sheath. (b) Find the distribution of the surface charge in the cable.

9.35. Show that the time needed to dissipate as much energy in Joule's heating of an ohmic conductor carrying a steady current as is stored in the electric field within this conductor is

$$t = \frac{\varepsilon_0 \varepsilon}{2\sigma},$$

where ε is the permittivity, and σ is the conductivity, both assumed constant throughout the conductor.

9.36. Show that as a result of the deformation of the conducting bar described in Example 9-4.3 the power loss due to Joule's heating of the bar decreases 1.125 times.

9.37. A cubic vessel of side l has the bottom and the sides made of nonconducting material and the two ends made of perfect conductors serving as electrodes. Show that if a voltage V is applied between the electrodes, and if the vessel is filled with liquid of conductivity σ, specific heat c, and density δ, the temperature T of the liquid will rise at the rate

$$\frac{dT}{dt} = \frac{°\sigma V^2}{c \delta l^2}.$$

9.38. Find the power lost in Joule's heating per unit length of the dielectric in the cable described in Problem 9.11.

9.39. Find the rate at which heat is generated in Joule's heating of the leaky dielectric in the capacitor described in Problem 9.13.

9.40. Find the energy of the electric field in the space inside the tube described in Example 9-6.1.

9.41. Show that the force with which the inner surfaces of the conducting plates described in Problem 9.32 are attracted to the shorting bar is

$$F = {}^{\circ}2 \, \frac{\varepsilon_0 V^2 b}{l \cos \alpha} \tan \alpha \left(\frac{1}{2} \sin^2 \alpha + \cos^2 \alpha \right),$$

and show that the force with which the inner surface of the shorting bar is attracted to the plates is

$$F = {}^{\circ}\varepsilon_0 \, \frac{V^2 b}{l \cos^2 \alpha} \sin \alpha \, ,$$

where b is the width of the plates and the bar.

9.42. Find the force resulting from the accumulation of surface charge on the dielectric interface described in Problem 9.28.

9.43. Show that as a result of charge accumulation in the wax slab (electret) described in Example 9-5.2 the slab is subjected to a volume force (force per unit volume)

$$\mathbf{F}_v = {}^{\circ}\pi \varepsilon_0 k_1 k_2 \, \frac{V^2}{d^3} \cos \frac{\pi x}{d} \, \mathbf{i},$$

and show that the maximum pressure inside the wax due to the charge accumulation is

$$p_{\max} = \frac{{}^{\circ}\varepsilon_0 k_1 k_2 V^2}{d^2} \, .$$

9.44. A hollow, perfectly conducting sphere of radius b is half filled with a liquid of conductivity σ and permittivity ε. A smaller perfectly conducting sphere of radius a is half submerged in the liquid, and the centers of the spheres coincide. The two spheres are connected to a battery of terminal voltage V, so that a current is present in the liquid. Neglecting the effect of the lead wires, show that the smaller sphere is subjected to the electric force

$$F = \frac{{}^{\circ}\varepsilon_0 (\varepsilon - 1) \pi V^2 b^2}{2(b - a)^2} \, ,$$

and then show that the same force acts on the sphere if the liquid is nonconducting.

10

STATIONARY MAGNETIC
FIELD IN VACUUM

The basic definitions, formulas, and equations used for the quantitative representation of magnetic phenomena are analogous to those used for the quantitative representation of electric phenomena. Moreover, most of the fundamental electric quantities have magnetic counterparts. Thus, the electric field vector $\mathbf{E}[V/m]$ corresponds to the magnetic field vector $\mathbf{H}[A/m]$, the electric displacement vector $\mathbf{D}[As/m^2]$ corresponds to the magnetic induction vector $\mathbf{B}[Vs/m^2]$, capacitance $C[As/V]$ corresponds to inductance $L[Vs/A]$, etc. (the dimensions of analogous electric and magnetic quantities have the same structure, but $[V]$ and $[A]$ are interchanged).[1] This symmetry of quantities contributes greatly to the internal unity and harmony of electromagnetic theory, simplifies its mathematical formulation considerably, and is very helpful for practical applications of the theory. In particular, this symmetry will enable us to present the theory of magnetic phenomena in a form parallel to that in which the theory of electric phenomena was presented, and thus will allow us to utilize again many of the already familiar logical and mathematical deductions and techniques developed in the preceding chapters.

10-1. Magnetic Field and Magnetic Field Vector H

It has been known since ancient times that certain bodies, called *magnets*, respond to a special force known as the *magnetic force*.

---

[1] We are using here the short form of unit notations, writing A for ampere, V for volt, m for meter, and s for second.

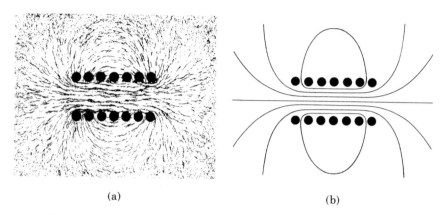

(a)   (b)

FIG. 10.1   (a) Magnetic lines of force in the field of a solenoid. (b) Magnetic
field map for the same solenoid.

A region of space where a stationary magnet experiences a
magnetic force (or torque) is called a *magnetic field*. Experiments show
that all magnets themselves are accompanied by magnetic fields and,
what is most important, that all current-carrying conductors are
accompanied by magnetic fields.[1] Magnetic fields of various characteristics can therefore be obtained by using magnets of various shapes or by
using appropriately arranged current-carrying conductors. Especially
convenient for this purpose are current-carrying coils.

A magnetic field can be made "visible" by sprinkling iron filings
on a glass plate and placing this plate in the field. In the magnetic field
the filings arrange themselves in regular chain-like filaments, thus
making a picture of the "magnetic lines of force" (Figs. 10.1, 10.2,
and 10.3).

Different magnetic fields can be quantitatively compared with each
other with the aid of a magnetic-field-indicator or a *magnetoscope*. An
example of a magnetoscope is a small compass needle suspended on an
elastic wire or supported by a torsion spring that can exert a restoring
torque upon the needle (Fig. 10.4). If two magnetic fields produce the
same deflection of a magnetoscope, the fields are considered equal (subject to proper orientation of the magnetoscope, as will be clear from the
following discussion).

The study of various magnetic fields with the aid of magnetoscopes
and lines-of-force pictures shows that the simplest magnetic field is the
field inside a straight, tightly wound, current-carrying coil whose length

[1] Compare with Section 10-3.

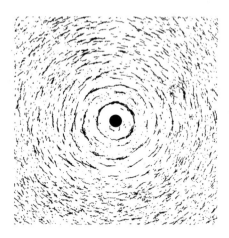

FIG. 10.2   Magnetic lines of force around a current-carrying wire directed at a right angle of the page.

FIG. 10.3   Magnetic lines of force in the field of a toroidal coil.

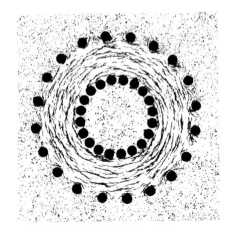

FIG. 10.4   A magnetic field indicator, or magnetoscope, for comparing different magnetic fields.

is much larger than the diameter ("solenoid"). Except near the ends of the coil, this field is homogeneous; it causes the same deflection of a magnetoscope no matter at what point of the field the magnetoscope is placed, and its lines of force are straight, parallel lines (Fig. 10.1) (thus the magnetic field inside a long coil corresponds to the electric field inside a thin parallel-plate capacitor).[1]

If, using a magnetoscope, we compare the magnetic fields in different long coils, we find that the fields in those coils which have the same ratio

$$\frac{\text{number of turns} \times \text{current in the coil}}{\text{length of the coil}}$$

cause equal deflections of the magnetoscope regardless of any other characteristics of the coils. Therefore this ratio can be used as the measure of the magnetic field inside a long coil.

Since the field in a long coil has a well defined structure, is easily reproducible, and can be used conveniently for producing standard laboratory conditions for experiments with magnetic fields, we shall adopt this field as the *standard magnetic field H_s* and, in agreement with the ratio stated above, shall define its magnitude as

$$H_s = \frac{nI}{l}, \tag{10-1.1}$$

where n is the number of turns in the coil, I is the current in the coil, and l is the length of the coil.

The magnitude of any magnetic field can be defined in terms of the magnitude of the standard field. We shall define it as follows: *the magnitude of an arbitrary magnetic field H is measured by and is equal to the magnitude of the standard field H_s which exactly equalizes the field H.* The units of a magnetic field are, according to this definition, ampere/meter.

The principle of measurement of an arbitrary magnetic field is illustrated in Fig. 10.5. The standard field is on the left; it is adjusted by means of a variable current source until the torsion balance carrying on the ends of its axle two identical compass needles which are placed in the standard and the unknown field, respectively, is in equilibrium.

The method of direct field measurement shown in Fig. 10.5 is seldom used in practice. Instead, magnetic fields are usually measured indirectly in two steps. First the effect of the standard field upon some magnetic-field-indicator is determined (calibration of the indicator). Then this effect

---

[1] A homogeneous magnetic field can be produced also between the plates of a parallel-plate capacitor by establishing opposite currents in the two plates (see Problem 10.8 and Example 13-6.2).

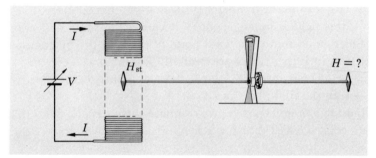

FIG. 10.5   Magnetic fields can be measured by comparison with a standard magnetic field.

is compared with the effect produced upon the same indicator by the field that is being measured. An example of an instrument for such an indirect field measurement is shown in Fig. 10.6. The indicator is a small piece of soft iron attached to a pointer. The iron piece and the pointer are deflected under the action of the magnetic field that is being measured, and the deflection is read on the scale calibrated previously with the aid of a standard field. Magnetic field meters of this type are known as *oerstedmeters*.

Magnetic fields, like electric fields, are vector fields. With each point of a magnetic field one can associate the *magnetic field vector* **H**, whose magnitude is equal to the magnitude of the magnetic field at that point and whose direction is indicated by a compass needle placed at that point (by convention, the positive direction of **H** is that indicated by the north-seeking pole of the needle).

It has been found that maps of magnetic vector fields (see page 36) are closely represented by pictures of the magnetic lines of force (filaments of iron filings on a glass plate) produced by the same fields (Fig. 10.1). The easily obtainable pictures of the magnetic lines of force are therefore often used as the approximate maps of the magnetic fields.

The magnetic field and the magnetic field vector **H** are the counterparts of the electric field and the electric field vector **E**. It is useful to note the similarity of the dimensions of **H** and **E**. Both dimensions have the same form, [A/m] and [V/m], respectively, but [V] and [A] are interchanged.

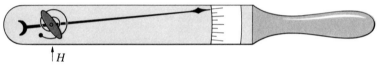

FIG. 10.6   An oerstedmeter.

10-2. Induction Field and Induction Vector B

Let us take two thin conducting rods, connect them to a ballistic voltmeter, and place across them a short piece of bare wire that can be slid over them. Let us then insert the rods with the slide wire into a current-carrying coil through a slot made in the coil at a right angle to the axis of the coil (Fig. 10.7a). If we now slide the wire along the rods, the voltmeter registers a voltage impulse, indicating in this way that a voltage has appeared in the wire. Thus we can "generate" voltage (and, hence, current) in a wire by merely moving the wire inside a current-carrying coil. This type of voltage generation is called *generation by electromagnetic induction*. The region of space where this generation can take place is called the *field of electromagnetic induction*, or, simply, the *induction field*. Experiments show that the induction field is intimately related to the magnetic field defined in the preceding section and can be produced by the same means as the latter.

If we measure voltage-impulses produced by small slide wires of different sizes which are moved with different speeds over different small distances Δl (Fig. 10.7b) we find that, as long as all wires are inserted at the same point of the field and are oriented in exactly the same manner, the ratio

$$\frac{\int V dt}{\Delta S} = \frac{\text{voltage-impulse produced by the slide wire}}{\text{area swept during the motion of the slide wire}}$$

is the same for all wires. This ratio may therefore be regarded as the measure of the induction field and may be used for the quantitative definition of this field. Using this possibility, we shall quantitatively define the induction field as follows: *the magnitude of the induction field at a*

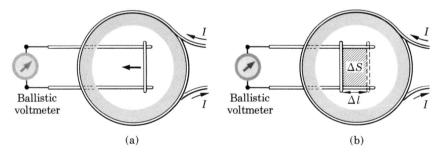

(a)   (b)

FIG. 10.7 Voltage can be generated in a wire by moving the wire across a current-carrying coil.

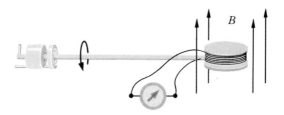

FIG. 10.8   "Flip coil" for measuring B.

given point is measured by and is equal to the ratio $(\int V dt)/\Delta S$ *obtained with a small slide wire inserted at this point and oriented so that this ratio is a maximum.* We shall designate the magnitude of the induction field by the symbol B and shall call it, for brevity, the *induction*. The units of B are, according to this definition, volt $\cdot$ sec/m².

In practice, B is measured with the aid of a small test coil, rather than with a slide wire. When the test coil is turned about a diameter, a voltage-impulse is induced in it. A properly oriented test coil of one turn and of area ΔS produces the same voltage impulse when turned through 90° as a slide wire sweeping an equal area ΔS; a coil of n turns produces a voltage impulse n times larger. A test coil is usually permanently connected to a ballistic voltmeter calibrated directly in terms of the induction B. A spring "flips" the coil (Fig. 10.8) through 180° when the measurement is made (turning the coil through 180° instead of 90° increases the voltage impulse by a factor of 2). Test coils of this type, also known as "flip coils," "search coils," and "induction coils" are important instruments for the study of magnetic fields. A test coil for studying the earth magnetic field is called the "earth inductor."

Induction fields are vector fields also. With each point of an induction field one can associate the *induction vector* **B** whose magnitude is equal to the induction at this point and whose direction is normal to the surface swept by the slide wire when the wire is oriented to produce the largest ratio $(\int V dt)/\Delta S$. By convention, the sense of the direction of **B** is then such that the induced current density vector in the slide wire, $\mathbf{J}_{\text{ind}}$, the velocity vector of the slide wire, **v**, and the induction vector, **B**, form a right-handed system in the order stated (Fig. 10.9).

A simple way to determine the direction of **B** when using a test coil is to orient the axis of rotation so that no voltage is induced in the coil. The axis of rotation will then be parallel to **B**.

The induction field and the induction field vector **B** are the counterparts of the displacement field and the displacement field vector **D**.

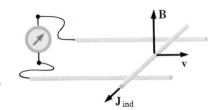

FIG. 10.9 Directional relations for current induced in a slide wire.

It is useful to note the similarity of the dimensions of **B** and **D**. Both dimensions have the same form, $[Vs/m^2]$ and $[As/m^2]$, respectively, but $[V]$ and $[A]$ are interchanged.

It is customary to use the expression "magnetic field" as a general term for designating both the magnetic field proper, defined in the preceding section, and the induction field. When using this expression in such a general sense, we shall refer to both the induction vector **B** and the magnetic field vector **H** as the magnetic field vectors.

The definitions of the magnetic field vectors are given in Table 4-I parallel to the definitions of the electric field vectors.

10-3. Magnetic Fields as a Property of Moving Electric Charges

As we have seen in the preceding chapters, the time-independent electric fields can always be attributed to electric charges, which thus may be always considered as the sources of the fields. It is natural to ask whether the time-independent magnetic fields could be similarly attributed to some "magnetic charges" as the sources of these fields.

All experiments conducted in search of such magnetic charges gave negative results. Magnetic charges have never been found.

These and other experiments have shown, however, that all time-independent magnetic fields can ultimately be traced to moving electric charges. Thus, for example, it has been established that the magnetic fields of permanent magnets are a result of rotation and revolution of electric charges within atoms and molecules, and that the magnetic fields of current-carrying conductors are a result of translational motion of the electric charges within the conductors.

It has also been found that a stream of electric charges of density ρ and velocity **v** produces the same magnetic field as that produced by a conductor carrying a current of density $\mathbf{J} = \rho\mathbf{v}$. A stream of charged particles is therefore frequently called a *convection current*. Its current density is defined, in accordance with the observation just mentioned, as

$$\mathbf{J}_{\text{conv}} = \rho\mathbf{v}. \qquad (10\text{-}3.1)$$

10-4. Fundamental Magnetostatic Field Laws

The simplest magnetic fields are the time-independent, or the *magnetostatic*, fields. The fundamental laws of magnetostatic fields in vacuum may be deduced as follows.

The Circulation (Curl) Law. If we compare the lines-of-force pictures obtained with the aid of iron filings in the magnetostatic fields of various current-carrying conductors, we shall find that all the pictures have one remarkable property in common: there are only closed lines of force in all of them; no lines have a beginning or an end. Since the lines-of-force pictures essentially represent the vector maps of the corresponding magnetic fields, and since closed field lines are the characteristic property of vector fields with nonvanishing curl and circulation integral, we must suspect that the circulation integral and curl of a magnetostatic field are different from zero. A further study of the lines-of-force pictures shows that the lines of force always encircle current-carrying conductors. This suggests that the circulation integral of magnetostatic fields is intimately related to the current enclosed by the path of integration. If we now observe that the dimensions of the circulation integral of the field vector **H** are the same as the dimensions of the electric current, we are immediately led to the assumption that in a magnetostatic field $\oint\mathbf{H}\cdot d\mathbf{l}$ is simply equal to the current enclosed by the path of integration: $\oint\mathbf{H}\cdot d\mathbf{l} = I_{\text{enclosed}}$. Expressing the enclosed current as the surface integral of current density, we thus obtain

$$\oint \mathbf{H}\cdot d\mathbf{l} = \int \mathbf{J}\cdot d\mathbf{S}. \qquad (10\text{-}4.1\text{a})$$

The curl of **H**, according to Stoke's theorem, is then

$$\nabla \times \mathbf{H} = \mathbf{J}. \qquad (10\text{-}4.1\text{b})$$

The validity and generality of these equations have been confirmed by all presently known phenomena involving the correlations between electric currents and magnetostatic fields. According to Section 3-2, these equations therefore constitute a fundamental magnetostatic field law in its integral and differential forms, respectively. The circulation law expressed by Eq. (10-4.1a) is usually called *Ampere's law*, and the path of integration used for evaluating the circulation integral in Eq. (10-4.1a) is usually called an *Amperian loop*.

The Flux (Divergence) Law. There is another deduction that we can make from the study of magnetic lines of force. As already noted, these lines have neither a beginning nor an end. This is also, however, the characteristic property of field lines in vector fields whose divergence is zero. Observing now that in the electric fields it was the displacement vector **D** that entered the divergence law, and remembering that the magnetic counterpart of **D** is the induction vector **B**, we are led to the assumption that in the time-independent induction fields

$$\nabla \cdot \mathbf{B} = 0. \tag{10-4.2a}$$

By Gauss's theorem, we can then also write

$$\oint \mathbf{B} \cdot d\mathbf{S} = 0. \tag{10-4.2b}$$

These equations too have been confirmed by all presently known phenomena involving the induction fields. Therefore, according to Section 3-2, they constitute a fundamental law of the induction fields in its differential and integral forms, respectively.

Equation (10-4.2b) shows that the field vector **B** represents the flux density of the magnetic induction field. It is therefore customary to call **B** the *flux density vector*, or the *magnetic flux density vector*.

Additional experiments show that both the time-independent **H** and time-independent **B** fields are always regular at infinity.

The Flux Density Law. The set of field laws that we have thus far introduced is incomplete, since we do not have the circulation (curl) law for **B** and the flux (divergence) law for **H**. These laws can be obtained, however, from the ones that we already have, if the correlation between the vectors **B** and **H** is known. This correlation can be determined by making simultaneous measurements of **B** and **H** in various magnetic fields. On the basis of such measurements it has been found that in vacuum **H** and **B** are bound to each other by the equation

$$\mathbf{B} = \mu_0 \mathbf{H}, \tag{10-4.3}$$

where μ_0 is an experimentally determined universal constant, called the permeability of space; its value is $1.256 \cdot 10^{-6}$ volt $\cdot$ sec/amp $\cdot$ m.[1] The correlation expressed by this equation is called the *flux density law*. This

---

[1] As has been stated in Section 7-1, the units of current and voltage in the *mksva* system are so defined as to make μ_0 equal to $4\pi \cdot 10^{-7}$ volt $\cdot$ sec/amp $\cdot$ meter.

law is a constitutive law and, in the above form, is valid only for magnetic fields in vacuum (and, practically, also in air) but not for the fields in material media, as we shall see later.

The flux density law is the magnetic counterpart of the displacement law of electrostatics, and the constant μ_0 is the magnetic counterpart of the constant ε_0. Observe that both constants have the same dimensional structure, [Vs/Am] and [As/Vm], respectively, but [V] and [A] are interchanged.

The flux density law completes the set of the fundamental magnetostatic field laws expressed in Eqs. (10-4.1) and (10-4.2), since both the circulation (curl) law and the flux (divergence) law for **H** as well as for **B** can now be obtained from these equations, and hence, by Helmholtz's theorem of vector analysis, both vector fields **H** and **B** are now specified completely.[1]

This means that if somehow we find an expression for **H** or **B** which for a given magnetic system in vacuum satisfies all three equations (10-4.1), (10-4.2), and (10-4.3) at all points of space and is regular at infinity, we may be sure that this expression is correct and that the field represented by this expression is the only possible field for the system under consideration.

What is more, just like the corresponding equations for electric fields, these three equations uniquely specify the vector fields **H** and **B** within a given region of space even if these equations are known for the points of this region only, provided that the normal component of **H** or **B** is known for all points of the boundaries of the region (the proof of this statement is left to Problem 10.1).

▼
Example 10-4.1   Find the magnetic field outside and inside a long wire of radius a carrying a uniform current I.

Let us describe a circular Amperian loop C of radius r around the wire, as shown in Fig. 10.10a. Applying Ampere's law to this loop we have

$$\oint \mathbf{H} \cdot d\mathbf{l} = I_{\text{enclosed}}.$$

By the symmetry of the system, the magnetic field lines must be circles centered on the axis of the wire, and the magnitude of **H** must be the same at all points of each such circle. Therefore, at any point of the Amperian loop, the magnetic field vector **H** must be parallel to $d\mathbf{l}$ and constant in magnitude,

---

[1] As usual, we are referring to Eqs. (10-4.1a) and (10-4.1b) as to Eq. (10-4.1), and we are referring to Eqs. (10-4.2a) and (10-4.2b) as to Eq. (10-4.2).

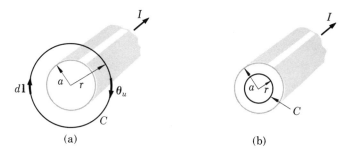

FIG. 10.10   Calculation of the magnetic field of a current-carrying wire.

so that $\oint \mathbf{H} \cdot d\mathbf{l} = \oint H dl = H \oint dl$. Since $\oint dl = 2\pi r$, Ampere's law for this problem reduces to

$$H 2\pi r = I_{enclosed},$$

and hence

$$H = \frac{I_{enclosed}}{2\pi r}.$$

Taking into account the direction of $\mathbf{H}$ and dropping the subscript on I, we finally obtain

$$\mathbf{H} = \frac{I}{2\pi r} \mathbf{\theta}_u \qquad (r \geq a), \qquad (10\text{-}4.4)$$

where $\mathbf{\theta}_u$ is a unit vector in the circular direction forming a right-handed system with the direction of the current. To find the field inside the wire, we likewise describe a circular Amperian loop of radius r inside the wire, as shown in Fig. 10.10b. Applying Ampere's law to this loop, we obtain, as before,

$$H = \frac{I_{enclosed}}{2\pi r}.$$

However, the enclosed current is now $I_{enclosed} = (I/\pi a^2)\pi r^2 = I(r^2/a^2)$, where a is the radius of the wire. The field is therefore

$$\mathbf{H} = \frac{Ir}{2\pi a^2} \mathbf{\theta}_u \qquad (r \leq a). \qquad (10\text{-}4.5)$$

Example 10-4.2   A long cylindrical beam of charged particles has a uniform space charge density ρ and moves with a constant velocity $\mathbf{v}$ in the direction of its axis (Fig. 10.11). The radius of the beam is a. Find the magnetic field inside and outside the beam.

By the symmetry of the system, the magnetic field is everywhere circular. To find the field inside the beam we apply Ampere's law to a circular loop of radius $r \leq a$ centered on the axis of the beam. We then have

$$\oint \mathbf{H} \cdot d\mathbf{l} = \int \mathbf{J}_{conv} \cdot d\mathbf{S},$$

FIG. 10.11   Calculation of the magnetic field of a beam of charged particles.

where $\mathbf{J}_{conv}$ is the convection current density of the beam. By Eq. (10-3.1), $\mathbf{J}_{conv} = \rho\mathbf{v}$. Since both ρ and $\mathbf{v}$ are constant, $\mathbf{J}_{conv}$ is constant. We can therefore write[1] $\int\mathbf{J}\cdot d\mathbf{S} = \int J\, dS = J\int dS = JS = J\pi r^2 = \rho v\pi r^2$, and since $\oint\mathbf{H}\cdot d\mathbf{l} = H2\pi r$, we obtain $H2\pi r = \rho v\pi r^2$, so that the field inside the beam is

$$H = \frac{\rho v r}{2} \qquad (r \leq a).$$

To find the field outside the beam we apply Ampere's law to a circle of radius $r > a$ centered on the axis. Since the beam is now completely enclosed by the path of integration, $\int\mathbf{J}\cdot d\mathbf{S} = J\pi a^2 = \rho v\pi a^2$, and therefore the field outside the beam is

$$H = \frac{\rho v a^2}{2r} \qquad (r \geq a).$$

Taking into account the direction of the field, we can write

$$\mathbf{H} = \rho\,\frac{\mathbf{v} \times \mathbf{r}}{2} \quad \text{for} \quad r \leq a, \quad \text{and} \quad \mathbf{H} = \rho a^2\,\frac{\mathbf{v} \times \mathbf{r}_u}{2r} \quad \text{for} \quad r \geq a.$$

Example 10-4.3   A large conducting slab of thickness t carries a uniform current of density $\mathbf{J}$ along the length of the slab. Find the magnetic field inside and outside the slab, neglecting the edge effects.

Let us construct a rectangular Amperian loop of length l and width $w < t$, as shown in Fig. 10.12a. Applying Ampere's law to this loop, we have

$$\oint \mathbf{H}\cdot d\mathbf{l} = \int \mathbf{J}\cdot d\mathbf{S}.$$

By the symmetry of the system, the field $\mathbf{H}$ is parallel to $d\mathbf{l}$ on the horizontal portions of the loop and is constant at all points of these portions, so that on them $\int\mathbf{H}\cdot d\mathbf{l} = \int H\,dl = H\int dl = Hl$. On the vertical portions of the loop the field $\mathbf{H}$ is perpendicular to $d\mathbf{l}$, so that there $\int\mathbf{H}\cdot d\mathbf{l} = 0$. Designating the corners of the loop by the symbols a, b, c, and d, as shown in Fig. 10.12a,

---

[1] We naturally assume that the surface of integration S is simply a disk normal to the axis of the beam. One should emphasize, however, that Ampere's law is valid for *any* surface of integration as long as this surface is bounded by the line along which the circulation integral is being evaluated; it may be a cone, a hemisphere, a cylinder closed at one end, or any other surface. For practical applications of Ampere's law one selects, of course, the surface that makes the integration simplest.

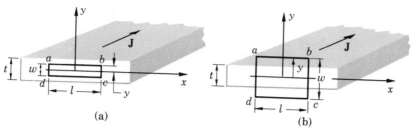

FIG. 10.12   Calculation of the magnetic field of a current-carrying slab.

we then have

$$\oint \mathbf{H} \cdot d\mathbf{l} = \int_a^b \mathbf{H} \cdot d\mathbf{l} + \int_b^c \mathbf{H} \cdot d\mathbf{l} + \int_c^d \mathbf{H} \cdot d\mathbf{l} + \int_d^a \mathbf{H} \cdot d\mathbf{l}$$
$$= Hl + 0 + Hl + 0 = 2Hl,$$

and since for this loop $\int \mathbf{J} \cdot d\mathbf{S} = 2Jly$, we obtain for the field inside the slab

$$H = Jy \qquad (y \leq t/2),$$

where y is as shown in Fig. 10.12a. Taking into account the direction of $\mathbf{H}$ (the $\mathbf{H}$-lines form a right-handed system with the vector $\mathbf{J}$), we can write then for $\mathbf{H}$

$$\mathbf{H} = Jy\,\mathbf{i} \qquad (y \leq t/2).$$

Constructing a rectangular Amperian loop of length l and width $w > t$, as shown in Fig. 10.12b, we likewise obtain for the magnetic field outside the slab

$$H = \frac{1}{2} Jt, \quad \text{or} \quad \mathbf{H} = \frac{1}{2} Jt \frac{y}{|y|} \mathbf{i} \qquad (y \geq t/2).$$

Example 10-4.4   In a field emission microscope, charged particles (electrons) leave a hemispherical tip (radius a) of a needle-shaped cathode and move toward a concave, concentric, hemispherical anode (radius b), as shown in Fig. 10.13. The current in the cathode and anode is I, and the

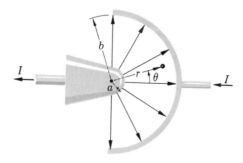

FIG. 10.13   Calculation of the magnetic field within a stream of electrons moving from a hemispherical cathode to a hemispherical anode.

charged particles constitute an equal convection current while they are on their way from the cathode to the anode. Assuming that the flux density of the particles is constant at all points of the tip, and that the particles move radially, find the magnetic field at any point (r, θ) between the cathode and the anode.

By the symmetry of the system, the field is everywhere circular. Applying Ampere's law to a circle of radius R constructed between the cathode and anode and centered on the symmetry axis, we have therefore $\oint \mathbf{H} \cdot d\mathbf{l} = \int\int \mathbf{J}_{conv} \cdot d\mathbf{S}$, and since $\oint \mathbf{H} \cdot d\mathbf{l} = H2\pi R = H2\pi r \sin \theta$, we obtain

$$H = \frac{\int \mathbf{J}_{conv} \cdot d\mathbf{S}}{2\pi r \sin \theta},$$

where θ is the polar angle, as shown in Fig. 10.13. Since the convection current is spherically symmetric, $\mathbf{J}_{conv}$ at a distance r from the center of the tip is

$$\mathbf{J}_{conv} = -\frac{I}{2\pi r^2} \mathbf{r}_u.$$

Using as the surface of integration a spherical cup of radius r and polar angle θ, we then have for the surface integral

$$\int \mathbf{J}_{conv} \cdot d\mathbf{S} = \int \frac{I}{2\pi r^2} dS = \int_0^\theta \frac{I}{2\pi r^2} 2\pi r^2 \sin \theta \, d\theta = I(1 - \cos \theta).$$

The field is therefore

$$H = \frac{I(1 - \cos \theta)}{2\pi r \sin \theta} = \frac{I}{2\pi r} \tan \frac{\theta}{2}.$$

Example 10-4.5   Two parallel wires separated by a distance $2d$ carry equal currents I in the same direction (Fig. 10.14). Find the magnetic field outside the wires and determine the limiting value of this field for points far away from the wires.

Each wire alone has the field given by Eq. (10-4.4). The combined field of the two wires is the vector sum of their individual fields. To find this sum we shall express Eq. (10-4.4) in terms of the rectangular coordinates shown in Fig. 10.14. Using subscript 1 to indicate quantities pertaining to the wire on the left and subscript 2 for quantities pertaining to the wire on the right, we then have

$$r_1 = \sqrt{(x + d)^2 + y^2}, \qquad r_2 = \sqrt{(x - d)^2 + y^2},$$

$$\boldsymbol{\theta}_{u1} = \sin \theta_1 \mathbf{i} + \cos \theta_1 \mathbf{j} = \frac{y}{\sqrt{(x + d)^2 + y^2}} \mathbf{i} - \frac{x + d}{\sqrt{(x + d)^2 + y^2}} \mathbf{j},$$

$$\boldsymbol{\theta}_{u2} = \sin \theta_2 \mathbf{i} + \cos \theta_2 \mathbf{j} = \frac{y}{\sqrt{(x - d)^2 + y^2}} \mathbf{i} - \frac{x - d}{\sqrt{(x - d)^2 + y^2}} \mathbf{j},$$

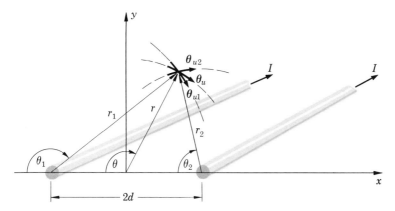

FIG. 10.14   Calculation of the magnetic field of two parallel wires carrying equal currents.

so that

$$\mathbf{H}_1 = \frac{I}{2\pi[(x+d)^2 + y^2]} [y\mathbf{i} - (x+d)\mathbf{j}]$$

and

$$\mathbf{H}_2 = \frac{I}{2\pi[(x-d)^2 + y^2]} [y\mathbf{i} - (x-d)\mathbf{j}].$$

The total field, $\mathbf{H} = \mathbf{H}_1 + \mathbf{H}_2$, is then

$$\mathbf{H} = \frac{I}{2\pi} \left\{ y\left[\frac{1}{(x+d)^2 + y^2} + \frac{1}{(x-d)^2 + y^2} \right] \mathbf{i} \right.$$
$$\left. - \left[\frac{x+d}{(x+d)^2 + y^2} + \frac{x-d}{(x-d)^2 + y^2} \right] \mathbf{j} \right\}.$$

For the points far away from the wires, d in the denominator of the last equation can be neglected. We then have

$$\mathbf{H} = \frac{I}{2\pi} \left(\frac{2y}{x^2 + y^2} \mathbf{i} - \frac{2x}{x^2 + y^2} \mathbf{j} \right)$$
$$= \frac{2I}{2\pi\sqrt{x^2 + y^2}} \left(\frac{y}{\sqrt{x^2 + y^2}} \mathbf{i} - \frac{x}{\sqrt{x^2 + y^2}} \mathbf{j} \right),$$

or

$$\mathbf{H} = \frac{I'}{2\pi r} \boldsymbol{\theta}_u \qquad (r \gg d),$$

where $I' = 2I$, and r and $\boldsymbol{\theta}_u$ are as shown in Fig. 10.14. If $r \gg d$, the field is thus the same as that of a single wire carrying the current $2I$.

Example 10-4.6   Prove that any two current distributions, $\mathbf{J}_1$ and $\mathbf{J}_2$, confined to a finite region of space (as all real currents are), satisfy the reciprocation relation

$$\int_{\text{All space}} \mathbf{B}_1 \times \mathbf{J}_2 dv = \int_{\text{All space}} \mathbf{J}_1 \times \mathbf{B}_2 dv,$$

where $\mathbf{B}_1$ is the induction field associated with the current $\mathbf{J}_1$, and $\mathbf{B}_2$ is the induction field associated with the current $\mathbf{J}_2$.

Using the flux density law (10-4.3), the curl law (10-4.1b), and the vector identity (V-2), we can write

$$\int \mathbf{B}_1 \times \mathbf{J}_2 dv = \frac{1}{\mu_0} \int \mathbf{B}_1 \times (\boldsymbol{\nabla} \times \mathbf{B}_2) dv$$

$$= \frac{1}{\mu_0} \int \boldsymbol{\nabla}(\mathbf{B}_1 \cdot \mathbf{B}_2) dv - \frac{1}{\mu_0} \int (\mathbf{B}_1 \cdot \boldsymbol{\nabla}) \mathbf{B}_2 dv - \frac{1}{\mu_0} \int (\mathbf{B}_2 \cdot \boldsymbol{\nabla}) \mathbf{B}_1 dv$$

$$- \frac{1}{\mu_0} \int \mathbf{B}_2 \times (\boldsymbol{\nabla} \times \mathbf{B}_1) dv,$$

where the integrals are extended over all space. We shall show now that the first three integrals in the last expression vanish. The first integral in this expression can be transformed into a surface integral by means of the vector identity (V-20):

$$\int \boldsymbol{\nabla}(\mathbf{B}_1 \cdot \mathbf{B}_2) dv = \oint \mathbf{B}_1 \cdot \mathbf{B}_2 d\mathbf{S}.$$

But since $\mathbf{J}_1$ and $\mathbf{J}_2$ are confined to a finite region of space, $\mathbf{B}_1$ and $\mathbf{B}_2$ are regular at infinity. Therefore the surface integral vanishes, and so does the volume integral. The second and third integrals in the expression under consideration can be transformed by means of the vector identity (V-23) as follows:

$$\int (\mathbf{B}_1 \cdot \boldsymbol{\nabla}) \mathbf{B}_2 dv = \oint \mathbf{B}_2 (\mathbf{B}_1 \cdot d\mathbf{S}) - \int (\boldsymbol{\nabla} \cdot \mathbf{B}_1) \mathbf{B}_2 dv,$$

and

$$\int (\mathbf{B}_2 \cdot \boldsymbol{\nabla}) \mathbf{B}_1 dv = \oint \mathbf{B}_1 (\mathbf{B}_2 \cdot d\mathbf{S}) - \int (\boldsymbol{\nabla} \cdot \mathbf{B}_2) \mathbf{B}_1 dv.$$

But since $\mathbf{B}_1$ and $\mathbf{B}_2$ are regular at infinity, and since $\boldsymbol{\nabla} \cdot \mathbf{B}_1 = \boldsymbol{\nabla} \cdot \mathbf{B}_2 = 0$ by the divergence law (10-4.2a), the integrals on the right vanish, and so do the integrals on the left. Thus only the last integral in the expression under consideration remains, and we have

$$\int \mathbf{B}_1 \times \mathbf{J}_2 dv = -\frac{1}{\mu_0} \int \mathbf{B}_2 \times (\boldsymbol{\nabla} \times \mathbf{B}_1) dv.$$

Substituting $(\boldsymbol{\nabla} \times \mathbf{B}_1)/\mu_0 = \mathbf{J}_1$, we finally obtain

$$\int \mathbf{B}_1 \times \mathbf{J}_2 dv = -\int \mathbf{B}_2 \times \mathbf{J}_1 dv = \int \mathbf{J}_1 \times \mathbf{B}_2 dv,$$

which was to be proved.

▲

10-5. Inductance

An important problem in the domain of magnetic phenomena is the calculation of magnetic fields associated with a given current distribution. In the next section we shall solve this problem in its general form. In this section we shall consider a special case of the problem: the calculation of the magnetic flux

$$\Phi = \int \mathbf{B} \cdot d\mathbf{S} \tag{10-5.1}$$

associated with currents in conductors, by means of a special quantity called *inductance*.

Inductance is defined for single conductors and also for pairs of conductors.

The inductance of a single conductor, or the *self inductance*, is defined, in general, as the ratio

$$L = \frac{\Phi}{I}, \tag{10-5.2}$$

where I is the current in the conductor, and Φ is the total magnetic flux due to this current. However, the inductance of a tightly wound coil with negligible end effects is defined as

$$L = \frac{n\Phi}{I}, \tag{10-5.3}$$

where n is the number of turns in the coil and Φ is the total magnetic flux of the coil.

Frequently the inductance is determined by using only that part of the flux Φ which is produced by the magnetic field outside the conductor. The inductance so obtained is called the *external inductance*.

For pairs of conductors, the so-called *mutual inductance* is defined. The mutual inductance of a conductor i with respect to a conductor j is, in general, defined as the ratio

$$L_{ij} = \frac{\Phi_{ij}}{I_j}, \tag{10-5.4}$$

where I_j is the current in the conductor j, and Φ_{ij} is the magnetic flux due to this current evaluated over a surface bounded by the conductor i. However, the mutual inductance of a tightly wound coil with respect to another conductor is defined as the sum of the mutual inductance of each individual turn of the coil with respect to this conductor. In the particular case when the current in the conductor causes the same flux Φ_{ij} through each turn of the coil, the mutual inductance is therefore

$$L_{ij} = \frac{n_i \Phi_{ij}}{I_j}, \qquad (10\text{-}5.5)$$

where I_j is the current in the conductor, n_i is the number of turns in the coil, and Φ_{ij} is the flux through a turn of the coil due to the current in the conductor.

The units of inductance are volt · sec/amp. These units are usually called the "henry."

It must be pointed out that the above definitions of self and mutual inductance ordinarily do not permit a unique determination of the inductance, and that other definitions are possible (a more satisfactory definition is given in Chapter 14). Therefore different authors frequently give different expressions for inductances of the same systems.

Inductance is the magnetic counterpart of capacitance (mutual inductance is the counterpart of the coefficient of mutual capacitance). Observe that the dimensions of inductance and capacitance have the same structure, [Vs/A] and [As/V], respectively, but [V] and [A] are interchanged.

Like the capacitance, the inductance is a function of geometrical relations only. Therefore, once it has been calculated (or measured) for a system to which one of the four equations (10-5.2) to (10-5.5) applies, the flux in the system can be immediately found from these equations if the corresponding current is known. The problem of calculating the magnetic flux in such a system reduces therefore to that of determining the inductance of the system.

▼

Example 10-5.1   A coaxial cable consists of an inner thin-walled cylinder of radius a carrying a current I, and an outer thin-walled cylinder of radius b returning this current. Find the inductance of a portion of this cable of length l (Fig. 10.15).

By the symmetry of the system, the magnetic field must be everywhere circular, with the field lines forming circles centered on the axis of the cable. Applying Ampere's law to an Amperian circle of radius r centered on the axis (Fig. 10.15a), we have, as in Example 10-4.1,

$$\oint \mathbf{H} \cdot d\mathbf{l} = \oint H \, dl = H \oint dl = H 2\pi r = I_{\text{enclosed}},$$

or

$$H = \frac{I_{\text{enclosed}}}{2\pi r}.$$

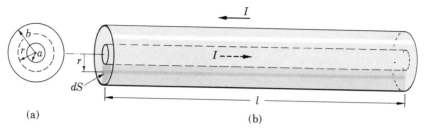

FIG. 10.15 Calculation of the inductance of coaxial cable.

For $r < a$, $I_{\text{enclosed}} = 0$, so that H and B are also zero. For $a < r < b$, $I_{\text{enclosed}} = I$, so that

$$H = \frac{I}{2\pi r},$$

and (by the flux density law)

$$B = \frac{\mu_0 I}{2\pi r}.$$

For $r > b$, $I_{\text{enclosed}} = I - I = 0$ (the conductors carry *equal* currents in *opposite* directions), so that H and B are again zero. Thus the magnetic field is confined to the space between the cylinders. The magnetic flux

$$\Phi = \int \mathbf{B} \cdot d\mathbf{S}$$

associated with a portion l of the cable can be obtained therefore by evaluating the flux integral over a rectangular plane surface of length l in the space between the cylinders (Fig. 10.15b). The surface element of such a surface can be taken as $dS = l \, dr$. Since $\mathbf{B}$, being circular, is perpendicular to this surface (parallel to the vector element $d\mathbf{S}$), we can replace in the flux integral the dot product $\mathbf{B} \cdot d\mathbf{S}$ with the product $B \, dS$. The flux is therefore

$$\Phi = \int B \, dS = \int_a^b \frac{\mu_0 I}{2\pi r} l \, dr = \frac{\mu_0 I l}{2\pi} \ln \frac{b}{a}.$$

The inductance is then, by Eq. (10-5.2),

$$L = \frac{\Phi}{I} = \frac{\mu_0 l}{2\pi} \ln \frac{b}{a}.$$

Example 10-5.2   Two parallel wires whose centers are a distance d apart carry equal currents in opposite directions (Fig. 10.16). The radius of each wire is a. Find the external inductance of a length l of these wires.

By Example 10-4.1, each wire produces in the external space a circular field

$$H = \frac{I}{2\pi r},$$

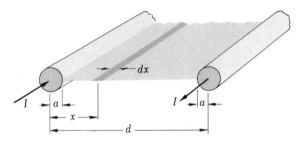

FIG. 10.16   Calculation of the inductance of a two-wire transmission line.

where r is the distance from the wire in question and I is the current in this wire. The total field at a point x between the wires is therefore

$$H = \frac{I}{2\pi x} + \frac{I}{2\pi(d - x)} .$$

Since all field lines of this field pass between the wires, the total flux produced by this field is just the flux through the plane surface extending from $x = a$ to $x = d - a$ in the space between the wires. Taking into account that the field lines are normal to this surface and that $\mathbf{B} = \mu_0\mathbf{H}$, we then have for a length l of the wires

$$\Phi = \int \mathbf{B} \cdot d\mathbf{S} = \int B \, dS = \int_a^{d-a} \left[\frac{\mu_0 I}{2\pi x} + \frac{\mu_0 I}{2\pi(d - x)} \right] l \, dx$$

$$= \mu_0 \frac{Il}{2\pi} \ln \frac{x}{d - x} \Big|_a^{d-a} = \mu_0 \frac{Il}{\pi} \ln \frac{d - a}{a} .$$

The inductance is therefore

$$L = \frac{\Phi}{I} = \mu_0 \frac{l}{\pi} \ln \frac{d - a}{a} .$$

Example 10-5.3   Find the inductance of a long, thin-walled coil of n turns, length l, and cross-sectional area A.

Let the current in the coil be I. The magnetic field in the coil is then

$$H = \frac{nI}{l} ,$$

and the flux density is

$$B = \frac{\mu_0 nI}{l} .$$

Since the field in the coil is homogeneous and is directed along the coil's axis, the magnetic flux produced by the coil is

$$\Phi = BA = \frac{\mu_0 nI}{l} A.$$

The inductance is therefore, by Eq. (10-5.3),

$$L = \frac{n\Phi}{I} = \frac{\mu_0 n^2 A}{l}.$$

Example 10-5.4 A rectangular loop of wire of width a and height b is placed at a distance d from a long straight wire, as shown in Fig. 10.17. Find the mutual inductance of the loop with respect to the wire.

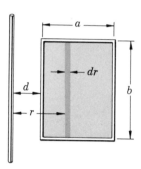

Fig. 10.17 Calculation of the mutual inductance between a long wire and a rectangular loop (only a small portion of the wire is shown).

Let the current in the wire be I_1. The magnetic field of the wire is then

$$H = \frac{I_1}{2\pi r},$$

and the flux density is

$$B = \frac{\mu_0 I_1}{2\pi r}.$$

The flux produced by this field through the rectangular loop is

$$\Phi_{21} = \int \mathbf{B} \cdot d\mathbf{S} = \int B \, dS = \int_d^{d+a} Bb \, dr = \int_d^{d+a} \frac{\mu_0 I}{2\pi r} b \, dr,$$

or

$$\Phi_{21} = \frac{\mu_0 I_1 b}{2\pi} \ln \frac{d+a}{d}.$$

The mutual inductance of the loop with respect to the wire is therefore, by Eq. (10-5.4),

$$L_{21} = \frac{\Phi_{21}}{I_1} = \frac{\mu_0 b}{2\pi} \ln \frac{d+a}{d}.$$

Example 10-5.5 A tightly wound, thin-walled toroidal coil of rectangular cross section, inner radius R, width a, and height b is placed at a right angle to a long straight wire coinciding with the symmetry axis of the coil, as shown in Fig. 10.18. The coil has n turns. Find the mutual inductance of the coil with respect to the wire and the mutual inductance of the wire with respect to the coil.

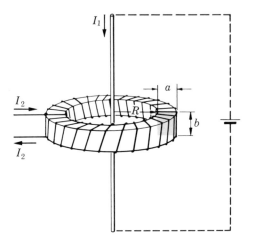

Fig. 10.18   Calculation of the mutual inductance between a toroidal coil and a straight wire.

By symmetry, the current in the wire causes the same flux through each turn of the coil. According to the preceding example, this flux is (using R in place of d)

$$\Phi_{21} = \frac{\mu_0 b I_1}{2\pi} \ln \frac{R + a}{R}.$$

By Eq. (10-5.5), the mutual inductance of the coil with respect to the wire is therefore

$$L_{21} = \frac{n \mu_0 b}{2\pi} \ln \frac{R + a}{R}.$$

To find the mutual inductance of the wire with respect to the coil, we assume that the coil carries a current I_2. Describing a circular Amperian loop of radius r within the coil, with the center on the coil's axis, we have, by Ampere's law,

$$\oint \mathbf{H} \cdot d\mathbf{l} = H 2\pi r = I_{\text{enclosed}} = n I_2.$$

The field in the coil is therefore

$$H = \frac{n I_2}{2\pi r},$$

and the flux density is

$$B = \frac{\mu_0 n I_2}{2\pi r}.$$

The flux in the coil is then

$$\Phi = \int \mathbf{B} \cdot d\mathbf{S} = \int B \, dS = \int_R^{R+a} \frac{\mu_0 n I_2}{2\pi r} b \, dr$$

$$= \frac{n \mu_0 I_2 b}{2\pi} \ln \frac{R + a}{R}.$$

But this is also the flux caused by I_2 through the area bounded by the wire (the area is semi-infinite), so that

$$\Phi_{12} = \frac{n\mu_0 I_2 b}{2\pi} \ln \frac{R + a}{R} .$$

The mutual inductance of the wire with respect to the coil is therefore

$$L_{12} = \frac{n\mu_0 b}{2\pi} \ln \frac{R + a}{R} .$$

As one can see, this is the same expression as that obtained for the mutual inductance of the coil with respect to the wire.

▲

10-6. Calculation of Magnetostatic Fields from Current Distributions

The method of calculating magnetostatic fields by direct application of Ampere's law (see examples in Section 10-4) is limited to fields of very simple structure, because only then can the equation $\oint \mathbf{H} \cdot d\mathbf{l} = \int \mathbf{J} \cdot d\mathbf{S}$ be easily solved for $\mathbf{H}$. There are other methods, however, based on immediate consequences of the basic laws, which can be used for calculating fields of arbitrary structure. One of the most important of these methods is the method of calculating magnetostatic fields from the corresponding current distributions by direct integration. This method can be deduced from the basic magnetostatic laws combined with Poisson's theorem of vector analysis, as follows.

Applying Poisson's theorem, Eq. (2-13.3), to the field vector $\mathbf{H}$, we have

$$\mathbf{H} = -\frac{1}{4\pi} \int_{\text{All space}} \frac{\mathbf{\nabla}'(\mathbf{\nabla}' \cdot \mathbf{H}) - \mathbf{\nabla}' \times (\mathbf{\nabla}' \times \mathbf{H})}{r} \, dv',$$

where we are using primed operators to avoid ambiguity in the transformations that follow. By the curl law, Eq. (10-4.1b), $\mathbf{\nabla}' \times \mathbf{H} = \mathbf{J}$, while by the divergence law, Eq. (10-4.2a), and by the flux density law, Eq. (10-4.3), $\mathbf{\nabla}' \cdot \mathbf{H} = \mathbf{\nabla}' \cdot \mathbf{B}/\mu_0 = 0$. We can therefore write

$$\mathbf{H} = \frac{1}{4\pi} \int_{\text{All space}} \frac{\mathbf{\nabla}' \times \mathbf{J}}{r} \, dv'. \qquad (10\text{-}6.1)$$

Let us now apply to the integrand of this integral the operational relation (V-28). We have

$$\frac{\mathbf{\nabla}' \times \mathbf{J}}{r} = \mathbf{\nabla}' \times \frac{\mathbf{J}}{r} - \mathbf{r}_u \times \frac{\mathbf{J}}{r^2} = \mathbf{\nabla}' \times \frac{\mathbf{J}}{r} + \frac{\mathbf{J} \times \mathbf{r}_u}{r^2},$$

so that

$$\mathbf{H} = \frac{1}{4\pi} \int_{\text{All space}} \mathbf{\nabla}' \times \frac{\mathbf{J}}{r} \, dv' + \frac{1}{4\pi} \int_{\text{All space}} \frac{\mathbf{J} \times \mathbf{r}_u}{r^2} \, dv'. \qquad (10\text{-}6.2)$$

The first integral can be transformed into a surface integral by means of vector identity (V-21), which gives

$$\int_{\text{All space}} \mathbf{\nabla}' \times \frac{\mathbf{J}}{r} \, dv' = - \oint_{\text{All space}} \frac{\mathbf{J}}{r} \times d\mathbf{S}'. \qquad (10\text{-}6.3)$$

In all cases of practical interest, however, $\mathbf{J}$ vanishes outside a finite region of space, and since the surface of integration in the above surface integral encloses all space and thus lies outside the region where $\mathbf{J}$ differs from zero, the surface integral is zero. Therefore the first volume integral is also zero, and we finally obtain

$$\mathbf{H} = \frac{1}{4\pi} \int_{\text{All space}} \frac{\mathbf{J} \times \mathbf{r}_u}{r^2} \, dv'. \qquad (10\text{-}6.4)$$

Thus the magnetostatic field is determined by the distribution of electric currents and can be calculated with the aid of Eq. (10-6.4) if this distribution is known everywhere in space. Note that in this integral $\mathbf{r}_u$ is directed from the source point x', y', z' (the point where $\mathbf{J} \, dv'$ is located) to the point of observation x, y, z.

The integral of Eq. (10-6.4) can be simplified in the following two cases of special current distribution.

Surface Current. Very often current is confined to a layer whose thickness t is much smaller than the distances r from the source points of this layer to the point of observation (Fig. 10.19). In this case the current distribution is called a *surface current.* For this type of current distribution the variation of r with the depth of the source points inside the layer may be neglected. Integrating over the thickness of the layer,

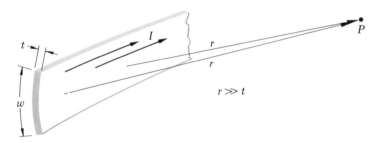

FIG. 10.19   Definition of the surface current.

we then have

$$\mathbf{H} = \frac{1}{4\pi} \int \frac{\mathbf{J} \times \mathbf{r}_u}{r^2} \, dv' = \frac{1}{4\pi} \int \frac{\mathbf{J} \times \mathbf{r}_u}{r^2} \, dS' dt' = \frac{1}{4\pi} \int \left(\int \mathbf{J} \, dt' \right) \times \frac{\mathbf{r}_u}{r^2} \, dS',$$

or

$$\mathbf{H} = \frac{1}{4\pi} \int \frac{\mathbf{J}^{(s)} \times \mathbf{r}_u}{r^2} \, dS', \qquad (10\text{-}6.5)$$

where $\mathbf{J}^{(s)} = \int \mathbf{J} \, dt'$ is the so-called *surface current density*. Since one must integrate $\mathbf{J}^{(s)}$ over the width w (Fig. 10.19) of the layer to obtain the total current in the layer, $\mathbf{J}^{(s)}$ is simply the current per unit width of the layer.

Thus, in the case of a current confined to a layer whose thickness is much smaller than r, the element $\mathbf{J} \, dv'$ may be replaced by $\mathbf{J}^{(s)} dS'$ and the volume integral may be replaced by the surface integral over the area of the layer to which the current is confined.

Filamentary Current. Another frequently encountered case of special current distribution is a current confined to a filament-like region of space whose cross section d is much smaller than the distance r from the points of this region to the point of observation (Fig. 10.20). In this case the current distribution is called a *line current*, or, more frequently, a *filamentary current*. The variation of r over the cross-section area S' of a filamentary current may be neglected. Since the current in a filament must be directed along the filament, we can write

$$\mathbf{J} \, dv' = \mathbf{J} \, dS' dl' = J \, dS' d\mathbf{l}',$$

where the vector notation has been transferred from $\mathbf{J}$ to $d\mathbf{l}'$. The magnetic field of a filamentary current is then

$$\mathbf{H} = \frac{1}{4\pi} \int \frac{\mathbf{J} \times \mathbf{r}_u}{r^2} \, dv' = \frac{1}{4\pi} \int \left(\int J \, dS' \right) \frac{d\mathbf{l}' \times \mathbf{r}_u}{r^2}.$$

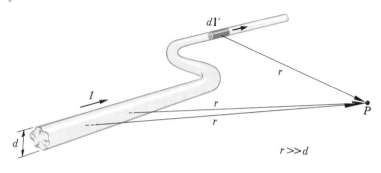

FIG. 10.20   Definition of the line current.

But $\int J\,dS'$ is simply the total current I in the filament. This current is constant throughout the entire length of the filament (because $\oint \mathbf{J} \cdot d\mathbf{S}' = 0$) and can be factored out from under the integral sign. Furthermore, the filament must be closed (for the same reason), so that the last integral must be a circulation integral. We therefore obtain for the magnetic field of a filamentary current

$$\mathbf{H} = \frac{I}{4\pi} \oint \frac{d\mathbf{l}' \times \mathbf{r}_u}{r^2} \qquad (10\text{-}6.6)$$

(the sense of the direction of $d\mathbf{l}'$ is the same as that of the current I). This formula is called the *formula of Biot and Savart*.

▼
Example 10-6.1   A circular ring carries a current I. The radius of the ring is R. Find the magnetic field produced by this ring at a point of the symmetry axis (Fig. 10.21).

Let us rewrite Eq. (10-6.6) as

$$\mathbf{H} = \frac{I}{4\pi} \oint \frac{d\mathbf{l}' \times \mathbf{r}}{r^3} . \qquad (10\text{-}6.7)$$

According to Fig. 10.21, vector $\mathbf{r}$ can be expressed as $\mathbf{r} = \mathbf{z} - \mathbf{R}$. We can therefore write

$$\mathbf{H} = \frac{I}{4\pi} \oint \frac{d\mathbf{l}' \times (\mathbf{z} - \mathbf{R})}{r^3} = \frac{I}{4\pi} \oint \frac{d\mathbf{l}' \times \mathbf{z}}{r^3} - \frac{I}{4\pi} \oint \frac{d\mathbf{l}' \times \mathbf{R}}{r^3} .$$

Since $\mathbf{z}$ and r are both constant, we can factor them out from under the integral signs, obtaining

$$\mathbf{H} = -\frac{I}{4\pi r^3} \mathbf{z} \times \oint d\mathbf{l}' - \frac{I}{4\pi r^3} \oint d\mathbf{l}' \times \mathbf{R}.$$

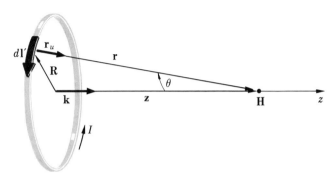

Fɪɢ. 10.21   Calculation of the magnetic field on the axis of a current-carrying ring.

But $\oint d\mathbf{l}' = 0$ (by the polygon law of vector addition) and $d\mathbf{l}' \times \mathbf{R} = -\mathbf{k}R\,dl'$ (by Fig. 10.21). The last expression for $\mathbf{H}$ therefore reduces to

$$\mathbf{H} = \mathbf{k}\,\frac{IR}{4\pi r^3}\oint dl' = \mathbf{k}\,\frac{IR}{4\pi r^3}\,2\pi R.$$

Using now the relation $r = (R^2 + z^2)^{1/2}$, we finally obtain

$$\mathbf{H} = \frac{IR^2}{2(R^2 + z^2)^{3/2}}\,\mathbf{k}, \quad \text{or} \quad \mathbf{H} = \frac{I}{2R}\sin^3\theta\,\mathbf{k}. \qquad (10\text{-}6.8\text{a, b})$$

It is interesting to note that in the center of the ring ($z = 0$, $\theta = \pi/2$) the field is simply

$$\mathbf{H}_{center} = \frac{I}{2R}\,\mathbf{k}. \qquad (10\text{-}6.9)$$

Example 10-6.2   Find the contribution of a straight segment of current-carrying wire to the magnetic field determined by the formula of Biot and Savart.

Let the current in the wire be I, and let the length of the segment under consideration be l, as shown in Fig. 10.22. The formula of Biot and Savart for this segment can be written as

$$\mathbf{H} = \frac{I}{4\pi}\int \frac{d\mathbf{z}' \times \mathbf{r}_u}{r^2}.$$

In this integral $d\mathbf{z}' \times \mathbf{r}_u = dz'\sin(d\mathbf{z}', \mathbf{r}_u)\,\boldsymbol{\theta}_u = dz'\cos\varphi\,\boldsymbol{\theta}_u$, where φ is as shown in Fig. 10.22, and $\boldsymbol{\theta}_u$ is a unit vector in the circular direction normal

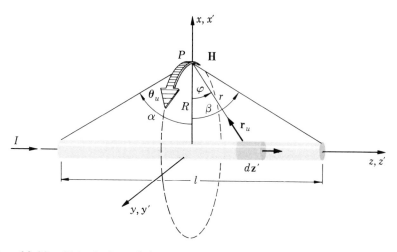

FIG. 10.22   Calculation of the magnetic field associated with a segment of a current-carrying wire.

to the wire and forming a right-handed system with the current I. Let us now assume that the point of observation P is at a distance R from the wire. As one can see from Fig. 10.22, $z' = R \tan \varphi$ so that $dz' = (R/\cos^2 \varphi)d\varphi$, and $r = R/\cos \varphi$. Substituting these values in the above integral, we obtain

$$\mathbf{H} = \boldsymbol{\theta}_u \frac{1}{4\pi} \int_{-\alpha}^{\beta} \frac{(R/\cos^2 \varphi) \cos \varphi \, d\varphi}{(R/\cos \varphi)^2} = \boldsymbol{\theta}_u \frac{I}{4\pi R} \int_{-\alpha}^{\beta} \cos \varphi \, d\varphi$$

$$= \frac{I}{4\pi R} (\sin \beta + \sin \alpha) \boldsymbol{\theta}_u.$$

Observe that for a very long segment $(\alpha \approx \beta \approx \pi/2)$ this expression reduces to that found in Example 10-4.1 by direct application of Ampère's law.

Example 10-6.3   A thin-walled cylinder of radius R and length l carries a uniform circular current I as shown in Fig. 10.23. Find $\mathbf{H}$ at a point of the cylinder's axis.

Since the cylinder is thin-walled, the current in the cylinder may be regarded as a surface current and Eq. (10-6.5) may be used for finding $\mathbf{H}$. It is, however, simpler to consider the cylinder merely as a system of current-carrying rings of width dl and current $dI = (I/l)dl$, one of which is shown in Fig. 10.23. The contribution of such a ring to the magnetic field of the cylinder is, by Eq. (10-6.8b) obtained in Example 10-6.1,

$$d\mathbf{H} = \mathbf{k} \frac{I}{2Rl} \sin^3 \theta \, dl.$$

But as can be seen from Fig. 10.23,

$$dl = \frac{r \, d\theta}{\sin \theta} = \frac{R \, d\theta}{\sin^2 \theta}.$$

Substituting this expression in the above formula for $d\mathbf{H}$ and integrating, we obtain

$$\mathbf{H} = \mathbf{k} \frac{I}{2Rl} \int_{\theta_1}^{\theta_2} \frac{\sin^3 \theta R \, d\theta}{\sin^2 \theta} = \mathbf{k} \frac{I}{2l} \int_{\theta_1}^{\theta_2} \sin \theta \, d\theta,$$

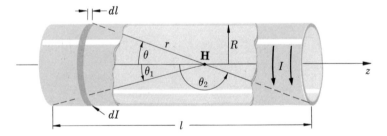

FIG. 10.23   Calculation of the magnetic field on the axis of a thin-walled current-carrying cylinder.

or

$$\mathbf{H} = \frac{I}{2l} (\cos \theta_1 - \cos \theta_2)\mathbf{k}.$$

At the center of the cylinder, $\theta_2 = \pi - \theta_1$, and

$$\cos \theta_1 = -\cos \theta_2 = \frac{l}{\sqrt{l^2 + 4R^2}}.$$

Therefore

$$\mathbf{H}_{\text{center}} = \frac{I}{\sqrt{l^2 + 4R^2}} \mathbf{k}.$$

In the plane of one end of the cylinder, the field is similarly

$$\mathbf{H}_{\text{end}} = \frac{I}{2\sqrt{l^2 + R^2}} \mathbf{k}.$$

For a very long cylinder, $R \ll l$, so that these formulas become

$$\mathbf{H}_{\text{center}} = \frac{I}{l} \mathbf{k} \quad \text{and} \quad \mathbf{H}_{\text{end}} = \frac{I}{2l} \mathbf{k}.$$

Example 10-6.4   A spherical shell of radius **R** and uniform surface charge density σ is rotated with angular velocity **ω** about a diameter (Fig. 10.24). Find the magnetic field in the center of the shell.

Let the thickness of the shell be t. The space charge density in the shell is then $\rho = \sigma/t$. By Eq. (10-3.1), the shell constitutes a current distribution of density $\mathbf{J} = \rho\mathbf{v} = (\sigma/t)\mathbf{v}$, where **v** is the linear velocity at a point of the shell. Since the shell is thin, this current distribution may be regarded as a surface current of surface current density $\mathbf{J}^{(s)} = \mathbf{J}t = \sigma\mathbf{v}$. The magnetic field of the shell can therefore be found from Eq. (10-6.5). Since

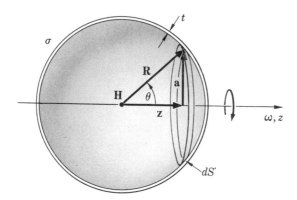

FIG. 10.24   Calculation of the magnetic field at the center of a charged, rotating spherical shell.

$\mathbf{v} = \boldsymbol{\omega} \times \mathbf{R}$, Eq. (10-6.5) for the shell can be written as

$$\mathbf{H} = -\frac{\sigma}{4\pi} \oint \frac{(\boldsymbol{\omega} \times \mathbf{R}) \times \mathbf{R}}{R^3} \, dS'$$

(the minus sign is needed because $\mathbf{R}$ in Fig. 10.24 is directed *toward* the source points). Now, according to Fig. 10.24, $\mathbf{R} = \mathbf{z} + \mathbf{a}$, so that $\boldsymbol{\omega} \times \mathbf{R} = \boldsymbol{\omega} \times \mathbf{z} + \boldsymbol{\omega} \times \mathbf{a}$. But $\boldsymbol{\omega} \times \mathbf{z} = 0$ because $\boldsymbol{\omega}$ is parallel to $\mathbf{z}$. We can therefore write, making use of the "bac cab" expansion,

$$\mathbf{H} = -\frac{\sigma}{4\pi} \oint \frac{(\boldsymbol{\omega} \times \mathbf{a}) \times \mathbf{R}}{R^3} \, dS' = \frac{\sigma}{4\pi} \oint \frac{\boldsymbol{\omega}(\mathbf{a} \cdot \mathbf{R})}{R^3} \, dS' - \frac{\sigma}{4\pi} \oint \frac{\mathbf{a}(\boldsymbol{\omega} \cdot \mathbf{R})}{R^3} \, dS'.$$

The last integral is, however, zero because to every $\mathbf{a}(\boldsymbol{\omega} \cdot \mathbf{R})$ there corresponds an equally large $-\mathbf{a}(\boldsymbol{\omega} \cdot \mathbf{R})$, and R^3 is a constant. Thus the field is

$$\mathbf{H} = \frac{\sigma}{4\pi} \oint \frac{\boldsymbol{\omega}(\mathbf{a} \cdot \mathbf{R})}{R^3} \, dS'.$$

Taking into account that $\boldsymbol{\omega}(\mathbf{a} \cdot \mathbf{R}) = \boldsymbol{\omega} R^2 \sin^2 \theta$ and that dS' may be written as $dS' = 2\pi R^2 \sin \theta \, d\theta$, we obtain therefore

$$\mathbf{H} = \boldsymbol{\omega} \, \frac{\sigma R}{2} \int_0^\pi \sin^3 \theta \, d\theta,$$

or

$$\mathbf{H} = \frac{2}{3} \sigma R \boldsymbol{\omega}.$$

▲

10-7. Calculation of Magnetostatic Fields from Current Inhomogeneities

Let us examine Eq. (10-6.1), which we obtained in the preceding section,

$$\mathbf{H} = \frac{1}{4\pi} \int_{\text{All space}} \frac{\nabla' \times \mathbf{J}}{r} \, dv'. \tag{10-6.1}$$

The remarkable feature of this equation is that it correlates the magnetic field with the *curl* of the current distribution rather than with the current distribution itself. Hence the equation may be interpreted as indicating that the magnetic field is associated not with the electric current as such, but with the inhomogeneities in the distribution of the current (a homogeneous, or uniform, current has zero curl). As we shall presently see, this point of view is useful for analyzing and solving certain types of magnetostatic problems.

For practical applications Eq. (10-6.1) can be transformed into a somewhat different form, which is more convenient to use in the case of currents changing abruptly from one value to another across a thin boundary layer. For a current distribution of this type, the integral of Eq. (10-6.1) can be split into two integrals

$$\underset{\text{All space}}{\int} \frac{\mathbf{\nabla'} \times \mathbf{J}}{r}\, dv' = \underset{\text{Boundary layer}}{\int} \frac{\mathbf{\nabla'} \times \mathbf{J}}{r}\, dv' + \underset{\text{Remaining space}}{\int} \frac{\mathbf{\nabla'} \times \mathbf{J}}{r}\, dv'.$$

$$(10\text{-}7.1)$$

Using vector identity (V-28), we can write the first integral on the right as

$$\underset{\text{Boundary layer}}{\int} \frac{\mathbf{\nabla'} \times \mathbf{J}}{r}\, dv'$$

$$= \underset{\text{Boundary layer}}{\int} \mathbf{\nabla'} \times \frac{\mathbf{J}}{r}\, dv' - \underset{\text{Boundary layer}}{\int} \mathbf{r}_u \times \frac{\mathbf{J}}{r^2}\, dv'. \quad (10\text{-}7.2)$$

Since $\mathbf{J}$ and $\mathbf{r}_u/r^2$ are finite, however, the last integral vanishes if the boundary layer is sufficiently thin, which we assume to be the case. The first integral on the right of Eq. (10-7.2) can be transformed into a surface integral by means of vector identity (V-21). This reduces Eq. (10-7.2) to

$$\underset{\text{Boundary layer}}{\int} \frac{\mathbf{\nabla'} \times \mathbf{J}}{r}\, dv' = - \underset{\text{Boundary layer}}{\oint} \frac{\mathbf{J}}{r} \times d\mathbf{S'},$$

where the surface integral is extended over *both* surfaces of the boundary layer. Since for a sufficiently thin layer these surfaces are equal, the last equation can also be written as

$$\underset{\text{Boundary layer}}{\int} \frac{\mathbf{\nabla'} \times \mathbf{J}}{r}\, dv' = \underset{\text{Boundary}}{\oint} \frac{\mathbf{J}_1 - \mathbf{J}_2}{r} \times d\mathbf{S'}_{12}, \quad (10\text{-}7.3)$$

where $\mathbf{J}_1$ and $\mathbf{J}_2$ are the current densities on side 1 and side 2 of the boundary, and $d\mathbf{S'}_{12}$ is directed from side 1 to side 2.

Combining Eqs. (10-7.3), (10-7.1), and (10-6.1), we obtain

$$\mathbf{H} = \frac{1}{4\pi} \underset{\text{Boundary}}{\oint} \frac{\mathbf{J}_1 - \mathbf{J}_2}{r} \times d\mathbf{S'}_{12} + \frac{1}{4\pi} \underset{\text{Remaining space}}{\int} \frac{\mathbf{\nabla'} \times \mathbf{J}}{r}\, dv'. \quad (10\text{-}7.4)$$

This equation becomes especially simple in the case of a curl-free current distribution surrounded by a current-free space. In this case we may set $\mathbf{J}_2 = 0$, $\mathbf{J}_1 = \mathbf{J}$ and $d\mathbf{S'}_{12} = d\mathbf{S'}$, where $d\mathbf{S'}$ points from the current distribution into the surrounding space. We then obtain

$$\mathbf{H} = \frac{1}{4\pi} \oint_{\text{Boundary}} \frac{\mathbf{J} \times d\mathbf{S}'}{r}. \tag{10-7.5}$$

Since $d\mathbf{S}'$ is normal to the boundary, and since $\mathbf{J}$ must be tangent to the boundary, $\mathbf{J} \times d\mathbf{S}'$ must also be tangent to the boundary. A magnetic field due to a boundary surface is therefore always parallel to this surface.

▼
Example 10-7.1   An axially symmetric channel is made in a conducting bar of length l, as shown in Fig. 10.25. A voltage V is applied between the ends of the bar. Neglecting end effects, find how the magnetic field on the symmetry axis of the channel is affected by the linear dimensions of the channel.

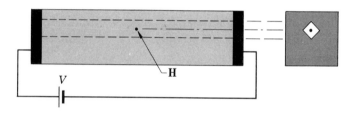

Fɪɢ. 10.25   Effect of the size of a channel on the magnetic field on the axis of the channel.

The current in the bar is curl-free, so that Eq. (10-7.5) applies. By symmetry, the walls of the channel do not contribute to the magnetic field on the axis. The magnetic field on the axis is therefore entirely due to the external surfaces of the bar. Since these surfaces are not affected by the channel, the field on the axis can vary with the size of the channel only if the channel affects the current density in the bar. The current density is $\mathbf{J} = \sigma \mathbf{E} = \sigma V/l$, however, and does not depend on the presence or size of the channel. The linear dimensions of the channel therefore have no effect on the field on the symmetry axis of the channel.

Example 10-7.2   To measure the magnetic field inside a homogeneous current-carrying conductor, a spherical cavity is made in the conductor, and the magnetic field at the center of the cavity is measured. The cavity is so small that neither the total current in the conductor nor the current density at the surfaces of the conductor is affected by its presence. Find how the magnetic field at the center of the cavity depends on the radius of the cavity (Fig. 10.26).

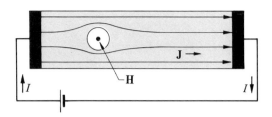

FIG. 10.26   Effect of the size of a spherical cavity on the magnetic field at the center of the cavity.

Since the conductor is homogeneous, $\mathbf{\nabla} \times \mathbf{J} = 0$, and the magnetic field is given by Eq. (10-7.5). By symmetry, the surface of the cavity has no effect on the magnetic field at the center of the cavity. The remaining surfaces are, however, not affected by the presence of the cavity, and the currents at these surfaces, by supposition, are not affected either. Therefore the magnetic field under consideration does not depend on the radius of the cavity.

Example 10-7.3   A thin, uniformly charged disk of charge density ρ, radius R, and thickness t rotates with angular velocity $\mathbf{\omega}$ about the axis of symmetry, as shown in Fig. 10.27. Find the magnetic field at the center of the disk.

By Eq. (10-3.1), the disk may be regarded as a current of density $\mathbf{J} = \rho\mathbf{v} = \rho\mathbf{\omega} \times \mathbf{r}$, where $\mathbf{r}$ is the radius vector from the axis of the disk to a source point within the disk. With the aid of the "bac cab" expansion we obtain

$$\mathbf{\nabla'} \times \mathbf{J} = \mathbf{\nabla'} \times (\rho\mathbf{\omega} \times \mathbf{r}) = \rho[\mathbf{\omega}(\mathbf{\nabla'} \cdot \mathbf{r}) - (\mathbf{\omega} \cdot \mathbf{\nabla'})\mathbf{r}],$$

and since $\mathbf{r}$ can be written as $x'\mathbf{i} + y'\mathbf{j}$, while $\mathbf{\omega} \cdot \mathbf{\nabla'}$ can be written as $\omega\partial/\partial z'$, we have

$$\mathbf{\nabla'} \times \mathbf{J} = 2\rho\mathbf{\omega}.$$

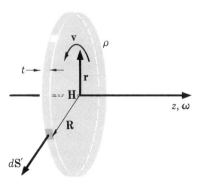

FIG. 10.27   Calculation of the magnetic field at the center of a rotating charged disk.

The magnetic field is then, according to Eq. (10-7.4),

$$\mathbf{H} = \frac{1}{4\pi} \oint_{\substack{\text{Boundary}}} \frac{\rho(\boldsymbol{\omega} \times \mathbf{r}) \times d\mathbf{S}'}{r} + \frac{1}{4\pi} \int_{\substack{\text{Interior}}} \frac{2\rho\boldsymbol{\omega}}{r} \, dv' \; .$$

By symmetry, the flat surfaces of the disk make no contribution to the field at the center of the disk, so that only the curved surface of the disk needs be considered in the first integral. For the curved surface, however, $r = R$, and

$$(\boldsymbol{\omega} \times \mathbf{r}) \times d\mathbf{S}' = (\boldsymbol{\omega} \times \mathbf{R}) \times d\mathbf{S}'$$
$$= -\boldsymbol{\omega}(\mathbf{R} \cdot d\mathbf{S}') + \mathbf{R}(\boldsymbol{\omega} \cdot d\mathbf{S}') = -\boldsymbol{\omega} R \, dS'.$$

In the last integral we can write $dv' = 2\pi r t \, dr$. The magnetic field is therefore

$$\mathbf{H} = -\frac{1}{4\pi} \int_{\substack{\text{Curved surface}}} \frac{\rho\boldsymbol{\omega} R}{R} \, dS' + \frac{1}{4\pi} \int_0^R \frac{2\rho\boldsymbol{\omega} 2\pi r t}{r} \, dr$$

$$= -\boldsymbol{\omega}\frac{\rho}{4\pi} \int_{\substack{\text{Curved surface}}} dS' + \boldsymbol{\omega}\rho t \int_0^R dr$$

$$= -\boldsymbol{\omega}\frac{\rho}{4\pi} 2\pi R t + \boldsymbol{\omega}\rho t R,$$

or

$$\mathbf{H} = \frac{1}{2}\rho t R \boldsymbol{\omega}.$$

Example 10-7.4 Find the magnetic field associated with a very long, plane boundary surface, one side of which is in a current-free region, while the other is in a region of constant current density $\mathbf{J}$ directed along the surface (Fig. 10.28).

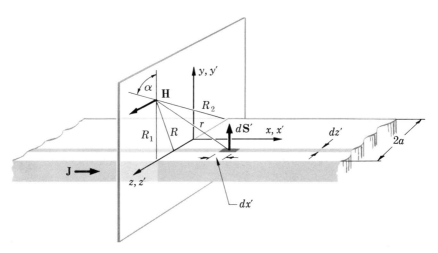

Fig. 10.28 Calculation of the magnetic field associated with a very long, plane boundary surface.

According to Eq. (10-7.5), the field is given by

$$\mathbf{H} = \frac{1}{4\pi} \int \frac{\mathbf{J} \times d\mathbf{S}'}{r},$$

where $d\mathbf{S}'$ is directed into the current-free region. Let the coordinates be as shown in Fig. 10.28, and let the surface extend from $x' = -L$ to $x' = +L$, and from $z' = -a$ to $z' = a$. Since $\mathbf{J} \times d\mathbf{S}'$ is directed along the z-axis, the magnetic field has only the z-component. The contribution of an elementary ribbon of width dz' to the total field of the surface is

$$d\mathbf{H} = \mathbf{k}\frac{J\,dz'}{4\pi}\int_{-L}^{L}\frac{dx'}{\sqrt{x'^2 + R^2}} = \mathbf{k}\frac{J\,dz'}{2\pi}\int_{0}^{L}\frac{dx'}{\sqrt{x'^2 + R^2}}$$

$$= \mathbf{k}\frac{J\,dz'}{2\pi}\ln(x' + \sqrt{x'^2 + R^2})\Big|_{0}^{L} = \mathbf{k}\frac{J\,dz'}{2\pi}\ln\frac{L + \sqrt{L^2 + R^2}}{R},$$

and since $L \gg R$,

$$d\mathbf{H} = \mathbf{k}\frac{J}{2\pi}(\ln 2L - \ln R)dz'.$$

The total field of the surface is

$$\mathbf{H} = \mathbf{k}\frac{J}{2\pi}\int_{-a}^{+a}(\ln 2L - \ln R)dz' = \mathbf{k}\frac{J}{2\pi}\left(2a \ln 2L - \int_{-a}^{+a}\ln R\,dz'\right).$$

Since $R = \sqrt{y^2 + (z - z')^2}$, we have

$$\mathbf{H} = \mathbf{k}\frac{J}{4\pi}\left\{4a \ln 2L - \int_{-a}^{+a}\ln[y^2 + (z - z')^2]dz'\right\}.$$

Noting that $dz' = -d(z - z')$, and integrating by parts, we obtain

$$\mathbf{H} = \mathbf{k}\frac{J}{4\pi}\left\{4a \ln 2L + (z - z')\ln[y^2 + (z - z')^2]\Big|_{-a}^{+a}\right.$$

$$\left. -\int_{-a}^{+a}\frac{2(z - z')^2}{y^2 + (z - z')^2}d(z - z')\right\} = \mathbf{k}\frac{J}{4\pi}\left\{4a \ln 2L\right.$$

$$\left. + 2(z - z')\ln R - 2\left[(z - z') - y\tan^{-1}\frac{z - z'}{y}\right]\right\}\Big|_{-a}^{+a},$$

which after the substitution of the limits simplifies to

$$\mathbf{H} = \mathbf{k}\frac{J}{2\pi}(2a \ln 2L + z \ln R_1/R_2 - a \ln R_1 R_2 + 2a - y\alpha),\quad (10\text{-}7.6)$$

where R_1, R_2, and α are as in Fig. 10.28.

Example 10-7.5   Find the magnetic field produced by a long, thin, straight conducting ribbon of width $2a$ carrying a uniform current I (the thickness of the ribbon is $2t$).

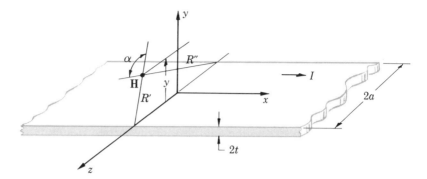

FIG. 10.29   Calculation of the magnetic field of a thin current-carrying ribbon.

The field of the ribbon can be obtained by adding the fields associated with each surface of the ribbon. Let the coordinates be as shown in Fig. 10.29. The z-component of the field is produced by the horizontal surfaces. The contribution of the upper surface to the field is given by Eq. (10-7.6) of the preceding example. The contribution of the lower surface is given by the same equation, except that **k** in this equation is now replaced by $-\mathbf{k}$, and y is replaced by $y + 2t$. Since both surfaces are of the same length and width, and since the ribbon is thin, so that R_1 and R_2 are the same for both surfaces, we obtain upon adding the two contributions

$$H_z = \frac{Jt}{\pi}\,\alpha,$$

and since $J = I/4at$, the z-component of the field is

$$H_z = \frac{I}{4\pi a}\,\alpha.$$

The y-component of the field is produced by the vertical surfaces of the ribbon. The contribution of the back surface is given by Eq. (10-7.6) with **k** replaced by **j**, a replaced by t, R_1 and R_2 replaced by R'' (this surface in a thin ribbon is so narrow that both R's may be considered equal to R''), and with α set equal to zero (because the ribbon is thin). The contribution of the front surface is also given by Eq. (10-7.6), but with **k** replaced by $-\mathbf{j}$, a replaced by t, R_1 and R_2 replaced by R', and with α set again equal to zero. Adding the two contributions gives

$$H_y = \frac{Jt}{\pi}\ln\frac{R'}{R''},$$

or

$$H_y = \frac{I}{4\pi a}\ln\frac{R'}{R''}.$$

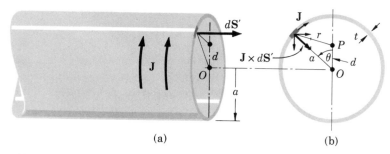

(a) (b)

FIG. 10.30 Calculation of the radial magnetic field in an end plane of a current-carrying cylinder.

Example 10-7.6 A long thin-walled cylinder of radius a and wall thickness t carries a circular current of density $\mathbf{J}$, as shown in Fig. 10.30. Find the radial component of the magnetic field at a point near the symmetry axis in one of the two end planes of the cylinder.

Only the end surfaces of the cylinder can contribute to the radial field. Since the cylinder is long, the contribution of the far end is negligible. Let the point of observation P be at a distance d from the axis, as shown in Fig. 10.30b. According to Eq. (10-7.5), the radial field at this point is then given by

$$\mathbf{H}_r = \frac{1}{4\pi} \int \frac{\mathbf{J} \times d\mathbf{S}'}{r} = \frac{1}{4\pi} \int \frac{\mathbf{J} \times d\mathbf{S}'}{\sqrt{a^2 + d^2 - 2ad\cos\theta}},$$

where the integral is extended over the end surface shown in Fig. 10.30b. The direction of $\mathbf{J} \times d\mathbf{S}'$ on this surface is radial, toward the axis. By symmetry, however, the component of $\mathbf{J} \times d\mathbf{S}'$ parallel to the line PO is the only one which makes a net contribution to the field. The magnitude of this component is $J \cos\theta \, dS'$. Taking now into account that, by supposition, $d \ll a$, and making use of the well-known rules for operations with small quantities, we have for the magnitude of the radial field

$$H_r = \frac{1}{4\pi} \int_0^{2\pi} \frac{J\cos\theta}{\sqrt{a^2 + d^2 - 2ad\cos\theta}} \, ta \, d\theta$$

$$\approx \frac{Jta}{2\pi} \int_0^\pi \frac{\cos\theta \, d\theta}{a\left(1 - \dfrac{d}{a}\cos\theta\right)} \approx \frac{Jt}{2\pi} \int_0^\pi \cos\theta \left(1 + \frac{d}{a}\cos\theta\right) d\theta$$

$$= -\frac{Jt}{2\pi} \sin\theta \Big|_0^\pi + \frac{Jtd}{2\pi a} \left(\frac{\theta}{2} - \frac{1}{4}\sin 2\theta\right)\Big|_0^\pi,$$

or

$$H_r \approx \frac{Jtd}{4a}.$$

▲

Problems

10.1. Prove that the basic laws given by Eqs. (4-4.1) to (4-4.3) uniquely specify the fields **H** and **B** within a limited region of space, provided that the normal component of **H** or **B** is known for all points of the surface by which the region is bounded.

10.2. A long cylindrical wire of 1 mm radius carries a current of 1 amp. Calculate and plot the magnetic field and the magnetic flux density, for both external and internal points, as a function of the distance from the axis of the wire.

10.3. Find the magnetic field produced by a lightning bolt carrying a current of 1000 amp confined to a long cylindrical channel of 10 cm in diameter at a point just outside the channel and at a point 100 m distant from the channel.

10.4. A cylindrical channel is drilled in a long conducting cylinder so that the axis of the channel is parallel to the axis of the cylinder but is displaced from it by a distance **a**. Show that if the cylinder carries a uniform current of density **J** in the direction of its length, the magnetic field anywhere in the channel is

$$\mathbf{H} = \frac{\mathbf{J} \times \mathbf{a}}{2}.$$

10.5. Find the magnetic field for both internal and external points of the cylinder described in the preceding problem.

10.6. Show that the magnetic field inside a long solenoid

$$H = \frac{nI}{l}$$

is compatible with Ampere's law and can be obtained by a direct application of this law to the solenoid.

10.7. Show that the magnetic field inside a toroidal coil of n turns carrying a current I is the same as that which would be produced by a straight wire carrying a current nI along the symmetry axis of the toroid.

10.8. Two large parallel conducting plates of width w are separated by a small distance (they form a parallel-plate capacitor) and carry a current I in opposite directions. Show that if the edge effects are neglected, the magnetic field in the space between the plates is

$$H = \frac{I}{w}.$$

10.9. A transmission line is formed by two parallel conducting ribbons of width w separated from each other by a small distance d (the broad sides of the ribbons are facing one another). Show that if the edge effects are neglected, the self inductance per unit length of this transmission line is

$$L = \mu_0 \frac{d}{w}.$$

10.10. Show that the self inductance of a "double" solenoid consisting of two long, thin-walled coaxial coils placed one inside the other and carrying a current I in opposite directions is

$$L = \frac{\pi \mu_0 n^2 (b^2 - a^2)}{l},$$

where b and a are the radii of the outer and inner coils, respectively, l is the length of each coil, and n is the number of turns in each coil.

10.11. Show that the self inductance of a tightly wound toroidal coil of rectangular cross section is

$$L = \frac{\mu_0 n^2 w}{2\pi} \ln \frac{b}{a},$$

where a and b are the internal and external radii of the coil, w is the width of the coil, and n is the number of turns in the coil.

10.12. Show that the self inductance of a toroidal coil of n turns, cross-sectional radius a, and mean radius b is

$$L = \mu_0 n^2 [b - (b^2 - a^2)^{1/2}].$$

10.13. A toroidal ring of mean radius a and cross-sectional radius b is wound with two windings of n_1 and n_2 turns, respectively. Find the mutual inductance between the two windings.

10.14. Find the mutual inductance of two parallel coaxial circular loops of radii a and b, respectively, separated by a large distance R ($R \gg a,b$).

10.15. Show that the mutual inductance of two coaxial solenoids of radii r_1 and r_2 having n_1 and n_2 turns, respectively, and separated by a distance R which is much larger than the linear dimensions of either solenoid, is

$$L_{12} = \frac{\pi \mu_0 n_1 n_2 r_1^2 r_2^2}{2R^3}.$$

10.16. Show that a current-carrying wire forming a circular arc contributes to the magnetic field at the center of curvature of the arc an amount

$$H = \frac{I}{4\pi r} \alpha,$$

where I is the current in the wire, r is the radius of the arc, and α is the angle subtended by the arc at the center of curvature.

10.17. Show that the magnetic field at the center of a square loop of length l on a side carrying a current I is

$$H = \frac{2\sqrt{2}\,I}{\pi l}.$$

10.18. A conducting loop made in the form of a regular polygon of n sides carries a current I. Show that the field at the center of the polygon is

$$H = \frac{nI}{2\pi R} \tan \frac{\pi}{n},$$

where R is the radius of the circle which may be described about the polygon.

10.19. A "current disk" of radius R is made of insulated wire wound as a close flat spiral of n turns carrying a current I from the terminal at the center to the terminal at circumference. Show that on the axis of the disk

$$H = \frac{1}{2} \frac{nI}{R} [\cosh^{-1} (\sec \theta) - \sin \theta],$$

where θ is the angle subtended by the radius of the disk at the point of observation.

10.20. Show that the magnetic field on the axis inside a solenoid is

$$H = \frac{nI}{2l} (\cos \theta_1 + \cos \theta_2),$$

where n is the number of turns in the solenoid, I is the current in the solenoid, l is the length of the solenoid, and θ_1, θ_2 are the angles subtended at the point of observation by the radii of the end surfaces of the solenoid.

10.21. A helix of angle α and radius a is formed by n complete turns of a wire carrying a current I. Show that the magnetic field at the center of the helix is

$$H = \frac{nI}{2a} (1 + \pi^2 n^2 \tan^2 \alpha)^{-1/2}.$$

10.22. A current I flows along an elliptical path of length l and area A. Show that the field at the center of the ellipse is $Il/4A$.

10.23. Prove by means of dimensional analysis, or otherwise, that the magnetic field H of a current-carrying conductor can be expressed as a function of the power dissipated in the conductor, P, the conductivity of the conductor, σ, a characteristic linear dimension of the conductor, a, and the energy constant, $^\circ$, as

$$H = G \sqrt{\frac{\sigma P}{^\circ a}},$$

where G is a numerical factor, a function of geometrical parameters of the conductor only (G may be called the "efficiency factor" of the conductor).

10.24. Consider the magnetic field at the center of a thin-walled cylinder carrying a circular current. Show that if the characteristic linear dimension of the cylinder is assumed to be its radius r, then the efficiency factor of the cylinder, as defined in the preceding problem, is

$$G = \sqrt{\frac{tl}{2\pi(l^2 + 4r^2)}},$$

where l is the length of the cylinder and t is its wall thickness. Show also that for given r and t the cylinder will consume least power to maintain a prescribed field if $l = 2r$.

10.25. A spherical capacitor consisting of two concentric spherical shells of radii a and b carrying charges $+q$ and $-q$, respectively, is rotated with angular velocity $\boldsymbol{\omega}$ about a diameter. Show that a magnetic field

$$\mathbf{H} = \boldsymbol{\omega} \frac{q}{6\pi} \left(\frac{1}{a} - \frac{1}{b} \right)$$

will appear at the center of the capacitor.

10.26. A thin, uniformly charged disk of surface charge density σ and radius R is rotating with angular velocity $\boldsymbol{\omega}$ about the axis of symmetry. Show that the magnetic field at a point of this axis is

$$\mathbf{H} = \frac{\boldsymbol{\omega}\sigma}{2} \left[(R^2 + 2z^2)(R^2 + z^2)^{-1/2} - 2z \right],$$

where z is the distance from the disk.

10.27. Show that the components of the field of a long rectangular bar carrying a uniformly distributed current I in the x-direction are:

$$H_x = 0$$

$$H_y = \frac{I}{2\pi A} \left(y_1 \ln \frac{r_4}{r_1} + y_3 \ln \frac{r_2}{r_3} + z_1 \alpha_1 - z_3 \alpha_3 \right)$$

$$H_z = \frac{I}{2\pi A} \left(z_1 \ln \frac{r_1}{r_2} + z_3 \ln \frac{r_3}{r_4} - y_1 \alpha_4 + y_3 \alpha_2 \right).$$

In this formula A is the cross-sectional area of the bar; r_1, r_2, r_3, and r_4 are the respective distances from the observation point in the positive quadrant to the edges of the bar starting with the nearest and proceeding clockwise around the x-axis; y_1, z_1 and y_3, z_3 are the Cartesian components of r_1 and r_3, respectively. The angles α_1, α_2, α_3, and α_4 are those between successive r's. The current is directed away from the observer.

10.28. Show that the field of a long rectangular bar approaches the field of a cylindrical wire for points far remote from the bar.

10.29. Show that at the end of a long solenoid the magnetic field near the axis of the solenoid has a radial component

$$H_r \approx \frac{nI}{4l} \frac{d}{a},$$

where n is the number of turns, I is the current, l is the length, and a is the radius of the solenoid, while d is the distance of the point of observation from the axis.

10.30. Show that near the center of a long solenoid the magnetic field has a radial component

$$H_r \approx 24nI \left(\frac{a^2 z d}{l^5} \right),$$

where the symbols are the same as in the preceding problem and z is the distance of the point of observation from the central plane of the solenoid.

10.31. Consider a cylindrical boundary surface the inner side of which is in a region of circular current of density $\mathbf{J}$, while the outer side is in a current-free region. Show that on the symmetry axis the magnetic field associated with this surface can be expressed as

$$\mathbf{H} = \frac{\mathbf{J} \times \mathbf{a}}{2} \ln \frac{z_2 + \sqrt{a^2 + z_2^2}}{z_1 + \sqrt{a^2 + z_1^2}},$$

where z_1 and z_2 are the coordinates of the planes of the near and far ends of the surface, respectively, measured along the symmetry axis from the origin at the point of observation, and $\mathbf{a}$ is the radius of the surface measured in the direction away from the axis.

10.32. Consider a ring of rectangular cross section, inner radius a_1, outer radius a_2, width w, and conductivity σ. A narrow slot is cut through the ring in a plane containing the ring's axis, and two plane electrodes are attached to the exposed surfaces. A voltage V is then applied to the electrodes, and a circular current is thus set up in the ring. Show that the magnetic field on the axis of the ring can be expressed as

$$H = \frac{\sigma V}{4\pi} \ln \frac{(z_2 + \sqrt{a_1^2 + z_2^2})(z_1 + \sqrt{a_2^2 + z_1^2})}{(z_2 + \sqrt{a_2^2 + z_2^2})(z_1 + \sqrt{a_1^2 + z_1^2})},$$

where z_1 and z_2 are the coordinates of the end planes of the ring, as defined in the preceding problem. (Rings of this type can be used for producing very strong magnetic fields.)

10.33. Using Eq. (10-7.4), show that outside a current distribution the magnetic field of this distribution can be expanded in a series of inverse powers of R—the distance from the current-carrying region—and show that the first nonvanishing term in this series is that with R^{-3} (this series expresses the field as a superposition of multipole fields).

11

MAGNETIC POTENTIALS

A magnetostatic field can be described not only by the vectors **H** and **B** but also by another vector: the magnetostatic vector potential **A**. What is more, in a current-free region a magnetostatic field can also be described by a scalar quantity: the magnetostatic scalar potential φ. All four of these quantities are intimately related to each other, and can be derived one from another. However, the potentials **A** or φ are frequently easier to calculate than the field vectors **H** or **B**. It is therefore frequently more convenient to use one of these potentials instead of a field vector for describing a magnetostatic field. The basic properties and applications of magnetostatic potentials are discussed in this chapter.

11-1. Magnetic Vector Potential

According to the corollary to Poisson's theorem of vector analysis, any vector field whose divergence is zero can be expressed as the curl of the vector potential defined by Eq. (2-13.6). Therefore, since the divergence of the magnetic induction field **B** is zero, this field can be expressed as

$$\mathbf{B} = \nabla \times \mathbf{A}, \tag{11-1.1}$$

where **A**, by Eq. (2-13.6), is

$$\mathbf{A} = \frac{1}{4\pi} \int_{\text{All space}} \frac{\nabla \times \mathbf{B}}{r} \, dv' + \mathbf{A}_\circ. \tag{11-1.2}$$

363

Setting $\mathbf{A}_o = 0$, for simplicity, and substituting $\nabla \times \mathbf{B} = \nabla \times \mu_0\mathbf{H} = \mu_0\nabla \times \mathbf{H} = \mu_0\mathbf{J}$, we can write Eq. (11-1.2) as

$$\mathbf{A} = \frac{\mu_0}{4\pi} \int_{\substack{\text{All space}}} \frac{\mathbf{J}}{r}\, dv', \qquad (11\text{-}1.3)$$

or, in terms of the Cartesian components, as

$$A_x = \frac{\mu_0}{4\pi} \int \frac{J_x}{r}\, dv', \qquad (11\text{-}1.4a)$$

$$A_y = \frac{\mu_0}{4\pi} \int \frac{J_y}{r}\, dv', \qquad (11\text{-}1.4b)$$

$$A_z = \frac{\mu_0}{4\pi} \int \frac{J_z}{r}\, dv', \qquad (11\text{-}1.4c)$$

where each integral is extended over all space.

The vector potential $\mathbf{A}$ defined by Eq. (11-1.2) or Eq. (11-1.3) is called the *magnetostatic vector potential*. It constitutes a vector point function which determines a new vector field $\mathbf{A}$ associated with the induction field $\mathbf{B}$.

The integral in Eq. (11-1.3) can be simplified in the case of a filamentary current-distribution. For a filamentary current (see Section 10-6), $\mathbf{J}\, dv = I\, d\mathbf{l}$, I is constant over the entire length of the filament, and the filament is closed. Therefore Eq. (11-1.3) reduces in this case to

$$\mathbf{A} = \frac{\mu_0 I}{4\pi} \oint \frac{d\mathbf{l}'}{r} \qquad (11\text{-}1.5)$$

(the sense of the direction of $d\mathbf{l}$ is the same as that of the current I).

The vector potential defined by Eq. (11-1.3) is characterized by two important properties: its divergence is zero

$$\nabla \cdot \mathbf{A} = 0, \qquad (11\text{-}1.6)$$

and it satisfies Poisson's equation

$$\nabla^2\mathbf{A} = -\mu_0\mathbf{J}, \qquad (11\text{-}1.7)$$

which can be written in the scalar form

$$\nabla^2 A_x = -\mu_0 J_x \qquad (11\text{-}1.8a)$$
$$\nabla^2 A_y = -\mu_0 J_y \qquad (11\text{-}1.8b)$$
$$\nabla^2 A_z = -\mu_0 J_z. \qquad (11\text{-}1.8c)$$

That $\mathbf{V} \cdot \mathbf{A} = 0$ can be shown as follows. From Eq. (11-1.3) we have

$$\mathbf{V} \cdot \mathbf{A} = \frac{\mu_0}{4\pi} \mathbf{V} \cdot \left(\int\limits_{\text{All space}} \frac{\mathbf{J}}{r} \, dv' \right).$$

Since the integration here is to be done over the primed coordinates (source point coordinates), while $\mathbf{V}$ operates upon the unprimed coordinates only, we can introduce $\mathbf{V}$ under the integral sign, obtaining

$$\mathbf{V} \cdot \mathbf{A} = \frac{\mu_0}{4\pi} \int\limits_{\text{All space}} \mathbf{V} \cdot \frac{\mathbf{J}}{r} \, dv',$$

or, since $\mathbf{J}$ is a function of primed coordinates only,

$$\mathbf{V} \cdot \mathbf{A} = \frac{\mu_0}{4\pi} \int\limits_{\text{All space}} \mathbf{J} \cdot \mathbf{V} \frac{1}{r} \, dv'.$$

But $\mathbf{V}(1/r) = -\mathbf{V}'(1/r)$, and therefore

$$\mathbf{V} \cdot \mathbf{A} = - \frac{\mu_0}{4\pi} \int\limits_{\text{All space}} \mathbf{J} \cdot \mathbf{V}' \frac{1}{r} \, dv'.$$

Now, by vector identity (V-4),

$$\mathbf{J} \cdot \mathbf{V}' \frac{1}{r} = \mathbf{V}' \cdot \left(\frac{\mathbf{J}}{r} \right) - \frac{1}{r} \mathbf{V}' \cdot \mathbf{J},$$

and since $\mathbf{V}' \cdot \mathbf{J} = 0$, we have

$$\mathbf{J} \cdot \mathbf{V}' \frac{1}{r} = \mathbf{V}' \cdot \left(\frac{\mathbf{J}}{r} \right).$$

Substituting this expression into the last integral, transforming the integral by means of Gauss's theorem, and observing that $\mathbf{J} = 0$ on a surface enclosing all space (the currents are assumed to be limited in space), we obtain

$$\mathbf{V} \cdot \mathbf{A} = - \frac{\mu_0}{4\pi} \oint\limits_{\text{All space}} \frac{\mathbf{J}}{r} \cdot d\mathbf{S}' = 0.$$

That $\nabla^2\mathbf{A} = -\mu_0\mathbf{J}$ can be shown as follows. Using vector identity (V-12), we can write

$$\mathbf{V} \times (\mathbf{V} \times \mathbf{A}) = \mathbf{V}(\mathbf{V} \cdot \mathbf{A}) - \nabla^2\mathbf{A},$$

and since $\mathbf{V} \times (\mathbf{V} \times \mathbf{A}) = \mathbf{V} \times \mathbf{B} = \mu_0\mathbf{J}$, while $\mathbf{V} \cdot \mathbf{A} = 0$, we obtain $\nabla^2\mathbf{A} = -\mu_0\mathbf{J}$.

The significance of the magnetostatic vector potential for the calculation of magnetostatic fields is contained in the fact that once the distribution of electric currents is known, the magnetic field associated with these currents can be found by first finding **A** from Eqs. (11-1.3) or (11-1.7) and then finding **B** from Eq. (11-1.1).

Sometimes it is desirable to determine **A** from **B**, rather than the other way around. This can be done either by means of Eq. (11-1.1), or by means of the integral form of Eq. (11-1.1)

$$\oint \mathbf{A} \cdot d\mathbf{l} = \int \mathbf{B} \cdot d\mathbf{S} = \Phi_{\text{enclosed}}, \qquad (11\text{-}1.9)$$

where Φ_{enclosed} is the flux through the surface bounded by the path of integration [this relation is obtained from Eq. (11-1.1) by applying Stokes's theorem of vector analysis to it].

▼

Example 11-1.1   Find the contribution made by a long, straight segment of a thin current-carrying wire to the magnetostatic vector potential outside the segment at a point equidistant from the ends of the segment and then find the corresponding contribution to the magnetic flux density.

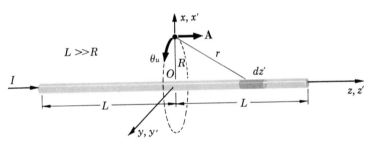

FIG. 11.1   Calculation of the magnetic vector potential associated with a segment of a current-carrying wire.

Let the current be in the z-direction, and let the point of observation lie on the x-axis a distance R from the origin. Let the ends of the segment be at a distance L from the origin, as shown in Fig. 11.1. By Eq. (11-1.5), we then have

$$
\begin{aligned}
\mathbf{A} &= \mathbf{k}\,\frac{\mu_0 I}{4\pi}\int_{-L}^{L}\frac{dz'}{\sqrt{z'^2 + R^2}} \\
&= \mathbf{k}\,\frac{\mu_0 I}{2\pi}\int_{0}^{L}\frac{dz'}{\sqrt{z'^2 + R^2}} = \mathbf{k}\,\frac{\mu_0 I}{2\pi}\ln\left(z' + \sqrt{z'^2 + R^2}\right)\Big|_0^L \\
&= \mathbf{k}\,\frac{\mu_0 I}{2\pi}\ln\frac{L + \sqrt{L^2 + R^2}}{R}.
\end{aligned}
$$

Since the segment is long, $L^2 \gg R^2$, so that R^2 in the last expression may be neglected. The potential is therefore

$$\mathbf{A} = \mathbf{k} \frac{\mu_0 I}{2\pi} \ln \frac{2L}{R}.$$

The flux density associated with this potential is $\mathbf{B} = \nabla \times \mathbf{A}$. Using the expression for the curl in circular cylindrical coordinates (Table 2-I) and observing that $A_\theta = A_R = 0$ and that A_z is a function of R only, we have for the flux density

$$\mathbf{B} = -\frac{\partial A_z}{\partial R} \boldsymbol{\theta}_u,$$

or

$$\mathbf{B} = \frac{\mu_0 I}{2\pi R} \boldsymbol{\theta}_u,$$

which agrees with the expression obtained by means of Ampere's law in Example 10-4.1.

Example 11-1.2   Show that the magnetostatic vector potential outside a long current-carrying cylinder in which the current density is a function of the distance from the cylinder's axis only is the same as if the total current of the cylinder were confined to the axis.

Let the current in the cylinder be along the z-axis. The vector potential is then, by Eq. (11-1.3),

$$\mathbf{A} = \mathbf{k} \frac{\mu_0}{4\pi} \int \frac{J}{r} \, dv'.$$

Although we can prove the required property of the vector potential by a direct transformation of this equation, we shall use a simpler procedure based on the analogy between this equation and Eq. (5-3.1)

$$\varphi = \frac{1}{4\pi\varepsilon_0} \int \frac{\rho}{r} \, dv'$$

representing the *electrostatic potential* of a charge distribution (we have set $\varphi_0 = 0$, as usual). As can be seen, except for the vector notation in the equation for $\mathbf{A}$, these equations can be obtained from each other by a mere substitution of symbols

$$J \rightarrow \rho \quad \text{and} \quad \mu_0 \rightarrow 1/\varepsilon_0.$$

Therefore the solutions of these equations for systems of identical geometry can differ only in the symbols appearing in these solutions, but not in the functional dependences. Now, from the chapters on electrostatics we know that φ for a cylindrically symmetric charge distribution outside the distribution is the same as if the entire charge were confined to the axis. Consequently, $\mathbf{A}$ for the current distribution under consideration is also the same as if the entire current were confined to the axis.

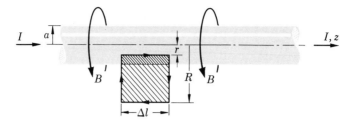

FIG. 11.2   Calculation of the magnetic vector potential inside and outside a current-carrying cylinder.

Example 11-1.3   For both external and internal points find the magnetostatic vector potential due to a long cylinder of length $2L$ and radius a carrying a current I uniformly distributed over the cross section of the cylinder.

Let the cylinder be parallel to the z-axis. By Examples 11-1.1 and 11-1.2, the potential outside the cylinder is then

$$\mathbf{A}_{\text{outside}} = \mathbf{k}\,\frac{\mu_0 I}{2\pi}\ln\frac{2L}{R}.$$

The potential inside the cylinder can be found from Eq. (11-1.9)

$$\oint \mathbf{A}\cdot d\mathbf{l} = \int \mathbf{B}\cdot d\mathbf{S}.$$

Using the path of integration shown in Fig. 11.2 and taking into account that $\mathbf{A}$ is parallel to the cylinder's axis, we have for the circulation integral

$$\oint \mathbf{A}\cdot d\mathbf{l} = A_{\text{inside}}\Delta l - A_{\text{outside}}\Delta l$$

$$= A_{\text{inside}}\Delta l - \frac{\mu_0 I}{2\pi}\Delta l\ln\frac{2L}{R},$$

so that

$$A_{\text{inside}} = \frac{1}{\Delta l}\oint \mathbf{A}\cdot d\mathbf{l} + \frac{\mu_0 I}{2\pi}\ln\frac{2L}{R}.$$

The flux density produced by the cylinder is, according to Example 10-4.1,

$$\mathbf{B} = \frac{\mu_0 I}{2\pi r}\,\boldsymbol{\theta}_u$$

outside the cylinder, and

$$\mathbf{B} = \frac{\mu_0 I r}{2\pi a^2}\,\boldsymbol{\theta}_u$$

inside the cylinder. The flux enclosed by the path of integration is then

$$\int \mathbf{B}\cdot d\mathbf{S} = \int_r^a \frac{\mu_0 I r}{2\pi a^2}\Delta l\, dr + \int_a^R \frac{\mu_0 I}{2\pi r}\Delta l\, dr$$

$$= \frac{\mu_0 I \Delta l}{2\pi}\left(\frac{1}{2} - \frac{r^2}{2a^2} + \ln\frac{R}{a}\right).$$

The potential inside the cylinder is therefore

$$A_{\text{inside}} = \frac{1}{\Delta l} \oint \mathbf{A} \cdot d\mathbf{l} + \frac{\mu_0 I}{2\pi} \ln \frac{2L}{R} = \frac{1}{\Delta l} \int \mathbf{B} \cdot d\mathbf{S} + \frac{\mu_0 I}{2\pi} \ln \frac{2L}{R}$$

or

$$\mathbf{A}_{\text{inside}} = \mathbf{k} \frac{\mu_0 I}{2\pi} \left(\frac{1}{2} - \frac{r^2}{2a^2} + \ln \frac{2L}{a} \right).$$

Example 11-1.4   A current distribution $\mathbf{J}(\xi, \eta, \zeta)$ is located in an external magnetic field $\mathbf{B}'(x + \xi, y + \eta, z + \zeta)$ whose vector potential is $\mathbf{A}'(x + \xi, y + \eta, z + \zeta)$. Prove that

$$\nabla \int_{\text{All space}} (\mathbf{J} \cdot \mathbf{A}') d\tau = \int_{\text{All space}} (\mathbf{J} \times \mathbf{B}') d\tau,$$

where ∇ operates upon x, y, z, and $d\tau$ is a volume element in the system ξ, η, ζ (we shall use this relation in Chapter 13 for deriving magnetic force equations).

Since the integration is to be performed with respect to ξ, η, ζ, upon which ∇ does not operate, we can introduce ∇ under the integral sign:

$$\nabla \int (\mathbf{J} \cdot \mathbf{A}') d\tau = \int \nabla(\mathbf{J} \cdot \mathbf{A}') d\tau,$$

where the integrals are extended over all space. Using now vector identity (V-2) to transform the last integral, we have

$$\int \nabla(\mathbf{J} \cdot \mathbf{A}') d\tau = \int (\mathbf{J} \cdot \nabla)\mathbf{A}' d\tau + \int \mathbf{J} \times (\nabla \times \mathbf{A}') d\tau$$
$$+ \int (\mathbf{A}' \cdot \nabla)\mathbf{J} d\tau + \int \mathbf{A}' \times (\nabla \times \mathbf{J}) d\tau.$$

Since $\mathbf{J}$ is a function of ξ, η, ζ only, upon which ∇ does not operate, the last two integrals vanish. The first integral on the right also vanishes, as can be seen by transforming it with the aid of the vector identity (V-23):

$$\int (\mathbf{J} \cdot \nabla)\mathbf{A}' d\tau = \oint \mathbf{A}'(\mathbf{J} \cdot d\mathbf{S}) - \int (\nabla \cdot \mathbf{J})\mathbf{A}' d\tau.$$

Here, the surface integral vanishes because there is no $\mathbf{J}$ at infinity, and the volume integral on the right vanishes because $\mathbf{J}$ is not a function of x, y, z. Thus we are left with

$$\nabla \int (\mathbf{J} \cdot \mathbf{A}') d\tau = \int \mathbf{J} \times (\nabla \times \mathbf{A}') d\tau,$$

and since $\nabla \times \mathbf{A}' = \mathbf{B}'$, we obtain

$$\nabla \int (\mathbf{J} \cdot \mathbf{A}') d\tau = \int (\mathbf{J} \times \mathbf{B}') d\tau.$$

▲

11-2. Neumann's Formula

With the aid of the magnetostatic vector potential we can derive a useful expression for the calculation of the coefficient of mutual inductance of two filamentary current systems (circuits).

By definition, the mutual inductance coefficient L_{12} is

$$L_{12} = \frac{\Phi_{12}}{I_2}.$$

Writing the flux Φ_{12} as the surface integral of the flux density $\mathbf{B}_{12}$ and expressing the flux density as the curl of the vector potential $\mathbf{A}_{12}$, we have

$$L_{12} = \frac{1}{I_2} \int \mathbf{B}_{12} \cdot d\mathbf{S}_1 = \frac{1}{I_2} \int \nabla \times \mathbf{A}_{12} \cdot d\mathbf{S}_1.$$

Transforming the last surface integral with the aid of Stokes's theorem and using Eq. (11-1.5), we obtain

$$L_{12} = \frac{1}{I_2} \oint \mathbf{A}_{12} \cdot d\mathbf{l}_1 = \frac{1}{I_2} \cdot \frac{\mu_0 I_2}{4\pi} \oint \oint \frac{d\mathbf{l}_1 \cdot d\mathbf{l}_2}{r_{12}},$$

or

$$L_{12} = \frac{\mu_0}{4\pi} \oint \oint \frac{d\mathbf{l}_1 \cdot d\mathbf{l}_2}{r_{12}}. \tag{11-2.1}$$

This formula is called *Neumann's formula*. A very important consequence of Neumann's formula is the equivalence of the two inductance coefficients L_{12} and L_{21}. Indeed, since $r_{12} = r_{21}$ this formula shows at once that

$$L_{12} = L_{21}, \tag{11-2.2}$$

so that two circuits have but a single mutual inductance $M = L_{12} = L_{21}$.

Equation (11-2.1) can be written in a somewhat different manner if the two circuits are made up of straight line segments all of which are either parallel or perpendicular to each other. This is a much more general case than may at first appear, since any two circuits may be approximated by such straight line circuits with parallel and perpendicular segments, as shown in Fig. 11.3. The approximation can be made with any degree of accuracy by making the number of segments sufficiently large. For such circuits, $d\mathbf{l}_1 \cdot d\mathbf{l}_2$ in Eq. (11-2.1) is zero whenever the two segments are mutually perpendicular, and $d\mathbf{l}_1 \cdot d\mathbf{l}_2 = \pm dl_1 dl_2$ whenever the segments are parallel or antiparallel

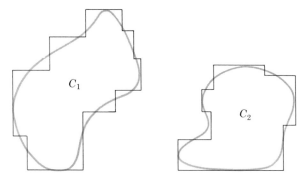

FIG. 11.3   Circuits can be regarded as made up of straight line segments along perpendicular directions.

(opposite currents). Equation (11-2.1) can be written then as

$$M = \frac{\mu_0}{4\pi} \sum_i \sum_k \left[\pm \int_i \int_k \frac{dl_i \, dl_k}{r_{ik}} \right] \qquad (dl_i \parallel dl_k),$$

where the integration is extended over each pair of the mutually parallel $(+)$ or antiparallel $(-)$ segments of the two circuits, and where the subscript i refers to different segments of one circuit, while the subscript k refers to different segments of the other circuit.

The double integral for the segments of the two circuits can be evaluated in terms of the parameters shown in Fig. 11.4. Integrating

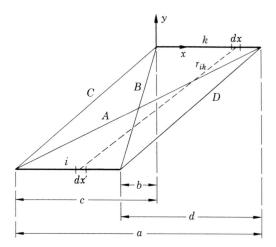

FIG. 11.4   Mutual inductance of two parallel segments can be expressed in terms of the parameters a, b, c, d and A, B, C, D shown here.

over the segment i, we have

$$\int_i \frac{dl_i}{r_{ik}} = \int_i \frac{dx'}{\sqrt{(x-x')^2 + y^2}} = -\sinh^{-1}\frac{x-x'}{y}\Big|_{-c}^{-b}$$

$$= -\left[\sinh^{-1}\frac{x+b}{y} - \sinh^{-1}\frac{x+c}{y}\right].$$

Integrating this expression over the segment k, we have

$$\int_i \int_k \frac{dl_i dl_k}{r_{ik}} = -\int_k \left[\sinh^{-1}\frac{x+b}{y} - \sinh^{-1}\frac{x+c}{y}\right]dx$$

$$= -\left[(x+b)\sinh^{-1}\frac{x+b}{y} - \sqrt{(x+b)^2 + y^2}\right.$$

$$\left. - (x+c)\sinh^{-1}\frac{x+c}{y} + \sqrt{(x+c)^2 + y^2}\right]\Big|_0^{d-b}.$$

Substituting the limits and changing the hyperbolic functions to logarithms, we finally obtain

$$\int_i \int_k \frac{dl_i dl_k}{r_{ik}} = \left[\ln\frac{(a+A)^a(b+B)^b}{(c+C)^c(d+D)^d} + (D+C) - (B+A)\right]_{ik}.$$

Thus the mutual inductance of two circuits can be written as

$$M = \sum_i \sum_k \Delta M_{ik}, \tag{11-2.3}$$

where, referring to Fig. 11.4,

$$\Delta M_{ik} = \pm\frac{\mu_0}{4\pi}\left[\ln\frac{(a+A)^a(b+B)^b}{(c+C)^c(d+D)^d} + (D+C) - (B+A)\right]_{ik}. \tag{11-2.4}$$

▼

Example 11-2.1   Find the coefficient of mutual inductance of two coaxial, parallel, square circuits of length l on a side separated by a distance h (Fig. 11.5).

The problem is most conveniently solved with the aid of Eqs. (11-2.3) and (11-2.4). For the sides directly opposing each other the parameters of Eq. (11-2.4) are (see Fig. 11.4) $a = l$, $b = -l$, $A = B = \sqrt{l^2 + h^2}$, $c = d = 0$, $C = D = h$, so that the contribution to the mutual inductance from these sides is

$$4\Delta M_{11} = \frac{\mu_0}{\pi}\left[\ln\frac{(l + \sqrt{l^2 + h^2})^l}{(-l + \sqrt{l^2 + h^2})^l} + 2h - 2\sqrt{l^2 + h^2}\right]$$

$$= \frac{\mu_0}{\pi}\left[2l \cdot \ln\frac{l + \sqrt{l^2 + h^2}}{h} + 2h - 2\sqrt{l^2 + h^2}\right].$$

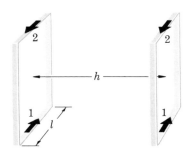

FIG. 11.5 Calculation of the mutual inductance of two square circuits.

For the sides diagonally opposing each other the parameters are $a = l$, $b = -l$, $A = B = \sqrt{2l^2 + h^2}$, $c = d = 0$, $C = D = \sqrt{l^2 + h^2}$, so that the contribution of these sides to the mutual inductance is

$$4\Delta M_{12} = -\frac{\mu_0}{\pi}\left[\ln\frac{(l + \sqrt{2l^2 + h^2})^l}{(-l + \sqrt{2l^2 + h^2})^l} + 2\sqrt{l^2 + h^2} - 2\sqrt{2l^2 + h^2}\right]$$

$$= -\frac{\mu_0}{\pi}\left[2l\cdot\ln\frac{l + \sqrt{2l^2 + h^2}}{\sqrt{l^2 + h^2}} + 2\sqrt{l^2 + h^2} - 2\sqrt{2l^2 + h^2}\right]$$

(the minus sign is needed because the currents here are antiparallel). Adding the above expressions, we obtain for the total mutual inductance of the two circuits

$$M = \frac{2\mu_0}{\pi}\left[l\cdot\ln\frac{(l + \sqrt{l^2 + h^2})\sqrt{l^2 + h^2}}{h(l + \sqrt{2l^2 + h^2})} + h + \sqrt{2l^2 + h^2} - 2\sqrt{l^2 + h^2}\right].$$

▲

11-3. Magnetostatic Scalar Potential

The curl of a gradient is always zero. The curl of the magnetostatic field **H** in a current-free space, by the basic law (10-4.1b), is also always zero. It should therefore be possible to express the magnetostatic field in a current-free space by the equation

$$\mathbf{H} = -\nabla\varphi, \tag{11-3.1}$$

provided that this equation is compatible with the remaining two basic laws given by Eqs. (10-4.2) and (10-4.3). That Eq. (11-3.1) is compatible with Eq. (10-4.3) is obvious. That Eq. (11-3.1) is compatible also with Eq. (10-4.2) follows from the following considerations. Substituting Eq. (10-4.3) into Eq. (10-4.2a) and using Eq. (11-3.1), we have

$$\nabla\cdot\mathbf{B} = 0 = \nabla\cdot\mu_0\mathbf{H} = -\mu_0\nabla\cdot\nabla\varphi,$$

or

$$\nabla^2\varphi = 0. \tag{11-3.2}$$

Therefore Eq. (11-3.1) is compatible with Eq. (10-4.2) if φ satisfies Laplace's equation (11-3.2).

Thus, it is always possible to express the magnetostatic field **H** in a current-free space by Eq. (11-3.1), where φ is a harmonic function. This function is called the *magnetostatic scalar potential*.

In the particular case of a magnetostatic field produced by a closed filamentary current at points outside the current, φ can be expressed directly in terms of the current, as follows. Applying vector identity (V-16) to Eq. (11-1.5), we have

$$\mathbf{A} = \frac{\mu_0 I}{4\pi} \oint \frac{d\mathbf{l}'}{r} = \frac{\mu_0 I}{4\pi} \int d\mathbf{S}' \times \nabla' \frac{1}{r},$$

where we are using the primed operator ∇' in order to avoid ambiguity in the transformations that follow. Combining this equation with Eqs. (11-1.1) and (10-4.3), we obtain

$$\mathbf{H} = \frac{1}{\mu_0} \nabla \times \mathbf{A} = \frac{I}{4\pi} \nabla \times \int d\mathbf{S}' \times \nabla' \frac{1}{r}.$$

Since the last integral is to be evaluated with respect to the primed coordinates only, and since the unprimed ∇ does not operate upon these coordinates, ∇ can be placed under the integral sign. We have then

$$\mathbf{H} = \frac{I}{4\pi} \int \nabla \times \left(d\mathbf{S}' \times \nabla' \frac{1}{r} \right).$$

But $\nabla'(1/r) = -\nabla(1/r)$, so that we can write

$$\mathbf{H} = -\frac{I}{4\pi} \int \nabla \times \left(d\mathbf{S}' \times \nabla \frac{1}{r} \right) = \frac{I}{4\pi} \int \nabla \times \left(\nabla \frac{1}{r} \times d\mathbf{S}' \right).$$

Using vector identity (V-8) to transform the last integral and noting that $\nabla^2(1/r) = 0$, we now obtain[1]

$$\mathbf{H} = \frac{I}{4\pi} \int (d\mathbf{S}' \cdot \nabla) \nabla \frac{1}{r}.$$

Using vector identity (V-2) and observing that $\nabla \times \nabla(1/r) = 0$, we can transform this equation into

$$\mathbf{H} = \frac{I}{4\pi} \int \nabla \left(d\mathbf{S}' \cdot \nabla \frac{1}{r} \right),$$

[1] Observe that operations of the type $\nabla \times d\mathbf{S}'$, $\nabla \cdot d\mathbf{S}'$, etc. are always zero because $d\mathbf{S}'$ is not a point function.

and factoring out ∇ from under the integral sign, we finally obtain

$$\mathbf{H} = \nabla\left(\frac{I}{4\pi}\int\nabla\frac{1}{r}\cdot d\mathbf{S}'\right). \tag{11-3.3}$$

Comparing this equation with Eq. (11-3.1), we see that the expression in parenthesis may be regarded as the negative of the magnetostatic scalar potential, so that for a closed filamentary current the scalar potential can be expressed as

$$\varphi = -\frac{I}{4\pi}\int\nabla\frac{1}{r}\cdot d\mathbf{S}'. \tag{11-3.4}$$

This equation has a simple geometrical meaning. The quantity

$$-\int\nabla\frac{1}{r}\cdot d\mathbf{S}' = \int\frac{\mathbf{r}_u\cdot d\mathbf{S}'}{r^2}$$

represents the solid angle Ω subtended at the point of observation by the loop formed by the current filament. Thus, the magnetostatic scalar potential can be written also as

$$\varphi = \frac{I}{4\pi}\Omega \tag{11-3.5}$$

(the solid angle Ω is considered positive if the direction of the current in the filament as seen from the point of observation is counterclockwise).

▼
Example 11-3.1   By using the magnetostatic scalar potential, find the magnetic field on the axis of a circular ring of radius R carrying a current I.

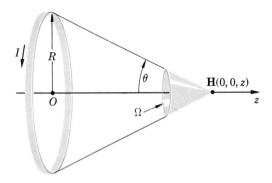

FIG. 11.6   Magnetic scalar potential can be used for magnetic field calculations.

The solid angle subtended by the ring at the point z of the axis (Fig. 11.6) is

$$\Omega = 2\pi(1 - \cos\theta) = 2\pi\left(1 - \frac{z}{\sqrt{R^2 + z^2}}\right).$$

The magnetic field is therefore

$$\mathbf{H} = -\frac{I}{4\pi}\,\boldsymbol{\nabla}\left\{2\pi\left[1 - \frac{z}{(R^2+z^2)^{1/2}}\right]\right\} = \frac{I}{2}\left[\frac{1}{(R^2+z^2)^{1/2}} - \frac{z^2}{(R^2+z^2)^{3/2}}\right]\mathbf{k}$$

$$= \frac{I}{2(R^2+z^2)^{3/2}}\,(R^2 + z^2 - z^2)\mathbf{k},$$

or

$$\mathbf{H} = \frac{IR^2}{2(R^2+z^2)^{3/2}}\,\mathbf{k},$$

which agrees with the results of Example 10-6.1.

▲

11-4. Special Methods for the Solution of Magnetostatic Problems

Various special methods are available for solving certain types of frequently encountered magnetostatic problems. The most important of these methods are based on the fact that in a current-free region of space, the magnetostatic potentials $\mathbf{A}$ and φ satisfy Laplace's equation.

We shall consider here two such special methods: the method of harmonics and the method of axial expansion. Both these methods are essentially the same as the corresponding methods for the solution of electrostatic problems, so that little additional explanation is needed here. It must be pointed out, however, that the correctness of solution of a magnetostatic problem is verified best not by means of the uniqueness of solution theorems for magnetostatic potentials (which will not be presented here), but rather by checking whether the solution is compatible with the basic magnetostatic laws (Section 10.4).

Although the potentials $\mathbf{A}$ and φ satisfy Laplace's equation only in a current-free region of space, the region may contain current-carrying surfaces (boundaries). A solution to a problem involving such surfaces is correct if it is compatible with the basic laws in the space external to the surfaces and with the boundary conditions

$$H_{t2} - H_{t1} = J^{(s)} \tag{11-4.1}$$

and

$$B_{n2} - B_{n1} = 0 \tag{11-4.2}$$

on the two sides of each surface ($J^{(s)}$ is the surface current density; see Section 10-6). The above boundary conditions are, of course, the special forms of the curl and divergence laws for a current-carrying surface and are analogous to the boundary conditions for electric fields which we have met in Sections 8-5 and 9-3. We shall derive these conditions later (Section 14-5). In the meantime, since they are almost obvious, we shall use them without derivation.

▼

Example 11-4.1   A spherical shell of radius R and surface charge density σ is rotated with angular velocity ω about a diameter (Fig. 11.7). Find the magnetic field inside and outside the shell.

We shall solve this problem by the method of harmonics. The symmetry of the system suggests that we should try the spherical harmonics (see Tables 6-I and 5-I)

$$\varphi_{\text{inside}} = A_i\, r \cos \theta \tag{11-4.3}$$

and

$$\varphi_{\text{outside}} = A_o\, \frac{\cos \theta}{r^2}, \tag{11-4.4}$$

where A_i and A_o are constants and the coordinates are those shown in Fig. 11.7. By Example 10-6.4, the sphere constitutes a surface current

$$J^{(s)} = \sigma \omega R \sin \theta.$$

According to Eqs. (11-4.1) and (11-4.2), the two potentials must therefore satisfy the following boundary conditions at the surface of the shell ($r = R$):

$$H_{t\ \text{outside}} - H_{t\ \text{inside}} = J^{(s)}$$

and

$$B_{n\ \text{outside}} = B_{n\ \text{inside}}.$$

But for the shell $H_t = -\dfrac{\partial \varphi}{r \partial \theta}$ and $B_n = -\mu_0 \dfrac{\partial \varphi}{\partial r}$, so that the boundary conditions become upon differentiating Eqs. (11-4.3) and (11-4.4)

$$A_o\, \frac{\sin \theta}{R^3} - A_i \sin \theta = \sigma \omega R \sin \theta$$

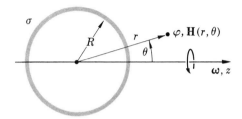

FIG. 11.7   Method of harmonics can be used to find the magnetic field inside and outside a charged, rotating spherical shell.

and

$$\mu_0 A_o \frac{2 \cos \theta}{R^3} = -\mu_0 A_i \cos \theta.$$

Solving these equations, we obtain

$$A_i = -\frac{2}{3} \sigma \omega R$$

$$A_o = \frac{\sigma \omega}{3} R^4,$$

so that the potentials are

$$\varphi_{\text{inside}} = -\frac{2}{3} \sigma \omega R r \cos \theta$$

and

$$\varphi_{\text{outside}} = \frac{\sigma \omega R^4}{3} \frac{\cos \theta}{r^2}.$$

Applying $\mathbf{H} = -\nabla \varphi$ to these potentials, we obtain

$$\mathbf{H}_{\text{inside}} = \frac{2}{3} \sigma \omega R \, \mathbf{k}$$

$$\mathbf{H}_{\text{outside}} = \frac{2 \sigma \omega R^4}{3 r^3} \cos \theta \, \mathbf{r}_u + \frac{\sigma \omega R^4}{3 r^3} \sin \theta \, \boldsymbol{\theta}_u.$$

As one can see, the field outside the shell is a dipole field (compare Section 11-5).

Example 11-4.2   Find the magnetic scalar potential of a circular loop of radius R carrying a current I for all points of space exclusive of the loop.

This problem can be solved by the method of axial expansion. According to Eq. (11-3.5) and Example 11-3.1, the potential on the axis of the loop is

$$\varphi_{\text{axis}} = \frac{I}{2}\left(1 - \frac{z}{\sqrt{R^2 + z^2}}\right),$$

where z is the distance from the center of the loop. Expanding this expression into a power series of z, we have for $z > R$ (compare with Example 6-4.1)

$$\varphi_{\text{axis}} = \frac{I}{2}\left[1 - \frac{1}{\sqrt{1 + (R/z)^2}}\right]$$

$$= \frac{I}{2}\left[1 - \left(1 - \frac{1}{2}\frac{R^2}{z^2} + \frac{1 \cdot 3}{2 \cdot 4}\frac{R^3}{z^3} - \cdots\right)\right]$$

$$= I\frac{R^2}{2}\left(\frac{1}{2}\frac{1}{z^2} - \frac{1 \cdot 3}{2 \cdot 4}\frac{R}{z^3} + \cdots\right).$$

Replacing now $\dfrac{1}{z^n}$ by $\dfrac{P_{n-1}(\cos\theta)}{r^n}$, we obtain

$$\varphi(r,\theta) = I\frac{R^2}{2}\left[\frac{1}{2}\frac{P_1(\cos\theta)}{r^2} - \frac{1\cdot 3}{2\cdot 4}\frac{P_2(\cos\theta)R}{r^3} + \cdots\right],$$

where r is the distance from the center of the loop and θ is the angle between r and the z-axis. Similarly, for $z < R$ we have

$$\begin{aligned}
\varphi_{\text{axis}} &= \frac{I}{2}\left[1 - \frac{z}{R\sqrt{1 + (z/R)^2}}\right]\\
&= \frac{I}{2}\left[1 - \frac{z}{R}\left(1 - \frac{1}{2}\frac{z^2}{R^2} + \frac{1\cdot 3}{2\cdot 4}\frac{z^4}{R^4} - \cdots\right)\right]\\
&= \frac{I}{2}\left(1 - \frac{z}{R} + \frac{1}{2}\frac{z^3}{R^3} - \frac{1\cdot 3}{2\cdot 4}\frac{z^5}{R^5} + \cdots\right),
\end{aligned}$$

and replacing z^n by $r^n P_n(\cos\theta)$, we obtain

$$\varphi(r,\theta) = \frac{I}{2}\left[1 - \frac{r}{R}P_1(\cos\theta) + \frac{1}{2}\frac{r^3}{R^3}P_3(\cos\theta) - \cdots\right].$$

Example 11-4.3   Two parallel coaxial coils of radius R are separated by a distance R (Helmholtz coils). The coils have n turns, each coil carries the same current I, and the dimensions of the cross-sectional area of the coils are small. Find the magnetic field in the central region between the coils.

Let one coil lie in the plane $z = R/2$, the other in the plane $z = -R/2$, as shown in Fig. 11.8. By the preceding example and Fig. 11.8, the magnetic

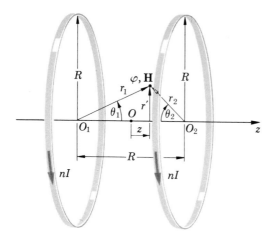

FIG. 11.8 Helmholtz coils are used for producing easily accessible, almost homogeneous magnetic fields in the central region between the coils.

scalar potential at the point P in the central region of the coil is

$$\varphi = \frac{nI}{2}\left[1 - \frac{r_1}{R} P_1(\cos\theta_1) + \frac{1}{2}\frac{r_1^3}{R^3} P_3(\cos\theta_1) + \cdots\right]$$
$$- \frac{nI}{2}\left[1 - \frac{r_2}{R} P_1(\cos\theta_2) + \frac{1}{2}\frac{r_2^3}{R^3} P_3(\cos\theta_2) + \cdots\right].$$

Let us now express the r's and the P's in terms of z and r' shown in Fig. 11.8. We have $r_1 = \sqrt{(R/2 + z)^2 + r'^2}$, $r_2 = \sqrt{(R/2 - z)^2 + r'^2}$, $\sin\theta_1 = r'/\sqrt{(R/2 + z)^2 + r'^2}$, $\sin\theta_2 = r'/\sqrt{(R/2 - z)^2 + r'^2}$, $\cos\theta_1 = (R/2 + z)/\sqrt{(R/2 + z)^2 + r'^2}$, $\cos\theta_2 = (R/2 - z)/\sqrt{(R/2 - z)^2 + r'^2}$. If we now expand all these quantities into power series of R, evaluate the P's with the aid of Table 5-I, and substitute the resultant expressions in the above formula for φ, we obtain

$$\varphi = -\frac{8nI}{5\sqrt{5}}\frac{z}{R}\left(1 - \frac{144}{625}\frac{z^4}{R^4} + \frac{18}{125}\frac{z^2 r'^2}{R^4} + \frac{6}{25}\frac{r'^4}{R^4} + \cdots\right).$$

Taking the gradient of this potential, we then obtain for the magnetic field

$$H_z = -\frac{\partial\varphi}{\partial z} = \frac{8nI}{5\sqrt{5}R}\left(1 - \frac{144}{125}\frac{z^4}{R^4} + \frac{54}{125}\frac{z^2 r'^2}{R^4} + \cdots\right)$$

and

$$H_{r'} = -\frac{\partial\varphi}{\partial r'} = \frac{8nI}{5\sqrt{5}R}\frac{12zr'(3z^2 + 10r'^2 + \cdots)}{125R^4}$$

for the axial and the radial components of the field, respectively. An important property of Helmholtz coils is that they produce a nearly homogeneous field in the central region. Indeed, as can be seen from the above equations, the axial component of the field in the central region is

$$H_z = \frac{8nI}{5\sqrt{5}R}$$

to the terms of the order $(l/R)^4$, where l is the linear dimensions of the region. The radial component is

$$H_{r'} = 0$$

to the terms of the order $(l/R)^4$. Helmholtz coils are frequently used in laboratories for producing easily accessible, almost homogeneous fields.

▲

11-5. Current Dipole

By Eq. (11-3.4), the magnetic scalar potential of a current-carrying loop is

$$\varphi = -\frac{I}{4\pi}\int\nabla\frac{1}{r}\cdot d\mathbf{S}' = \frac{I}{4\pi}\int\frac{\mathbf{r}_u \cdot d\mathbf{S}'}{r^2},$$

where $d\mathbf{S}'$ is an element of the surface bounded by the loop, and r is the distance from this element to the point of observation.

Let us apply this formula to a plane current-carrying loop whose linear dimensions are much smaller than the distance between the loop and the point of observation. For such a loop, the variation of r in the above integrals can be neglected, so that r can be factored out from under the integral sign. The potential becomes then

$$\varphi = -\frac{I}{4\pi}\,\boldsymbol{\nabla}\frac{1}{r}\cdot\mathbf{S}' = \frac{I}{4\pi}\,\frac{\mathbf{r}_u\cdot\mathbf{S}'}{r^2} = \frac{IS'\cos\theta}{4\pi r^2},$$

(in this formula θ is the angle between $\mathbf{r}_u$ and $\mathbf{S}'$; $\mathbf{S}'$ has a magnitude equal to the area of the loop; the direction of $\mathbf{S}'$ is normal to the plane of the loop and forms a right-handed system with the circulation of the current in the loop).

If we now define the vector

$$\mathbf{m} = \mu_0 I\mathbf{S}' \tag{11-5.1}$$

and rewrite the last equation for φ in terms of this vector, we obtain

$$\varphi = -\frac{\mathbf{m}}{4\pi\mu_0}\cdot\boldsymbol{\nabla}\frac{1}{r} = \frac{\mathbf{m}\cdot\mathbf{r}_u}{4\pi\mu_0 r^2} = \frac{m\cos\theta}{4\pi\mu_0 r^2}. \tag{11-5.2a, b, c}$$

But these formulas have exactly the same form as the formulas for the electrostatic potential of an electric dipole (Section 5-4), except that now $\mathbf{m}$ and μ_0 appear where $\mathbf{p}$ and ε_0 were standing in the formulas for the electrostatic dipole. Therefore a distant, plane current-carrying loop is called a *magnetic dipole*, or a *current dipole* (Fig. 11.9). The vector $\mathbf{m}$ defined by Eq. (11-5.1) is called, accordingly, the *magnetic dipole moment* of a current-carrying loop.

By applying $\mathbf{H} = -\boldsymbol{\nabla}\varphi$ to one of the formulas of Eqs. (11-5.2a, b, c), we obtain for the magnetic field of a distant current-carrying loop

$$\mathbf{H} = \frac{m\cos\theta}{2\pi\mu_0 r^3}\,\mathbf{r}_u + \frac{m\sin\theta}{4\pi\mu_0 r^3}\,\boldsymbol{\theta}_u \tag{11-5.3}$$

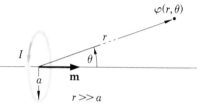

FIG. 11.9 A current-carrying loop viewed from a large distance constitutes a magnetic dipole.

and

$$H = \frac{m}{4\pi\mu_0 r^3} \sqrt{1 + 3\cos^2\theta} \, . \tag{11-5.4}$$

These equations, too, have the same form as the equations for the electric field of an electric dipole.

▼

Example 11-5.1   Find the magnetic dipole moment of a straight, long, tightly wound coil of n turns, length l, and cross-sectional area S if the coil carries a current I.

Each turn of the wire in the coil constitutes a dipole of moment $\mu_0 I S$. The total moment of the coil is just the sum of the moments of all individual turns, or

$$\mathbf{m} = n\mu_0 I \mathbf{S}.$$

This formula has a noteworthy consequence. Multiplying and dividing the right side by the length of the coil, we have

$$\mathbf{m} = \mu_0 \frac{nI\mathbf{S}}{l} \, l.$$

But

$$\frac{\mu_0 nI}{l} S = BS = \Phi.$$

Therefore we can write

$$m = \Phi l.$$

By comparing this formula with the formula for the dipole moment of an electric dipole, $p = ql$, we find that the magnetic counterpart of the electric charge q is the magnetic flux Φ (they also correspond dimensionally: As and Vs, respectively).

Example 11-5.2   Find the magnetic dipole moment of the spinning spherical shell described in Example 11-4.1.

Comparing the expression for $\mathbf{H}_{\text{outside}}$ obtained in Example 11-4.1 with Eq. (11-5.3), we immediately recognize that the dipole moment is

$$m = \frac{4\pi\mu_0\sigma\omega R^4}{3} \, .$$

Example 11-5.3   A thin, uniformly charged disk of surface charge density σ and radius a rotates with angular velocity ω about the axis of symmetry. Find the magnetic dipole moment of the disk.

Let us subdivide the disk into elementary rings of radius R. By Eqs. (11-5.1) and (10-3.1), each ring has a dipole moment

$$dm = \mu_0\sigma\omega\pi R^3 dR.$$

The total dipole moment of the disk is then

$$m = \int_0^a \mu_0 \sigma \omega \pi R^3 dR,$$

or

$$m = \mu_0 \sigma \omega \pi \frac{a^4}{4}.$$

▲

PROBLEMS

11.1. Show that the vector potential of a homogeneous field $\mathbf{B} = B_0\mathbf{k}$, in a rectangular system of coordinates, can be expressed as

$$\mathbf{A} = -\mathbf{i}C_1 B_0 y + \mathbf{j}C_2 B_0 x,$$

where C_1 and C_2 are constants, subject to the condition $C_1 + C_2 = 1$.

11.2. Show that the vector potential of a homogeneous field $\mathbf{B} = B_0\mathbf{k}$, in a cylindrical system of coordinates, can be expressed as

$$\mathbf{A} = \frac{B_0 r}{2}\, \mathbf{\theta}_u.$$

11.3. Show that the vector potential of a homogeneous field $\mathbf{B} = B_0\mathbf{k}$, in a spherical system of coordinates with $\mathbf{k}$ pointing along the polar axis, can be expressed as

$$\mathbf{A} = \frac{B_0 r}{2}\, (\sin \theta)\, \mathbf{\phi}_u.$$

11.4. Show that the magnetic vector potential at the center of curvature of a segment of wire having the shape of an arc of radius r subtending an angle $\delta = \theta_2 - \theta_1$ at the center and carrying a current I in the direction of $\mathbf{\theta}_u$, is (assuming that the wire lies in the xy-plane)

$$A_x = \frac{\mu_0 I}{4\pi}\, (\cos \theta_2 - \cos \theta_1)$$

$$A_y = \frac{\mu_0 I}{4\pi}\, (\sin \theta_2 - \sin \theta_1).$$

11.5. In a very long parallel-wire transmission line, one wire carries a current I and the other returns the current. (a) Show that the magnetic vector potential of the line is parallel to the line and is equal to

$$A = \frac{\mu_0 I}{2\pi} \ln \frac{r_1}{r_2},$$

where r_1 and r_2 are the distances from the point of observation to the wires. (b) Using this vector potential, find the magnetic field of the line.

11.6. Two square-shaped loops of wire, each of length a on a side, are placed opposite each other a distance a apart. Show that the coefficient of mutual inductance is

$$M = \frac{2\mu_0 a}{\pi}\left(\ln\frac{2 + \sqrt{2}}{1 + \sqrt{3}} + 1 + \sqrt{3} - 2\sqrt{2}\right).$$

11.7. Two coaxial circular loops of wire are placed a distance c apart with their planes normal to the axis. The radii of the loops are a and b. Show that the coefficient of mutual inductance, in a cylindrical system of coordinates, is

$$M = \frac{1}{2}\,\mu_0 ab \int_0^{2\pi} \frac{\cos\theta\,d\theta}{(c^2 + a^2 + b^2 - 2ab\cos\theta)^{1/2}}.$$

11.8. A thin, uniformly charged disk of surface charge density σ and radius a rotates with angular velocity ω about the axis of symmetry. Show that the magnetic scalar potential on the axis can be expressed as

$$\varphi = \frac{\sigma\omega}{2}\,z(z - \sqrt{a^2 + z^2}) + \frac{\sigma\omega}{4}\,a^2.$$

11.9. A narrow rectangular loop of wire has the length $2a$ and width $w(w \ll a)$. The loop carries a current I. Show that if the loop lies in the xy-plane with the center at the origin and long side parallel to the x-axis, the magnetic scalar potential at distances sufficiently far from the loop is

$$\varphi(x, y, z) = \frac{Iwz}{4\pi(y^2 + z^2)}\left[\frac{a - x}{\sqrt{(a - x)^2 + y^2 + z^2}} + \frac{a + x}{\sqrt{(a + x)^2 + y^2 + z^2}}\right].$$

11.10. A square loop of wire carries a current I. The loop is of length $2a$ on a side. Using the fact that the loop subtends the solid angle

$$\Omega = 2\pi - 4\sin^{-1}\left[1 - \frac{a^4}{(a^2 + z^2)^2}\right]^{1/2}$$

at a point of the symmetry axis at the distance z from the center of the loop, show that the magnetic field on the axis is

$$\mathbf{H} = \pm\frac{2Ia^2}{\pi(a^2 + z^2)(2a^2 + z^2)^{1/2}}\,\mathbf{k}.$$

11.11. A spherical capacitor consisting of two thin, concentric spherical shells of radii a and b carrying charges $+q$ and $-q$, respectively, rotates with angular velocity $\boldsymbol{\omega}$ about a diameter. Find the magnetic field at all points of space exclusive of the shells and show that the field in the space enclosed by the inner shell is largest when the radius of this shell approaches zero.

11.12. Helmholtz coils are used to produce an almost homogeneous field in a cubic region of length l on a side. The magnitude of the field may not deviate from its value at the center of the system by more than $(1/n)$ 100%. Show that the radius of the coils must be $R \geqslant n^{1/4}l$.

11.13. Show that the magnetic dipole moment of the spinning spherical shell discussed in Example 11-4.1 is

$$m = \mu_0 \omega q R^2/3,$$

where q is the total charge of the shell.

11.14. A uniformly charged cylinder of total charge q and radius a rotates with angular velocity ω about the axis of symmetry. Show that the magnetic dipole moment of the cylinder is

$$m = \frac{\mu_0 \omega q a^2}{4}.$$

11.15. Show that the shell referred to in Problem 11.13 has a gyromagnetic ratio (the ratio of the magnetic dipole moment to the angular momentum)

$$\frac{\mu_0 q}{2m'},$$

where m' is the mass of the shell.

11.16. Show that the disk discussed in Example 11-5.3 has a gyromagnetic ratio (see Problem 11.15)

$$\frac{\mu_0 q}{2m'},$$

where m' is the mass of the disk.

11.17. Show that the cylinder discussed in Problem 11.14 has a gyromagnetic ratio (see Problem 11.15)

$$\frac{\mu_0 q}{2m'},$$

where m' is the mass of the cylinder.

11.18. A homogeneous solid sphere of mass m' has a charge q uniformly distributed throughout its volume. The sphere rotates about a diameter. Show that the gyro-magnetic ratio of the sphere (see Problem 11.15) is

$$\frac{\mu_0 q}{2m'}.$$

11.19. A sphere of radius a has a charge $+q$ uniformly distributed over its surface and a charge $-q$ uniformly distributed throughout its volume. Show that if the sphere rotates with angular velocity ω about a diameter, the magnetic dipole moment of the sphere is

$$m = \frac{2}{15}\mu_0 a^2 q \omega.$$

11.20. A tightly wound coil of n turns has the shape of a half-ring. The cross-sectional area of the coil is S. Show that if the coil carries a current I, the magnetic dipole moment of the coil is

$$m \approx \frac{2\mu_0 nSI}{\pi}$$

directed along the line joining the ends of the coil.

11.21. Two identical, small coaxial rings are perpendicular to their common axis of symmetry and are separated by a small distance a. They carry equal currents, but the direction of the current in one ring is opposite to that in the other. Show by direct calculation that at a point far from the rings the magnetic scalar potential of the rings is

$$\varphi = \frac{ma}{4\pi\mu_0 r^3}(3\cos^2\theta - 1),$$

where r is the distance from the rings, θ is the angle between r and the symmetry axis, and m is the magnetic dipole moment of each ring. Then, consulting Section 5-4, show that the rings constitute a *magnetic quadrupole* whose moment is

$$m^{(2)} = 2ma.$$

11.22. The rings described in Problem 11.21 are now placed in a single plane, with their centers again separated by a small distance a. Show by direct calculation that the magnetic scalar potential of the rings is now

$$\varphi = \frac{3ma}{4\pi\mu_0 r^3}\cos\theta\sin\theta,$$

where r is the distance from the rings, and θ is the angle between r and a normal to the plane. Then show that the rings still constitute a magnetic quadrupole whose moment is the same as before.

12

MOTION OF BODIES
AND PARTICLES
IN MAGNETIC
AND ELECTRIC FIELDS

In this chapter we shall present the fundamentals of the electromagnetic theory of moving systems. The importance of this theory can be recognized from the fact that it constitutes the most essential part of the foundation upon which such new branches of physics as cosmical electrodynamics, magnetohydrodynamics, and plasma physics are built. To stay within the scope and purpose of this book, however, we shall present only the most elementary equations and ideas involved in this theory. The reason for taking up this subject now, rather than in one of the later chapters, is the fact that it will provide us with equations needed for developing the theory of energy and force relations in magnetic fields. These relations, in turn, will provide us with relations needed for a further development of the theory of electric and magnetic phenomena.

12-1. Dependence of Magnetic and Electric Fields
on Reference Frame

On the basis of various experiments it has been established that the results of magnetic and electric field measurements depend on the velocity of the instruments which are used for these measurements.

Let us denote the field vectors measured in a given region of space by instruments considered to be stationary as **E**, **D**, **H**, and **B**, and let us denote as **E***, **D***, **H***, and **B*** the field vectors measured in the

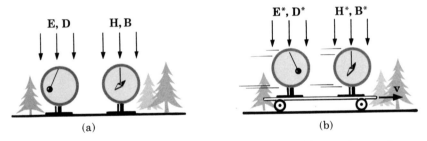

Fig. 12.1   (a) Electric and magnetic fields measured by stationary instruments. (b) When these instruments are placed on a moving platform, they indicate entirely different values of the fields in the same region of space.

same region of space by instruments considered to be moving (Fig. 12.1). Let the velocity of the latter instruments with respect to the former be $\mathbf{v}$. Experiments show that if $v \ll c$, where c is the velocity of light, then the two sets of field vectors are connected by the relations

$$\mathbf{E}^* = \mathbf{E} + \mathbf{v} \times \mathbf{B} \qquad (12\text{-}1.1)$$

and

$$\mathbf{H}^* = \mathbf{H} - \mathbf{v} \times \mathbf{D}. \qquad (12\text{-}1.2)$$

Thus the moving instruments measure additional fields

$$\mathbf{E}_L = \mathbf{v} \times \mathbf{B} \qquad (12\text{-}1.3)$$

and

$$\mathbf{H}_L = -\mathbf{v} \times \mathbf{D} \qquad (12\text{-}1.4)$$

which the stationary instruments do not measure. We shall call these fields *Lorentz's fields*.

Equations (12-1.1) and (12-1.2) show that magnetic and electric fields are intimately related to each other, and what is regarded as a purely electric or a purely magnetic field in one frame of reference will appear as a combination of electric and magnetic fields in another frame of reference if it is moving with respect to the first. To speak of electric or magnetic fields without specifying the reference frame in which these fields are measured is therefore meaningless.

In all reference frames which move without acceleration, the fundamental laws for electric and magnetic fields are, of course, the same as in a "stationary" reference frame. However, the fundamental laws stated in terms of a given coordinate system are usually not valid for field vectors measured by instruments moving with respect to this coordinate system. This follows from the fact that the divergence and curl of $\mathbf{v} \times \mathbf{B}$ and $\mathbf{v} \times \mathbf{D}$ in Eqs. (12-1.1) and (12-1.2) are not equal to zero unless **v**, **B**, and **D** are all constant or **v** is parallel to **B** and **D**, neither of which is usually the case (see Example 12-1.3).

▼

Example 12-1.1   According to Bohr's initial model, a hydrogen atom consists of a point charge nucleus of charge e around which an electron revolves in a circular orbit. Find the magnetic field experienced by the electron if its orbital angular velocity is **ω** and the radius of the orbit is r.

By Eq. (12-1.2), the electron experiences a magnetic field

$$\mathbf{H}^* = \mathbf{H} - \mathbf{v} \times \mathbf{D},$$

where **H** and **D** are the magnetic and displacement fields as "seen" by a stationary electron at a given point of the orbit, and **v** is the velocity of the electron (**H** can be produced by the spin of the nucleus and by sources external to the atom, **D** is produced by the charge of the nucleus). Since

$$\mathbf{D} = \frac{e}{4\pi r^3} \mathbf{r} \quad \text{and} \quad \mathbf{v} = \boldsymbol{\omega} \times \mathbf{r},$$

we have, using the "bac cab" expansion and noting that $\boldsymbol{\omega} \perp \mathbf{r}$,

$$\mathbf{v} \times \mathbf{D} = \frac{e}{4\pi r^3} [(\boldsymbol{\omega} \times \mathbf{r}) \times \mathbf{r}] = \frac{e}{4\pi r^3} [\mathbf{r}(\boldsymbol{\omega} \cdot \mathbf{r}) - \boldsymbol{\omega}(\mathbf{r} \cdot \mathbf{r})] = -\frac{e}{4\pi r} \boldsymbol{\omega}.$$

The magnetic field experienced by the electron is therefore

$$\mathbf{H}^* = \mathbf{H} + \frac{e}{4\pi r} \boldsymbol{\omega}.$$

Example 12-1.2   A particle of charge q moves with velocity **v** relative to an observer. Find the electric and magnetic fields produced by the particle at the location of the observer if $v \ll c$.

The simplest way to solve this problem is to assume that the particle is at rest and that the observer is moving. Let **r** be the radius vector joining the particle with the observer. A charged particle at rest produces an electric field $\mathbf{E} = (q/4\pi\varepsilon_0 r^3)\mathbf{r}$ but no magnetic field. From Eq. (12-1.1) we then obtain for the electric field which the observer will see

$$\mathbf{E}^* = \frac{q}{4\pi\varepsilon_0 r^3} \mathbf{r}.$$

Now, if the velocity of the particle with respect to the observer is **v**, the velocity of the observer with respect to the particle is −**v**. From Eq. (12-1.2) we then have for the magnetic field which the observer will see

$$\mathbf{H}^* = \frac{q}{4\pi r^3} \mathbf{v} \times \mathbf{r}.$$

Replacing the starred vectors in these equations by ordinary vectors, we obtain for the electric and magnetic fields produced by the particle at the location of the observer assumed to be at rest

$$\mathbf{E} = \frac{q}{4\pi\varepsilon_0 r^3}\mathbf{r} \quad \text{and} \quad \mathbf{H} = \frac{q}{4\pi r^3}\mathbf{v} \times \mathbf{r}.$$

Example 12-1.3   Can one determine the charges and currents present in a certain region of space by evaluating $\nabla \cdot \mathbf{D}^*$ and $\nabla \times \mathbf{H}^*$, where $\mathbf{D}^*$ and $\mathbf{H}^*$ are fields measured by instruments located on a rotating platform and ∇ is the ordinary operator expressed in terms of a stationary coordinate system?

Let the platform rotate with angular velocity $\boldsymbol{\omega}$. The linear velocity of an instrument on the platform is then $\mathbf{v} = \boldsymbol{\omega} \times \mathbf{r}$, where $\mathbf{r}$ is the distance to the instrument from the point about which the platform is rotated. Substituting $\mathbf{v}$ in Eqs. (12-1.1) and (12-1.2), multiplying Eq. (12-1.1) by ε_0, and differentiating, we have

$$\nabla \cdot \mathbf{D}^* = \nabla \cdot (\varepsilon_0\mathbf{E}^*) = \nabla \cdot (\varepsilon_0\mathbf{E}) + \varepsilon_0\nabla \cdot [(\boldsymbol{\omega} \times \mathbf{r}) \times \mathbf{B}] \quad (12\text{-}1.5)$$

and

$$\nabla \times \mathbf{H}^* = \nabla \times \mathbf{H} - \nabla \times [(\boldsymbol{\omega} \times \mathbf{r}) \times \mathbf{D}]. \quad (12\text{-}1.6)$$

The charges and currents in the region under consideration are given by

$$\rho = \nabla \cdot \mathbf{D} = \nabla \cdot (\varepsilon_0\mathbf{E}) \quad \text{and} \quad \mathbf{J} = \nabla \times \mathbf{H}.$$

The calculation in question yields therefore not ρ and $\mathbf{J}$, but

$$\rho + \rho_S \quad \text{and} \quad \mathbf{J} + \mathbf{J}_S,$$

where

$$\rho_S = \varepsilon_0\nabla \cdot [(\boldsymbol{\omega} \times \mathbf{r}) \times \mathbf{B}] \quad \text{and} \quad \mathbf{J}_S = -\nabla \times [(\boldsymbol{\omega} \times \mathbf{r}) \times \mathbf{D}].$$

The quantities ρ_S and $\mathbf{J}_S$ are sometimes called *Schiff's charges* and *Schiff's currents*. They represent the illusory charges and currents that one obtains by using the calculation in question. It is instructive to calculate them for the special case of constant $\boldsymbol{\omega}$, $\mathbf{B}$, and $\mathbf{D}$. Using vector identities (V-5) and (V-8), we have

$$\rho_S = \varepsilon_0\nabla \cdot [(\boldsymbol{\omega} \times \mathbf{r}) \times \mathbf{B}] = \varepsilon_0\mathbf{B} \cdot [\nabla \times (\boldsymbol{\omega} \times \mathbf{r})]$$
$$= \varepsilon_0\mathbf{B} \cdot [\boldsymbol{\omega}(\nabla \cdot \mathbf{r}) - (\boldsymbol{\omega} \cdot \nabla)\mathbf{r}].$$

Since $\nabla \cdot \mathbf{r} = 3$ and $(\boldsymbol{\omega} \cdot \nabla)\mathbf{r} = \boldsymbol{\omega}$ (see Problem 2.25), we obtain

$$\rho_S = 2\varepsilon_0\boldsymbol{\omega} \cdot \mathbf{B}. \quad (12\text{-}1.7)$$

Using the "bac cab" expansion and vector identities (V-7) and (V-2), we likewise have

$$\mathbf{J}_S = -\nabla \times [(\boldsymbol{\omega} \times \mathbf{r}) \times \mathbf{D}] = \nabla \times [\boldsymbol{\omega}(\mathbf{r} \cdot \mathbf{D}) - \mathbf{r}(\boldsymbol{\omega} \cdot \mathbf{D})]$$
$$= -\boldsymbol{\omega} \times \nabla(\mathbf{r} \cdot \mathbf{D}) = -\boldsymbol{\omega} \times (\mathbf{D} \cdot \nabla)\mathbf{r},$$

or, since $(\mathbf{D} \cdot \nabla)\mathbf{r} = \mathbf{D}$,

$$\mathbf{J}_S = \mathbf{D} \times \boldsymbol{\omega}. \tag{12-1.8}$$

Thus Schiff's charges and currents are not zero even when $\boldsymbol{\omega}$, $\mathbf{B}$, and $\mathbf{D}$ are constant, so that the calculation in question yields wrong values even in this simplest case (the calculation yields charges and currents equal to ρ_S and $\mathbf{J}_S$, while in reality no charges or currents are present in the region under consideration if $\mathbf{D}$ and $\mathbf{B}$ are constant, as we have assumed).

▲

12-2. Motion of Bodies in Magnetic and Electric Fields

In this section we shall present an elementary discussion of the electromagnetic phenomena associated with the motion of material media in magnetic and electric fields. The purpose of this discussion is to introduce the reader into the domain of these phenomena, rather than to present a consequent mathematical treatment of them. Plausibility arguments and empirical methods will be used therefore in the discussion. A consequent treatment of the subject matter will be presented in Sections 12-3 and 12-4. The arguments and methods which we shall use now will then appear as a consequence of a rigorous, although somewhat complex, theory.

Suppose that a body moves with a velocity $\mathbf{v}_m$ in an electric or magnetic field. Taking into account Eqs. (12-1.1) and (12-1.2), we can write for the field vectors measured in the body by instruments moving with the body

$$\mathbf{E}^* = \mathbf{E}_m + \mathbf{v}_m \times \mathbf{B}_m \tag{12-2.1}$$

and

$$\mathbf{H}^* = \mathbf{H}_m - \mathbf{v}_m \times \mathbf{D}_m, \tag{12-2.2}$$

where the subscript m is used to point out the fact that the vectors on the right refer to the interior of a moving body and are not to be confused with the vectors $\mathbf{E}$, $\mathbf{D}$, $\mathbf{H}$, and $\mathbf{B}$ measured in a vacuum.

Like Eqs. (12-1.1) and (12-1.2), Eqs. (12-2.1) and (12-2.2) correlate the starred vectors measured in a moving frame of reference with vectors which a stationary observer uses in his frame of reference. As we shall see in Section 12-3, however, vectors $\mathbf{E}_m$, $\mathbf{D}_m$, $\mathbf{H}_m$, and $\mathbf{B}_m$, unlike vectors $\mathbf{E}$, $\mathbf{D}$, $\mathbf{H}$, and $\mathbf{B}$, usually cannot be measured and must be calculated from the starred vectors. In fact, in the rigorous theory, Eqs. (12-2.1) and (12-2.2) together with two other equations are used to define the vectors $\mathbf{E}_m$, $\mathbf{D}_m$, $\mathbf{H}_m$, and $\mathbf{B}_m$ in terms of the starred vectors.

From Eqs. (12-2.1) and (12-2.2) it follows that in the interior of a moving body there are Lorentz's fields

$$\mathbf{E}_L = \mathbf{v}_m \times \mathbf{B}_m \qquad (12\text{-}2.3)$$

and

$$\mathbf{H}_L = -\mathbf{v}_m \times \mathbf{D}_m. \qquad (12\text{-}2.4)$$

Since $\mathbf{B}_m$ and $\mathbf{D}_m$ are usually different from $\mathbf{B}$ and $\mathbf{D}$ measured outside the body, these fields are usually different from Lorentz's fields measured in the space external to the body.

Experiments show, however, that in the case of nonmagnetic bodies,[1] $\mathbf{B}_m$ is practically equal to the field vector $\mathbf{B}_0$ which a stationary observer would measure at the location of the body if the body were absent. For a nonmagnetic uniformly moving body ($\mathbf{v}_m$ constant in magnitude and direction) and homogeneous $\mathbf{B}_0$, the Lorentz field $\mathbf{E}_L$ is therefore the same throughout all space. The body appears then to be *at rest* in a homogeneous electric field $\mathbf{E}_L = \mathbf{v}_m \times \mathbf{B}_0$ ("background field").

The fact that a body moving in an electric or magnetic field becomes subjected to the Lorentz fields is the most important aspect of the electromagnetic phenomena associated with moving bodies. The main effects produced by the Lorentz field $\mathbf{E}_L$ are the polarization of dielectrics and the induction of charges and currents in conductors.

In a conducting body the Lorentz field $\mathbf{E}_L$ induces charges which pile up on the surface (and sometimes in the interior) of the body until the field $\mathbf{E}_m$ produced by them, and by all other charges present inside or outside the body, balances the field $\mathbf{E}_L$ throughout the body. The motion of charges in the process of induction constitutes an induced conduction current. Under certain conditions it may happen that the induced charges cannot set up a field $\mathbf{E}_m$ which would balance the field $\mathbf{E}_L$. The induced current is then present as long as the body is moving. This happens, for example, when a conductor moves through a magnetic field and the charges are allowed to escape from this moving conductor into a stationary conductor which connects the regions of the moving conductor where charges of opposite polarity pile up. Electric current generators are built on this principle.

---

[1] Bodies whose permeability is $\mu = 1$ (see Section 14-2).

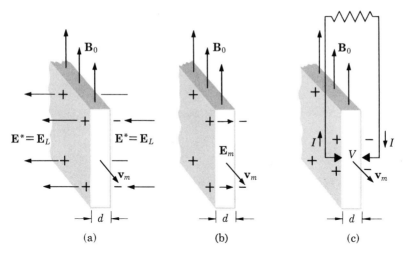

FIG. 12.2   Conducting plate moving through a magnetic field $\mathbf{B}_0$. (a) Observer moving with the plate finds an electric field $\mathbf{E}^* = \mathbf{E}_L$ outside the plate but no field inside the plate. (b) Stationary observer finds an electric field $\mathbf{E}_m$ inside the plate but no field outside the plate. (c) Current is generated in a circuit connected to the plate by sliding contacts.

Experiments show that the density of conduction currents in moving ohmic conductors satisfies the modified Ohm's law

$$\mathbf{J} = \sigma \mathbf{E}^* = \sigma(\mathbf{E}_m + \mathbf{v}_m \times \mathbf{B}_m), \qquad (12\text{-}2.5)$$

where σ and $\mathbf{v}_m$ are the conductivity and the velocity of the conductor, and all other symbols are the same as before. As it follows from this equation and from Eq. (12-2.3), there is no current in a moving conductor if

$$\mathbf{E}_m = -\mathbf{E}_L. \qquad (12\text{-}2.6)$$

This agrees with the mechanism of induced currents just described.

The relations between the vectors $\mathbf{E}^*$, $\mathbf{E}_m$, and $\mathbf{E}_L$ for the simple case of a nonmagnetic conducting plate moving parallel to itself with a velocity $\mathbf{v}_m$ in a homogeneous magnetic field $\mathbf{B}_0 \perp \mathbf{v}_m$ are demonstrated in Fig. 12.2.

An observer moving with the plate (Fig. 12.2a) finds it immersed in an electric field $\mathbf{E}^*_{\text{outside}} = \mathbf{v}_m \times \mathbf{B}_0$ (this is the Lorentz field $\mathbf{E}_L$).[1] He finds no electric field inside the plate and considers therefore the

---

[1] If the observer does not know that the plate is moving, he probably will not recognize the field $\mathbf{E}^*_{\text{outside}}$ as a Lorentz field. He may simply accept the fact that in his "world" there exists a general background electric field.

plate as an equipotential body. He finds that the plate carries a surface charge, which he associates with $\mathbf{E}^*_{\text{outside}}$ according to the relation $\sigma = \pm\varepsilon_0 \left|\mathbf{E}^*_{\text{outside}}\right|$ so that $\sigma = \pm\varepsilon_0 v_m B_0$.

An observer at rest (Fig. 12.2b) sees no electric field outside the plate (the Lorentz field $\mathbf{E}_L$ disappears in his reference frame). He finds, of course, the same surface charges which the moving observer finds, because the number of electrons and ions on the plate does not depend on a reference frame. He associates these charges, however, with the field $\mathbf{E}_m$ *inside* the plate according to the relation $\sigma = \pm\varepsilon_0 \left|\mathbf{E}_m\right|$.[1] By Eqs. (12-2.6) and (12-2.3), $\mathbf{E}_m = -\mathbf{E}_L = -\mathbf{v}_m \times \mathbf{B}_0$ so that $\sigma = \pm\varepsilon_0 v_m B_0$ just as for the moving observer. Since $\mathbf{E}_m$ is not zero, the plate is not an equipotential body for the stationary observer. He finds that there is a voltage $V = E_m d = v_m B_0 d$ across the plate. He utilizes the current-producing property of this voltage (see Section 3-4) by using the plate as a current generator. For this purpose he connects the positive and the negative side of the plate by a stationary wire with the help of sliding contacts (Fig. 12.2c). The charges escape now from the plate into the wire and produce a current in the wire (at the same time newly induced charges produce a current in the plate, as was already explained; under steady-state conditions the current in the plate is equal to the current in the wire).

In concluding this section, it is useful to emphasize the fact that physical systems to which Eq. (12-2.1) applies are encountered much more frequently than physical systems to which Eq. (12-2.2) applies. For this reason we have been concerned here almost exclusively with Eq. (12-2.1).

▼

Example 12-2.1   A nonmagnetic, conducting, spherical artificial satellite of radius a moves in an equatorial orbit with a constant velocity v (Fig. 12.3). The space around the satellite may be considered nonconducting (vacuum). The earth's magnetic field at the location of the satellite is $\mathbf{B}$. Show that the satellite acquires induced surface charges which make it an electric dipole of moment $p = 4\pi\varepsilon_0 v B a^3$.

This problem is best solved in the frame of reference moving with the satellite. In this frame of reference the satellite appears to be immersed in a homogeneous electric Lorentz field $\mathbf{E}_L$ (background field), which is equal

---

[1] More exactly, he associates these charges with the field $\mathbf{D}_m$ inside the plate. As is shown in Section 12-3, in the case under consideration $\mathbf{D}_m = \varepsilon_0 \mathbf{E}_m$ regardless of the dielectric constant of the plate. Hence $\sigma = \pm\left|\mathbf{D}_m\right| = \pm\varepsilon_0 \left|\mathbf{E}_m\right|$.

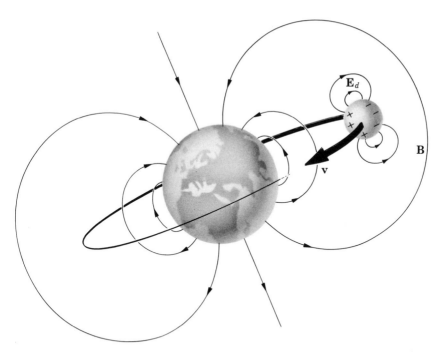

FIG. 12.3   Electric dipole field $\mathbf{E}_d$ produced by charges induced by the earth's magnetic field on an artificial satellite.

to $\mathbf{v}_m \times \mathbf{B} = \mathbf{v} \times \mathbf{B}$. The problem then reduces to that discussed in Example 6-3.2. According to this example, the field $\mathbf{E}^*$ around the satellite is (the coordinates are shown in Fig. 12.11)

$$\mathbf{E}^* = E_L\left(1 + \frac{2a^3}{r^3}\right) \cos \theta \, \mathbf{r}_u - E_L\left(1 - \frac{a^3}{r^3}\right) \sin \theta \, \mathbf{\theta}_u$$

$$= E_L \cos \theta \, \mathbf{r}_u + E_L \frac{2a^3}{r^3} \cos \theta \, \mathbf{r}_u - E_L \sin \theta \, \mathbf{\theta}_u + E_L \frac{a^3}{r^3} \sin \theta \, \mathbf{\theta}_u$$

$$= \mathbf{E}_L + E_L \frac{2a^3}{r^3} \cos \theta \, \mathbf{r}_u + E_L \frac{a^3}{r^3} \sin \theta \, \mathbf{\theta}_u.$$

Since $\mathbf{E}^*$ must be the sum of the field $\mathbf{E}_L$ and the field produced by the charges induced on the satellite, the last two terms represent the field produced by these charges. If we compare these terms with Eq. (5-4.13)

$$\mathbf{E}_{\text{dipole}} = \frac{p}{2\pi\varepsilon_0} \frac{\cos \theta}{r^3} \mathbf{r}_u + \frac{p}{4\pi\varepsilon_0} \frac{\sin \theta}{r^3} \mathbf{\theta}_u,$$

we recognize that the charges induced on the satellite constitute a dipole distribution of moment $p = 4\pi\varepsilon_0 E_L a^3$, where $E_L = |\mathbf{v} \times \mathbf{B}| = vB$. The dipole moment of the satellite is therefore

$$p = 4\pi\varepsilon_0 vBa^3,$$

which was to be shown.

Example 12-2.2   Two nonmagnetic, conducting, spherical space probes move parallel to each other through a magnetic cloud (Fig. 12.4). The radius of each probe is a, the velocity of the probes is $\mathbf{v}$, the probes are at a distance r one from the other, and the magnetic field of the cloud is $\mathbf{B} \perp \mathbf{v}$. Show that the probes will exert an electric force on each other and find this force if r is large compared with a.

In the frame of reference moving with the probes, the probes appear to be immersed in an electric field $\mathbf{E}_L$. According to Example 12-2.1, each probe becomes then an electric dipole of moment $p = 4\pi\varepsilon_0 vBa^3$ (since the probes are far from each other, the charges which they induce on each other may be ignored). Like all electric dipoles, the probes produce electric fields. The electric field produced by one probe at the location of the other is, by Eq. (5-4.13),

$$\mathbf{E} = \frac{2vBa^3}{r^3}\, \mathbf{r}_u,$$

where $\mathbf{r}_u$ points from the first to the second probe. The force between the probes is therefore, by Eq. (7-10.2),

$$\mathbf{F} = °4\pi\varepsilon_0 vBa^3 \frac{\partial}{\partial r}\left(\frac{2vBa^3}{r^3}\right)\mathbf{r}_u = -\frac{°24\pi\varepsilon_0 v^2 B^2 a^6}{r^4}\,\mathbf{r}_u$$

and is an attraction.

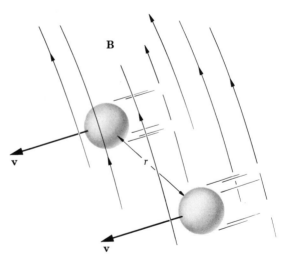

FIG. 12.4   Two space probes moving through a magnetic cloud exert electric forces on each other.

FIG. 12.5 A river as an electric current generator. In 1832 Faraday attempted to produce current in this manner at Waterloo Bridge on the river Thames. The current was, however, too small to be measured. A modern version of this current generator is the *magnetohydrodynamic current generator* described in Problem 12.14.

Example 12-2.3   The bed of a river has a rectangular cross section of width w and depth h. Two long electrodes of length l are placed along the vertical sides of the river bed, as shown in Fig. 12.5. The velocity of the river is v, the conductivity of the water in the river is σ, and the vertical component of the earth's magnetic field at the location of the river is B. If the river is used as an electric current generator, and if the end effects of the electrodes can be neglected, what current is produced in the load resistance R connected to the electrodes?

By inspection we see that the electric field $\mathbf{E}^*$ in the river is homogeneous (we neglect the end effects of the electrodes). The current in the river is then, by Eq. (12-2.5),

$$I = \int \mathbf{J} \cdot d\mathbf{S} = \sigma E^* lh = \sigma(-E_m + v_m B)lh = \sigma(vB - E_m)lh$$

($-E_m$ is used because E_m is produced by induced charges accumulating on the electrodes under the action of $E_L = vB$ and is therefore opposite to E_L). Since $\mathbf{E}^*$ and E_L are homogeneous, E_m is also homogeneous. The voltage measured between the electrodes by a stationary observer is then

$$V = E_m w,$$

and the current in the load resistance is

$$I = \frac{V}{R} = \frac{E_m w}{R}.$$

Solving this equation for E_m, we obtain

$$E_m = \frac{RI}{w}.$$

Substituting E_m in the first equation for I, we have

$$I = \sigma\left(vB - \frac{RI}{w}\right)lh.$$

Solving this equation for I, we finally obtain

$$I = \frac{\sigma lhvB}{1 + \sigma lhR/w}.$$

▲

12-3. Minkowski's Equations for Moving Media⋆

The electromagnetic phenomena associated with motion of material media in electric and magnetic fields can be described rigorously by means of three sets of equations first obtained by Minkowski.[1]

The first set of Minkowski's equations consists of equations defining the vectors $\mathbf{E}_m$, $\mathbf{D}_m$, $\mathbf{H}_m$, and $\mathbf{B}_m$, which we shall call Minkowski's vectors.[2] If the velocities of the media are much smaller than the velocity of light, these equations are

$$\mathbf{E}_m + \mathbf{v}_m \times \mathbf{B}_m = \mathbf{E}^*, \qquad \mathbf{D}_m + \varepsilon_0\mu_0\mathbf{v}_m \times \mathbf{H}_m = \mathbf{D}^* \qquad (12\text{-}3.1a,b)$$

$$\mathbf{H}_m - \mathbf{v}_m \times \mathbf{D}_m = \mathbf{H}^*, \qquad \mathbf{B}_m - \varepsilon_0\mu_0\mathbf{v}_m \times \mathbf{E}_m = \mathbf{B}^*, \qquad (12\text{-}3.1c,d)$$

where $\mathbf{v}_m$ is the velocity of a medium at the point for which the vectors are being determined, and the starred vectors are field vectors measured in the medium at this point by instruments moving with the medium (the instruments are located in needle-shaped or coin-shaped cavities, as required by the definitions stated in Sections 8-1 and 14-1).

A remarkable property of Minkowski's vectors is the fact that, although they represent the fields in moving media, they satisfy in a

---

⋆ Sections 12-3 and 12-4 may be omitted without loss of continuity.

[1] H. Minkowski, "Raum-Zeit-Vektor II Art," Göttinger Nachrichten, 1908, p. 53.

[2] They are the same vectors which we used in Section 12-2. From now on, however, we shall regard the subscript m as an abbreviation for "Minkowski."

coordinate system at rest the same ordinary field laws which are satisfied by field vectors representing electric and magnetic fields in media at rest with respect to this coordinate system. For time-independent fields these laws are in a differential form

$$\nabla \times \mathbf{E}_m = 0, \qquad \nabla \cdot \mathbf{D}_m = \rho, \qquad (12\text{-}3.2a,b)$$

$$\nabla \times \mathbf{H}_m = \mathbf{J}, \qquad \nabla \cdot \mathbf{B}_m = 0, \qquad (12\text{-}3.2c,d)$$

and in an integral form

$$\oint \mathbf{E}_m \cdot d\mathbf{l} = 0, \qquad \oint \mathbf{D}_m \cdot d\mathbf{S} = \int \rho \, dv, \quad (12\text{-}3.3a,b)$$

$$\oint \mathbf{H}_m \cdot d\mathbf{l} = \int \mathbf{J} \cdot d\mathbf{S}, \qquad \oint \mathbf{B}_m \cdot d\mathbf{S} = 0, \qquad (12\text{-}3.3c,d)$$

where $\mathbf{J}$ is the total conduction and convection current density, and ρ is the charge density, both as seen by an observer at rest. At surfaces of discontinuity (discontinuity in the velocity or in the constitution of the media) these laws become, as usual,

$$E_{mt2} - E_{mt1} = 0, \qquad D_{mn2} - D_{mn1} = \sigma_{\text{charge}} \quad (12\text{-}3.4a,b)$$

$$H_{mt2} - H_{mt1} = J^{(s)}, \qquad B_{mn2} - B_{mn1} = 0 \qquad (12\text{-}3.4c,d)$$

$$J_{n2} - J_{n1} = 0. \qquad (12\text{-}3.4e)$$

Equations (12-3.2) and (12-3.3) constitute the second set of Minkowski's equations (for time-independent fields). They can be deduced from ordinary electric and magnetic field laws by using Einstein's special theory of relativity. We shall regard them here, however, as experimentally established correlations.

The third, and the last, set of Minkowski's equations consists of equations representing the constitutive relations for Minkowski's vectors. These equations are obtained from the first set by using the constitutive relations for the starred vectors. In the case of linear and isotropic media we have[1] $\mathbf{D}^* = \varepsilon_0\varepsilon\mathbf{E}^*$ and $\mathbf{B}^* = \mu_0\mu\mathbf{H}^*$. Using these relations to eliminate the starred vectors from Eqs. (12-3.1), we obtain

$$\mathbf{D}_m = \varepsilon_0\varepsilon\mathbf{E}_m - \varepsilon_0\mu_0\mathbf{v}_m \times \mathbf{H}_m + \varepsilon_0\varepsilon\mathbf{v}_m \times \mathbf{B}_m \quad (12\text{-}3.5a)$$

and

$$\mathbf{B}_m = \mu_0\mu\mathbf{H}_m + \varepsilon_0\mu_0\mathbf{v}_m \times \mathbf{E}_m - \mu_0\mu\mathbf{v}_m \times \mathbf{D}_m. \quad (12\text{-}3.5b)$$

---

[1] For readers not familiar with the basic relations between magnetic field vectors in material media we would like to point out that in a linear isotropic medium $\mathbf{B} = \mu_0\mu\mathbf{H}$, where μ is a factor of proportionality called the permeability of the medium (see Section 14-2).

If the media are conducting, these equations must be supplemented by a constitutive relation for the conduction current density. Assuming ohmic conductors, we have by Ohm's law $\mathbf{J}^*_{\text{conduction}} = \sigma \mathbf{E}^*$. However, as it follows from Section 9.2, a conduction current depends only on the relative motion of electrons and atoms (ions) that make up the medium. In the first approximation this relative motion is independent of the velocity of the medium. Hence we may set $\mathbf{J}_{\text{conduction}} = \mathbf{J}^*_{\text{conduction}}$. Ohm's law for moving conductors becomes then, as we already know from Section 12-2,

$$\mathbf{J}_{\text{conduction}} = \sigma \mathbf{E}^* = \sigma(\mathbf{E}_m + \mathbf{v}_m \times \mathbf{B}_m). \qquad (12\text{-}3.5c)$$

Within the limitations stated above ($v_m \ll c$, time-independent fields, linear isotropic media) we have now a complete system of Minkowski's equations. These equations, and Eqs. (12-3.2) and (12-3.3) in particular, allow one to treat electromagnetic phenomena associated with moving media in essentially the same manner in which the electromagnetic phenomena associated with stationary media are treated. All calculations can be made in a single frame of reference ("laboratory"), and one can use the same familiar field laws which are used for fields with no moving media present. Thus through Minkowski's equations the electromagnetic theory of moving media essentially reduces to the theory of stationary media.[1]

The complexity of the constitutive equations (12-3.5a) and (12-3.5b), however, makes practical applications of Minkowski's equations difficult except in certain special cases. Two such cases are stated below.

Special Case I. Frequently the terms containing magnetic vectors in Eq. (12-3.5a) are much smaller than the terms containing electric vectors. This happens, for example, when a body with $\mu \approx 1$ moves in an electric field; the magnetic field appears then as a field "induced" by the motion of the body and, as a secondary effect, is relatively small. In this case the terms containing magnetic vectors in Eq. (12-3.5a) can be neglected, and we obtain from Eqs. (12-3.5a) and (12-3.5b)

$$\mathbf{D}_m = \varepsilon_0 \varepsilon \mathbf{E}_m \qquad (12\text{-}3.6a)$$

---

[1] There is some disagreement among different authors concerning the applicability of Minkowski's equations to materials with $\mu \neq 1$ and concerning the meaning of $\mathbf{B}_m$ in such materials. For a discussion see R. M. Fano, L. J. Chu, and R. B. Adler, *Electromagnetic Fields, Energy, and Forces*, John Wiley and Sons, New York (1960).

and

$$\mathbf{B}_m = \mu_0\mu\mathbf{H}_m - \varepsilon_0\mu_0(\varepsilon\mu - 1)\mathbf{v}_m \times \mathbf{E}_m. \qquad (12\text{-}3.6b)$$

If, in addition, $\varepsilon = 1$, and the charge in the medium is negligible, then $\mathbf{E}_m$ becomes equal to the field $\mathbf{E}_0$ which would exist at the location of the medium if the medium were absent (see Example 12-3.1). In this case the constitutive equations become

$$\mathbf{D}_m = \varepsilon_0\mathbf{E}_0 = \mathbf{D}_0 \qquad (12\text{-}3.6c)$$

and

$$\mathbf{B}_m = \mu_0\mu\mathbf{H}_m - \varepsilon_0\mu_0(\mu - 1)\mathbf{v}_m \times \mathbf{E}_0. \qquad (12\text{-}3.6d)$$

Special Case II. Frequently the terms containing electric vectors in Eq. (12-3.5b) are much smaller than the terms containing magnetic vectors. This happens, for example, when a neutral body moves in a magnetic field; the electric field appears then as a field "induced" by the motion of the body and, as a secondary effect, is relatively small. In this case the terms containing electric vectors in Eq. (12-3.5b) can be neglected, and we obtain from Eqs. (12-3.5b) and (12-3.5a)

$$\mathbf{D}_m = \varepsilon_0\varepsilon\mathbf{E}_m + \varepsilon_0\mu_0(\varepsilon\mu - 1)\mathbf{v}_m \times \mathbf{H}_m \qquad (12\text{-}3.7a)$$

and

$$\mathbf{B}_m = \mu_0\mu\mathbf{H}_m. \qquad (12\text{-}3.7b)$$

If, in addition, $\mu = 1$, and all currents in the medium are negligible, then $\mathbf{H}_m$ becomes equal to the field $\mathbf{H}_0$ which would exist at the location of the medium if the medium were absent (see Example 12-3.1). In this case the constitutive equations become

$$\mathbf{D}_m = \varepsilon_0\varepsilon\mathbf{E}_m + \varepsilon_0\mu_0(\varepsilon - 1)\mathbf{v}_m \times \mathbf{H}_0 \qquad (12\text{-}3.7c)$$

and

$$\mathbf{B}_m = \mu_0\mathbf{H}_0 = \mathbf{B}_0. \qquad (12\text{-}3.7d)$$

In concluding this section, it is well to stress that Minkowski's vectors in a moving medium are not the electric and magnetic field vectors as they are defined in Sections 8-1 and 14-1. According to Sections 8-1 and 14-1, the fields in a material medium are the fields measured in cavities made in the medium. In general, however, one cannot make a cavity which does not move with a medium if the medium is moving. Therefore, in general, only the starred vectors of Eqs. (12-3.1) can be regarded as electric and magnetic field vectors in a moving medium. Outside a moving medium, however, Minkowski's vectors are identical with the ordinary vectors $\mathbf{E}$, $\mathbf{D}$, $\mathbf{H}$, and $\mathbf{B}$ measured by stationary instruments. This follows from the fact that everywhere except in a moving medium $\mathbf{v}_m = 0$. Therefore, by Eqs. (12-3.1), all

Minkowski's vectors outside a moving medium are equal to the starred vectors. But the starred vectors are measured by instruments moving with the velocity $\mathbf{v}_m$. Since $\mathbf{v}_m = 0$ in this case, the instruments must be stationary, which proves our statement.

Example 12-3.1   Show that if the electric terms in Eq. (12-3.5b) can be neglected and if $\mu = 1$, then Minkowski's field $\mathbf{H}_m$ for a current-free, charge-free medium is identical with the field $\mathbf{H}_0$ which would exist at the location of the medium if the medium were absent.

Under the conditions stated we have from Eq. (12-3.5b)

$$\mathbf{B}_m = \mu_0 \mathbf{H}_m.$$

The curl and divergence equations for $\mathbf{H}_m$ are then, by Eqs. (12-3.2c,d)

$$\nabla \times \mathbf{H}_m = \mathbf{J}, \qquad \nabla \cdot \mathbf{H}_m = 0.$$

By the basic magnetostatic laws, Eqs. (10-4.1b), (10-4.2a), and (10-4.3), the curl and divergence equations for $\mathbf{H}_0$ are

$$\nabla \times \mathbf{H}_0 = \mathbf{J} \qquad \nabla \cdot \mathbf{H}_0 = 0,$$

where the current density $\mathbf{J}$ is the same as in the curl equation for $\mathbf{H}_m$ (because, by supposition, the medium carries no conduction or convection current). As we see, the field $\mathbf{H}_0$ has the same curl and divergence as the field $\mathbf{H}_m$. Furthermore, since all media of interest are limited in space, the medium cannot produce a field at infinity. Hence, by Helmholtz's theorem of vector analysis,

$$\mathbf{H}_m = \mathbf{H}_0.$$

The corresponding theorem for electric fields (see Special Case I, above) can be proved in the same manner.

Example 12-3.2   Show that the voltage measured by a stationary observer between points a and b on the surface of a moving body is correctly given by

$$V_{ab} = \int_a^b \mathbf{E}_{m\ \text{inside}} \cdot d\mathbf{l}, \tag{12-3.8}$$

where the path of integration is inside the body.

The voltage measured by a stationary observer between the two points is

$$V_{ab} = \int_a^b \mathbf{E}_{\text{outside}} \cdot d\mathbf{l},$$

where the path of integration is outside the body. Outside the body, however, $\mathbf{E} = \mathbf{E}_m$, and hence

$$\int_a^b \mathbf{E}_{\text{outside}} \cdot d\mathbf{l} = \int_a^b \mathbf{E}_{m\ \text{outside}} \cdot d\mathbf{l}.$$

Now, by the circulation law (12-3.3a),

$$\oint \mathbf{E}_m \cdot d\mathbf{l} = 0$$

for any closed path. Therefore

$$\int_a^b \mathbf{E}_{m \text{ outside}} \cdot d\mathbf{l} = \int_a^b \mathbf{E}_{m \text{ inside}} \cdot d\mathbf{l},$$

and hence

$$V_{ab} = \int_a^b \mathbf{E}_{m \text{ inside}} \cdot d\mathbf{l},$$

which was to be shown.

Example 12.3.3   Show that if Special Case II applies, the displacement law for a current-free nonmagnetic conductor reduces to

$$\mathbf{D}_m = \varepsilon_0 \mathbf{E}_m \qquad (12\text{-}3.9)$$

regardless of the permittivity of the conductor.

If there is no current in the conductor, $\mathbf{E}^*$ in the conductor must be zero. Therefore, by Eq. (12-3.1a)

$$\mathbf{E}_m = -\mathbf{v}_m \times \mathbf{B}_m$$

in the conductor. Substituting this expression in Eq. (12-3.7c) and taking into account Eq. (12-3.7d), we then have

$$\mathbf{D}_m = \varepsilon_0 \varepsilon \mathbf{E}_m + \varepsilon_0 (\varepsilon - 1)\mathbf{v}_m \times \mathbf{B}_0$$

$$= \varepsilon_0 \varepsilon \mathbf{E}_m + \varepsilon_0 \varepsilon \mathbf{v}_m \times \mathbf{B}_0 - \varepsilon_0 \mathbf{v}_m \times \mathbf{B}_0$$

$$= \varepsilon_0 \varepsilon \mathbf{E}_m - \varepsilon_0 \varepsilon \mathbf{E}_m + \varepsilon_0 \mathbf{E}_m,$$

or

$$\mathbf{D}_m = \varepsilon_0 \mathbf{E}_m.$$

Example 12-3.4   A long, uncharged, nonmagnetic dielectric cylinder of dielectric constant ε rotates about its axis with angular velocity $\boldsymbol{\omega}$. The cylinder is located in a uniform magnetic field $\mathbf{H}_0$ parallel to $\boldsymbol{\omega}$. Neglecting end effects, find the polarization of the cylinder.

Special Case II and Eqs. (12-3.7c) and (12-3.7d) apply to the system under consideration. The cylinder carries no charge, and there is no charge in the surrounded space. By symmetry and by Gauss's law (12-3.3b), vector $\mathbf{D}_m$ must then be everywhere zero. By Eq. (12-3.7c), this means that vector $\mathbf{E}_m$ in the cylinder is

$$\mathbf{E}_m = -\frac{\mu_0}{\varepsilon}(\varepsilon - 1)\mathbf{v}_m \times \mathbf{H}_0 = -\frac{\mu_0}{\varepsilon}(\varepsilon - 1)(\boldsymbol{\omega} \times \mathbf{r}) \times \mathbf{H}_0,$$

where $\mathbf{r}$ is the distance from the cylinder's axis. From Eqs. (12-3.1a), (12-3.1b), and (12-3.7d) we have therefore

$$\mathbf{E}^* = -\frac{\mu_0}{\varepsilon}(\varepsilon - 1)(\boldsymbol{\omega} \times \mathbf{r}) \times \mathbf{H}_0 + \mu_0(\boldsymbol{\omega} \times \mathbf{r}) \times \mathbf{H}_0$$

$$= \frac{\mu_0}{\varepsilon}(\boldsymbol{\omega} \times \mathbf{r}) \times \mathbf{H}_0$$

and

$$\mathbf{D}^* = \varepsilon_0 \mu_0 (\boldsymbol{\omega} \times \mathbf{r}) \times \mathbf{H}_0.$$

Hence the polarization, $\mathbf{P} = \mathbf{D}^* - \varepsilon_0 \mathbf{E}^*$, is

$$\mathbf{P} = \frac{\varepsilon_0 \mu_0}{\varepsilon}(\varepsilon - 1)(\boldsymbol{\omega} \times \mathbf{r}) \times \mathbf{H}_0,$$

or, after the vector product is simplified by means of "bac cab" expansion,

$$\mathbf{P} = \frac{\varepsilon_0 \mu_0}{\varepsilon}(\varepsilon - 1)H_0 \omega \mathbf{r}.$$

Example 12-3.5   A long, hollow, uncharged, nonmagnetic dielectric cylinder of dielectric constant ε, inner radius a, and outer radius b rotates with angular velocity $\boldsymbol{\omega}$ about its axis. The cylinder is located in a uniform magnetic field $\mathbf{H}_0$ parallel to $\boldsymbol{\omega}$. The inner and outer walls of the cylinder are coated with a thin layer of conducting material, and a stationary electrostatic voltmeter is connected to these walls by means of sliding contacts (Fig. 12.6a). Neglecting end effects, find the voltage indicated by the voltmeter.

Proceeding as in Example 12-3.4, we have for the vector $\mathbf{E}_m$ in the dielectric

$$\mathbf{E}_m = -\frac{\mu_0}{\varepsilon}(\varepsilon - 1)\mathbf{v}_m \times \mathbf{H}_0 = -\frac{\mu_0}{\varepsilon}(\varepsilon - 1)(\boldsymbol{\omega} \times \mathbf{r}) \times \mathbf{H}_0$$

$$= -\frac{\mu_0}{\varepsilon}(\varepsilon - 1)H_0 \omega \mathbf{r},$$

where $\mathbf{r}$ is the distance from the axis of the cylinder. The voltage is then, by Example 12-3.2,

$$V_{ab} = \int_a^b \mathbf{E}_m \cdot d\mathbf{r} = -\int_a^b \frac{\mu_0}{\varepsilon}(\varepsilon - 1)H_0 \omega r\, dr,$$

or

$$V_{ab} = \frac{\mu_0}{2\varepsilon}(\varepsilon - 1)(a^2 - b^2)\omega H_0.$$

Example 12-3.6   A long, hollow, uncharged, nonmagnetic conducting cylinder of inner radius a and outer radius b rotates with angular velocity $\boldsymbol{\omega}$ about its axis. The cylinder is located in a uniform magnetic field $\mathbf{H}_0$ parallel to $\boldsymbol{\omega}$. A stationary electrostatic voltmeter is connected to the inner and outer walls of the cylinder by means of sliding contacts (Fig. 12.6b).

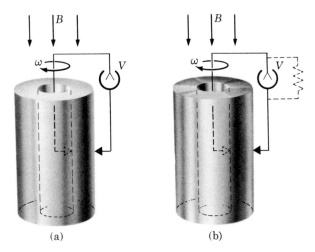

(a)   (b)

FIG. 12.6   (a) Voltage is produced by a dielectric cylinder rotating in a magnetic field. (b) Voltage is produced by a metal cylinder rotating in a dielectric field. If the voltmeter is replaced by a load resistance, electric current will be produced in the resistance and cylinder. The cylinder acts then as a current generator. Such current generators are called *unipolar current generators*. They are used for producing extremely high currents (of the order of 10^6 A).

Assuming that Special Case II applies to the system under consideration, find the voltage indicated by the voltmeter and find the charge induced inside and on the surface of the cylinder. Neglect edge effects.

Since there is no current in the cylinder, the vector $\mathbf{E}_m$ in the cylinder must be, by Eq. (12-3.5c),

$$\mathbf{E}_m = -\mathbf{v}_m \times \mathbf{B}_m,$$

or, since Eq. (12-3.7d) applies to the system under consideration,

$$\mathbf{E}_m = -\mu_0 \mathbf{v}_m \times \mathbf{H}_0 = -\mu_0(\boldsymbol{\omega} \times \mathbf{r}) \times \mathbf{H}_0 = -\mu_0 H_0 \omega \mathbf{r}, \quad (12\text{-}3.10)$$

where $\mathbf{r}$ is the distance from the axis of the cylinder. The voltage is then, by Example 12-3.2,

$$V_{ab} = \int_a^b \mathbf{E}_m \cdot d\mathbf{r} = -\int_a^b \mu_0 H_0 \omega r \, dr,$$

or

$$V_{ab} = \frac{\mu_0}{2} (a^2 - b^2) \omega H_0.$$

To find the charge induced in the cylinder we use Eqs. (12-3.10), (12-3.9), and (12-3.2b). By Eqs. (12-3.9) and (12-3.10),

$$\mathbf{D}_m = \varepsilon_0 \mathbf{E}_m = -\varepsilon_0 \mu_0 H_0 \omega \mathbf{r}. \quad (12\text{-}3.11)$$

From Eq. (12-3.2b) we then have

$$\rho = -2\varepsilon_0\mu_0 H_0\omega$$

(since $\mathbf{r}$ is a radius vector in cylindrical coordinates, $\nabla \cdot \mathbf{r} = 2$).

To find the charge induced on the surfaces of the cylinder we use Eqs. (12-3.3b), (12-3.4b), and (12-3.11). We note that since the cylinder has no net charge and since no charge is present in the space external to the cylinder, the displacement $\mathbf{D}_m$, by Eq. (12-3.3b) and by symmetry, must be zero in the external space. From Eqs. (12-3.11) and (12-3.4b) we then have

$$\sigma = -\varepsilon_0\mu_0 H_0\omega a$$

for the inner surface ($r = a$) and

$$\sigma = \varepsilon_0\mu_0 H_0\omega b$$

for the outer surface ($r = b$).[1]

Example 12-3.7   A thin parallel-plate capacitor of plate separation d and plate area A is placed in a uniform magnetic field $\mathbf{H}_0$ which is parallel to the capacitor's plates. A large nonmagnetic dielectric plate of thickness d and permittivity ε is moving between the plates with a velocity $\mathbf{v}_m$ perpendicular to $\mathbf{H}_0$. (a) Find the voltage between the plates if the capacitor carries no charge (Fig. 12.7a). (b) Find the charge on the plates if the plates are connected by a wire (Fig. 12.7b). (c) Find the voltage between the plates if charges $\pm q$ are placed on the plates (Fig. 12.7c). (d) Find the charges on the plates if a voltage V is applied between the plates (Fig. 12.7d). Neglect end effects and assume that Special Case II is valid in all four cases.

In the case (a) the capacitor carries no charge. Therefore if we construct a Gaussian surface as in Fig. 8.3 and apply Gauss's law (12-3.3b) to this surface, we obtain in the dielectric $D_m = 0$. From Eq. (12-3.7c), we then have (taking into account that $\mathbf{v}_m \perp \mathbf{H}_0$ so that $|-\mathbf{v}_m \times \mathbf{H}_0|$ is $v_m H_0$)

$$E_m = \frac{\mu_0}{\varepsilon}(\varepsilon - 1)v_m H_0,$$

which, by Eq. (12-3.8), gives for the voltage between the plates

$$V = \frac{\mu_0}{\varepsilon}(\varepsilon - 1)v_m H_0 d.$$

In the case (b) the plates are connected by a wire so that there is no voltage between them. Therefore, by the symmetry of the system and by

---

[1] It is important to emphasize that all these charges (ρ and σ) are real macroscopic charges. They are needed in order to make $\mathbf{E}^* = 0$ in the cylinder. The fact that such charges may reside under steady-state conditions on the surface of and within conducting bodies moving through magnetic fields is an important property of electromagnetic phenomena associated with moving bodies.

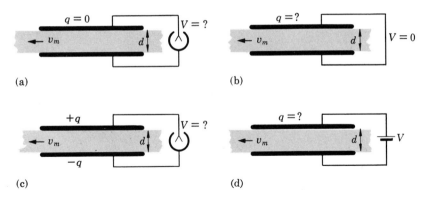

(a)   (b)

(c)   (d)

FIG. 12.7   Dielectric plate moving in a parallel-plate capacitor in the presence of a magnetic field (directed into the page). The relation between the charge and the voltage of the capacitor is entirely different from that which exists when the dielectric is at rest.

Eq. (12-3.8), we have in the dielectric $E_m = 0$. From Eq. (12-3.7c) we then obtain

$$D_m = \varepsilon_0 \mu_0 (\varepsilon - 1) v_m H_0,$$

which, by Gauss's law (12-3.3b), gives for the charge on the plates

$$\pm q = \varepsilon_0 \mu_0 (\varepsilon - 1) v_m H_0 A.$$

In the case (c) there are charges $\pm q$ on the plates. Therefore, by Gauss's law (12-3.3b), we have in the dielectric $D = q/A$. From Eq. (12-3.7c), we then obtain

$$E_m = \frac{q}{\varepsilon_0 \varepsilon A} \pm \frac{\mu_0}{\varepsilon} (\varepsilon - 1) v_m H_0,$$

where the $\pm$ sign is needed because the contributions of the two terms on the right may be in opposite directions. By Eq. (12-3.8), this gives for the voltage between the plates

$$V = \frac{q}{\varepsilon_0 \varepsilon A} d \pm \frac{\mu_0}{\varepsilon} (\varepsilon - 1) v_m H_0 d.$$

In the case (d) a voltage V is applied between the plates. Therefore, by the symmetry of the system and by Eq. (12-3.8), we have in the dielectric $E_m = V/d$. From Eq. (12-3.7c) we then obtain

$$D_m = \varepsilon_0 \varepsilon \frac{V}{d} \pm \varepsilon_0 \mu_0 (\varepsilon - 1) v_m H_0,$$

where the $\pm$ sign is needed for the same reason as in case (c), above. By Gauss's law (12-3.3b), this gives for the charges on the plates

$$\pm q = \varepsilon_0 \varepsilon \frac{V}{d} A \pm \varepsilon_0 \mu_0 (\varepsilon - 1) v_m H_0 A.$$

▲

12-4. Method of Harmonics for Fields of Moving Bodies[*]

The similarity between the field laws for Minkowski's vectors and field laws for ordinary electric and magnetic vectors suggests that the special methods devised for solving electrostatic and magnetostatic field problems can be applied to problems involving electric and magnetic fields of moving media. Minkowski's vectors, however, satisfy constitutive relations very different from those satisfied by the ordinary electric and magnetic field vectors. As a result, only the method of harmonics remains sufficiently simple and general to justify a discussion in this book. We shall discuss this method for three different systems: dielectrics of constant ε moving in vacuum, conductors moving in vacuum, and conductors of constant σ moving in conducting media of constant σ. We shall assume that Special Case II and Eqs. (12-3.7c) and (12-3.7d) apply to all three systems and that the motion is either a uniform translation or a uniform rotation.

According to Eq. (12-3.2a), we can always set

$$\mathbf{E}_m = -\nabla\varphi. \tag{12-4.1}$$

Let us see now what conditions must be satisfied by φ in the three systems under consideration.

In the case of a dielectric of constant ε, we have by Eqs. (12-3.2b), (12-3.7c), and (12-3.7d),

$$\nabla \cdot \mathbf{D}_m = \rho = \varepsilon_0\varepsilon \nabla \cdot \mathbf{E}_m + \varepsilon_0(\varepsilon - 1)\nabla \cdot (\mathbf{v}_m \times \mathbf{B}_0),$$

or, substituting $\nabla \cdot \mathbf{E}_m = -\nabla^2\varphi$ [which follows from Eq. (12-4.1)] and solving for $\nabla^2\varphi$,

$$\nabla^2\varphi = -\frac{\rho}{\varepsilon_0\varepsilon} + \frac{\varepsilon - 1}{\varepsilon}\nabla \cdot (\mathbf{v}_m \times \mathbf{B}_0). \tag{12-4.2}$$

For a uniform translation, $\nabla \cdot (\mathbf{v}_m \times \mathbf{B}_0) = 0$, and we have

$$\nabla^2\varphi = -\frac{\rho}{\varepsilon_0\varepsilon} \quad \text{(uniform translation)}. \tag{12-4.3}$$

For a uniform rotation with angular velocity $\boldsymbol{\omega}$, $\nabla \cdot (\mathbf{v}_m \times \mathbf{B}_0) = 2\boldsymbol{\omega} \cdot \mathbf{B}_0$ (see, for instance, Example 12-1.3), and hence

$$\nabla^2\varphi = -\frac{\rho}{\varepsilon_0\varepsilon} + 2\frac{\varepsilon - 1}{\varepsilon}\boldsymbol{\omega} \cdot \mathbf{B}_0 \quad \text{(uniform rotation)}. \tag{12-4.4}$$

[*] May be omitted without loss of continuity.

At the surface of the dielectric, the boundary conditions (12-3.4a) and (12-3.4b) must be satisfied. Obviously, the first condition can be written as

$$\varphi_1 = \varphi_2, \tag{12-4.5}$$

where subscripts 1 and 2 refer to the dielectric and vacuum, respectively. The second condition, by Eqs. (12-4.1), (12-3.7c), and (12-3.7d), can be written as

$$\varepsilon_0\varepsilon \frac{\partial \varphi_1}{\partial n_{12}} - \varepsilon_0 \frac{\partial \varphi_2}{\partial n_{12}} = \sigma_{\text{charge}} + \varepsilon_0(\varepsilon - 1)(\mathbf{v}_m \times \mathbf{B}_0) \cdot \mathbf{n}_{12}, \tag{12-4.6}$$

where $\mathbf{n}_{12}$ is a unit vector in the direction of an outward normal at the surface of the dielectric, and σ_{charge} is the density of the real surface charge on the surface.

In the case of a current-free conductor moving in vacuum, we have by Eq. (12-3.5c),

$$\mathbf{E}_m = -\mathbf{v}_m \times \mathbf{B}_0. \tag{12-4.7}$$

Taking the divergence of this expression and substituting $\mathbf{V} \cdot \mathbf{E}_m = -\nabla^2\varphi$, we obtain

$$\nabla^2\varphi = \mathbf{V} \cdot (\mathbf{v}_m \times \mathbf{B}_0), \tag{12-4.8}$$

which reduces to

$$\nabla^2\varphi = 0 \quad \text{(uniform translation)}, \tag{12-4.9}$$

and

$$\nabla^2\varphi = 2\boldsymbol{\omega} \cdot \mathbf{B}_0 \quad \text{(uniform rotation)}. \tag{12-4.10}$$

At the surface of the conductor, the boundary conditions (12-3.4a) and (12-3.4b) must be satisfied. Again, the condition (12-3.4a) can be written as

$$\varphi_1 = \varphi_2. \tag{12-4.5}$$

The condition (12-3.4b), however, by Eqs. (12-3.9) and (12-4.1), becomes

$$\varepsilon_0 \frac{\partial \varphi_1}{\partial n_{12}} - \varepsilon_0 \frac{\partial \varphi_2}{\partial n_{12}} = \sigma_{\text{charge}}, \tag{12-4.11}$$

where the notations are the same as in Eq. (12-4.6).

Finally, in the case of a conductor of constant σ moving in a conducting medium of constant σ, we have, by Eq. (12-3.5c),

$$\mathbf{E}_m = \frac{1}{\sigma}\mathbf{J}_{\text{conduction}} - \mathbf{v}_m \times \mathbf{B}_0,$$

so that

$$\mathbf{V} \cdot \mathbf{E}_m = \frac{1}{\sigma} \mathbf{V} \cdot \mathbf{J}_{\text{conduction}} - \mathbf{V} \cdot (\mathbf{v}_m \times \mathbf{B}_0).$$

According to Eq. (12-3.2c), however,

$$\mathbf{V} \cdot \mathbf{J}_{\text{conduction}} = 0 \qquad (12\text{-}4.12)$$

(because divergence of a curl is always zero, and a convection current carried by a solid body can have no divergence). Therefore, substituting $\mathbf{V} \cdot \mathbf{E}_m = -\nabla^2 \varphi$ in the preceding equation, we obtain

$$\nabla^2 \varphi = \mathbf{V} \cdot (\mathbf{v}_m \times \mathbf{B}_0), \qquad (12\text{-}4.13)$$

which reduces to

$$\nabla^2 \varphi = 0 \quad \text{(uniform translation)} \qquad (12\text{-}4.14)$$

and

$$\nabla^2 \varphi = 2\boldsymbol{\omega} \cdot \mathbf{B}_0 \quad \text{(uniform rotation).} \qquad (12\text{-}4.15)$$

Note that the last three equations are exactly the same as for a current-free conductor. At the interface, the boundary conditions (12-3.4a) and (12-3.4e) must be satisfied. The first condition is, as before,

$$\varphi_1 = \varphi_2. \qquad (12\text{-}4.5)$$

The second condition, by Eqs. (12-4.1) and (12-3.5c), can be written as

$$\sigma_1 \frac{\partial \varphi_1}{\partial n_{12}} - \sigma_2 \frac{\partial \varphi_2}{\partial n_{12}} = \sigma_1 (\mathbf{v}_m \times \mathbf{B}_0) \cdot \mathbf{n}_{12}, \qquad (12\text{-}4.16)$$

where the subscripts 1 and 2 refer to the moving conductor and the surrounding medium, respectively.

▼
Example 12-4.1   A nonmagnetic dielectric cylinder of constant ε and radius a moves along its axis with uniform velocity $\mathbf{v}$ in a magnetic field $\mathbf{B}_0 \perp \mathbf{v}$ (Fig. 12.8). Neglecting end effects, find the electric field outside the cylinder and the polarization of the cylinder.

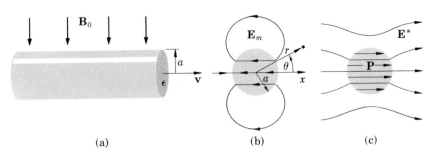

(a)   (b)   (c)

FIG. 12.8   (a) Dielectric cylinder moving across a magnetic field. (b) Minkowski's field $\mathbf{E}_m$ of the cylinder. (c) $\mathbf{E}^*$ field and the polarization $\mathbf{P}$ of the cylinder.

Special Case II applies to the system under consideration. Since there is no charge in the system, we have, by Eq. (12-4.3),

$$\nabla^2 \varphi = 0$$

inside as well as outside the cylinder. By Eqs. (12-4.5) and (12-4.6), the following boundary conditions must be satisfied at the surface of the cylinder $(r = a)$

(1) $\varphi_{\text{inside}} = \varphi_{\text{outside}}$ at $r = a$,

(2) $\varepsilon \dfrac{\partial \varphi_{\text{inside}}}{\partial r} - \dfrac{\partial \varphi_{\text{outside}}}{\partial r} = (\varepsilon - 1)vB_0 \cos \theta$ at $r = a$,

where r and θ are as shown in Fig. 12.8, and $vB_0 \cos \theta$ is the term $(\mathbf{v}_m \times \mathbf{B}_0) \cdot \mathbf{n}_{12}$ of Eq. (12-4.6). Consulting Table 6-I, we find that these conditions can be satisfied by the part of cylindrical harmonics (H-3) containing $\cos \theta$. Calculating in the usual manner the constants appearing in these harmonics, we obtain

$$\varphi_{\text{inside}} = \frac{\varepsilon - 1}{\varepsilon + 1} vB_0 r \cos \theta$$

and

$$\varphi_{\text{outside}} = \frac{\varepsilon - 1}{\varepsilon + 1} \frac{a^2}{r} vB_0 \cos \theta.$$

Taking the gradient of φ_{inside} and φ_{outside}, we have

$$\mathbf{E}_{m \text{ inside}} = -\frac{\varepsilon - 1}{\varepsilon + 1} vB_0 \mathbf{i}$$

$$\mathbf{E}_{m \text{ outside}} = \frac{\varepsilon - 1}{\varepsilon + 1} \frac{a^2}{r^2} vB_0 (\cos \theta \, \mathbf{r}_u + \sin \theta \, \boldsymbol{\theta}_n).$$

Since outside a moving medium $\mathbf{E}_m = \mathbf{E}$, the last expression represents the electric field outside the cylinder. The polarization of the cylinder is given by

$$\mathbf{P} = \mathbf{D}^* - \varepsilon_0 \mathbf{E}^* = \varepsilon_0 (\varepsilon - 1) \mathbf{E}^*.$$

Substituting $\mathbf{E}^* = \mathbf{E}_{m \text{ inside}} + \mathbf{v}_m \times \mathbf{B}_m = \mathbf{E}_{m \text{ inside}} + vB_0 \mathbf{i}$, we obtain

$$\mathbf{P} = \varepsilon_0 (\varepsilon - 1) \left(-\frac{\varepsilon - 1}{\varepsilon + 1} vB_0 \mathbf{i} + vB_0 \mathbf{i} \right) = 2\varepsilon_0 \frac{\varepsilon - 1}{\varepsilon + 1} vB_0 \mathbf{i}.$$

Example 12-4.2   An uncharged nonmagnetic conducting sphere rotates with constant angular velocity $\boldsymbol{\omega}$ about a diameter in a uniform magnetic field $\mathbf{B}_0 \parallel \boldsymbol{\omega}$ (Fig. 12.9). Assuming that Special Case II and Eqs. (12-3.7c) and (12-3.7d) apply to the system under consideration, find the electric field outside the sphere and find the charge distribution inside and on the surface of the sphere.

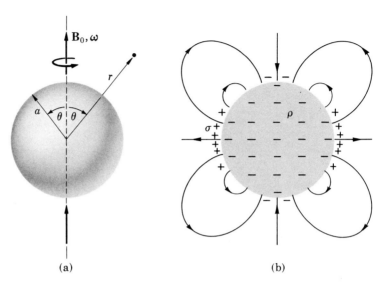

(a)   (b)

FIG. 12.9   (a) Conducting sphere rotating in a magnetic field $\mathbf{B}_0$. (b) Induced charges and electric field of the sphere.

The geometry of the system suggests the use of spherical coordinates shown in Fig. 12.9a. By Eq. (12-4.7), we must have inside the sphere

$$\mathbf{E}_{m\,\text{inside}} = -(\mathbf{v}_m \times \mathbf{B}_0) = -(\boldsymbol{\omega} \times \mathbf{r}) \times \mathbf{B}_0. \qquad (12\text{-}4.17)$$

Since there is no charge outside the sphere, we have for the potential in the space external to the sphere

$$\nabla^2 \varphi_{\text{outside}} = 0.$$

This potential must be regular at infinity and must reduce on the surface of the sphere to the potential φ_{surface} determined by $\mathbf{E}_{m\,\text{inside}}$. We can find φ_{surface} from Eqs. (12-3.8) and (12-4.17). Taking the potential of the upper pole of the sphere $(\theta = 0)$ as the reference potential φ_0, and integrating $\mathbf{E}_m$ along the surface of the sphere in the direction of $\boldsymbol{\theta}_u$, we have

$$\varphi_{\text{surface}} = -\int_\theta^0 [(\boldsymbol{\omega} \times \mathbf{a}) \times \mathbf{B}_0] \cdot \boldsymbol{\theta}_u a\, d\theta + \varphi_0$$

$$= a\int_0^\theta [\mathbf{a}(\boldsymbol{\omega} \cdot \mathbf{B}_0) - \boldsymbol{\omega}(\mathbf{a} \cdot \mathbf{B}_0)] \cdot \boldsymbol{\theta}_u\, d\theta + \varphi_0,$$

where we have used the "bac cab" expansion. Since $\mathbf{a} \perp \boldsymbol{\theta}_u$, we obtain

$$\varphi_{\text{surface}} = -a\int_0^\theta (\mathbf{a} \cdot \mathbf{B}_0)(\boldsymbol{\omega} \cdot \boldsymbol{\theta}_u)\, d\theta + \varphi_0$$

$$= a^2\omega B_0 \int_0^\theta \cos\theta \sin\theta\, d\theta + \varphi_0,$$

or

$$\varphi_{\text{surface}} = \frac{a^2\omega B_0}{2}(1 - \cos^2\theta) + \varphi_0.$$

Consulting Tables 6-I and 5-I, we find that a potential function which can reduce to this expression at the surface of the sphere and is regular at infinity is the part of the spherical harmonics (H-4) containing $\cos^2\theta$:

$$\varphi = C\frac{1}{r^3}P_2(\cos\theta) = C\frac{1}{2r^3}(3\cos^2\theta - 1).$$

By inspection, we see that this function will reduce to φ_{surface} at the surface of the sphere ($r = a$) if

$$C = -\frac{a^5\omega B_0}{3} \quad \text{and} \quad \varphi_0 = -\frac{a^2\omega B_0}{3}.$$

The potential outside the sphere is therefore

$$\varphi_{\text{outside}} = \frac{a^5\omega B_0}{6r^3}(1 - 3\cos^2\theta).$$

The corresponding electric field is calculated from $\mathbf{E} = -\nabla\varphi$. Taking the gradient of φ_{outside}, we obtain

$$\mathbf{E}_{\text{outside}} = \frac{a^5\omega B_0}{2r^4}(1 - 3\cos^2\theta)\mathbf{r}_u - \frac{a^5\omega B_0}{r^4}\cos\theta\sin\theta\,\boldsymbol{\theta}_u.$$

This is a quadrupole field. It is shown schematically in Fig. 12.9b.

To determine the charge distribution in the sphere, we use Eq. (12-3.2b)

$$\rho = \nabla \cdot \mathbf{D}_m.$$

According to Example 12-3.3, we have in the sphere

$$\mathbf{D}_m = \varepsilon_0\mathbf{E}_m. \tag{12-4.18}$$

Taking into account Eq. (12-4.17) and noting that in the case under consideration $\nabla \cdot [(\boldsymbol{\omega} \times \mathbf{r}) \times \mathbf{B}_0] = 2\omega B_0$, we then have for the charge within the sphere

$$\rho = -\varepsilon_0\nabla \cdot [(\boldsymbol{\omega} \times \mathbf{r}) \times \mathbf{B}_0] = -2\varepsilon_0\omega B_0.$$

To determine the charge distribution on the surface of the sphere, we use Eq. (12-3.4b), which for the case under consideration can be written as

$$\sigma = D_{n\,\text{outside}} - D_{mn\,\text{inside}}.$$

Using the expression for $\mathbf{E}_{\text{outside}}$ obtained above, we have for the normal component of $\mathbf{D}_{\text{outside}}$ at the surface of the sphere

$$D_{n\,\text{outside}} = \varepsilon_0 E_{n\,\text{outside}} = \varepsilon_0 E_{r\,\text{outside}} = \frac{\varepsilon_0 a\omega B_0}{2}(1 - 3\cos^2\theta).$$

Taking into account Eqs. (12-4.18) and (12-4.17), we have for the normal component of $\mathbf{D}_{m \text{ inside}}$ at the surface of the sphere

$$D_{mn \text{ inside}} = \varepsilon_0 E_{mn \text{ inside}} = -\varepsilon_0[(\boldsymbol{\omega} \times \mathbf{a}) \times \mathbf{B}_0] \cdot \mathbf{r}_u$$
$$= -\varepsilon_0[\mathbf{a}(\boldsymbol{\omega} \cdot \mathbf{B}_0) - \boldsymbol{\omega}(\mathbf{a} \cdot \mathbf{B}_0)] \cdot \mathbf{r}_u$$
$$= -\varepsilon_0(a\omega B_0 - a\omega B_0 \cos^2 \theta) = \varepsilon_0 a\omega B_0(\cos^2 \theta - 1).$$

The surface charge is therefore

$$\sigma = \frac{\varepsilon_0 a\omega B_0}{2}(1 - 3\cos^2 \theta) - \varepsilon_0 a\omega B_0(\cos^2 \theta - 1),$$

or

$$\sigma = \frac{\varepsilon_0 a\omega B_0}{2}(1 - 3\cos^2 \theta) + \varepsilon_0 a\omega B_0 \sin^2 \theta.$$

This charge distribution is shown schematically in Fig. 12.9b. The total charge on the surface is, of course, equal to the total charge inside the sphere.

Example 12-4.3   The bottom of a river flowing across a horizontal plane has the cross-section in the shape of a semi-circle of radius a. The diameter of the semi-circle coincides with the surface of the river, and the surface of the river is on the same level as the ground in the vicinity of

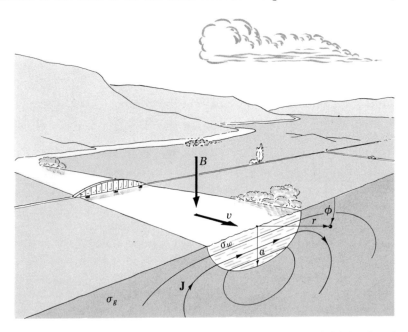

FIG. 12.10   Current is induced by the earth's magnetic field in the river and in the ground near the river.

the river. The velocity of water in the river is $\mathbf{v}$, the conductivity of water is σ_w, the conductivity of the ground is σ_g. There is a magnetic field with a vertical component B at the location of the river. Assuming that Special Case II applies, find the current distribution in the river and in the ground near the river.

The geometry of the system suggests the use of cylindrical coordinates shown in Fig. 12.10. By Eq. (12-4.14), we have in the water as well as in the ground

$$\nabla^2\varphi = 0.$$

Let the potentials in the water and in the ground be φ_w and φ_g, respectively. By Eqs. (12-4.5) and (12-4.16), these potentials must satisfy the following boundary conditions at $r = a$:

(1) $\varphi_w = \varphi_g$

(2) $\sigma_w \dfrac{\partial \varphi_w}{\partial r} - \sigma_g \dfrac{\partial \varphi_g}{\partial r} = \sigma_w vB \cos \theta,$

where $\sigma_w vB \cos \theta$ is the term $\sigma_1(\mathbf{v}_m \times \mathbf{B}_0) \cdot \mathbf{n}_{12}$ of Eq. (12-4.16). Consulting Table 6-I, we find that these conditions are satisfied by the cylindrical harmonics

$$\varphi_w = C_w \, r \cos \theta$$

and

$$\varphi_g = \frac{C_g}{r} \cos \theta,$$

if we set

$$C_w = \frac{\sigma_w}{\sigma_w + \sigma_g} vB \quad \text{and} \quad C_g = \frac{\sigma_w}{\sigma_w + \sigma_g} vBa^2.$$

Hence the potentials must be

$$\varphi_w = \frac{\sigma_w}{\sigma_w + \sigma_g} vBr \cos \theta$$

and

$$\varphi_g = \frac{\sigma_w}{\sigma_w + \sigma_g} vB \frac{a^2}{r} \cos \theta.$$

By Eqs. (12-4.1) and (12-3.5c), we then have for the current in the water

$$\mathbf{J}_w = \sigma_w(-\nabla\varphi_w + \mathbf{v} \times \mathbf{B}) = \sigma_w\left(-\frac{\sigma_w}{\sigma_w + \sigma_g} vB\mathbf{i} + vB\mathbf{i}\right),$$

or

$$\mathbf{J}_w = \frac{\sigma_w \sigma_g}{\sigma_w + \sigma_g} vB\mathbf{i}.$$

For the current in the ground we have likewise

$$\mathbf{J}_g = \sigma_g(-\nabla\varphi_g),$$

or

$$\mathbf{J}_g = \frac{\sigma_w \sigma_g}{\sigma_w + \sigma_g} \frac{a^2}{r^2} vB \cos \theta \, \mathbf{r}_u + \frac{\sigma_w \sigma_g}{\sigma_w + \sigma_g} \frac{a^2}{r^2} vB \sin \theta \, \boldsymbol{\theta}_u.$$

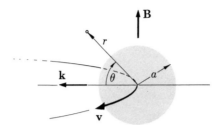

Fig. 12.11 Geometrical relations for finding current induced in an artificial satellite.

Example 12-4.4   Suppose that the artificial satellite of Example 12-2.1 has the conductivity σ_1 and the medium (assumed to be at rest) outside the satellite has the conductivity σ_2. Find the current generated in the satellite and in the surrounding medium, assuming that Special Case II applies to the system under consideration.

The geometry of the system suggests the use of spherical coordinates shown in Fig. 12.11. By Eq. (12-4.14), we have in the satellite as well as in the surrounding medium

$$\nabla^2 \varphi = 0.$$

Let the potentials in the satellite and in the medium be φ_1 and φ_2, respectively. By Eqs. (12-4.5) and (12-4.16), these potentials must satisfy the following boundary conditions at the surface of the satellite $(r = a)$:

$$(1)\ \varphi_1 = \varphi_2$$

$$(2)\ \sigma_1 \frac{\partial \varphi_1}{\partial r} - \sigma_2 \frac{\partial \varphi_2}{\partial r} = \sigma_1 vB \cos \theta,$$

where $\sigma_1 vB \cos \theta$ is the term $\sigma_1 (\mathbf{v}_m \times \mathbf{B}_0) \cdot \mathbf{n}_{12}$ of Eq. (12-4.16). Consulting Table 6-I we find that these conditions are satisfied by the spherical harmonics

$$\varphi_1 = C_1 r \cos \theta$$

and

$$\varphi_2 = \frac{C_2}{r^2} \cos \theta$$

if we set

$$C_1 = \frac{\sigma_1}{\sigma_1 + 2\sigma_2} vB \quad \text{and} \quad C_2 = \frac{\sigma_1}{\sigma_1 + 2\sigma_2} vBa^3.$$

Hence the potentials must be

$$\varphi_1 = \frac{\sigma_1}{\sigma_1 + 2\sigma_2} vBr \cos \theta$$

and

$$\varphi_2 = \frac{\sigma_1}{\sigma_1 + 2\sigma_2} vB \frac{a^3}{r^2} \cos \theta.$$

The currents are therefore, by Eqs. (12-4.1) and (12-3.5c)

$$\mathbf{J}_{\text{satellite}} = \sigma_1(-\nabla\varphi_1 + \mathbf{v} \times \mathbf{B}) = \sigma_1\left(-\frac{\sigma_1}{\sigma_1 + 2\sigma_2}\,vB\mathbf{k} + vB\mathbf{k}\right),$$

or

$$\mathbf{J}_{\text{satellite}} = \frac{2\sigma_1\sigma_2}{\sigma_1 + 2\sigma_2}\,vB\mathbf{k},$$

and likewise

$$\mathbf{J}_{\text{medium}} = \sigma_2(-\nabla\varphi_2),$$

or

$$\mathbf{J}_{\text{medium}} = \frac{2\sigma_1\sigma_2}{\sigma_1 + 2\sigma_2}\,vB\,\frac{a^3}{r^3}\cos\theta\,\mathbf{r}_u + \frac{\sigma_1\sigma_2}{\sigma_1 + 2\sigma_2}\,vB\,\frac{a^3}{r^3}\sin\theta\,\mathbf{\theta}_u.$$

12-5. Motion of Charged Particles through a Magnetic and Electric Field

Although we are concerned in this book with the macroscopic theory of electric and magnetic phenomena, some mention must be made of the motion of charged particles in electric and magnetic fields.

Since an electric field is, by definition, a region of space where a charged particle at rest experiences a purely electric force, the electric force experienced by a moving charged particle is, according to Eqs. (7-8.3) and (12-1.1),

$$\mathbf{F} = {}^{\circ}q\mathbf{E}^* = {}^{\circ}q(\mathbf{E} + \mathbf{v} \times \mathbf{B}), \qquad (12\text{-}5.1\text{a,b})$$

where $\mathbf{E}^*$ is the electric field in the frame of reference moving with the particle, and $\mathbf{v}$ is the velocity of the particle. If the electric field measured by a stationary observer at the location of the particle, $\mathbf{E}$, is zero, the particle experiences a force

$$\mathbf{F}_L = {}^{\circ}q\mathbf{v} \times \mathbf{B}, \qquad (12\text{-}5.2)$$

known as the *Lorentz force*. Note that according to this equation a particle moving through a purely magnetic field experiences a force normal to the velocity of the particle, and hence has a radial but no tangential acceleration. The trajectory of a charged particle in such a field is therefore helix-like.

In general, however, $\mathbf{E} \neq 0$. In this case the motion of a charged particle can be rather complex. The general characteristics of this motion can be deduced as follows.

Let us assume that $\mathbf{v} \perp \mathbf{B}$ and then rewrite Eq. (12-5.1b) for a frame of reference moving with velocity $\mathbf{v}_d \perp \mathbf{B}$ with respect to the reference frame in which $\mathbf{E}$ and $\mathbf{B}$ are measured. The velocity of the particle in this new frame of reference is $\mathbf{v}' = \mathbf{v} - \mathbf{v}_d$, and the force acting upon the particle is, according to Eq. (12-5.1b),

$$\mathbf{F} = {}^\circ q (\mathbf{E} + \mathbf{v}' \times \mathbf{B} + \mathbf{v}_d \times \mathbf{B}).$$

Suppose now that $\mathbf{v}_d$ is such that

$$\mathbf{E} + \mathbf{v}_d \times \mathbf{B} = 0. \tag{12-5.3}$$

Then the above force equation reduces to

$$\mathbf{F} = {}^\circ q (\mathbf{v}' \times \mathbf{B}),$$

so that in the frame of reference moving with velocity $\mathbf{v}_d$, the trajectory of the particle is a circle. Hence, if $\mathbf{v} \perp \mathbf{B}$ and if Eq. (12-5.3) can be satisfied, the trajectory of a particle in the stationary frame of reference is a cycloid in a plane normal to $\mathbf{B}$. However, Eq. (12-5.3) cannot be satisfied if $\mathbf{E}$ has a component parallel to $\mathbf{B}$. In this case this component of $\mathbf{E}$ exerts a force on the particle along the direction of $\mathbf{B}$. The motion of the particle is then a translation along $\mathbf{B}$ superimposed upon the motion along a cycloidal path normal to $\mathbf{B}$. Similar superposition of motions takes place if $\mathbf{v}$ has a component along $\mathbf{B}$.

The motion of a particle along the cycloidal path is called the *drift* of the particle, and $\mathbf{v}_d$ defined by Eq. (12-5.3) is called the *drift velocity* (this is the velocity of the "guiding center" of the cycloid).

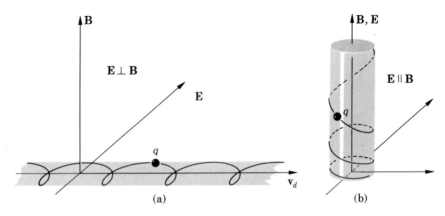

Fig. 12.12   Examples of trajectories of charged particles in electric and magnetic fields.   (a) $\mathbf{E} \perp \mathbf{B}$ and $\mathbf{v} \perp \mathbf{B}$.   (b) $\mathbf{E} \parallel \mathbf{B}$.

Two typical trajectories for a charged particle moving in homogeneous fields are shown in Fig. 12.12. If the fields are not homogeneous, the trajectories become much more intricate.[1]

▼

Example 12-5.1   Show that all particles of equal charge-to-mass ratio q/m moving through a uniform magnetic field **B** which is perpendicular to their velocity vector **v** circulate with the same angular velocity ω

Since **B** $\perp$ **v**, the trajectories of the particles under consideration are circles. From Newton's second law and Lorentz's force equation we then have

$$°qvB = m\omega^2 r,$$

where r is the radius of the circle described by a particle. Since $v = \omega r$, we can write

$$°q\omega r B = m\omega^2 r,$$

and, solving for ω, we obtain

$$\omega = \frac{°q}{m}B.$$

By supposition, however, q/m is the same for all particles, and B is uniform. Therefore ω is the same for all particles. This means, incidentally, that all particles require the same time (period) $T = 2\pi/\omega$ to complete one revolution along the circle. The reciprocal of T is sometimes called the *cyclotron frequency* because particles circulate at this frequency in a cyclotron.

Example 12-5.2   A slightly divergent beam of electrons is emitted from a point electrode along a uniform magnetic field **B**. Show that at a certain

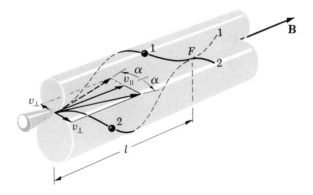

FIG. 12.13   A slightly divergent beam of electrons emitted from a point electrode along a magnetic field is "focused" at the point F. The trajectories of two electrons with different α's are shown.

---

[1] For details the reader is referred to books on plasma physics and magnetogasdynamics.

distance from the electrode all electrons will pass through the same single point ("focus") and find the location of this point if the velocity of the electrons is v and the half-angle of the beam at the electrode is α (small).

Let us denote the component of v along B as $v_{\parallel}$, and the component normal to B as $v_{\perp}$. The motion of the electrons in the beam is a superposition of a translation along B with velocity $v_{\parallel}$ and a circular motion with velocity $v_{\perp}$ in a plane normal to B, the latter motion being a result of the Lorentz force $^{\circ}qv_{\perp}B$. According to Example 12-5.1, the time required for each electron to complete one cycle of the circular motion is

$$T = \frac{2\pi m}{^{\circ}qB},$$

where m is the mass, and q is the charge of an electron. Therefore all electrons emitted from the electrode at the instant $t = 0$ will pass through a point directly in front of the electrode at the instant $t_1 = T$. Since the translational velocity of the electrons is $v_{\parallel} = v \cos \alpha \approx v$, this point is located at the distance

$$l \approx vT = v \frac{2\pi m}{^{\circ}qB}$$

from the electrode (Fig. 12.13).[1]

Example 12-5.3   A long cylindrical beam of charged particles moves with velocity v along its length. The radius of the beam is a and the charge density in the beam (measured in a reference frame moving with the beam) is ρ. Find the total force acting upon a particle of charge q located on the surface of the beam.

In the reference frame moving with the beam the electric field at the surface of the beam is, by Gauss's law and the displacement law,

$$E^* = \frac{\rho a}{2\varepsilon_0}$$

in the outward direction. Since the beam is at rest in this reference frame, the magnetic field in this reference frame is zero. The force on the particle is therefore, by Eq. (12-5.1a),

$$F = {}^{\circ}q \frac{\rho a}{2\varepsilon_0}$$

and represents an ordinary electrostatic repulsion.

Example 12-5.4   Find the drift velocity of a charged particle in an electric field $\mathbf{E}$ and magnetic field $\mathbf{B}$, if $\mathbf{E} \perp \mathbf{B}$.

---

[1] By measuring this distance, one can determine q/m if v and B are known. This method of determining q/m is called the *Busch method*.

According to Eq. (12-5.3), the drift velocity $\mathbf{v}_d$ is given by

$$\mathbf{E} + \mathbf{v}_d \times \mathbf{B} = 0.$$

Multiplying by $\mathbf{B}$, we have

$$\mathbf{E} \times \mathbf{B} + (\mathbf{v}_d \times \mathbf{B}) \times \mathbf{B} = 0.$$

Using the "bac cab" expansion, we obtain

$$\mathbf{E} \times \mathbf{B} + \mathbf{B}(\mathbf{v}_d \cdot \mathbf{B}) - \mathbf{v}_d B^2 = 0.$$

But by the definition of $\mathbf{v}_d$, $\mathbf{v}_d$ is perpendicular to $\mathbf{B}$, so that the second term in the above equation is zero. Therefore

$$\mathbf{v}_d = \frac{\mathbf{E} \times \mathbf{B}}{B^2}.$$

▲

Problems

12.1. Assuming that the sun has a magnetic dipole moment $\mathbf{m}$ along the polar axis, find the electric field experienced by a planet due to its orbital motion (the radius of the orbit is R, the orbital velocity of the planet is $\mathbf{v}$, the plane of the orbit is normal to $\mathbf{m}$).

12.2. A speed boat moves with a velocity of 20 m/sec. The earth's electric field at the surface of the water is 120 V/m and vertical. If the horizontal component of the earth's magnetic field is 0.2×10^{-4} Vs/m^2, what is the maximum angular deviation of the boat's compass caused by the motion of the boat?

12.3. A long, thin parallel-plate capacitor moves parallel to itself with a velocity v in the direction of its length. The capacitor is charged, and the surface charge density on its plates is $\pm\sigma$. Show that the magnetic field measured in the capacitor by stationary instruments is

$$H = \sigma v,$$

and demonstrate that this result can be obtained from Eq. (12-1.2) as well as from Eq. (10-3.1).

12.4. Show that elongated nonmagnetic particles moving across a magnetic field will orient themselves in a direction perpendicular to the field.

12.5. A large nonmagnetic dielectric plate moves with velocity v in the direction of its length across a magnetic field B. Find the polarization of the plate if (a) B is parallel to the plate, (b) B is perpendicular to the plate.

12.6. Two small nonmagnetic dielectric needle-shaped particles of cosmic dust move with velocity $\mathbf{v}$ normal to a galactic magnetic field $\mathbf{B}$.

The volume of each particle is τ, and the distance, r, between them is much larger than their linear dimensions. The particles are oriented along a single line perpendicular to $\mathbf{v}$ and $\mathbf{B}$. Show that the particles are attracted to each other with a force

$$F = \frac{°3\varepsilon_0(\varepsilon - 1)^2\tau^2v^2B^2}{2\pi r^4} + F_g,$$

where F_g is the gravitational force between the particles.

12.7. A conducting, nonmagnetic spherical space vehicle of radius a moves with velocity $\mathbf{v}$ through a magnetic cloud whose magnetic field $\mathbf{B}$ is perpendicular to $\mathbf{v}$. Show that an electric force

$$F = \frac{°9}{4}\,\pi\varepsilon_0 a^2 v^2 B^2$$

acts on each half of the vehicle along a direction perpendicular to $\mathbf{v}$ and $\mathbf{B}$ tending to break the vehicle in two.

12.8. A long nonmagnetic conducting rod of radius a moves with velocity $\mathbf{v}$ along its axis through a magnetic field $\mathbf{B}$ which is perpendicular to $\mathbf{v}$. Show that a stationary observer will see an electric field outside the rod

$$\mathbf{E} = \frac{a^2}{r^2}\,vB(\cos\theta\,\mathbf{r}_u + \sin\theta\,\mathbf{\theta}_u),$$

where r and θ are cylindrical coordinates about the axis of the rod (the end effects are neglected).

12.9. Show that the surface charge density on the artificial satellite described in Example 12-2.1 is

$$\sigma = 3\varepsilon_0 vB\cos\theta.$$

12.10. An uncharged parallel-plate capacitor moves along its length through a magnetic field B which is perpendicular to the direction of the motion of the capacitor and parallel to its plates. A stationary electrostatic voltmeter is connected between the plates by means of sliding contacts. What voltage will the voltmeter indicate?

12.11. The magnetic field of the earth can be assumed to be nearly homogeneous throughout the interior of the earth, with $B = 6 \times 10^{-4}$ Vs/m^2. Show that for an observer not participating in the rotation of the earth there is a voltage of $\approx 10^5$ V between the pole and the equator.

12.12. The plates of a large parallel-plate capacitor are separated by a distance d and are perfect conductors. A long thin plate of conductivity σ, length a, thickness t, and width d is inserted between the capacitor's plates and makes perfect contact with them, while a load resistance R is connected between the plates outside the capacitor. A magnetic field B is then applied parallel to all three plates, and the thin plate is moved with velocity v in the direction normal to the magnetic field. Show that a current

$$I \approx \frac{vBd}{R + d/\sigma at}$$

will be produced in the load.

12.13. A disk of radius b, thickness t, and conductivity σ rotates about its axis with angular velocity ω in a magnetic field B which is parallel to the axis of the disk. The disk is mounted on a perfectly conducting axle of radius a, and is surrounded by a stationary, perfectly conducting ring, also of thickness t, which makes perfect contact with the disk. A resistance R is connected between the axle and the ring. Show that the disk constitutes a current generator (unipolar generator) and that the current in R is

$$I = \frac{\pi \omega \sigma t (b^2 - a^2) B}{2 \pi \sigma t R + \ln (b/a)}.$$

12.14. In a magnetohydrodynamic current generator a stream of conducting gas passes between the plates of a parallel-plate capacitor

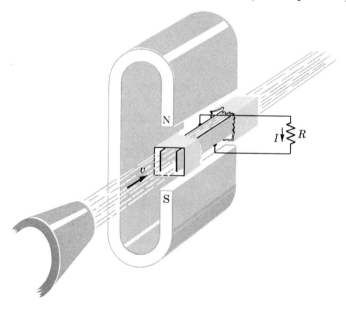

Fɪɢ. 12.14   Magnetohydrodynamic current generator.

located in a magnetic field which is parallel to the plates and perpendicular to the stream (Fig. 12.14). Show that the current generated in an external load R is, in the first approximation,

$$I = \frac{\sigma v B a b d}{d + \sigma a b R},$$

where a, b, and d are the width, length, and separation of the capacitor's plates, respectively, σ and v are the conductivity and velocity of the gas, respectively, and B is the magnetic field.

12.15. Prove that if the magnetic terms in Eq. (12-3.5a) can be neglected and if $\varepsilon = 1$, then Minkowski's field $\mathbf{E}_m$ for a charge-free medium is identical with the field $\mathbf{E}_0$ which would exist at the location of the medium if the medium were absent.

12.16. Show that if the terms of the order $(v/c)^2$ can be neglected, the constitutive equations (12-3.5a) and (12-3.5b) reduce to

$$\mathbf{D}_m = \varepsilon_0 \varepsilon \mathbf{E}_m + \varepsilon_0 \mu_0 (\varepsilon \mu - 1) \mathbf{v}_m \times \mathbf{H}_m$$

and

$$\mathbf{B}_m = \mu_0 \mu \mathbf{H}_m - \varepsilon_0 \mu_0 (\varepsilon \mu - 1) \mathbf{v}_m \times \mathbf{E}_m.$$

12.17. Show by direct calculation that the fictitious charges and currents found in Example 12-1.3 do not appear if Minkowski's vectors are used for charge and current calculation.

12.18. Show that if the coatings of the cylinder discussed in Example 12-3.5 are replaced by stationary conducting cylinders, the voltage indicated by the voltmeter will not change.

12.19. Show that if the parallel-plate capacitor discussed in Example 12-3.7 moves together with the dielectric, the results obtained in all four cases (a), (b), (c), and (d) of that example will be the same.

12.20. Two conductors are in contact along an interface. One conductor moves with velocity $\mathbf{v}_1$, the other with velocity $\mathbf{v}_2$ parallel to the interface. There is a Minkowski's vector $\mathbf{B}_m$ at the interface. Show that if there is no current in the conductors, then there appears a surface charge

$$\sigma = \pm \varepsilon_0 [(\mathbf{v}_1 - \mathbf{v}_2) \times \mathbf{B}_m] \cdot \mathbf{n}_u$$

on the interface, where $\mathbf{n}_u$ is a unit vector normal to the interface.

12.21. Two conductors are in contact along an interface. One conductor moves with velocity $\mathbf{v}_1$, the other with velocity $\mathbf{v}_2$ parallel to the interface. There is a Minkowski's vector $\mathbf{H}_m$ at the interface. Show that if there is a current in the conductors, and if Special Case II applies, then there appears a surface charge

$$\sigma_{\text{charge}} = \pm \left\{ \varepsilon_0 J_n \left(\frac{\varepsilon_2}{\sigma_2} - \frac{\varepsilon_1}{\sigma_1} \right) + \varepsilon_0 \mu_0 [(\mathbf{v}_1 - \mathbf{v}_2) \times \mathbf{H}_m] \cdot \mathbf{n}_u \right\}$$

at the interface, where J_n is the normal component of the current density, ε and σ are the permittivity and conductivity of the conductors, respectively, and $\mathbf{n}_u$ is a unit vector normal to the interface.

12.22. Show that if Special Case II applies, the charge density in a rotating current-carrying conductor as well as in a rotating current-free conductor is given by the same expression

$$\rho = -2\varepsilon_0 \mu_0 \boldsymbol{\omega} \cdot \mathbf{H}_m,$$

where ω is the angular velocity of the conductor, and $\mathbf{H}_m$ is Minkowski's vector in the conductor.

12.23. Show by direct calculation that the total charge of the cylinder and the sphere discussed in Examples 12-3.6 and 12-4.2, respectively, is zero.

12.24. Show that the potential inside the sphere discussed in Example 12-4.2 is

$$\varphi = \frac{\omega B_0}{2} r^2 (1 - \cos^2 \theta) - \frac{\omega B_0}{3} a^2.$$

Is this a harmonic function?

12.25. Find the surface charges accumulating along the river bed discussed in Example 12-4.3.

12.26. Using Example 12-4.2 and the data given in Problem 12.11, find the space and surface charge of the earth.

12.27. A dielectric sphere rotates in a uniform magnetic field. Find the polarization assuming that Special Case II applies.

12.28. Suppose that the sphere discussed in Example 12-4.2 is located in a nonmagnetic conducting medium, and that the conductivities of the sphere and the medium are σ_1 and σ_2, respectively. Show that the currents

$$\mathbf{J}_{\text{inside}} = -\omega r B_0 \frac{\sigma_1 \sigma_2}{2\sigma_1 + 3\sigma_2} [(3 \cos^2 \theta - 1)\mathbf{r}_u - 3 \sin \theta \cos \theta \, \boldsymbol{\theta}_u]$$

and

$$\mathbf{J}_{\text{outside}} = -\frac{\omega a^5 B_0}{r^4} \frac{\sigma_1 \sigma_2}{2\sigma_1 + 3\sigma_2} [(3 \cos^2 \theta - 1)\mathbf{r}_u + 2 \sin \theta \cos \theta \, \boldsymbol{\theta}_u]$$

will be generated inside and outside the sphere. Then find the surface charges accumulating on the sphere.

12.29. A nonmagnetic, incompressible conducting liquid is forced between two closely spaced parallel dielectric disks through an opening made at the center of one of them. There is a homogeneous magnetic field B normal to the disks. Show that a circular current of density

$$\mathbf{J} = \frac{C}{r} B \boldsymbol{\theta}_u,$$

where C is a constant depending on the rate of liquid flow at the opening and on the conductivity of the liquid, is set up between the plates. (The reverse of this arrangement constitutes a magnetohydrodynamic pump: a circular current is set up by means of appropriate electrodes, and the magnetic field forces the liquid to flow.)

12.30. Find the power dissipated in Joule's heating of the river and resistor described in Example 12-2.3 and hence show that the electromagnetic force resisting the flow of water in the river between the two electrodes ("induction drag") is

$$F = \frac{^\circ \sigma l h w v B^2}{(1 + \sigma l h R / w)}.$$

(Hint: The force of resistance is given by $P = vF$, where v is the velocity of motion and P is the rate of energy dissipation.)

12.31. Find the induction drag (see Problem 12.30) on the satellite described in Example 12-4.4.

12.32. Suppose that a submarine is a long thin-walled cylinder of radius a and length l. The submarine moves at a great depth with a horizontal velocity v through a region where the vertical component of the earth's magnetic field is B. The conductivity of the sea-water is σ_w and the conductivity of the submarine is $\sigma_s = \infty$. Neglecting edge effects, find the distribution of electric currents in and outside the submarine, find the power dissipated in Joule's heating of the submarine and the water, and find the induction drag (see Problem 12.30) on the submarine (assume that the water around the submarine is stationary).

12.33. Show that in a perfect conductor the relation between $\mathbf{E}_m$, $\mathbf{v}_m$, and $\mathbf{B}_m$ is always

$$\mathbf{E}_m = -\mathbf{v}_m \times \mathbf{B}_m$$

regardless of whether or not there is a current in the conductor.

12.34. Find the natural period of rotation of an electron ($q = 1.6 \times 10^{-19}$ As) in the magnetic field of the earth ($B = 0.4 \times 10^{-4}$ Vs/m²).

12.35. A "magnetic wall" is formed by a uniform magnetic field B confined to a region of space whose boundaries are two planes parallel to B separated by a distance t. Show that a particle of charge q and mass m cannot penetrate the wall unless its velocity is

$$v \geq \frac{°qtB}{2m}.$$

12.36. Show that the maximum energy to which a particle of charge q and mass m (assumed to be constant) can be accelerated in a cyclotron is

$$U_{\max} = \frac{°q^2R^2B^2}{2m},$$

where B is the magnetic field of the cyclotron and R is the largest possible radius for the particle's orbit in the cyclotron.

13

ENERGY AND FORCE RELATIONS IN THE MAGNETOSTATIC FIELD IN VACUUM

A magnetostatic field is a carrier of *magnetic energy*. Like any other energy, magnetic energy satisfies the principle of conservation. In this chapter we shall study various energy relations in magnetostatic fields, after which, using the principle of conservation of energy, we shall study force relations in magnetostatic systems.

13-1. The Energy of a Magnetostatic Field

Look at the lines-of-force picture of the magnetic field between a compass needle and a horseshoe magnet (Fig. 13.1). It seems as if the ends of the needle are pulled to the magnet by a set of elastic strings or springs. This analogy led Faraday and later Maxwell to the idea that a magnetic field could be regarded as an elastic medium in a state of stress. But then a magnetic field should be a carrier of a definite amount of energy, just as a compressed or a stretched spring is. According to Maxwell's views, the energy stored in a magnetostatic field should be

$$U = \frac{°\mu_0}{2} \int_{\text{All space}} H^2 dv. \qquad (13\text{-}1.1a)$$

This equation has been found to be in complete agreement with all presently known phenomena involving energy and force relations in magnetostatic fields. What is more, all such relations have been found to be derivable from this equation, and no equation for the energy of a

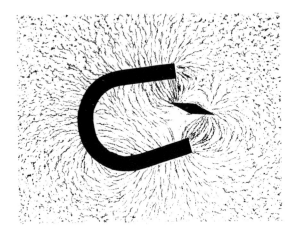

FIG. 13.1   Lines-of-force picture for a compass needle and a horseshoe magnet. The picture suggests that there is a tension along the lines of force combined with pressure in perpendicular directions.

magnetostatic field (in vacuum) more general than this one has been discovered. Therefore Eq. (13-1.1a) is considered to represent the fundamental magnetostatic energy law.

Since in vacuum $\mu_0\mathbf{H} = \mathbf{B}$, this law is frequently written in the symmetrical form

$$U = \overset{\circ}{\frac{1}{2}} \int\limits_{\text{All space}} \mathbf{H} \cdot \mathbf{B} \, dv. \qquad (13\text{-}1.1)$$

This law is sometimes written also in the differential form

$$U_v = \overset{\circ}{\frac{1}{2}} \mathbf{H} \cdot \mathbf{B}, \qquad (13\text{-}1.2)$$

where U_v is the energy density of the magnetostatic field.

It is useful to note the similarity between the above equations and the corresponding equations for electric energy (Section 7-1). This similarity between the basic magnetic and electric energy equations leads to a similarity between the corresponding special forms of these equations, as will be seen from the following sections.

▼
Example 13-1.1   Find the ratio of the magnetic and electric energies of a uniformly charged spherical shell of total charge q and radius a rotating with angular velocity ω about a diameter.

By Example 11-4.1, the magnetic field of the shell is

$$\mathbf{H} = \frac{2\sigma\omega a}{3} \mathbf{k} \qquad (r \leq a)$$

and

$$\mathbf{H} = \frac{2\sigma\omega a^4 \cos\theta}{3r^3} \mathbf{r}_u + \frac{\sigma\omega a^4 \sin\theta}{3r^3} \boldsymbol{\theta}_u \qquad (r \geq a).$$

The magnetic energy of the shell is then, by Eq. (13-1.1a),

$$U = \frac{°\mu_0}{2}\left(\frac{2\sigma\omega a}{3}\right)^2 \frac{4}{3}\pi a^3$$

$$+ \frac{°\mu_0}{2}\left(\frac{\sigma\omega a^4}{3}\right)^2 \int_a^\infty \left[\int_0^\pi \frac{(1 + 3\cos^2\theta)}{r^6} 2\pi r^2 \sin\theta \, d\theta\right] dr$$

$$= \frac{°8\pi\mu_0\sigma^2\omega^2 a^5}{27} + \frac{°4\pi\mu_0\sigma^2\omega^2 a^5}{27}$$

or, substituting $\sigma = q/4\pi a^2$ and simplifying,

$$U = \frac{°\mu_0 q^2\omega^2 a}{36\pi}.$$

The electric energy of the shell is, by Example 7-1.2,

$$U = \frac{°q^2}{8\pi\varepsilon_0 a}.$$

The ratio of the two energies is therefore

$$\frac{U_{\text{mag}}}{U_{\text{elec}}} = \frac{2\varepsilon_0\mu_0\omega^2 a^2}{9}.$$

Since $\varepsilon_0\mu_0$ is $1/c^2$, where c is the velocity of light (see Chapter 15), and since $\omega^2 a^2$ must be always smaller than c^2, this ratio is always less than one.

▲

13-2. Energy in Terms of Current Distribution

The fundamental energy law (13-1.1) can be transformed into various special forms which in many instances are more convenient to use than the original expression itself. One of the most important special forms of the energy law is the equation representing the energy of the magnetostatic field in terms of the current distribution producing this field. It may be obtained as follows.

Substituting $\mathbf{B} = \nabla \times \mathbf{A}$ into Eq. (13-1.1), we have

$$U = \frac{°1}{2} \int_{\text{All space}} \mathbf{H} \cdot \mathbf{B} \, dv = \frac{°1}{2} \int_{\text{All space}} \mathbf{H} \cdot (\nabla \times \mathbf{A}) \, dv.$$

Using the vector identity (V-5), which may be written as

$$\nabla \cdot (\mathbf{H} \times \mathbf{A}) = \mathbf{A} \cdot (\nabla \times \mathbf{H}) - \mathbf{H} \cdot (\nabla \times \mathbf{A}),$$

or

$$\mathbf{H} \cdot (\nabla \times \mathbf{A}) = \mathbf{A} \cdot (\nabla \times \mathbf{H}) - \nabla \cdot (\mathbf{H} \times \mathbf{A}),$$

we obtain (omitting for brevity the subscripts "all space")

$$U = \frac{1}{2} \int \mathbf{A} \cdot (\nabla \times \mathbf{H}) \, dv - \frac{1}{2} \int \nabla \cdot (\mathbf{H} \times \mathbf{A}) \, dv.$$

The last integral can be transformed into a surface integral by using Gauss's theorem of vector analysis, and since $\mathbf{H}$ and $\mathbf{A}$ are regular at infinity, this integral vanishes. In the first integral we can substitute $\nabla \times \mathbf{H} = \mathbf{J}$. We then obtain

$$U = \frac{1}{2} \int \mathbf{A} \cdot \mathbf{J} \, dv. \tag{13-2.1}$$

This equation can be written in an alternative form by also expressing the potential $\mathbf{A}$ in terms of current distribution. Using Eq. (11-1.3), we then obtain

$$U = \frac{\mu_0}{8\pi} \iint \frac{\mathbf{J}_1 \cdot \mathbf{J}_2}{r_{12}} \, dv_1 dv_2, \tag{13-2.2}$$

where r_{12} is the distance between the two volume elements dv_1 and dv_2, while $\mathbf{J}_1$ and $\mathbf{J}_2$ are the current densities in these elements.

13-3. Energy of a System of Current Distributions

Several special forms of the energy equation (13-1.1) can be obtained for the magnetic energy associated with a system of discrete current distributions.

Let us consider a system of current distributions consisting of n separate current-carrying regions. Taking into account that the current density outside the current-carrying regions is zero, we can write Eq. (13-2.1) as

$$U = \frac{1}{2} \sum_i \int \mathbf{A}_i \cdot \mathbf{J}_i dv_i, \tag{13-3.1}$$

where $\mathbf{A}_i$ and $\mathbf{J}_i$ are the potential and the current density in the volume element dv_i of the i-th region.

Each potential $\mathbf{A}_i$ in Eq. (13-3.1) may be regarded as the sum of two potentials

$$\mathbf{A}_i = \mathbf{A}_i'' + \mathbf{A}_i',$$

where $\mathbf{A}_i''$ is the "internal" potential due to the current in the i-th current-carrying region itself, while $\mathbf{A}_i'$ is the "external" potential due to the currents in all other current-carrying regions of the system. Substituting these potentials into Eq. (13-3.1), we have

$$U = \overset{\circ}{\frac{1}{2}} \sum_i \int \mathbf{A}_i'' \cdot \mathbf{J}_i dv_i + \overset{\circ}{\frac{1}{2}} \sum_i \int \mathbf{A}_i' \cdot \mathbf{J}_i dv_i. \tag{13-3.2}$$

As in the corresponding equation for the electrostatic energy, the first term on the right represents the *internal energy*, or the *self-energy*, U_s, of the individual current distributions comprising the system under consideration, while the last term represents the *mutual energy*, or the *interaction energy*, U', of these current distributions.

Using the symbol U_s for the self-energy, we can write Eq. (13-3.2) in the simpler form

$$U = \overset{\circ}{\frac{1}{2}} \sum_i \int \mathbf{A}_i' \cdot \mathbf{J}_i dv_i + U_s. \tag{13-3.3}$$

13-4. Energy of a Current Distribution in an External Field

It is often desirable to know the energy of the interaction between a current distribution and an external magnetic field. This energy can be found as follows.

Let $\mathbf{J}$ be some current distribution and let $\mathbf{J}'$ be the current distribution which produces the external magnetic field at the location of $\mathbf{J}$. Let the field produced by $\mathbf{J}$ be $\mathbf{H}$, and that produced by $\mathbf{J}'$ be $\mathbf{H}'$, so that the total field at any point of space is $\mathbf{H}_{\text{total}} = \mathbf{H} + \mathbf{H}'$.

The total magnetic energy of the system is then, by the energy law (13-1.1a),

$$U = \overset{\circ}{\frac{\mu_0}{2}} \int H_{\text{total}}^2 dv = \overset{\circ}{\frac{\mu_0}{2}} \int \mathbf{H}_{\text{total}} \cdot \mathbf{H}_{\text{total}} dv$$

$$= \overset{\circ}{\frac{\mu_0}{2}} \int (\mathbf{H} + \mathbf{H}') \cdot (\mathbf{H} + \mathbf{H}') dv$$

or

$$U = \overset{\circ}{\frac{\mu_0}{2}} \int H^2 dv + \overset{\circ}{\frac{\mu_0}{2}} \int H'^2 dv + {}^{\circ}\mu_0 \int \mathbf{H} \cdot \mathbf{H}' dv. \tag{13-4.1}$$

The first term on the right of this equation depends only on the field produced by the current distribution $\mathbf{J}$, and the second term depends only on the field produced by the current distribution $\mathbf{J}'$; these two terms represent therefore the self-energy U_s of the two distributions.

The last term, however, depends on both fields and, consequently, represents the mutual, or interaction, energy U' of these current distributions.

Writing this term as

$$U' = {}^{\circ}\!\!\int \mathbf{H} \cdot \mathbf{B}'dv = {}^{\circ}\!\!\int \mathbf{H} \cdot (\boldsymbol{\nabla} \times \mathbf{A}')\,dv$$

and repeating the transformations employed in Section 13-2, we obtain for U'

$$U' = {}^{\circ}\!\!\int \mathbf{J} \cdot \mathbf{A}'dv. \tag{13-4.2}$$

Since the integral in this equation depends only on the current distribution $\mathbf{J}$ and the external potential $\mathbf{A}'$, the equation may be interpreted as representing the interaction energy of the current distribution with the external field, or, as one usually says, the energy of the current distribution *in* the external field.

As it follows from the derivation, this energy is the same as the mutual, or interaction, energy of the current distribution $\mathbf{J}$ and the current distribution $\mathbf{J}'$ which produces the external field at the location of $\mathbf{J}$.

▼

Example 13-4.1   Consider two mutually external uniformly charged spherical shells, each spinning about its diameter (Fig. 13.2a). Show that the magnetic interaction energy of the shells is equal to that of two magnetic dipoles located at the centers of the shells, each having a dipole moment (magnitude and direction) equal to the dipole moment of the respective shell.

According to Eq. (13-4.2), the magnetic interaction energy of the shells is

$$U' = {}^{\circ}\!\!\int \mathbf{J} \cdot \mathbf{A}'dv,$$

where $\mathbf{A}'$ is the vector potential produced by one shell at the location of the other. A spinning charged shell, by Example 11-4.1 and Problem 11.13, produces a dipole field in the external space. Therefore the "field-producing" shell may be replaced by an equivalent dipole at the center without affecting the interaction energy (Fig. 13.2b). Now, the interaction energy of this new system can be expressed as

$$U' = {}^{\circ}\!\!\int \mathbf{J} \cdot \mathbf{A}'dv,$$

where $\mathbf{J}$ is the current in the dipole and $\mathbf{A}'$ is the potential produced at the location of the dipole by the remaining sphere. In view of the considerations

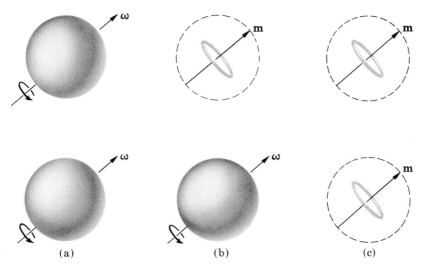

Fɪɢ. 13.2   Magnetic interaction energy of two mutually external, charged, spinning shells is equal to the interaction energy of two magnetic dipoles.

just presented, this energy will not be affected either if the sphere is replaced by an equivalent dipole at the center (Fig. 13.2c). Thus the magnetic interaction energy of two spinning, uniformly charged spherical shells is indeed equal to the magnetic interaction energy of the two dipoles at the centers of the shells.

▲

13-5. Energy of a System of Filamentary Currents or Circuits

Special forms of the energy law (13-1.1) are also frequently used for representing the magnetic energy of a system of stationary filamentary currents.

Let us consider a system of n mutually external currents carried by n separate wires (circuits). The magnetic energy of this system can be expressed, by Eq. (13-3.1), as

$$U = \frac{1}{2} \sum_i \int \mathbf{J}_i \cdot \mathbf{A}_i dv_i.$$

Since the currents are all filamentary, we can write

$$\mathbf{J}_i dv_i = \mathbf{J}_i a_i dl_i = I_i d\mathbf{l}_i,$$

where a_i is the cross-sectional area of the wire carrying the current I_i, and dl_i is the length element of the wire. The current in a wire is, however, the same at all points of the wire, so that we can write the above energy equation as

$$U = {}^{\circ}\frac{1}{2} \sum_i I_i \oint \mathbf{A}_i \cdot d\mathbf{l}_i$$

(the integral is closed because only closed wires can carry stationary currents). Using Stokes's theorem of vector analysis, we can transform the integral in this equation into a surface integral over a surface S_i bounded by the i-th wire. We then obtain

$$U = {}^{\circ}\frac{1}{2} \sum_i I_i \int \nabla \times \mathbf{A}_i \cdot d\mathbf{S}_i = {}^{\circ}\frac{1}{2} \sum_i I_i \int \mathbf{B}_i \cdot d\mathbf{S}_i,$$

where $\mathbf{B}_i$ is the magnetic flux density at the location of the surface element dS_i. Since the last integral represents the magnetic flux Φ_i linking the i-th wire (circuit), we finally obtain for the magnetic energy of a system of stationary filamentary currents

$$U = {}^{\circ}\frac{1}{2} \sum_i I_i \Phi_i. \qquad (13\text{-}5.1)$$

(In using this equation, we should remember that the product $I_i \Phi_i$ can be positive as well as negative. As it follows from the derivation, the product is positive if I_i and Φ_i form a right-handed system; the product is negative if they form a left-handed system.)

If we designate the contribution of the current I_k of the k-th wire to the flux Φ_i linking the i-th wire as Φ_{ik}, we can express Φ_i as

$$\Phi_i = \sum_k \Phi_{ik},$$

or, using the inductance coefficient $L_{ik} = \dfrac{\Phi_{ik}}{I_k}$, as

$$\Phi_i = \sum_k L_{ik} I_k. \qquad (13\text{-}5.2)$$

Substituting this expression into Eq. (13-5.1), we obtain an alternative expression for the energy of the filamentary currents

$$U = {}^{\circ}\frac{1}{2} \sum_i \sum_k I_i I_k L_{ik}. \qquad (13\text{-}5.3)$$

From this equation we can easily obtain the expression for the energy of a filamentary current in an external field. For this purpose let us rewrite Eq. (13-5.3) as

$$U = {}^{\circ}\frac{1}{2} I_1^2 L_{11} + {}^{\circ}\frac{1}{2} I_1 \sum_{k>1} I_k L_{1k} + {}^{\circ}\frac{1}{2} I_1 \sum_{i>1} I_i L_{i1} + {}^{\circ}\frac{1}{2} \sum_{i>1} \sum_{k>1} I_i I_k L_{ik},$$

where we have written explicitly all terms involving the wire number 1. Since $L_{1k} = L_{k1}$ (see Section 11-2), we can combine the second and third terms by replacing the index of summation i in the third term by k. Then we obtain

$$U = \frac{°1}{2} I_1^2 L_{11} + °I_1 \sum_{k>1} I_k L_{1k} + \frac{°1}{2} \sum_{i>1} \sum_{k>1} I_i I_k L_{ik},$$

or, using Eq. (13-5.2),

$$U = \frac{°1}{2} I_1^2 L_{11} + °I_1 \Phi_1' + \frac{°1}{2} \sum_{i>1} \sum_{k>1} I_i I_k L_{ik},$$

where the prime on Φ_1' indicates that the flux Φ_1' is due to currents other than I_1 (that is, due to sources external to the circuit number 1). The first term in this expression depends only on the current I_1 and therefore represents the self-energy of this current. The last term depends on currents other than I_1 and therefore represents the energy of the remaining currents in the system. The second term, however, depends on the current I_1 and also on the currents which produce the external field (causing Φ_1') at the location of this current. Consequently this term represents the mutual, or interaction energy, of the current I_1 with all other currents of the system, or, which is the same, the energy of I_1 in the field of these currents.

Thus, for the magnetic energy of a filamentary current I in an external magnetic field we have

$$U' = °I\Phi', \tag{13-5.4}$$

where Φ' is the flux through the circuit carrying the current I due to this external field. [Eq. (13-5.4) can be obtained, of course, directly from Eq. (13-4.2); see Problem 13.3.]

For a single circuit, Eqs. (13-5.1), (13-5.3), and (10-5.2) yield

$$U = \frac{°1}{2} \Phi I = \frac{°1}{2} L I^2 = \frac{°1}{2} \frac{\Phi^2}{L}, \tag{13-5.5a, b, c}$$

where Φ is the flux linking the circuit, I is the current in the circuit, and L is the self-inductance of the circuit. These equations are the magnetic counterpart of the equations for the electrostatic energy of a single capacitor.

One frequently uses Eq. (13-5.5b) as the *definition* of self-inductance for systems in which the currents are not filamentary. This definition avoids the ambiguity inherent in the definition stated in Section 10-5. When this definition is used, Eq. (13-5.5b) is usually combined with

Eq. (13-1.1a) and the self-inductance is calculated from

$$L = \frac{\mu_0}{I^2} \int\limits_{\text{All space}} H^2 \, dv. \qquad (13\text{-}5.6)$$

▼
Example 13-5.1   Neglecting end effects, find the self-inductance of a coaxial cable of length l consisting of a central wire of radius a and a sheath of inner radius b and outer radius c (Fig. 13.3).

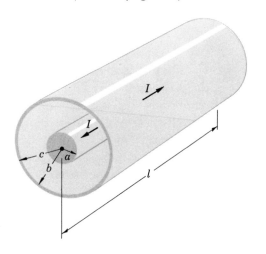

FIG. 13.3   Example of self-inductance calculation by energy method.

If the central wire carries a current I and the sheath returns this current, the magnetic field in the wire is, by Ampere's law,

$$H = \frac{Ir}{2\pi a^2} \qquad (r \leq a),$$

where r is the distance from the axis of the wire. The field in the space between the wire and the sheath is, similarly,

$$H = \frac{I}{2\pi r} \qquad (a \leq r \leq b).$$

The field in the sheath is

$$H = \frac{I}{2\pi r}\left[1 - \left(\frac{r^2 - b^2}{c^2 - b^2}\right)\right] = \frac{I}{2\pi r}\left(\frac{c^2 - r^2}{c^2 - b^2}\right) \qquad (b \leq r \leq c).$$

The field outside the sheath $(r > c)$ is zero. We thus have, by Eq. (13-5.6),

$$L = \frac{\mu_0}{I^2}\left[\int_0^a \left(\frac{Ir}{2\pi a^2}\right)^2 l2\pi r \, dr + \int_a^b \left(\frac{I}{2\pi r}\right)^2 l2\pi r \, dr + \int_b^c \left(\frac{I}{2\pi r}\right)^2 \left(\frac{c^2 - r^2}{c^2 - b^2}\right)^2 l2\pi r \, dr\right]$$

which upon integration and simplification yields

$$L = \frac{\mu_0}{8\pi} l \left\{ 1 + 4 \ln \frac{b}{a} + 4 \left[\frac{c^4}{(c^2 - b^2)^2} \ln \frac{c}{b} - \frac{3c^2 - b^2}{4(c^2 - b^2)} \right] \right\}.$$

▲

13-6. Correlation between Magnetic Energy and Magnetic Force

With the aid of Eq. (13-4.2) and the principle of conservation of energy, we shall now determine the magnetic force which a current distribution experiences in a magnetic field.

Let us consider an isolated system consisting of a conductor carrying a current distribution $\mathbf{J}_1$ placed in a magnetic field of a current distribution $\mathbf{J}_2$ carried by another conductor or conductors (the system also contains all devices necessary for maintaining the currents and keeping the conductors in equilibrium). The total energy of this system may be subdivided into the following components:

(1) The magnetic energy of the currents, U.

(2) The electric energy of the battery and other sources which maintain the currents, U_e.

(3) The energy dissipated in Joule's heating of the conductors carrying the currents, U_h.

(4) The mechanical energy of the devices keeping the conductors in equilibrium, W.

The principle of conservation of energy requires that the sum of these four energies remains constant, or that

$$dU + dU_e + dU_h + dW = 0.$$

Suppose now that under the action of the magnetic force $\mathbf{F}$ the first conductor undergoes a small displacement (translation) $d\mathbf{l}$ in a time interval dt, so that the velocity of the conductor during this displacement is $\mathbf{v} = d\mathbf{l}/dt$. Suppose also that during this displacement both the current density in the first conductor, $\mathbf{J}_1$, and the current density in the second conductor, $\mathbf{J}_2$, are maintained constant. In this case the magnetic self-energies of $\mathbf{J}_1$ and $\mathbf{J}_2$ remain constant and the change in the total magnetic energy of the system is equal to the change in the magnetic interaction energy U' of $\mathbf{J}_1$ with $\mathbf{J}_2$, or

$$dU\big|_{\mathbf{J}=\text{constant}} = dU'\big|_{\mathbf{J}=\text{constant}}.$$

The above energy relation can then be written as

$$dW = -(dU + dU_e + dU_h)\,|_{\mathbf{J}=\text{constant}}$$
$$= -(dU' + dU_e + dU_h)\,|_{\mathbf{J}=\text{constant}}.$$

The increment in the mechanical energy dW is, however, equal to the work $\mathbf{F} \cdot d\mathbf{l}$ done by the force $\mathbf{F}$ in displacing the current distribution along $d\mathbf{l}$, so that we have

$$\mathbf{F} \cdot d\mathbf{l} = -(dU' + dU_e + dU_h)\,|_{\mathbf{J}=\text{constant}}. \qquad (13\text{-}6.1)$$

Let us now evaluate the term on the right of this equation. When the conductors are at rest, and the currents are steady, the energy of the batteries is needed only to supply the steady-state heat losses, so that $dU_e + dU_h = 0$. When conductor 1 undergoes a displacement, however, it moves through the external magnetic field (flux density $\mathbf{B}_1'$) produced by the current distribution of conductor 2. An electric field (see Section 12-2)

$$\mathbf{E}_1^* = \mathbf{v} \times \mathbf{B}_1' \qquad (13\text{-}6.2)$$

is then induced in conductor 1. At the same time, conductor 2 may be regarded as moving with velocity $-\mathbf{v}$ through the magnetic field (flux density $\mathbf{B}_2'$) produced by the current distribution of conductor 1. An electric field

$$\mathbf{E}_2^* = -\mathbf{v} \times \mathbf{B}_2' \qquad (13\text{-}6.3)$$

is therefore induced in conductor 2. These induced fields cause an additional dissipation of energy, $dU_h^* = dU_e + dU_h$, during the displacement of conductor 1 (time interval dt).

By Joule's law and by Eqs. (13-6.2) and (13-6.3), we have

$$dU_h^* = \left(\overset{\circ}{\int} \mathbf{J}_1 \cdot \mathbf{E}_1^* dv + \overset{\circ}{\int} \mathbf{J}_2 \cdot \mathbf{E}_2^* dv \right) dt$$
$$= \left(\overset{\circ}{\int} \mathbf{J}_1 \cdot \mathbf{v} \times \mathbf{B}_1' dv - \overset{\circ}{\int} \mathbf{J}_2 \cdot \mathbf{v} \times \mathbf{B}_2' dv \right) dt$$
$$= \overset{\circ}{\int} \mathbf{J}_1 \cdot d\mathbf{l} \times \mathbf{B}_1' dv - \overset{\circ}{\int} \mathbf{J}_2 \cdot d\mathbf{l} \times \mathbf{B}_2' dv,$$

and using the permutation property of the "box product" (Section 2-7), we obtain

$$dU_h^* = -\overset{\circ}{\int} d\mathbf{l} \cdot \mathbf{J}_1 \times \mathbf{B}_1' dv + \overset{\circ}{\int} d\mathbf{l} \cdot \mathbf{J}_2 \times \mathbf{B}_2' dv,$$

or

$$dU_h^* = -\overset{\circ}{d\mathbf{l}} \cdot \int \mathbf{J}_1 \times \mathbf{B}_1' dv + \overset{\circ}{d\mathbf{l}} \cdot \int \mathbf{J}_2 \times \mathbf{B}_2' dv.$$

Now, by Example 10-4.6,[1]

$$\int \mathbf{J}_2 \times \mathbf{B}_2' dv = -\int \mathbf{J}_1 \times \mathbf{B}_1' dv,$$

so that

$$dU_h^* = -{}^\circ 2 \, d\mathbf{l} \cdot \int \mathbf{J}_1 \times \mathbf{B}_1' dv.$$

Therefore we can write Eq. (13-6.1) as

$$\mathbf{F} \cdot d\mathbf{l} = -\left(dU' - {}^\circ 2 \, d\mathbf{l} \cdot \int \mathbf{J}_1 \times \mathbf{B}_1' dv \right)\bigg|_{\mathbf{J}=\text{constant}}. \qquad (13\text{-}6.4)$$

If $\mathbf{J}$ is kept constant, however,

$$dU' = \nabla U' \cdot d\mathbf{l},$$

and hence

$$\mathbf{F} \cdot d\mathbf{l} = -d\mathbf{l} \cdot \left(\nabla U' - {}^\circ 2 \int \mathbf{J}_1 \times \mathbf{B}_1' dv \right)\bigg|_{\mathbf{J}=\text{constant}}.$$

Since $d\mathbf{l}$ is arbitrary, this relation demands that

$$\mathbf{F} = -\left(\nabla U' - {}^\circ 2 \int \mathbf{J}_1 \times \mathbf{B}_1' dv \right)\bigg|_{\mathbf{J}=\text{constant}}.$$

Now, by Eq. (13-4.2) and Example 11-1.4,

$$\nabla U' = \nabla \left({}^\circ \int \mathbf{J}_1 \cdot \mathbf{A}_1' dv \right) = {}^\circ \int \mathbf{J}_1 \times \mathbf{B}_1' dv,$$

and we finally obtain (eliminating ${}^\circ 2 \int \mathbf{J}_1 \times \mathbf{B}_1' dv$ from the preceding equation)

$$\mathbf{F} = \nabla U' \big|_{\mathbf{J}=\text{constant}}, \qquad (13\text{-}6.5)$$

and (eliminating $\nabla U'$ from the same equation)

$$\mathbf{F} = {}^\circ \int \mathbf{J}_1 \times \mathbf{B}_1' dv. \qquad (13\text{-}6.6)$$

Equation (13-6.5) constitutes the general relation between the magnetic energy of a current distribution in the magnetic field of external currents and the magnetic force acting upon this current distribution. Since for $\mathbf{J} = $ constant, $\nabla U'$ is equal to ∇U, this relation can be written also as

$$\mathbf{F} = \nabla U \big|_{\mathbf{J}=\text{constant}}. \qquad (13\text{-}6.7)$$

Observe that in Eqs. (13-6.5) and (13-6.7) the force is given by the *positive* gradient of the energy.

---

[1] Note that the field previously designated as $\mathbf{B}_1$ is now designated as $\mathbf{B}_2'$, and the field previously designated as $\mathbf{B}_2$ is now designated as $\mathbf{B}_1'$.

Equation (13-6.6) can be written without subscripts as

$$\mathbf{F} = {}^{\circ}\!\int \mathbf{J} \times \mathbf{B}' dv. \qquad (13\text{-}6.8)$$

This is the basic equation representing the magnetic force acting upon a current distribution in an external magnetic field.

Since the self-energy $U_s = \int \mathbf{J} \cdot \mathbf{A}'' dv$ does not change if $\mathbf{J}$ is kept constant (compare with Section 7-8), this equation is equivalent to

$$\mathbf{F} = {}^{\circ}\!\int \mathbf{J} \times \mathbf{B} \, dv, \qquad (13\text{-}6.9)$$

where $\mathbf{B}$ is the total field at the location of volume element dv.

For filamentary currents, Eq. (13-6.7) becomes

$$\mathbf{F} = \nabla U \big|_{I = \text{constant}}. \qquad (13\text{-}6.10)$$

By Eqs. (13-5.3), (10-5.4), and (11-2.2), however

$$
\begin{aligned}
\nabla U \Big|_{I = \text{constant}} &= {}^{\circ}\frac{1}{2} \sum_i \sum_k I_i I_k \nabla L_{ik} \\
&= {}^{\circ}\frac{1}{2} \sum_i \sum_k \frac{\Phi_{ki}}{L_{ki}} \frac{\Phi_{ik}}{L_{ik}} \nabla L_{ik} = {}^{\circ}\frac{1}{2} \sum_i \sum_k \frac{\Phi_{ki}\Phi_{ik}}{L_{ik}^2} \nabla L_{ik} \\
&= -{}^{\circ}\frac{1}{2} \nabla \sum_i \sum_k \frac{\Phi_{ki}\Phi_{ik}}{L_{ik}} \bigg|_{\Phi = \text{constant}} = -{}^{\circ}\frac{1}{2} \sum_i \sum_k \Phi_{ki} I_k \bigg|_{\Phi = \text{constant}} \\
&= -\nabla U \big|_{\Phi = \text{constant}}.
\end{aligned}
$$

Therefore for filamentray currents we have also

$$\mathbf{F} = -\nabla U \big|_{\Phi = \text{constant}}. \qquad (13\text{-}6.11)$$

▼
Example 13-6.1   A long, flexible, cylindrical coil of negligible weight, radius a, and length l has n turns of wire. The coil is suspended from its upper end, and to its lower end a weight w is attached (Fig. 13.4). Neglecting end effects of the coil, find the current I that should be sent through the coil in order that the coil will support the weight w without stretching or contracting.

We shall solve this problem first by using Eq. (13-6.10) and then by using Eq. (13-6.11) in order to demonstrate that either equation can be used for magnetic force calculation in a system of filamentary currents.

Let z be the distance from the point from which the upper end of the coil is suspended to the center of gravity of w. Since the end effects of the coil may be neglected, we may assume that the field of the coil is just

$$H = \frac{nI}{l}$$

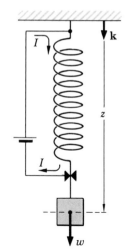

Fig. 13.4 If a current of certain magnitude is sent through the coil, the coil lifts the weight. A coil of this type is known as "Roget's spiral."

and is confined to the interior of the coil. The energy of this field is, by Eq. (13-1.1a),

$$U = \frac{\overset{\circ}{\mu_0}}{2} \int H^2 dv = \frac{\overset{\circ}{\mu_0}}{2} H^2 \pi a^2 l = \frac{\overset{\circ}{\mu_0}}{2} \frac{n^2 I^2}{l} \pi a^2. \qquad (13\text{-}6.12)$$

The force exerted by the coil on the weight w is, by Eq. (13-6.10),

$$\mathbf{F} = \frac{\partial U}{\partial z} \mathbf{k} \Big|_{I=\text{constant}},$$

and since $\Delta z = \Delta l$,

$$\mathbf{F} = \frac{\partial U}{\partial l} \mathbf{k} \Big|_{I=\text{constant}} = - \frac{\overset{\circ}{\mu_0}}{2} \frac{n^2 I^2}{l^2} \pi a^2 \mathbf{k}.$$

For equilibrium we must have

$$\mathbf{F} = -w\mathbf{k},$$

so that

$$I = \frac{l}{na} \sqrt{\frac{2w}{\overset{\circ}{\mu_0}\pi}}.$$

The same result can be obtained from Eq. (13-6.11). Indeed, the magnetic flux Φ in the coil is

$$\Phi = B\pi a^2 = \mu_0 H \pi a^2 = \mu_0 \frac{nI}{l} \pi a^2, \qquad (13\text{-}6.13)$$

so that the energy of the coil, Eq. (13-6.12), can be expressed in terms of Φ as

$$U = \frac{\overset{\circ}{\Phi^2} l}{2\mu_0 \pi a^2}.$$

The force is then, by Eq. (13-6.11),

$$\mathbf{F} = -\frac{\partial U}{\partial z} \mathbf{k}\bigg|_{\Phi=\text{constant}},$$

or, since as before $\Delta z = \Delta l$,

$$\mathbf{F} = -\frac{{}^{\circ}\Phi^2}{2\mu_0\pi a^2}\mathbf{k}.$$

Substituting Φ from Eq. (13-6.13), we again obtain

$$\mathbf{F} = -\frac{{}^{\circ}\mu_0}{2}\frac{n^2I^2}{l^2}\pi a^2\mathbf{k},$$

so that Eqs. (13-6.10) and (13-6.11) yield identical results.

Example 13-6.2   A parallel-plate capacitor of plate separation x and length l on a side is a part of the circuit shown in Fig. 13.5. Assuming that the plates are perfect conductors and neglecting edge effects, find the magnetic force acting on the capacitor's plates and compare it with the electric force acting on the plates.

If the edge effects are neglected and the plates are sufficiently thin, the magnetic field of the capacitor is confined to the region between the plates. By Ampere's law, this field is (compare with Example 10-4.3)

$$H = \frac{I}{l}.$$

The magnetic energy of the capacitor is then, by Eq. (13-1.1a),

$$U = \frac{{}^{\circ}\mu_0}{2} H^2 l^2 x = \frac{{}^{\circ}\mu_0 I^2}{2} x,$$

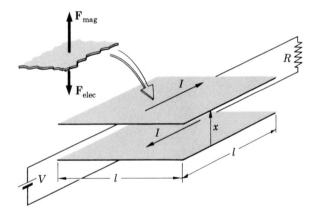

FIG. 13.5   If a current is sent through the plates of a parallel-plate capacitor, the plates are subjected to magnetic as well as electric forces which act in opposite directions.

and the magnetic force on the upper plate, for example, is, by Eq. (13-6.7),

$$\mathbf{F}_{\text{mag}} = \frac{\partial U}{\partial x} \mathbf{i} \Big|_{J=\text{constant}} = \frac{°\mu_0 I^2}{2} \mathbf{i}.$$

In terms of the applied voltage V and the resistance R this force is

$$\mathbf{F}_{\text{mag}} = \frac{°\mu_0 V^2}{2R^2} \mathbf{i}.$$

This force represents a *repulsion*.

The electric field of the capacitor is

$$E = \frac{V}{x},$$

and the electric energy is, by Eq. (7-1.1a),

$$U = \frac{°\varepsilon_0}{2} E^2 l^2 x = \frac{°\varepsilon_0 V^2 l^2}{2x}.$$

The electric force on the upper plate is then (see Example 7-7.1)

$$\mathbf{F}_{\text{elec}} = \frac{\partial U}{\partial x} \mathbf{i} \Big|_{V=\text{constant}} = -\frac{°\varepsilon_0 V^2 l^2}{2x^2} \mathbf{i}.$$

This force represents an *attraction*.

Thus, the plates of the capacitor are subjected to a magnetic as well as to an electric force, which act in opposite directions. The two forces become equal when

$$\frac{°\mu_0 V^2}{2R^2} = \frac{°\varepsilon_0 V^2 l^2}{2x^2},$$

or

$$R = \sqrt{\frac{\mu_0}{\varepsilon_0}} \frac{x}{l} \approx 377 \frac{x}{l} \text{ ohms.}$$

If R is larger than this value, the electric attraction predominates. If R is smaller than this value, the magnetic repulsion predominates.

The simultaneous presence of magnetic and electric forces in systems of current-carrying conductors is a very important phenomenon, which must be taken into account when magnetic forces are used for the measurement of electric currents or for calibration of standard current meters (as in the so-called "Ampere balance," for example). If electric forces acting on current-carrying conductors are disregarded in such measurements or calibrations, considerable errors may result.

Example 13-6.3   Find the induction drag (the force exerted by a magnetic field upon a current induced by this field) experienced by the artificial satellite discussed in Example 12-4.4.

By Eq. (13-6.8), the drag is

$$\mathbf{F} = \int^{\circ} \mathbf{J} \times \mathbf{B}' dv.$$

Let the velocity of the satellite be in the x-direction, and let the magnetic field be in the y-direction. This equation reduces then to

$$\mathbf{F} = -{}^{\circ}\mathbf{i} \int J_z B'_y dv = -{}^{\circ}\mathbf{i} \int J B' dv,$$

where the integral is extended over the volume of the satellite. Substituting the expression for J found in Example 12-4.4, dropping the prime on B', and designating the velocity of the satellite by u, we obtain for the drag

$$\mathbf{F} = -{}^{\circ}\mathbf{i} \int \frac{2\sigma_1\sigma_2 u B^2}{\sigma_1 + 2\sigma_2} dv = -\mathbf{i}\frac{2\sigma_1\sigma_2 u B^2}{\sigma_1 + 2\sigma_2} \cdot \frac{4}{3} \pi a^3,$$

or

$$\mathbf{F} = -\mathbf{i}\frac{8\sigma_1\sigma_2}{3(\sigma_1 + 2\sigma_2)} \pi u a^3 B^2.$$

Example 13-6.4   A thin, long conducting strip of width w and thickness t is moved with velocity $\mathbf{v}$ across a uniform magnetic field of flux density $\mathbf{B}$. Two sliding contacts are attached to the strip, as shown in Fig. 13.6. One contact delivers a current I to the strip, the other leads it away. Find the force needed to maintain the motion of the strip.

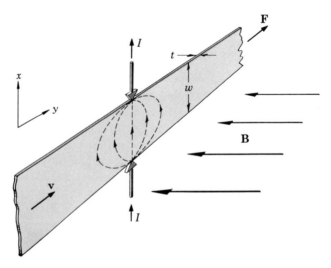

FIG. 13.6   Force is needed to move a current-carrying conductor across a magnetic field.

By Eq. (13-6.8), the magnetic force acting on the strip is (writing **B** for **B**′)

$$\mathbf{F} = {}^{\circ}\!\!\int \mathbf{J} \times \mathbf{B} \, dv,$$

where **J** is the current density in the strip, and the integration is extended over the volume of the strip. In terms of the coordinates shown in Fig. 13.6 this force is

$$\mathbf{F} = {}^{\circ}\!\!\iint (J_x\mathbf{i} + J_y\mathbf{j}) \times \mathbf{B}t \, dx \, dy,$$

and since **B** is a constant,

$$\mathbf{F} = -{}^{\circ}\mathbf{B} \times \iint (J_x\mathbf{i} + J_y\mathbf{j})t \, dx \, dy$$

$$= -{}^{\circ}\mathbf{B} \times \left(\mathbf{i} \iint J_x t \, dx \, dy + \mathbf{j} \iint J_y t \, dx \, dy\right).$$

By the symmetry of the system, however, the first integral of the last expression is

$$\iint J_x t \, dx \, dy = \int \left(\int J_x t \, dy\right) dx = \int I \, dx = Iw,$$

and the last integral is zero. The magnetic force acting on the strip is therefore

$$\mathbf{F} = -{}^{\circ}Blw\mathbf{j}.$$

The force needed to maintain the motion of the strip is then

$$\mathbf{F} = {}^{\circ}Blw\mathbf{j}.$$

▲

13-7. Energy and Force Relations for a Current Dipole

As we know from Chapter 11, a small, plane, current-carrying loop, or a current dipole, has the same significance in the theory of magnetic fields of current-carrying conductors as an electric dipole has in the theory of electric fields. We shall now obtain explicit expressions for the energy of a current dipole in an external magnetic field and for the magnetic force acting on such a dipole.

Starting from Eq. (13-4.2) and taking into account that a current dipole is a filamentary current, we can write

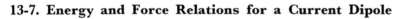

$$U' = {}^{\circ}\!\!\int \mathbf{J} \cdot \mathbf{A}' \, dv = {}^{\circ}I \oint \mathbf{A}' \cdot d\mathbf{l} = {}^{\circ}I \int \nabla \times \mathbf{A}' \cdot d\mathbf{S} = {}^{\circ}I \int \mathbf{B}' \cdot d\mathbf{S},$$

where the integral is extended over the area S of the loop forming the dipole. By the definition of the current dipole, S must be so small that the external field is essentially the same at all points of S. We can therefore write

$$U' = {}^{\circ}I\mathbf{B}' \cdot \int d\mathbf{S} = {}^{\circ}I\mathbf{B}' \cdot \mathbf{S} = {}^{\circ}I\mu_0\mathbf{H}' \cdot \mathbf{S}$$

and finally obtain

$$U' = {}^{\circ}\mathbf{m} \cdot \mathbf{H}', \tag{13-7.1}$$

where $\mathbf{m} = \mu_0 I\mathbf{S}$ is the dipole moment of the dipole.

Combining Eqs. (13-7.1) and (13-6.5), we obtain for the force acting upon a current dipole in an external magnetic field

$$\mathbf{F} = \boldsymbol{\nabla} U'\big|_{\mathbf{J}=\text{constant}} = \boldsymbol{\nabla} U'\big|_{I=\text{constant}} = \boldsymbol{\nabla} U'\big|_{\mathbf{m}=\text{constant}}$$

or

$$\mathbf{F} = {}^{\circ}\boldsymbol{\nabla}(\mathbf{m} \cdot \mathbf{H}')\big|_{\mathbf{m}=\text{constant}}. \tag{13-7.2}$$

Since $\boldsymbol{\nabla} \times \mathbf{H}' = 0$ at the location of the dipole, this equation, by vector identity (V-2), can be transformed into

$$\mathbf{F} = {}^{\circ}(\mathbf{m} \cdot \boldsymbol{\nabla})\mathbf{H}'. \tag{13-7.3}$$

As one can see, Eqs. (13-7.2) and (13-7.3) are the same as the corresponding equations for the force acting on an electric dipole in an external electric field. This implies that the torque acting on a current dipole in a magnetic field is, just as for an electric dipole in an electric field,

$$\mathbf{T} = {}^{\circ}\mathbf{m} \times \mathbf{H}'. \tag{13-7.4}$$

13-8. Maxwell's Stress Equation for a Magnetic Field

According to Section 13-6, the magnetic force experienced by a current distribution depends only on this distribution and on the external magnetic field. On the other hand, the *total* magnetic field around a current distribution also depends only on this current distribution and on the external field. It may therefore be anticipated that there should be a correlation between the force acting on a current distribution and the total magnetic field in the surrounding space. Such a correlation indeed exists and may be derived in the following manner.

Since in a vacuum $\boldsymbol{\nabla} \cdot \mathbf{B} = \boldsymbol{\nabla} \cdot \mathbf{H} = 0$ and $\mathbf{B} = \mu_0\mathbf{H}$, we can write for the magnetic field vector $\mathbf{H}$, according to the vector identity (V-22),

$$\mu_0\int (\boldsymbol{\nabla} \times \mathbf{H}) \times \mathbf{H}\, dv = -\frac{\mu_0}{2}\oint H^2 d\mathbf{S} + \mu_0\oint \mathbf{H}(\mathbf{H} \cdot d\mathbf{S}). \tag{13-8.1}$$

But $\mathbf{\nabla} \times \mathbf{H} = \mathbf{J}$, so that

$$\mu_0 \int (\mathbf{\nabla} \times \mathbf{H}) \times \mathbf{H} \, dv = \int \mathbf{J} \times \mu_0 \mathbf{H} \, dv = \int \mathbf{J} \times \mathbf{B} \, dv. \quad (13\text{-}8.2)$$

Substituting Eqs. (13-8.2) and (13-8.1) into Eq. (13-6.9), we obtain for the magnetic force acting upon a current distribution in a given region of space

$$\mathbf{F} = - \frac{°\mu_0}{2} \oint H^2 d\mathbf{S} + °\mu_0 \oint \mathbf{H}(\mathbf{H} \cdot d\mathbf{S}), \quad (13\text{-}8.3)$$

where the integrals are extended over the surface of the region under consideration.

We shall call this equation *Maxwell's stress equation for magnetic fields.* From this equation the force experienced by a current distribution can be determined if the total magnetic field at the points of some arbitrary surface of integration (Maxwellian surface) surrounding the current distribution is known. It is useful to note that this equation is the magnetic counterpart of the Maxwell stress equation for electric fields and has the same form as the latter.

Equation (13-8.3) is often written in a symmetric form

$$\mathbf{F} = - \frac{°1}{2} \oint \mathbf{H} \cdot \mathbf{B} \, d\mathbf{S} + °\oint \mathbf{H}(\mathbf{B} \cdot d\mathbf{S}). \quad (13\text{-}8.3a)$$

▼

Example 13-8.1   A long coil of n turns, length l, and cross-sectional area A is wound on two separate thin-walled cores (Fig. 13.7). Neglecting end effects, find the force needed to pull the two halves of the coil apart when the coil carries a current I.

Let us assume that there is a small gap between the two halves of the coil, and let us construct a Maxwellian surface passing through this gap, as shown in Fig. 13.7. Since when the end effects are neglected, the field may be assumed zero everywhere on this surface except in the gap, and since the

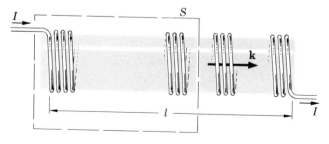

FIG. 13.7   The force needed to separate the two parts of the coil can be found from Maxwell's stress integral.

field in the gap is $H = nI/l$, Maxwell's stress equation for this surface becomes

$$\mathbf{F} = \left[-\frac{{}^{\circ}\mu_0}{2}\left(\frac{nI}{l}\right)^2 A + {}^{\circ}\mu_0 \frac{nI}{l}\left(\frac{nI}{l} A\right)\right]\mathbf{k},$$

where $\mathbf{k}$ is the unit vector shown in Fig. 13.7. The force needed to pull the two halves of the coil apart is therefore

$$F = \frac{{}^{\circ}\mu_0}{2}\left(\frac{nI}{l}\right)^2 A.$$

Example 13-8.2   A long coil of length l and radius a is made of n thin wires, each carrying a current I, as shown in Fig. 13.8. Neglecting edge effects, find the pitch θ that the coil should have in order to be "force free" (a system is called force free when the force acting on each element of the system is zero). Also, investigate how a variation of the pitch affects the forces acting on the coil.

By Ampere's law and by the geometry of the system, the magnetic field inside the coil is

$$H_{\text{inside}} = \left(\frac{nl}{2\pi a \cot \theta}\right)\frac{I}{l}\sin \theta = \frac{nI \sin^2 \theta}{2\pi a \cos \theta}$$

and just outside the coil

$$H_{\text{outside}} = \frac{nI \cos \theta}{2\pi a}.$$

Let us now apply Maxwell's stress equation

$$\mathbf{F} = -\frac{{}^{\circ}\mu_0}{2}\oint H^2 d\mathbf{S} + {}^{\circ}\mu_0 \oint \mathbf{H}(\mathbf{H} \cdot d\mathbf{S})$$

to a small element of the coil shown in the insert of Fig. 13.8. By symmetry, only the upper and the lower surfaces of the element contribute to the total

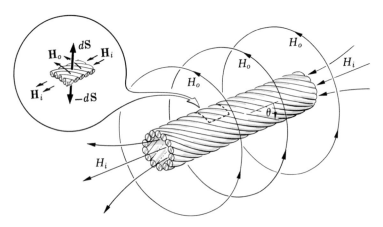

FIG. 13.8   A coil of 45° pitch is force free in radial direction.

force on the element. Furthermore, since $\mathbf{H}$ is perpendicular to $d\mathbf{S}$ on both these surfaces, the last term in Maxwell's stress equation makes no contribution. Designating the surface area of the element as ΔS, we therefore have for the force ΔF acting upon the element

$$\Delta F = \left[-\frac{{}^\circ\mu_0}{2}\left(\frac{nI\cos\theta}{2\pi a}\right)^2 + \frac{{}^\circ\mu_0}{2}\left(\frac{nI\sin^2\theta}{2\pi a\cos\theta}\right)^2 \right]\Delta S.$$

For the coil to be force free this force must vanish, so that

$$\frac{nI\cos\theta}{2\pi a} = \frac{nI\sin^2\theta}{2\pi a\cos\theta},$$

or

$$\cos^2\theta = \sin^2\theta,$$

which gives

$$\theta = 45°.$$

As one can easily see, for $\theta > 45°$ the force on the inner surface of the coil predominates so that the coil experiences a "magnetic pressure" from within tending to make the radius of the coil larger. On the other hand, for $\theta < 45°$, the force from the outside predominates and the coil experiences a magnetic pressure from without ("pinch effect") tending to make the radius of the coil smaller.

▲

PROBLEMS

13.1. Show that the ratio of the electric to the magnetic energy in a region where there is an electric field $E = n$ volt/meter and a magnetic field $H = n$ ampere/meter is

$$\frac{U_e}{U_m} \approx 7 \times 10^{-6}.$$

13.2. Show that the magnetic self-energy of a system of current distributions is always larger than the mutual, or interaction, energy of these distributions.

13.3. Starting with Eq. (13-4.2), show that the energy of a filamentary current I in an external field of flux density $\mathbf{B}'$ can be expressed as

$$U' = {}^\circ I\int \mathbf{B}' \cdot d\mathbf{S} = {}^\circ I\Phi',$$

where the integral is extended over a surface bounded by the current, and Φ' is the external flux linking this current.

13.4. Show that the magnetic energy of a system of i circuits can be written as the sum of self-energy terms ${}^\circ\frac{1}{2}\sum_i L_iI_i$ plus the sum of mutual energy terms ${}^\circ\sum_i\sum_j L_{ij}I_iI_j$, where $i < j$.

13.5. A current I_1 is carried by a circular loop of radius a, and a current I_2 is carried by an infinite coplanar straight wire at a distance $b > a$ from the center of the loop. Show that the mutual energy of this system is

$$U' = {}^\circ\mu_0 I_1 I_2 [b - (b^2 - a^2)^{1/2}].$$

13.6. A superconducting ring of weight w is placed over one end of a coil of wire whose axis is vertical. Show that if a current I is sent through the coil, the ring will rise to a maximum height

$$h = \frac{{}^\circ(M_0^2 - M_h^2)}{2wL} I^2,$$

where M_0 and M_h are the respective coefficients of mutual inductance between the ring and the coil initially and at the height h, and L is the self-inductance of the ring. (Hint: the magnetic flux linking a superconducting ring always remains the same.)

13.7. Show that in a system of n circuits the x-component of the force exerted upon the j-th circuit by all other circuits is

$$F_{jx} = {}^\circ\sum_n I_j I_n \frac{\partial L_{jn}}{\partial x} \qquad (n \neq j),$$

where I's are the currents in the corresponding circuits and L_{jn} is the mutual inductance between the j-th and the n-th circuit.

13.8. Show that a circular loop of wire carrying a current I will break if the breaking strength of the wire, T, is

$$T < \frac{{}^\circ I^2}{4\pi} \frac{\partial L}{\partial r},$$

where r is the radius and L is the self-inductance of the loop.

13.9. Two square loops, each of length a on a side, are placed parallel to each other and at right angles to the line joining their centers. The distance between the centers is h, and each loop carries a current I. Show that the force between the loops is

$$F = \frac{{}^\circ 2\mu_0 I^2}{\pi h} [h^2(2a^2 + h^2)^{1/2}(a^2 + h^2)^{-1} + h - (a^2 + 2h^2)(a^2 + h^2)^{-1/2}].$$

13.10. Show that a closed current-carrying circuit does not experience a net force in a homogeneous magnetic field.

13.11. Show that the loop described in Problem 13.5 is attracted to the infinite wire with the force

$$F = {}^\circ\mu_0 I_1 I_2 [1 - b(b^2 - a^2)^{-1/2}].$$

13.12. The self-inductance of a thin circular wire ring is

$$L = \mu_0 R\left(\ln \frac{8R}{r} - \frac{7}{4}\right),$$

where R is the radius of curvature of the ring, and r is the radius of the wire. Find the tension in the ring if the ring carries a current I.

13.13. Show that the force exerted by two closed filamentary currents I_1 and I_2 upon each other can be expressed as

$$\mathbf{F} = -\frac{{}^\circ\mu_0}{4\pi} I_1 I_2 \oint\oint \mathbf{r}_{u(12)} \frac{d\mathbf{l}_1 \cdot d\mathbf{l}_2}{r_{12}^2},$$

where $d\mathbf{l}_1$ and $d\mathbf{l}_2$ are length elements of the two currents in the direction of the currents, r_{12} is the distance between these elements, and $\mathbf{r}_{u(12)}$ is a unit vector pointing from length element $d\mathbf{l}_1$ to length element $d\mathbf{l}_2$.

13.14. A circular loop of wire of radius r carries a current I. Show that if the loop is placed in an external magnetic field of flux density B' parallel to the axis of the loop, and if the current is maintained constant, the loop will experience an additional tension

$$T = {}^\circ r I B'.$$

13.15. Two thin, very long, parallel wires carry currents I_1 and I_2, respectively. The wires are separated by a distance d. Show that each wire exerts a force per unit length of the other given by

$$f = -\frac{{}^\circ \mu_0 I_1 I_2}{2\pi d} \quad \text{or} \quad f = +\frac{{}^\circ \mu_0 I_1 I_2}{2\pi d},$$

depending on whether the two currents are parallel or antiparallel.

13.16. Find the force between the wire and the loop of Example 10-5.4.

13.17. A long coil of n_1 turns, length l_1 and cross-sectional area A is partially inserted into a larger coil of n_2 turns and length l_2. Neglecting end effects, show that if the coils carry currents I_1 and I_2, respectively, in the same direction, there is an attractive force between them

$$F = {}^\circ \mu_0 \frac{n_1 n_2}{l_1 l_2} A I_1 I_2.$$

13.18. A plane loop carrying a current I is placed in a uniform magnetic field of flux density B. The plane of the loop, whose area is S, forms an angle θ with the direction of B. Show that the loop experiences a torque

$$T = {}^\circ I B S \cos \theta.$$

13.19. Two parallel coaxial rings of radii a and b carry currents I_a and I_b, respectively. Show that if $a \gg b$ and if the centers of the rings are a distance d apart, the force between the rings is

$$F = \frac{{}^\circ 3 \mu_0 \pi a^2 b^2 I_a I_b}{2(a^2 + d^2)^{5/2}} d.$$

13.20. Two concentric circular loops of radii a and b carry currents I_a and I_b, respectively. The loops are free to turn about a common diameter.

Show that if $a < b$, a torque

$$T = \frac{^{\circ}\mu_0 \pi a^2}{2b}\left(1 - \frac{9a^2}{16b^2} + \cdots\right)I_a I_b$$

is required to hold the loops at a right angle to each other.

13.21. A long straight wire carries a current I. A current dipole of dipole moment m is placed at a distance r from the wire. Show that the dipole is subjected to an attractive or repulsive force F which, depending on the orientation of the dipole, lies in the interval

$$0 \leq F \leq \frac{^{\circ}mI}{2\pi r^2}.$$

13.22. Find the force between a large square loop of length a on a side carrying a current I and a small parallel, coaxial, square loop of length b on a side carrying a current i and placed at a distance d from the first.

13.23. Suppose that the rim of a "flying saucer" constitutes a circular conducting ring of radius a. The saucer is at a distance R from the earth, directly above earth's magnetic south pole. The plane of the saucer is normal to R. Assuming that $a \ll R$, show that in order to overcome the gravitational attraction of the earth a current

$$^{\circ}I = \frac{2M_s M_e R^2}{3ma^2}\, G$$

must be maintained in the rim. In this equation G is the gravitational constant, M_e is the mass of the earth, M_s is the mass of the saucer and m is the magnetic dipole moment of the earth. Considering that large currents require massive conductors, of what material could this rim be made?

13.24. A metal bar of weight w and length l falls without friction along a vertical track formed by two perfectly conducting metal rails, the ends of the bar being at all times in contact with the rails. The resistance of the bar is R, and a resistance R' is connected between the upper ends of the rails. Show that if there is a magnetic field B perpendicular to the plane of the track, the velocity of the bar cannot exceed

$$^{\circ}v = \frac{w(R + R')}{B^2 l^2}.$$

13.25. A circular loop of wire of radius a and resistance R rotates with angular velocity ω about a diameter which is perpendicular to a uniform magnetic field of flux density B. Show that a torque

$$T = \frac{^{\circ}\omega B^2 \pi^2 a^2}{R}\sin^2 \omega t$$

and a power

$$P = \frac{^{\circ}\omega^2 B^2 \pi^2 a^2}{R}\sin^2 \omega t$$

are needed to maintain the rotation of the loop.

13.26. A conducting disk is turning about a thin axle passing through the center at a right angle to the disk and parallel to a magnetic field H. A current I is delivered to the disk through a sliding contact on the periphery and is led away through a contact on the axle. Show that a torque

$$T = {}^{\circ}\tfrac{1}{2}\mu_0 H I a^2$$

is needed to maintain the rotation of the disk. (This device is called "Faraday's disk.")

13.27. A circular wire of conductivity σ_1 and radius a is bent to form a ring of radius R ($R \gg a$). The ring is embedded in a liquid of conductivity σ_2 and is turning around its axis with an angular velocity ω. A uniform magnetic field **B** is present at the location of the ring and is directed along the axis of the ring. Assuming that the liquid remains at rest, find the induction drag experienced by the ring. (Hint: consider a portion L of the ring, $R \gg L \gg a$, and treat it as a long cylinder.)

13.28. Suppose that a bolt of lightning constitutes a current of 10^4 ampere confined to a long, thin cylindrical shell of 10^{-1} meter radius. Show that the cylinder is subjected to an external magnetic pressure (pinch effect) of approximately 158 newton/(meter)^2.

13.29. A toroidal coil of rectangular cross section is wound on two separate thin-walled cores, each in the shape of a half-ring. The inner radius of the toroid is a, the outer radius is b, and the width is w. The toroid has n turns of wire and carries a current I. Show that the force needed to pull the two halves apart is

$$F = {}^{\circ}\mu_0 \frac{n^2 I^2 w}{4\pi^2} \left(\frac{1}{a} - \frac{1}{b} \right).$$

13.30. A thin long coil of n turns, length l, and cross-sectional area A carries a current I. The coil is placed along the axis of a large circular ring of radius R carrying a current I'. Find the force between the coil and the ring as a function of position of the center of the coil relative to the center of the ring.

14

MAGNETOSTATIC FIELD
IN MATERIAL MEDIA

Thus far we have dealt with magnetostatic fields in empty space, or vacuum. Magnetostatic fields can exist, however, in material media also. The properties of magnetostatic fields in material media will be discussed in this chapter.

14-1. Cavity Definition of Magnetic Field Vectors

The measurement procedures by means of which we have defined the field-vectors **H** and **B** in Sections 10-1 and 10-2 can be used directly for measurements in vacuum, gases, and liquids, but not in solids, since neither a compass needle nor a test coil can move freely inside solid bodies. Therefore more precise definitions of **H** and **B** must be made in order to make clear what we mean when we speak about magnetic fields inside material media and, in particular, inside solid bodies.

The only way to perform a field measurement in a solid body is to insert a measuring device (compass needle or test coil) into a hole, or cavity, made in the body. It has been found, however, that such a measurement is affected by the shape and orientation of the cavity. Therefore the shape and orientation of cavities to be used for field measurements must be specified in the definitions of **H** and **B** for material media. We shall define **H** and **B** for all media as follows.

*The magnetic field vector **H** at a point inside a material medium is defined*

454

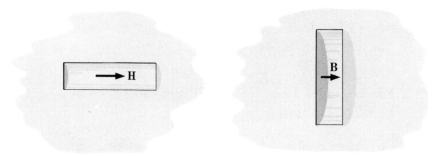

FIG. 14.1 To measure magnetic field in a material medium, a needle-shaped cavity or a long cylindrical cavity is used.

FIG. 14.2 To measure induction field in a material medium, a coin-shaped cavity or a short cylindrical cavity is used.

as the vector **H** *measured (by the method of Section 10.1) in a small, needle-shaped cavity made in this medium at that point and oriented so that the magnetic field in the cavity is in the direction of the axis of the cavity.* The essence of this definition is illustrated in Fig. 14.1. The requirement that the cavity be needle-shaped and oriented along the direction of the field is a result of investigations showing that the magnetic field measurements in liquids and gases by the direct method of Section 10-1 yield the same fields as the measurements inside small cavities of this type. The requirement that the cavity be small is needed in order to associate the magnetic field vector with a particular point of the medium (a "small" cavity is a cavity whose length is much smaller than the distance over which the field changes appreciably).

The induction vector **B** *at a point inside a material medium is defined as the vector* **B** *measured (by the method of Section 10.2) in a small, coin-shaped cavity made in this medium at that point and oriented so that the induction field in the cavity is in the direction of the axis of the cavity.* The essence of this definition is illustrated in Fig. 14.2. The requirement that the cavity be coin-shaped and oriented with its axis along the direction of the field is a result of investigations showing that the induction field measurements in liquids and gases by the direct method of Section 10-2 yield the same values as the measurements inside small cavities of this type. The requirement that the cavity be small is needed in order to associate the induction field vector with a particular point of the medium.

The two definitions which we have just introduced are frequently expressed symbolically as

$$\mathbf{H}_{\text{medium}} = \mathbf{H}_{\_} \quad \text{and} \quad \mathbf{B}_{\text{medium}} = \mathbf{B}_{\mathbf{I}}. \qquad (14\text{-}1.1a, b)$$

Observe that these definitions are analogous to those for the electric field vectors **E** and **D** stated in Section 8-1.

14-2. Fundamental Laws of the Magnetostatic Fields in Material Media

It has been established that the curl (circulation) law and the divergence (flux) law for the magnetostatic fields in material media are the same as for the magnetostatic fields in vacuum:

$$\nabla \times \mathbf{H} = \mathbf{J}, \qquad \oint \mathbf{H} \cdot d\mathbf{l} = \int \mathbf{J} \cdot d\mathbf{S} \qquad \text{(14-2.1a, b)}$$

and

$$\nabla \cdot \mathbf{B} = 0, \qquad \oint \mathbf{B} \cdot d\mathbf{S} = 0. \qquad \text{(14-2.2a, b)}$$

On the other hand, it has been established that, in contrast to the magnetostatic fields in vacuum, there is no general law which correlates **B** and **H** in an arbitrary medium, although for the majority of common materials the correlation between **B** and **H** can be expressed by the equation

$$\mathbf{B} = \mu_0 \mu \mathbf{H}. \qquad \text{(14-2.3)}$$

In this equation μ is a dimensionless factor of proportionality, different for different media, frequently different for different points of the same medium, and often depending on **H**. It is called the *permeability*. The media for which μ is not a function of **H** are called *magnetically linear media*. The media for which the correlation between **B** and **H** is independent of the direction of **H** are called *magnetically isotropic media*.

Frequently one expresses μ as

$$\mu = \chi_m + 1. \qquad \text{(14-2.4)}$$

The quantity χ_m defined by this equation is called *magnetic susceptibility*.

Equation (14-2.3) reduces to the flux density law for vacuum, $\mathbf{B} = \mu_0 \mathbf{H}$, if $\mu = 1$. Since the other two fundamental field laws for material media are identical with the corresponding laws for vacuum, a vacuum, as far as the magnetostatic field is concerned, is merely a special case of a material medium—a medium of permeability $\mu = 1$.

In a general case, a medium is neither linear nor isotropic—that is, in general, **B** is not a linear function of **H**, and the correlation between **B** and **H** depends on the direction of **H** relative to certain characteristic directions in the medium. An example of anisotropic media is a crystal. In a crystal, the correlation between **B** and **H** depends on the direction of **H** relative to crystal's axis. As a result, in a crystal, **B** and **H** are usually not even parallel to each other, each vector having a direction of its own.

It is customary to subdivide various media into three classes according to the magnitude of their permeability. The first class comprises media with $\mu < 1$; they are called the *diamagnetic media*. The second class comprises media with $\mu \gtrsim 1$; they are called the *paramagnetic media*. The third class comprises media with $\mu \gg 1$; they are called the *ferromagnetic media*.

Equations (14-2.1) to (14-2.3) determine the circulation law and the divergence law for both the magnetic field **H** and the induction field **B** and thus, by Helmholtz's theorem of vector analysis, constitute a complete set of equations uniquely specifying these fields.[1]

The similarity between Eqs. (14-2.1), (14-2.2), and (14-2.3) and the corresponding equations for the magnetostatic fields in vacuum suggests that many of the formulas which we have learned in the preceding chapters remain valid for the magnetostatic fields in material media. In particular, all formulas remain valid for the fields in the media of constant permeability μ occupying all space where the fields are present, provided that μ_0 in these formulas is replaced by the product $\mu_0\mu$.

14-3. Inductance of Conducting Systems in the Presence of Material Media

The inductance of conducting systems in material media is defined by the same equations as the inductance in vacuum—that is, by Eqs. (10-5.2), (10-5.3), (10-5.4), and (10-5.5).

▼

Example 14-3.1   A coaxial cable has two layers of different insulating materials between the core and the sheath. The length of the cable is l, the radius of the core is a, that of the sheath is b, the radius of the boundary between the two insulating layers is c, the permeability of the inner layer is μ_1, that of the outer layer is μ_2 (Fig. 14.3). Find the external inductance of the cable.

---

[1] Provided, of course, that the fields are regular at infinity, which we always assume to be the case.

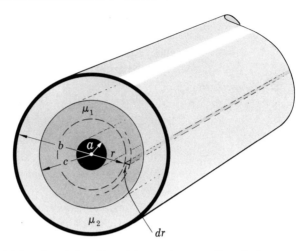

FIG. 14.3   Coaxial cable with two layers of insulating material.

Let the core carry a current I, and let the sheath return this current. By the symmetry of the system, the magnetic field must be circular, with field lines forming circles centered on the axis of the cable. Applying Ampere's law to an Amperian circle of radius r centered on the axis, we obtain for $a < r < b$

$$H = \frac{I}{2\pi r}.$$

The induction field is then, by Eq. (14-2.3),

$$B = \frac{\mu_0 \mu_1 I}{2\pi r}, \qquad a < r < c,$$

and

$$B = \frac{\mu_0 \mu_2 I}{2\pi r}, \qquad c < r < b.$$

The magnetic flux is

$$\Phi = \int \mathbf{B} \cdot d\mathbf{S} = \int_a^c \frac{\mu_0 \mu_1 I}{2\pi r} l \, dr + \int_c^b \frac{\mu_0 \mu_2 I}{2\pi r} l \, dr$$

$$= \frac{\mu_0 \mu_1 Il}{2\pi} \ln \frac{c}{a} + \frac{\mu_0 \mu_2 Il}{2\pi} \ln \frac{b}{c}.$$

The inductance is therefore, by Eq. (10-5.2),

$$L = \frac{\Phi}{I} = \frac{\mu_0 l}{2\pi} \left(\mu_1 \ln \frac{c}{a} + \mu_2 \ln \frac{b}{c} \right).$$

Example 14-3.2   A rectangular loop of wire of width a and height b is placed at a distance d from a long straight wire. The loop and the wire are

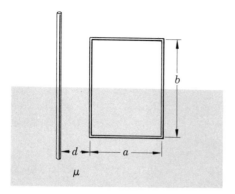

FIG. 14.4 Mutual inductance of a wire and a rectangular loop in the presence of a material medium (only a short segment of the wire is shown).

embedded halfway in a medium of permeability μ at a right angle to the surface of the medium, as shown in Fig. 14.4. Find the mutual inductance of the loop with respect to the wire.

Let the current in the wire be I_1. The magnetic field of the wire is then, by the symmetry of the system and by Eq. (14-2.1b),

$$H = \frac{I_1}{2\pi r},$$

and the flux density is, by Eq. (14-2.3),

$$B_u = \frac{\mu_0 I_1}{2\pi r} \quad \text{and} \quad B_l = \frac{\mu_0 \mu I_1}{2\pi r}$$

in the upper and lower halves of the system, respectively. The flux produced by this field through the rectangular loop is

$$\Phi_{21} = \int \mathbf{B} \cdot d\mathbf{S} = \int B \, dS = \int_d^{d+a} B_u \frac{b}{2} \, dr + \int_d^{d+a} B_l \frac{b}{2} \, dr$$

or

$$\Phi_{21} = \frac{\mu_0 I_1 b}{4\pi} \ln \frac{d+a}{d} + \frac{\mu_0 \mu I_1 b}{4\pi} \ln \frac{d+a}{d}$$

$$= \frac{\mu_0 I_1 b (1+\mu)}{4\pi} \ln \frac{d+a}{d}.$$

The mutual inductance of the loop with respect to the wire is therefore, by Eq. (10-5.4),

$$L_{21} = \frac{\Phi_{21}}{I_1} = \frac{\mu_0 b (1+\mu)}{4\pi} \ln \frac{d+a}{d}.$$

▲

14-4. Calculation of Magnetostatic Field and Magnetostatic Potentials within Material Media in Terms of Current Distribution

By Poisson's theorem, the field vector $\mathbf{H}$ can be expressed as

$$\mathbf{H} = -\frac{1}{4\pi} \int_{\text{All space}} \frac{\mathbf{\nabla}'(\mathbf{\nabla}' \cdot \mathbf{H}) - \mathbf{\nabla}' \times (\mathbf{\nabla}' \times \mathbf{H})}{r} \, dv'.$$

By the curl law (14-2.1a), we have $\mathbf{\nabla}' \times \mathbf{H} = \mathbf{J}$. By the divergence law (14-2.2a) and flux density law (14-2.3) (we are considering here only linear isotropic media), we have

$$\mathbf{\nabla}' \cdot \mathbf{H} = \mathbf{\nabla}' \cdot \frac{\mathbf{B}}{\mu_0 \mu} = \frac{1}{\mu_0 \mu} \mathbf{\nabla}' \cdot \mathbf{B} + \frac{\mathbf{B}}{\mu_0} \cdot \mathbf{\nabla}' \frac{1}{\mu} = \frac{\mathbf{B}}{\mu_0} \cdot \mathbf{\nabla}' \frac{1}{\mu}.$$

The above integral for the magnetic field therefore reduces to

$$\mathbf{H} = -\frac{1}{4\pi \mu_0} \int_{\text{All space}} \frac{\mathbf{\nabla}'[\mathbf{B} \cdot \mathbf{\nabla}'(1/\mu)]}{r} \, dv' + \frac{1}{4\pi} \int_{\text{All space}} \frac{\mathbf{\nabla}' \times \mathbf{J}}{r} \, dv'. \quad (14\text{-}4.1)$$

Obviously this equation, in general, is not very useful for calculating $\mathbf{H}$, since in order to evaluate the first integral one needs to know $\mathbf{B}$, and if $\mathbf{B}$ is known, then $\mathbf{H}$ is also known from Eq. (14-2.3).

However, in the particular case of a medium of constant permeability occupying all space, $\mathbf{\nabla}'(1/\mu) = 0$, and Eq. (14-4.1) becomes

$$\mathbf{H} = \frac{1}{4\pi} \int_{\text{All space}} \frac{\mathbf{\nabla}' \times \mathbf{J}}{r} \, dv', \quad (14\text{-}4.2)$$

which is the same equation as Eq. (10-6.1) for $\mathbf{H}$ in vacuum. All consequences derived from Eq. (10-6.1) in Chapters 10 and 11 are therefore also valid for the fields in material media of constant permeability occupying all space (μ_0 in the equations of Chapters 10 and 11 must be replaced, however, by $\mu_0 \mu$ to make these equations valid for material media). Specifically, for material media of constant permeability occupying all space, we have

$$\mathbf{H} = \frac{1}{4\pi} \int_{\text{All space}} \frac{\mathbf{J} \times \mathbf{r}_u}{r^2} \, dv', \quad (14\text{-}4.3)$$

$$\mathbf{A} = \frac{\mu_0 \mu}{4\pi} \int_{\text{All space}} \frac{\mathbf{J}}{r} \, dv', \quad (14\text{-}4.4)$$

and

$$\varphi = \frac{I}{4\pi} \Omega. \quad (14\text{-}4.5)$$

14-5. Boundary Conditions for Magnetic Fields at an Interface between Two Media

As we already know (see Section 8-5), if two media are in contact with each other, there exists between them a thin transitional zone over which the values of the characteristic parameters of the media gradually change from the values which these parameters have in one medium to the values which they have in the other medium. It is frequently convenient to disregard the existence of this transitional zone and to assume that the characteristic parameters change abruptly over the "interface" between the media. From the basic laws (14-2.1), (14-2.2), and (14-2.3) one can derive then the boundary conditions for the field-vectors measured on the opposite sides of the interface. At the points of the interface these boundary conditions replace the basic laws and are used in their place.

To obtain the boundary condition for $\mathbf{H}$, let us construct a small, very narrow rectangular loop crossing the interface between two media, 1 and 2, as shown in Fig. 14.5a. Applying the circulation law (14-2.1b) to this loop, we have

$$\oint \mathbf{H} \cdot d\mathbf{l} = \int_a^b \mathbf{H_2} \cdot d\mathbf{l} + \int_b^c \mathbf{H} \cdot d\mathbf{l} + \int_c^d \mathbf{H_1} \cdot d\mathbf{l} + \int_d^a \mathbf{H} \cdot d\mathbf{l} = \int \mathbf{J} \cdot d\mathbf{S}.$$

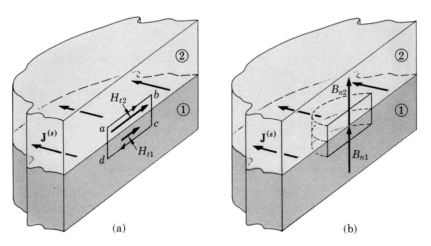

(a)   (b)

FIG. 14.5   (a) Boundary condition for $\mathbf{H}$ at an interface between two media. The tangential component of $\mathbf{H}$ is the same on each side of the interface if the interface carries no surface current. (b) Boundary condition for $\mathbf{B}$ at an interface between two media. The normal component of $\mathbf{B}$ is the same on each side of the interface.

Since the loop is very narrow, the line integrals over the segments bc and da vanish. Since the area of the loop is very small, the surface integral of the current density vanishes also, unless there is a surface current confined to the interface, in which case

$$\int \mathbf{J} \cdot d\mathbf{S} = \int_a^b \mathbf{J}^{(s)} \times \mathbf{n}_{12} \cdot d\mathbf{l},$$

where $\mathbf{J}^{(s)}$ is the surface current density, and $\mathbf{n}_{12}$ is a unit vector normal to the interface and directed from medium 1 into medium 2. We can therefore write

$$\int_a^b \mathbf{H}_2 \cdot d\mathbf{l} + \int_c^d \mathbf{H}_1 \cdot d\mathbf{l} = \int_a^b \mathbf{J}^{(s)} \times \mathbf{n}_{12} \cdot d\mathbf{l},$$

and since the loop is short,

$$\mathbf{H}_2 \cdot d\mathbf{l} + \mathbf{H}_1 \cdot (-d\mathbf{l}) = \mathbf{J}^{(s)} \times \mathbf{n}_{12} \cdot d\mathbf{l}.$$

Replacing in this equation $d\mathbf{l}$ by $dl\mathbf{t}_u$, where $\mathbf{t}_u$ is a unit vector in the direction of $d\mathbf{l}$ (and, hence, tangent to the interface) and cancelling dl, we finally obtain

$$(\mathbf{H}_2 - \mathbf{H}_1) \cdot \mathbf{t}_u = \mathbf{J}^{(s)} \times \mathbf{n}_{12} \cdot \mathbf{t}_u. \tag{14-5.1}$$

It is interesting to note that in contrast to the corresponding equation for the electric fields, Eq. (8-5.1), this equation does not require that $\mathbf{H}_1$ and $\mathbf{H}_2$ both be in a plane normal to the interface.

If there is no surface current on the interface, Eq. (14-5.1) reduces to

$$(\mathbf{H}_2 - \mathbf{H}_1) \cdot \mathbf{t}_u = 0, \quad \text{or} \quad H_{t1} = H_{t2}, \tag{14-5.1a, b}$$

so that in this particular case the tangential component of $\mathbf{H}$ is continuous across the interface.

To obtain the boundary condition for $\mathbf{B}$, we construct a Gaussian surface in the shape of a small, very thin pillbox crossing the interface under consideration, as shown in Fig. 14.5b. Applying flux law (14-2.2b) to this surface, we easily obtain

$$(\mathbf{B}_2 - \mathbf{B}_1) \cdot \mathbf{n}_u = 0, \quad \text{or} \quad B_{n1} = B_{n2}. \tag{14-5.2a, b}$$

Utilizing the analogy between Eqs. (14-5.1a, b) for magnetic fields at a current-free interface and Eqs. (8-5.1) and (8-5.2) for electric fields at a dielectric interface, and utilizing the analogy between the magneto-static and electrostatic potentials, we can immediately transform the boundary condition for the electrostatic potential, Eq. (8-5.5), into the boundary condition for the magnetostatic potential at a current-free interface, obtaining

$$\varphi_1 = \varphi_2. \tag{14-5.3}$$

When dealing with linear isotropic media involving a current-free interface, it is frequently desirable to express the boundary condition (14-5.2) for **B** in terms of the magnetostatic potential φ. Since by Eqs. (14-2.3) and (11-3.1) $B_n = -\mu_0\mu\, \partial\varphi/\partial n$, this boundary condition can be written as

$$\mu_1 \frac{\partial\varphi_1}{\partial n} = \mu_2 \frac{\partial\varphi_2}{\partial n}, \tag{14-5.4}$$

where n designates a direction along a normal to the interface.

▼

Example 14-5.1   Two long plungers of permeability μ are inserted in a long closely fitting coil of n turns and length l carrying a current I. The plungers are separated by a narrow gap of length d, as shown in Fig. 14.6. Neglecting all end effects, find the magnetic field within the coil.

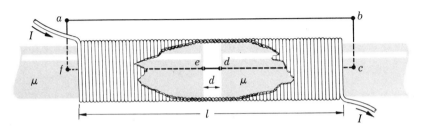

FIG. 14.6   Calculation of the magnetic field in a coil with two plungers.

Applying the circulation law (14-2.1b) to the path $abcdef$ shown in Fig. 14.6 and taking into account that if the end effects of the coil are neglected the only contribution to the circulation integral comes from the portion of the path $cdef$ within the coil, we have

$$\oint \mathbf{H}\cdot d\mathbf{l} = \int_{cdef} \mathbf{H}\cdot d\mathbf{l} = nI.$$

By symmetry, the magnetic field within the coil may be assumed to be everywhere parallel to the coil's axis, so that

$$\int_{cdef} \mathbf{H}\cdot d\mathbf{l} = \int_{cdef} H\, dl = \int_{\text{plungers}} H_p dl + \int_{\text{gap}} H_g dl = nI,$$

where the subscripts p and g stand for "plungers" and "gap," respectively. Furthermore, H_p and H_g may be considered constant if the end effects are neglected, so that we obtain

$$H_p(l - d) + H_g d = nI. \tag{14-5.5}$$

At the surfaces of the plungers facing the gap, the induction must satisfy
the boundary condition (14-5.2), which can be written as

$$B_p = B_g,$$

or, in view of the induction law (14-2.3),

$$\mu H_p = H_g. \tag{14-5.6}$$

Combining Eqs. (14-5.5) and (14-5.6), we finally obtain

$$H_p = \frac{nI}{l + d(\mu - 1)}, \qquad H_g = \frac{\mu nI}{l + d(\mu - 1)}.$$

▲

14-6. Special Methods for the Solution of Magnetostatic Problems Involving Media of Constant μ

As we already know, the magnetic field in a current-free region
can be expressed in terms of the magnetostatic potential φ as

$$\mathbf{H} = -\boldsymbol{\nabla}\varphi. \tag{14-6.1}$$

Combining Eqs. (14-6.1), (14-2.2a), and (14-2.3), we can write

$$\boldsymbol{\nabla} \cdot \mathbf{B} = \boldsymbol{\nabla} \cdot \mu_0\mu\mathbf{H} = -\mu_0\boldsymbol{\nabla} \cdot (\mu\boldsymbol{\nabla}\varphi) = 0,$$

and, using vector identity (V-4), we obtain

$$\nabla^2\varphi + \frac{1}{\mu}\boldsymbol{\nabla}\mu \cdot \boldsymbol{\nabla}\varphi = 0. \tag{14-6.2}$$

If μ is constant, $\boldsymbol{\nabla}\mu = 0$, and we obtain

$$\nabla^2\varphi = 0. \tag{14-6.3}$$

Thus, the magnetostatic potential in current-free media of constant μ
satisfies Laplace's equation (14-6.3), just as the electrostatic potential
in charge-free media of constant ε and the stationary electric field
potential in conductors of constant σ do. Therefore the magnetostatic
problems involving current-free media of constant μ can be solved by
essentially the same special methods as those used to solve the corresponding electrostatic or stationary electric field problems. The criteria
for the correctness of solutions obtained by such methods are furnished
by uniqueness theorems for magnetic fields, which can be easily deduced from Sections 6-2 and 14-2 [the boundary conditions (14-5.3)
and (14-5.4) must be satisfied, of course, at all interfaces].

The analogy between electric and magnetic systems frequently allows one to obtain solutions for magnetic problems from the known solutions for similar electric problems by merely replacing ε and ε_0 by μ and μ_0, or σ by $\mu_0\mu$.

Especially useful is the analogy between the magnetostatic problems involving current-free media of constant μ and the stationary electric field problems involving conductors of constant σ. This is because in both cases the problems are subject to the same types of fundamental laws:

$$\nabla \times \mathbf{H} = 0, \qquad \nabla \cdot \mathbf{B} = 0, \qquad \mathbf{B} = \mu_0\mu\mathbf{H}$$

for the magnetic problems and

$$\nabla \times \mathbf{E} = 0, \qquad \nabla \cdot \mathbf{J} = 0, \qquad \mathbf{J} = \sigma\mathbf{E}$$

for the electric problems. The only essential difference between these problems is in the fact that σ can vary from ∞ to 0, while $\mu_0\mu$ is always finite and always larger than 0. Magnetic systems therefore correspond to conducting systems in which conductors are embedded in an infinite conductor whose conductivity corresponds to μ_0, and where there are no perfect electrodes (because $\mu_0\mu$ is always less than ∞). Frequently, however, one neglects these differences between conducting and magnetic systems and obtains approximate solutions for magnetic problems by means of the methods developed for current-carrying conductors surrounded by nonconducting media. That this procedure is frequently well justified can be seen by comparing the electric and the magnetic field patterns produced by electric and magnetic systems of similar geometry (Fig. 14.7).

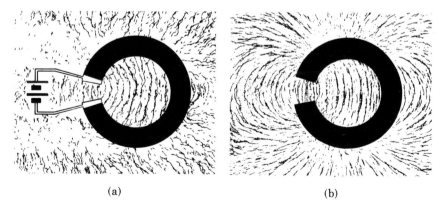

(a)   (b)

FIG. 14.7   (a) Electric lines of force of a current-carrying ring. (b) Magnetic lines of force of a circular magnet.

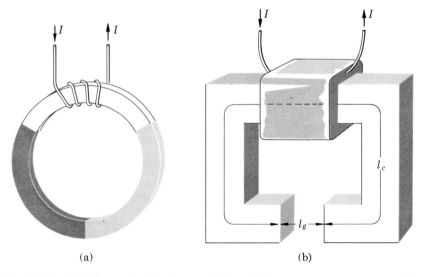

Fig. 14.8   (a) Magnetic circuit consisting of three segments connected in series. If the permeability of the material of these segments is sufficiently high, all magnetic flux is contained in the material. (b) Although an ideal magnetic circuit must form a filamentary path for the magnetic flux, the magnetic circuit method is frequently applied to systems where the flux is not filamentary. For example, the magnetic field of an electromagnet can be approximately calculated by using the magnetic circuit method.

Magnetic Circuits.   The analogy between current-carrying conductors and magnetic systems containing material media leads to the concept of the *magnetic circuit* (Fig. 14.8a).   A magnetic circuit is a filamentary path for the magnetic flux $\Phi = \int \mathbf{B} \cdot d\mathbf{S}$, just like a conducting circuit is a filamentary path for the electric current $I = \int \mathbf{J} \cdot d\mathbf{S}$.

The magnetic flux in a magnetic circuit can be represented by the formula

$$\Phi = \frac{\mathscr{V}}{\mathscr{R}}, \tag{14-6.4}$$

known as the "Ohm's law of magnetism." In this formula $\mathscr{V}$ is the "magnetic voltage," or *magnetomotance*, given by $\mathscr{V} = nI$, where n is the number of turns, and I is the current in the coil which produces the flux (see Fig. 14.8a). $\mathscr{R}$ is the "magnetic resistance," or *reluctance*. If the circuit contains only one medium, then

$$\mathscr{R} = \frac{l}{\mu_0 \mu S}, \tag{14-6.5}$$

where μ is the permeability of the medium, l is the length of the circuit, and S is the cross-sectional area of the circuit (cross-sectional area of the filament containing the flux). If the circuit has several segments formed by different media, however, then, depending on whether the segments are in series or in parallel, the reluctance of the circuit is, respectively,

$$\mathcal{R} = \mathcal{R}_1 + \mathcal{R}_2 + \cdots \qquad (14\text{-}6.6)$$

or

$$\mathcal{R} = \frac{1}{1/\mathcal{R}_1 + 1/\mathcal{R}_2 + \cdots}, \qquad (14\text{-}6.7)$$

where $\mathcal{R}_1$, $\mathcal{R}_2 \cdots$ are the reluctances of individual segments.

The derivation of these properties of magnetic circuits is left to Problem 14.8.

▼

Example 14-6.1   A sphere of radius a and permeability μ_1 is placed in a liquid of infinite extent and permeability μ_2. A uniform magnetic field **H** was originally present in the liquid. Find the resultant field inside and outside the sphere.

Using the analogy between electric and magnetic problems, we immediately obtain from the results of Example 8-6.1

$$\mathbf{H}_{\text{inside}} = \frac{3\mu_2}{\mu_1 + 2\mu_2} \mathbf{H}$$

$$\mathbf{H}_{\text{outside}} = H\left(1 + 2\,\frac{\mu_1 - \mu_2}{\mu_1 + 2\mu_2}\frac{a^3}{r^3}\right)\cos\theta\,\mathbf{r}_u$$

$$- H\left(1 - \frac{\mu_1 - \mu_2}{\mu_1 + 2\mu_2}\frac{a^3}{r^3}\right)\sin\theta\,\mathbf{\theta}_u,$$

where the coordinates are as shown in Fig. 8.10. The shape of the field lines in the sphere and in the liquid is exactly the same as the shape of the electric field lines shown in Fig. 8.11.

Example 14-6.2   Using the magnetic circuit method, find an approximate value for the magnetic field in the air gap of the electromagnet shown in Fig. 14.8b.

Let the coil of the magnet have n turns, and let the current in the coil be I. The magnetomotance is then

$$\mathcal{V} = nI.$$

The circuit has two segments in series: the core of the magnet and the gap. Let the average length of the core be l_c, and let the length of the gap be l_g. If the permeability of the core is μ, and the cross-sectional area of the core and the gap is S, we have from Eqs. (14-6.5) and (14-6.6)

$$\mathcal{R} = \frac{l_g}{\mu_0 S} + \frac{l_c}{\mu_0 \mu S} = \frac{\mu l_g + l_c}{\mu_0 \mu S}.$$

The flux in the magnet is then, by Eq. (14-6.4),

$$\Phi = \frac{\mu_0 \mu n I S}{\mu l_g + l_c}.$$

The magnetic field in the gap is therefore

$$H = \frac{\Phi}{\mu_0 S} = \frac{\mu n I}{\mu l_g + l_c}.$$

It follows from this equation that the shorter the gap, the stronger is the field in the gap.

▲

14-7. Magnetization and Magnetization Charges

The theory of magnetic phenomena in material media becomes especially informative and concise if in addition to the two field vectors **H** and **B**, the third field vector, the *magnetization vector* **M** is used. The magnetization vector is defined by the equation[1]

$$\mathbf{M} = \mathbf{B} - \mu_0 \mathbf{H}. \tag{14-7.1}$$

As we shall presently see, this vector allows a convenient description of magnetic phenomena in all media, linear and nonlinear, isotropic and anisotropic, with no restriction upon the magnetic properties of the media at all.

Using the magnetization vector, we shall now derive several important formulas for the magnetostatic field quantities associated with magnetized media (media for which $\mathbf{M} \neq 0$).

Let us take the divergence of Eq. (14-7.1). We have

$$\mathbf{\nabla} \cdot \mathbf{M} = \mathbf{\nabla} \cdot \mathbf{B} - \mu_0 \mathbf{\nabla} \cdot \mathbf{H},$$

and since $\mathbf{\nabla} \cdot \mathbf{B} = 0$ by the divergence law (14-2.2a),

$$\mathbf{\nabla} \cdot \mathbf{H} = -\frac{1}{\mu_0} \mathbf{\nabla} \cdot \mathbf{M}. \tag{14-7.2}$$

---

[1] The magnetization vector is frequently defined also as $\mathbf{M} = \mathbf{B}/\mu_0 - \mathbf{H}$.

Substituting Eq. (14-7.2) and the curl equation (14-2.1a) into Poisson's integral for $\mathbf{H}$,

$$\mathbf{H} = -\frac{1}{4\pi} \int_{\text{All space}} \frac{\nabla'(\nabla' \cdot \mathbf{H}) - \nabla' \times (\nabla' \times \mathbf{H})}{r} \, dv',$$

we obtain

$$\mathbf{H} = \frac{1}{4\pi\mu_0} \int_{\text{All space}} \frac{\nabla'(\nabla' \cdot \mathbf{M})}{r} \, dv' + \frac{1}{4\pi} \int_{\text{All space}} \frac{\nabla' \times \mathbf{J}}{r} \, dv'. \qquad (14\text{-}7.3)$$

As can be seen from this equation, the magnetostatic field $\mathbf{H}$ produced by a current distribution $\mathbf{J}$ in the presence of a magnetized medium can be regarded as the sum

$$\mathbf{H} = \mathbf{H}_V + \mathbf{H}_M \qquad (14\text{-}7.4)$$

of two partial fields: the ordinary "vacuum" field

$$\mathbf{H}_V = \frac{1}{4\pi} \int_{\text{All space}} \frac{\nabla' \times \mathbf{J}}{r} \, dv' \qquad (10\text{-}6.1)$$

identical with the field produced by $\mathbf{J}$ in the absence of the medium, and the "magnetization" field

$$\mathbf{H}_M = \frac{1}{4\pi\mu_0} \int_{\text{All space}} \frac{\nabla'(\nabla' \cdot \mathbf{M})}{r} \, dv', \qquad (14\text{-}7.5)$$

which is associated with the medium.

By comparing Eq. (14-7.5) with Eq. (4-5.1) representing the electrostatic field $\mathbf{E}$ associated with a charge distribution ρ,

$$\mathbf{E} = -\frac{1}{4\pi\varepsilon_0} \int_{\text{All space}} \frac{\nabla'\rho}{r} \, dv', \qquad (4\text{-}5.1)$$

it becomes clear that, as far as the calculation of $\mathbf{H}$ (or any quantity derivable from $\mathbf{H}$) is concerned, a magnetized medium is equivalent to a certain "magnetic charge" distribution that would produce the field $\mathbf{H}_M$ if the medium were replaced by this charge distribution. This fictitious charge distribution is called the *magnetization charge distribution* and is defined by

$$\rho_M = -\nabla \cdot \mathbf{M}. \qquad (14\text{-}7.6)$$

The magnetization field can therefore be expressed as

$$\mathbf{H}_M = -\frac{1}{4\pi\mu_0} \int_{\text{All space}} \frac{\nabla'\rho_M}{r} \, dv', \qquad (14\text{-}7.7)$$

which is an equation analogous to Eq. (4-5.1).

Like Eq. (4-5.1), Eq. (14-7.7) can be transformed in various special forms which frequently are more convenient to use than the original equation itself. One such special form is

$$\mathbf{H}_M = \frac{1}{4\pi\mu_0} \int_{\text{All space}} \frac{\rho_M \mathbf{r}_u}{r^2} \, dv', \tag{14-7.8}$$

which follows from Eq. (14-7.7) in the same manner in which Eq. (4-5.4) follows from Eq. (4-5.1) (see Section 4-5).

Ordinarily one deals with magnetized media of finite extent. For a medium of this type, the integral of Eq. (14-7.8) can be split into three integrals: an integral over the interior volume of the medium, an integral over the volume of the boundary layer of the medium, and an integral over the space external to the medium. Then Eq. (14-7.8) becomes

$$\mathbf{H}_M = \frac{1}{4\pi\mu_0} \int_{\text{Interior}} \frac{\rho_M \mathbf{r}_u}{r^2} \, dv' + \frac{1}{4\pi\mu_0} \int_{\text{Boundary layer}} \frac{\rho_M \mathbf{r}_u}{r^2} \, dv'$$

$$+ \frac{1}{4\pi\mu_0} \int_{\text{External space}} \frac{\rho_M \mathbf{r}_u}{r^2} \, dv'.$$

Outside the medium, $\mathbf{M} = \mu_0 \mathbf{H} - \mu_0 \mathbf{H} = 0$, so that $\rho_M = -\nabla \cdot \mathbf{M} = 0$, and the last integral is therefore zero. The second integral can be transformed by means of the vector identity (V-23) into a surface and a volume integral (using primed ∇' to avoid ambiguity)

$$\frac{1}{4\pi\mu_0} \int_{\text{Boundary layer}} \frac{\rho_M \mathbf{r}_u}{r^2} \, dv' = -\frac{1}{4\pi\mu_0} \int_{\text{Boundary layer}} (\nabla' \cdot \mathbf{M}) \frac{\mathbf{r}_u}{r^2} \, dv'$$

$$= -\frac{1}{4\pi\mu_0} \oint_{\text{Boundary layer}} \frac{\mathbf{r}_u}{r^2} (\mathbf{M} \cdot d\mathbf{S}') + \frac{1}{4\pi\mu_0} \int_{\text{Boundary layer}} (\mathbf{M} \cdot \nabla') \frac{\mathbf{r}_u}{r^2} \, dv',$$

so that

$$\mathbf{H}_M = \frac{1}{4\pi\mu_0} \int_{\text{Interior}} \frac{\rho_M \mathbf{r}_u}{r^2} \, dv' - \frac{1}{4\pi\mu_0} \oint_{\text{Boundary layer}} \frac{\mathbf{r}_u}{r^2} (\mathbf{M} \cdot d\mathbf{S}')$$

$$+ \frac{1}{4\pi\mu_0} \int_{\text{Boundary layer}} (\mathbf{M} \cdot \nabla') \frac{\mathbf{r}_u}{r^2} \, dv'.$$

The volume of the boundary layer may be assumed to be as small as one pleases, and since $\mathbf{M}$ is finite, the last integral of this equation vanishes. In the surface integral, the surface of integration consists of both the interior and exterior surfaces of the boundary layer, but since the exterior surface is outside the medium, $\mathbf{M} = 0$ there, and the only contribution to the surface integral comes from the interior surface (observe that on this surface dS is pointing into the medium). Furthermore, since the boundary layer may be assumed to be as thin as one wishes, the surface of integration is just the surface of the medium. Substituting $\mathbf{n}_{in}dS$ for $d\mathbf{S}$, where $\mathbf{n}_{in}$ is a unit vector in the direction of an inward normal to the surface of the medium, we then obtain from the last equation

$$\mathbf{H}_M = \frac{1}{4\pi\mu_0} \int_{\text{Interior}} \frac{\rho_M \mathbf{r}_u}{r^2} \, dv' - \frac{1}{4\pi\mu_0} \oint_{\text{Surface}} \frac{(\mathbf{M} \cdot \mathbf{n}_{in})}{r^2} \mathbf{r}_u dS'. \qquad (14\text{-}7.9)$$

If we now compare Eq. (14-7.9) with Eqs. (4-5.4) and (4-5.5) we recognize immediately that the magnetization field can be attributed to a volume distribution of magnetization charge

$$\rho_M = -\boldsymbol{\nabla} \cdot \mathbf{M} \qquad (14\text{-}7.6)$$

spread through the interior of the medium, and to a surface distribution of the magnetization charge defined as

$$\sigma_M = -\mathbf{M} \cdot \mathbf{n}_{in} \qquad (14\text{-}7.10)$$

spread over the surface of the medium. We can therefore write $\mathbf{H}_M$ in the form

$$\mathbf{H}_M = \frac{1}{4\pi\mu_0} \int_{\text{Interior}} \frac{\rho_M \mathbf{r}_u}{r^2} \, dv' + \frac{1}{4\pi\mu_0} \oint_{\text{Surface}} \frac{\sigma_M \mathbf{r}_u}{r^2} dS'. \qquad (14\text{-}7.11)$$

The curl of the magnetization field is always zero. This follows from the fact that the curl of the total magnetostatic field, by Eq. (14-7.4), can be written as

$$\boldsymbol{\nabla} \times \mathbf{H} = \boldsymbol{\nabla} \times \mathbf{H}_V + \boldsymbol{\nabla} \times \mathbf{H}_M, \qquad (14\text{-}7.12)$$

where by the basic laws (14-2.1a) and (10-4.1b), $\boldsymbol{\nabla} \times \mathbf{H} = \mathbf{J}$ and $\boldsymbol{\nabla} \times \mathbf{H}_V = \mathbf{J}$. We thus have

$$\boldsymbol{\nabla} \times \mathbf{H}_M = 0. \qquad (14\text{-}7.13)$$

The divergence of the magnetization field is, again by Eq. (14-7.4),

$$\boldsymbol{\nabla} \cdot \mathbf{H}_M = \boldsymbol{\nabla} \cdot \mathbf{H} - \boldsymbol{\nabla} \cdot \mathbf{H}_V,$$

and since $\boldsymbol{\nabla} \cdot \mathbf{H}_V = 0$ by Eqs. (10-4.2a) and (10-4.3), and

$$\boldsymbol{\nabla} \cdot \mathbf{H} = -\frac{1}{\mu_0} \boldsymbol{\nabla} \cdot \mathbf{M} = \frac{\rho_M}{\mu_0}$$

by Eqs. (4-7.2) and (14-7.6),

$$\boldsymbol{\nabla} \cdot \mathbf{H}_M = \frac{\rho_M}{\mu_0} . \qquad (14\text{-}7.14)$$

By the corollary to Poisson's theorem (p. 42), the magnetization field is therefore derivable from the *magnetization scalar potential*

$$\mathbf{H}_M = -\nabla \varphi_M, \tag{14-7.15}$$

where

$$\varphi_M = \frac{1}{4\pi\mu_0} \int_{\text{All space}} \frac{\rho_M}{r} \, dv' \tag{14-7.16}$$

or

$$\varphi_M = \frac{1}{4\pi\mu_0} \int_{\text{Interior}} \frac{\rho_M}{r} \, dv' + \frac{1}{4\pi\mu_0} \oint_{\text{Surface}} \frac{\sigma_M}{r} \, dS'. \tag{14-7.17}$$

Equation (14-7.16) for the magnetization potential can be transformed in the same manner in which the corresponding expression for the polarization potential [the last integral of Eq. (8-7.4)] was transformed in Section 8-7. The magnetization potential then becomes

$$\varphi_M = \frac{1}{4\pi\mu_0} \int_{\text{All space}} \mathbf{M} \cdot \nabla' \frac{1}{r} \, dv', \tag{14-7.18}$$

which is an equation analogous to Eq. (8-7.7b) for the polarization potential. Like the integrand in Eq. (8-7.7b), the integrand in Eq. (14-7.18) can be interpreted as the potential produced by a fictitious "magnetization" dipole of moment $d\mathbf{m} = \mathbf{M} \, dv'$. The magnetization vector $\mathbf{M}$ can therefore be interpreted as the dipole moment density (dipole moment per unit volume) of such magnetization dipoles

$$\mathbf{M} = \frac{d\mathbf{m}}{dv}. \tag{14-7.19}$$

The potential φ_M can then be regarded as the total potential produced by all these dipoles spread throughout the magnetized medium. This means that for the purpose of the calculation of φ_M (or any quantity derivable from φ_M) a magnetized medium may be replaced by a distribution of dipoles of moment density $d\mathbf{m}/dv = \mathbf{M}$.

Thus a magnetized medium can be replaced by either a magnetization space and surface charge distribution given by Eqs. (14-7.6) and (14-7.10), or by a magnetization dipole distribution given by Eq. (14-7.19). A choice between these two possibilities is merely a question of expediency.

The representation of a magnetized medium as an equivalent charge distribution is especially useful for dealing with magnets—that is, bodies possessing a permanent magnetization.

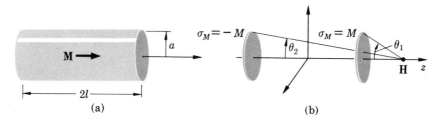

Fig. 14.9 (a) Cylindrical magnet. (b) Equivalent magnetization charge distribution.

▼

Example 14-7.1   A cylindrical magnet of length $2l$ and radius a has constant magnetization $\mathbf{M}$ directed along the axis of the magnet, as shown in Fig. 14.9a. Find the magnetic field produced by the magnet at an external axial point.

The field can be obtained easily from Example 8-7.2 by means of magneto-electric analogy. We shall, however, present here a more or less complete calculation, for clarity. We shall use Eq. (14-7.11) for this calculation.

Since $\mathbf{M}$ is constant in the interior of the magnet,

$$\rho_M = -\nabla \cdot \mathbf{M} = 0,$$

and the field can be found from σ_M alone. On the cylindrical surface of the magnet $\mathbf{M}$ is perpendicular to $\mathbf{n}_{\text{in}}$ so that $\sigma_M = -\mathbf{M} \cdot \mathbf{n}_{\text{in}} = 0$. The only contribution to the field comes therefore from σ_M on the flat bases of the magnet, where $\mathbf{M}$ and $\mathbf{n}_{\text{in}}$ are parallel. On the left base, $\mathbf{M}$ and $\mathbf{n}_{\text{in}}$ have the same direction so that $\sigma_M = -\mathbf{M} \cdot \mathbf{n}_{\text{in}} = -M$. On the right base, $\mathbf{M}$ is opposite to $\mathbf{n}_{\text{in}}$ so that $\sigma_M = -\mathbf{M} \cdot \mathbf{n}_{\text{in}} = M$. The problem thus reduces to finding the field of two uniformly charged disks located at the ends of the magnet and carrying surface charges $\pm M$ (Fig. 14.9b).

The field of a uniformly charged disk of charge density σ_M and radius a is, by Example 4-5.3 and by magneto-electric analogy,

$$\mathbf{H} = \frac{\sigma_M}{2\mu_0}\left(1 - \frac{z}{\sqrt{z^2 + a^2}}\right)\mathbf{k},$$

where z is the distance from the disk to the point of observation. The field of the magnet under consideration can therefore be obtained from this formula. Replacing in it σ_M by $\pm M$ and z by $z \mp l$ and adding the resulting expressions, we obtain

$$\mathbf{H} = \frac{M}{2\mu_0}\left[1 - \frac{z - l}{\sqrt{(z - l)^2 + a^2}}\right]\mathbf{k} - \frac{M}{2\mu_0}\left[1 - \frac{z + l}{\sqrt{(z + l)^2 + a^2}}\right]\mathbf{k},$$

which after simplification becomes

$$\mathbf{H} = \frac{\mathbf{M}}{2\mu_0}\left[\frac{z+l}{\sqrt{(z+l)^2 + a^2}} - \frac{z-l}{\sqrt{(z-l)^2 + a^2}}\right].$$

This can also be written in terms of the angles subtended by the radius of the bases of the magnet at the point of observation as

$$\mathbf{H} = \frac{\mathbf{M}}{2\mu_0}(\cos\theta_2 - \cos\theta_1).$$

It is instructive to note that this field is identical with the field produced by the current-carrying cylinder and coil discussed in Example 10-6.3 and Problem 10.20 (the fields are identical, however, only outside the magnet; see Problem 14.16 and compare with Examples 8-7.2 and 8-7.3).

Example 14-7.2   A small spherical cavity of radius a is made in a permanent magnet of uniform magnetization $\mathbf{M}$ in the region where the initial magnetic field was $\mathbf{H}_0$ (Fig. 14.10a). Find the final field inside and outside the cavity.

For the purpose of field calculation the cavity may be replaced by the magnetization surface charge distribution

$$\sigma_M = -\mathbf{M}\cdot\mathbf{n}_{\text{in}} = -M\cos\theta.$$

This charge produces a potential φ_M which must satisfy Laplace's equation at all points of space, except on the surface of the cavity. The potential must also satisfy the boundary conditions (14-5.3) and (14-5.2b) for φ_M and $\mathbf{B}$ on the surface of the cavity:

$$(1)\quad \varphi_{M1} = \varphi_{M2}\qquad (r = a),$$

and

$$(2)\quad B_{n1} = B_{n2}\qquad (r = a),$$

which, by Eqs. (14-7.1) and (14-7.15), can be written as

$$(2a)\quad M_{1r} - \mu_0\frac{\partial\varphi_{M1}}{\partial r} = M_{2r} - \mu_0\frac{\partial\varphi_{M2}}{\partial r}\qquad (r = a).$$

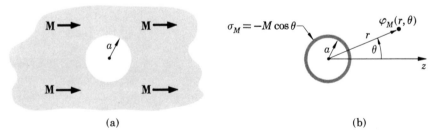

(a)   (b)

FIG. 14.10   (a) Spherical cavity in a magnet. (b) Equivalent magnetization charge distribution.

We seek the solution for φ_M in terms of spherical harmonics and, by inspection, select (see Table 6-I)

$$\varphi_{M1} = Ar \cos \theta$$

for the potential inside the cavity and

$$\varphi_{M2} = \frac{C}{r^2} \cos \theta$$

for the potential outside the cavity, where r and θ are as shown in Fig. 14.10b. From the boundary condition (1) we have

$$A = \frac{C}{a^3}.$$

From the boundary condition (2a) we have (noting that $M_1 = 0$ and $M_{2r} = M \cos \theta$)

$$-\mu_0 A = M + \frac{2C\mu_0}{a^3}.$$

Solving these equations, we obtain

$$A = -\frac{M}{3\mu_0}$$

and

$$C = -\frac{Ma^3}{3\mu_0}.$$

The potentials are therefore

$$\varphi_{\text{cavity}} = -\frac{M}{3\mu_0} r \cos \theta,$$

$$\varphi_{\text{outside}} = -\frac{Ma^3}{3\mu_0 r^2} \cos \theta.$$

The field due to cavity is then

$$\mathbf{H}_{\text{cavity}} = \frac{\mathbf{M}}{3\mu_0},$$

$$\mathbf{H}_{\text{outside}} = -\frac{2Ma^3}{3\mu_0 r^3} \cos \theta \, \mathbf{r}_u - \frac{Ma^3}{3\mu_0 r^3} \sin \theta \, \boldsymbol{\theta}_u.$$

The total field is the sum of this field and the initial field $\mathbf{H}_0$:

$$\mathbf{H}_{\text{total, cavity}} = \frac{\mathbf{M}}{3\mu_0} + \mathbf{H}_0,$$

$$\mathbf{H}_{\text{total, outside}} = -\frac{2Ma^3}{3\mu_0 r^3} \cos \theta \, \mathbf{r}_u - \frac{Ma^3}{3\mu_0 r^3} \sin \theta \, \boldsymbol{\theta}_u + \mathbf{H}_0.$$

▲

14-8. Magnetization Currents

In the preceding section we have found that for the purpose of the magnetic field calculation magnetized media can be replaced by fictitious magnetization charges. In this section we shall show that for the purpose of the magnetic induction (flux density) calculation magnetized media can be replaced by fictitious *magnetization currents*.

Let us take the curl of Eq. (14-7.1). We have

$$\mathbf{\nabla} \times \mathbf{M} = \mathbf{\nabla} \times \mathbf{B} - \mu_0 \mathbf{\nabla} \times \mathbf{H},$$

and since $\mathbf{\nabla} \times \mathbf{H} = \mathbf{J}$ by the curl law (14-2.1a),

$$\mathbf{\nabla} \times \mathbf{B} = \mathbf{\nabla} \times \mathbf{M} + \mu_0 \mathbf{J}. \tag{14-8.1}$$

Substituting this equation and the divergence equation (14-2.2a) into Poisson's integral for $\mathbf{B}$,

$$\mathbf{B} = -\frac{1}{4\pi} \int_{\text{All space}} \frac{\mathbf{\nabla}'(\mathbf{\nabla}' \cdot \mathbf{B}) - \mathbf{\nabla}' \times (\mathbf{\nabla}' \times \mathbf{B})}{r} \, dv',$$

we obtain

$$\mathbf{B} = \frac{1}{4\pi} \int_{\text{All space}} \frac{\mathbf{\nabla}' \times (\mathbf{\nabla}' \times \mathbf{M})}{r} \, dv' + \frac{\mu_0}{4\pi} \int_{\text{All space}} \frac{\mathbf{\nabla}' \times \mathbf{J}}{r} \, dv'. \tag{14-8.2}$$

As can be seen from this equation, the induction field $\mathbf{B}$ produced by a current distribution $\mathbf{J}$ in the presence of a magnetized medium can be regarded as the sum

$$\mathbf{B} = \mathbf{B}_V + \mathbf{B}_M \tag{14-8.3}$$

of two partial fields: the ordinary "vacuum" field

$$\mathbf{B}_V = \frac{\mu_0}{4\pi} \int_{\text{All space}} \frac{\mathbf{\nabla}' \times \mathbf{J}}{r} \, dv' \tag{14-8.4}$$

identical with the field produced by $\mathbf{J}$ in the absence of the medium, and the "magnetization" field

$$\mathbf{B}_M = \frac{1}{4\pi} \int_{\text{All space}} \frac{\mathbf{\nabla}' \times (\mathbf{\nabla}' \times \mathbf{M})}{r} \, dv' \tag{14-8.5}$$

which is associated with the medium. By comparing the last two equations it becomes clear that, as far as the calculation of $\mathbf{B}$ (or any quantity derivable from $\mathbf{B}$) is concerned, a magnetized medium is equivalent to a certain "magnetization current distribution" that would produce the field $\mathbf{B}_M$ if the medium were replaced by this current distribution. This fictitious current distribution is given by

$$\mathbf{J}_M = \frac{1}{\mu_0} \nabla \times \mathbf{M}. \qquad (14\text{-}8.6)$$

The magnetization field can therefore be expressed as

$$\mathbf{B}_M = \frac{\mu_0}{4\pi} \int_{\text{All space}} \frac{\nabla' \times \mathbf{J}_M}{r} \, dv'. \qquad (14\text{-}8.7)$$

Like Eq. (14-8.4), Eq. (14-8.7) can be transformed in various special forms which frequently are more convenient to use than the original equation itself. One such special form is

$$\mathbf{B}_M = \frac{\mu_0}{4\pi} \int_{\text{All space}} \frac{\mathbf{J}_M \times \mathbf{r}_u}{r^2} \, dv', \qquad (14\text{-}8.8)$$

which follows from Eq. (14-8.7) in the same manner in which Eq. (10-6.4) follows from Eq. (10-6.1).

Ordinarily, one deals with magnetized media of finite extent. For a medium of this type, Eq. (14-8.8) can be transformed after somewhat lengthy manipulations (see Example 14-8.3) into

$$\mathbf{B}_M = \frac{\mu_0}{4\pi} \int_{\text{Interior}} \frac{\mathbf{J}_M \times \mathbf{r}_u}{r^2} \, dv' + \frac{1}{4\pi} \oint_{\text{Surface}} \frac{(\mathbf{M} \times \mathbf{n}_{\text{out}}) \times \mathbf{r}_u}{r^2} \, dS', \quad (14\text{-}8.9)$$

where $\mathbf{n}_{\text{out}}$ is a unit vector parallel to $d\mathbf{S}'$. This equation shows that for magnetized media of finite extent the magnetization field can be attributed to a volume distribution of magnetization current

$$\mathbf{J}_M = \frac{1}{\mu_0} \nabla \times \mathbf{M} \qquad (14\text{-}8.6)$$

spread through the interior of the medium, and to a surface distribution of the magnetization current defined as

$$\mathbf{J}_M^{(s)} = \frac{1}{\mu_0} \mathbf{M} \times \mathbf{n}_{\text{out}} \qquad (14\text{-}8.10)$$

spread over the surface of the medium. We can therefore write for such media

$$\mathbf{B}_M = \frac{\mu_0}{4\pi} \int_{\text{Interior}} \frac{\mathbf{J}_M \times \mathbf{r}_u}{r^2} \, dv' + \frac{\mu_0}{4\pi} \oint_{\text{Surface}} \frac{\mathbf{J}_M^{(s)} \times \mathbf{r}_u}{r^2} \, dS'. \qquad (14\text{-}8.11)$$

The divergence of the magnetization induction field is always zero. Indeed, by Eqs. (14-8.3), (14-2.2a), and (10-4.2a),

$$\nabla \cdot \mathbf{B}_M = \nabla \cdot \mathbf{B} - \nabla \cdot \mathbf{B}_V = 0 - 0. \qquad (14\text{-}8.12)$$

Therefore

$$\nabla \cdot \mathbf{B}_M = 0. \qquad (14\text{-}8.13)$$

The curl of the magnetization induction field is

$$\nabla \times \mathbf{B}_M = \nabla \times \mathbf{B} - \nabla \times \mathbf{B}_V,$$

and since the terms on the right simplify to $\nabla \times \mathbf{B}_V = \mu_0 \mathbf{J}$ and $\nabla \times \mathbf{B} = \nabla \times (\mathbf{M} + \mu_0 \mathbf{H}) = \nabla \times \mathbf{M} + \mu_0 \nabla \times \mathbf{H} = \nabla \times \mathbf{M} + \mu_0 \mathbf{J} = \mu_0 \mathbf{J}_M + \mu_0 \mathbf{J}$,

$$\nabla \times \mathbf{B}_M = \mu_0 \mathbf{J}_M. \qquad (14\text{-}8.14)$$

By the corollary to Poisson's theorem (p. 42), the magnetization field is therefore derivable from the *magnetization vector potential*

$$\mathbf{B}_M = \nabla \times \mathbf{A}_M, \qquad (14\text{-}8.15)$$

where

$$\mathbf{A}_M = \frac{\mu_0}{4\pi} \int_{\text{All space}} \frac{\mathbf{J}_M}{r} \, dv'. \qquad (14\text{-}8.16)$$

Equation 14-8.6 constitutes an important link connecting the macroscopic theory of magnetic phenomena with the microscopic theory. The "fictitious" magnetization current of the macroscopic theory is, in the microscopic theory, a manifestation of spinning and orbiting charged particles within atomic and molecular systems. It is the task of the microscopic theory to explain how the magnetization current defined by Eq. (14-8.6) is produced.

▼

Example 14-8.1   A cylindrical magnet of length $2l$ and radius a has constant magnetization **M** directed along the axis of the magnet, as shown in Fig. 14.11a. Find the magnetization current and then, using the magnetization current, find the magnetic field produced by the magnet at an external axial point.

(a)   (b)

FIG. 14.11   (a) Cylindrical magnet. (b) Equivalent magnetization current distribution.

Since **M** is constant throughout the magnet, $\mathbf{J}_M = (1/\mu_0) \, \nabla \times \mathbf{M} = 0$. On the flat ends of the magnet **M** is perpendicular to the magnet's surface so that $\mathbf{J}_M^{(s)} = (1/\mu_0) \mathbf{M} \times \mathbf{n}_{\text{out}} = 0$. On the cylindrical surface we have

$$\mathbf{J}_M^{(s)} = \frac{1}{\mu_0} \mathbf{M} \times \mathbf{n}_{\text{out}} = \frac{1}{\mu_0} \, M \boldsymbol{\theta}_u,$$

where $\boldsymbol{\theta}_u$ is a unit vector, right-handed with respect to **M**. The magnetization current is thus confined to the cylindrical surface of the magnet and is circular. The field produced by such a current was found in Example 10-6.3 and is in terms of $J_M^{(s)}$

$$\mathbf{B} = \mu_0 \frac{J_M^{(s)}}{2} (\cos \theta_2 - \cos \theta_1)\mathbf{k},$$

or

$$\mathbf{B} = \frac{\mathbf{M}}{2} (\cos \theta_2 - \cos \theta_1).$$

It is instructive to note that this field is identical with the field produced by the current-carrying cylinder and coil discussed in Example 10-6.3 and Problem 10.20 both *outside* and *inside* the magnet (in contrast to the **H** field found in Example 14-7.1).

Example 14-8.2   A small spherical cavity of radius a is made in a permanent magnet of uniform magnetization **M** in the region where the initial induction field was $\mathbf{B}_0$ (Fig. 14.12a). Find the final field at the center of the cavity.

For the purpose of induction field calculation, the cavity may be replaced by the magnetization surface current

$$\mathbf{J}_M^{(s)} = \frac{1}{\mu_0} \mathbf{M} \times \mathbf{n}_{\text{out}},$$

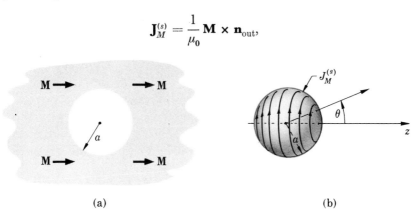

(a)   (b)

FIG. 14.12   (a) Spherical cavity in a magnet. (b) Equivalent magnetization current distribution.

and the field associated with the cavity can be found from the surface integral of Eq. (14-8.11). At the center of the cavity we then have, using the "bac cab" expansion,

$$\mathbf{B}_{\text{cavity}} = \frac{1}{4\pi} \oint \frac{(\mathbf{M} \times \mathbf{n}_{\text{out}}) \times \mathbf{r}_u}{a^2} \, dS'$$

$$= \frac{1}{4\pi} \oint \frac{(\mathbf{M} \cdot \mathbf{r}_u)\mathbf{n}_{\text{out}}}{a^2} \, dS' - \frac{1}{4\pi} \oint \frac{(\mathbf{r}_u \cdot \mathbf{n}_{\text{out}})\mathbf{M}}{a^2} \, dS'.$$

The surface element can be written as $dS' = 2\pi a^2 \sin\theta \, d\theta$. Taking now into account that both $\mathbf{r}_u$ and $\mathbf{n}_{\text{out}}$ are directed toward the center of the cavity and that, by the symmetry of the system, the magnetic field is parallel to the symmetry axis, we obtain

$$\mathbf{B}_{\text{cavity}} = \frac{\mathbf{k}}{4\pi} \int_0^\pi \frac{(M \cos\theta) \cos\theta}{a^2} \, 2\pi a^2 \sin\theta \, d\theta$$

$$- \frac{\mathbf{M}}{4\pi} \int_0^\pi \frac{1}{a^2} 2\pi a^2 \sin\theta \, d\theta$$

$$= \frac{\mathbf{M}}{2} \left(\int_0^\pi \cos^2\theta \sin\theta \, d\theta - \int_0^\pi \sin\theta \, d\theta \right),$$

or

$$\mathbf{B}_{\text{cavity}} = -\frac{2\mathbf{M}}{3}.$$

The total induction at the center of the cavity is then

$$\mathbf{B}_{\text{total, cavity}} = -\frac{2\mathbf{M}}{3} + \mathbf{B}_0 = -\frac{2\mathbf{M}}{3} + \mathbf{M} + \mu_0\mathbf{H}_0$$

or

$$\mathbf{B}_{\text{total, cavity}} = \frac{\mathbf{M}}{3} + \mu_0\mathbf{H}_0$$

in agreement with the result of Example 14-7.2.

Example 14-8.3   Derive Eq. (14-8.9).

Let us split the integral of Eq. (14-8.8) into three integrals: an integral over the interior volume of the medium, an integral over the boundary layer of the medium, and an integral over the space external to the medium. Since $\mathbf{M} = 0$ and therefore $\mathbf{J}_M = 0$ outside the medium, the last integral is zero, and we obtain

$$\int_{\text{All space}} \frac{\mathbf{J}_M \times \mathbf{r}_u}{r^2} \, dv' = \int_{\text{Interior}} \frac{\mathbf{J}_M \times \mathbf{r}_u}{r^2} \, dv' + \int_{\substack{\text{Boundary} \\ \text{layer}}} \frac{\mathbf{J}_M \times \mathbf{r}_u}{r^2} \, dv'.$$

$$(14\text{-}8.17)$$

The integral over the boundary layer can be transformed with the help of vector identities (V-29), (V-30), (V-21), and Eq. (14-8.6):

$$\int \frac{\mathbf{J}_M \times \mathbf{r}_u}{r^2}\, dv' = \int \nabla \times \frac{\mathbf{J}}{r}\, dv' = \nabla \times \int \frac{\mathbf{J}}{r}\, dv'$$

$$= \frac{1}{\mu_0} \nabla \times \int \frac{\nabla' \times \mathbf{M}}{r}\, dv' = \frac{1}{\mu_0} \nabla \times \left(\int \nabla \times \frac{\mathbf{M}}{r}\, dv' + \int \nabla' \times \frac{\mathbf{M}}{r}\, dv' \right)$$

$$= \frac{1}{\mu_0} \nabla \times \left(\nabla \times \int \frac{\mathbf{M}}{r}\, dv' - \oint \frac{\mathbf{M}}{r} \times d\mathbf{S}'_{in} \right),$$

where we have used the fact that $\mathbf{M} = 0$ on the outer surface of the boundary layer. Since the volume of the boundary layer can be assumed as small as one pleases, and since $\mathbf{M}$ is finite, the last volume integral is zero. We thus obtain (remembering that $\mathbf{M}$ is a function of primed coordinates only)

$$\int_{\substack{\text{Boundary} \\ \text{layer}}} \frac{\mathbf{J}_M \times \mathbf{r}_u}{r^2}\, dv' = -\frac{1}{\mu_0} \nabla \times \oint_{\text{Surface}} \frac{\mathbf{M}}{r} \times d\mathbf{S}'_{in}$$

$$= -\frac{1}{\mu_0} \oint_{\text{Surface}} \nabla \times \left(\frac{\mathbf{M}}{r} \times d\mathbf{S}'_{in} \right) = -\frac{1}{\mu_0} \oint_{\text{Surface}} \nabla \times \frac{1}{r} (\mathbf{M} \times d\mathbf{S}'_{in})$$

$$= \frac{1}{\mu_0} \oint_{\text{Surface}} \frac{\mathbf{r}_u}{r^2} \times (\mathbf{M} \times d\mathbf{S}'_{in}) = \frac{1}{\mu_0} \oint_{\text{Surface}} \frac{(\mathbf{M} \times d\mathbf{S}'_{out}) \times \mathbf{r}_u}{r^2},$$

or

$$\int_{\substack{\text{Boundary} \\ \text{layer}}} \frac{\mathbf{J}_M \times \mathbf{r}_u}{r^2}\, dv' = \frac{1}{\mu_0} \oint_{\text{Surface}} \frac{(\mathbf{M} \times \mathbf{n}_{out}) \times \mathbf{r}_u}{r^2}\, dS'.$$

Introducing this expression in Eq. (14-8.17), we obtain Eq. (14-8.9).

▲

14-9. Energy and Force Relations for Magnetostatic Fields in the Presence of Material Media

The basic energy law for magnetostatic systems containing material media can be expressed as[1]

$$U = \frac{\overset{\circ}{\mu_0}}{2} \int_{\text{All space}} H^2 dv + \overset{\circ}{\int}_{\text{All space}} \left(\int_0^{\mathbf{M}} \mathbf{H} \cdot d\mathbf{M} \right) dv. \qquad (14\text{-}9.1)$$

This equation represents: (a) the magnetic energy of systems containing permanent magnets and material media with changeable magnetization

[1] See the footnote on page 258.

M but not containing current-carrying conductors, and (b) the magnetic energy of systems containing current-carrying conductors and material media with changeable magnetization **M** but not containing permanent magnets.

The first term on the right of this equation is the so-called *field energy* U_f, the second term on the right is the so-called *magnetization energy* U_M.

The field energy

$$U_f = \frac{\overset{\circ}{\mu_0}}{2} \int H^2 dv \tag{14-9.2}$$

is attributed to the magnetic field as such and does not vanish even if there are no magnetizable media in the field.

The magnetization energy

$$U_M = \overset{\circ}{\int} \left(\int_0^{\mathbf{M}} \mathbf{H} \cdot d\mathbf{M} \right) dv \tag{14-9.3}$$

is attributed to the magnetization of magnetizable media and vanishes in the absence of such media. The designation of U_M as the magnetization energy is based upon the observation that an amount of energy given by Eq. (14-9.3) is absorbed by a medium when the magnetization of the medium changes from zero to **M**. Depending on the properties of the medium, the energy U_M may or may not be conserved (stored in the medium in a recoverable form). If **M** is a single-valued function of **H** the energy U_M is conserved, because then

$$\int_0^{\mathbf{M}} \mathbf{H} \cdot d\mathbf{M} = -\int_{\mathbf{M}}^0 \mathbf{H} \cdot d\mathbf{M}.$$

But if the correlation between **M** and **H** is such that the curve representing **M** as a function of **H** (magnetization curve) does not retrace itself when the field changes from $-\mathbf{H}$ to $+\mathbf{H}$ and back to $-\mathbf{H}$, as in Fig. 14.13, U_M is not conserved, because then

$$\int_0^{\mathbf{M}} \mathbf{H} \cdot d\mathbf{M} \neq -\int_{\mathbf{M}}^0 \mathbf{H} \cdot d\mathbf{M}.$$

In this latter case the material is said to exhibit a *hysteresis*. The loop formed by the magnetization curve is called the *hysteresis loop*. As one can see from Fig. 14.13 and Eq. (14-9.3), the area enclosed by the hysteresis loop is proportional to the energy dissipated in the material during each complete cycle in the change of **H**.

For a linear isotropic medium $\mathbf{M} = \mu_0(\mu - 1)\mathbf{H}$, so that

$$\int_0^{\mathbf{M}} \mathbf{H} \cdot d\mathbf{M} = \frac{\mu_0(\mu - 1)}{2} H^2,$$

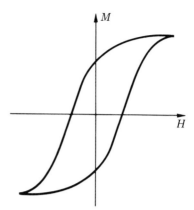

FIG. 14.13 Hysteresis loop for a magnetic material.

and the magnetization energy, according to Eq. (14-9.3), is

$$U_M = \frac{\overset{\circ}{\mu_0}}{2} \int (\mu - 1) H^2 dv. \tag{14-9.4}$$

Therefore, when all magnetic media present in a system under consideration are linear and isotropic, the magnetic energy of the system, according to Eq. (14-9.1), becomes

$$U = \frac{\overset{\circ}{\mu_0}}{2} \int H^2 dv + \frac{\overset{\circ}{\mu_0}}{2} \int (\mu - 1) H^2 dv = \frac{\overset{\circ}{\mu_0}}{2} \int \mu H^2 dv \tag{14-9.5}$$

which is usually written in the symmetric form

$$U = \frac{\overset{\circ}{1}}{2} \int \mathbf{H} \cdot \mathbf{B} \, dv. \tag{14-9.6}$$

When Eq. (14-9.1) is used to represent the energy of systems containing no electric currents, it can be transformed and interpreted in exactly the same manner as Eq. (8-8.1) describing the energy of electric fields in the presence of dielectrics. This is because in the absence of electric currents we have

$$\mathbf{H} = -\nabla \varphi \quad \text{and} \quad \mu_0 \nabla \cdot \mathbf{H} = \rho_M$$

in complete analogy with

$$\mathbf{E} = -\nabla \varphi \quad \text{and} \quad \varepsilon_0 \nabla \cdot \mathbf{E} = \rho + \rho_P$$

valid for dielectric media. Therefore all consequences of Eq. (8-8.1) obtained in Section 8-8 can be extended immediately to magnetic systems free of electric currents by merely replacing in the corresponding equations for electrostatic systems electric quantities with the analogous magnetic quantities and setting $\rho = 0$ (because there are no real magnetic charges).

In particular, we have for the force acting upon a magnetized body in a current-free system

$$\mathbf{F} = -\nabla U|_{\mathbf{M}=\text{constant}} - \nabla U'_f|_{\mathbf{M}=\text{constant}}, \qquad (14\text{-}9.7a, b)$$

where

$$U'_f = \int_0^{} \rho_M \varphi' dv \qquad (14\text{-}9.8)$$

(the prime indicates the external potential).

For the explicit expression of the magnetic force we similarly have, according to Eq. (8-8.9a, b),

$$\mathbf{F} = \int_0^{} \rho_M \mathbf{H}' dv = \int_0^{} \rho_M \mathbf{H}\, dv \qquad (14\text{-}9.9a, b)$$

(the prime indicates the external field).

Furthermore, since the magnetization $\mathbf{M}$ may be regarded as the dipole moment density associated with magnetization charges ρ_M, the force acting on a magnetized body can also be expressed by an equation analogous to Eq. (8-8.10):

$$\mathbf{F} = \int_0^{} (\mathbf{M} \cdot \nabla)\mathbf{H}' dv. \qquad (14\text{-}9.10)$$

Finally, the magnetic force can be expressed, in agreement with Eq. (8-8.11), by Maxwell's stress formula

$$\mathbf{F} = -\frac{\mu_0}{2} \oint^0 H^2 d\mathbf{S} + \mu_0 \oint^0 \mathbf{H}(\mathbf{H} \cdot d\mathbf{S}). \qquad (14\text{-}9.11)$$

The transformation and interpretation of Eq. (14-9.1) when it is used to represent the energy of magnetic systems with electric currents present is more difficult. Therefore we shall merely state that the magnetic force acting on a body or on a current in such a system can be obtained from the equation

$$\mathbf{F} = +\nabla U\bigg|_{\mathbf{J}=\text{constant}}, \qquad (14\text{-}9.12)$$

or, explicitly,

$$\mathbf{F} = \int_0^{} (\mathbf{J} + \mathbf{J}_M) \times \mathbf{B}' dv = \int_0^{} (\mathbf{J} + \mathbf{J}_M) \times \mathbf{B}\, dv. \qquad (14\text{-}9.13a, b)$$

For systems containing both permanent magnets and electric currents no simple energy relation is available. It is important to note, however, that the explicit force equations (14-9.9), (14-9.10), (14-9.11), and (14-9.13) are valid for *all* magnetic systems regardless of what particular system was used in obtaining these equations. The universal validity of these equations follows from the fact that magnetic fields, by definition, are force fields, so that if an object experiences a magnetic force in the magnetic field of some particular origin, it will experience the same force in the equal magnetic field of any other origin.

▼

Example 14-9.1   Two very long, identical bar magnets are placed with opposite poles facing each other, as shown in Fig. 14.14a. The poles are separated by a very short distance d. Each magnet has uniform magnetization **M** directed along the length of the magnet, and the area of each end surface (pole surface) is A. Find the force between the magnets.

The magnets may be replaced by the magnetization surface charge

$$\sigma_M = -\mathbf{M} \cdot \mathbf{n}_{\text{in}}$$

(the magnetization space charge is zero, because **M** = constant). Since **M** is directed along the length of the magnets, the magnetization surface charge is different from zero only on the end surfaces of the magnets. Since the magnets are very long, the charge due to the far ends has negligible effect on the forces between the magnets. For the purpose of force calculation the magnets may therefore be replaced by the charges shown in Fig. 14.14b. The magnetic field produced by these charges is identical in structure to the electric field produced by similar electric charges, and this latter field, in turn, closely resembles the field of a parallel-plate capacitor. Using the magneto-electric analogy and utilizing the result of Example 7-7.1, we can therefore write for the force between the two magnets

$$F = \frac{{}^{\circ}\sigma_M^2 A}{2\mu_0} = \frac{{}^{\circ}M^2 A}{2\mu_0}.$$

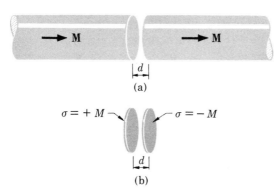

FIG. 14.14   (a) Two magnets facing each other. (b) For the purpose of force calculation the magnets are replaced by the equivalent magnetization charge distribution.

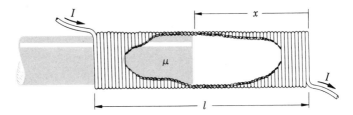

FIG. 14.15   Calculation of the force pulling a plunger into a current-carrying coil. If the end effect of the plunger is neglected, the calculated value for the force is reasonably accurate only as long as $l - x$ is much larger than the diameter of the plunger.

Example 14-9.2   A long plunger of permeability μ is partially inserted into a long closely fitting coil of n turns, length l, and cross-sectional area A (Fig. 14.15). Neglecting all end effects, find the magnetic force on the plunger if the coil carries a current I.

Let the free portion of the coil be of length x. If the end effects of the coil and plunger are neglected, the magnetic field in the coil is everywhere the same[1] and is

$$H = \frac{nI}{l}.$$

The energy of the system is then by Eq. (14-9.6)

$$U = \frac{1}{2} \int \mathbf{H} \cdot \mathbf{B} \, dv = \frac{\mu_0 \mu n^2 I^2}{2l^2} A(l - x) + \frac{\mu_0 n^2 I^2}{2l^2} Ax.$$

Using Eq. (14-9.12) and differentiating, we then obtain for the force on the plunger

$$\mathbf{F} = \frac{\partial U}{\partial x} \mathbf{i} \Big|_I = -\frac{\mu_0(\mu - 1)n^2 I^2 A}{2l^2} \mathbf{i}.$$

Example 14-9.3   Two long plungers of permeability μ are inserted in a long closely fitting coil of n turns, length l, and cross-sectional area A. The coil carries a current I. The plungers are separated by a narrow gap of length d, as shown in Fig. 14.16. Find the magnetic force acting on the plungers.

The energy of the system is, by Eq. (14-9.6),

$$U = \frac{1}{2} \int \mathbf{H} \cdot \mathbf{B} \, dv = \frac{1}{2} \mu_0 \mu H_p^2 A(l - d) + \frac{1}{2} \mu_0 H_g^2 Ad,$$

---

[1] This is in drastic contradiction with the requirement that $B_{n1} = B_{n2}$ at the ends of the plunger. The solution that follows is good therefore only if the portion $l - x$ of the plunger is much larger than the diameter of the coil. In this case the ends of the plunger contribute little to the total volume of the system.

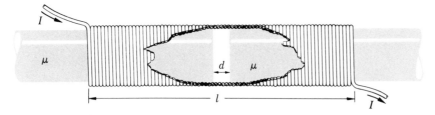

FIG. 14.16 Calculation of the force pulling two plungers into a current-carrying coil.

where subscripts p and g stand for "plunger" and "gap," respectively. The magnetic field H for the system under consideration is, by Example 14-5.1,

$$H_p = \frac{nI}{l + d(\mu - 1)}, \qquad H_g = \frac{\mu nI}{l + d(\mu - 1)}.$$

Substituting these values into the above expression for energy, we have

$$U = \frac{°\mu_0 \mu n^2 I^2}{2[l + d(\mu - 1)]^2} A(l - d) + \frac{°\mu_0 \mu^2 n^2 I^2}{2[l + d(\mu - 1)]^2} Ad$$

$$= \frac{°\mu_0 \mu n^2 I^2 A}{2[l + d(\mu - 1)]^2} l + \frac{°\mu_0 \mu (\mu - 1) n^2 I^2 A}{2[l + d(\mu - 1)]^2} d.$$

Using now Eq. (14-9.12) and differentiating, we obtain

$$F = \frac{\partial U}{\partial d}\bigg|_I = -\frac{°\mu_0 \mu n^2 I^2 A}{[l + d(\mu - 1)]^3} l(\mu - 1) + \frac{°\mu_0 \mu (\mu - 1) n^2 I^2 A}{2[l + d(\mu - 1)]^2}$$

$$- \frac{°\mu_0 \mu (\mu - 1) n^2 I^2 A}{[l + d(\mu - 1)]^3} d(\mu - 1)$$

or

$$F = -\frac{°\mu_0 \mu (\mu - 1) n^2 I^2 A}{2[l + d(\mu - 1)]^2}.$$

Example 14-9.4   A small sphere of radius a and permeability μ is placed at a distance $x \gg a$ from a small magnet of dipole moment **m**. The direction of **m** is along the line joining the magnet with the sphere. Find the force exerted by the magnet on the sphere (Fig. 14.17).

The magnetic field produced by the magnet at the location of the sphere is, by Eq. (11-5.3),

$$\mathbf{H'} = \frac{\mathbf{m}}{2\pi \mu_0 x^3}.$$

Since $x \gg a$, this field, in the first approximation, is uniform throughout the region occupied by the sphere. The magnetic field within the sphere

FIG. 14.17   Calculation of the force exerted on a sphere by a magnet.

is then, by Example 14-6.1,

$$\mathbf{H}_{\text{inside}} = \frac{3}{\mu + 2} \mathbf{H}'$$

and the magnetization of the sphere is

$$\mathbf{M} = \mathbf{B} - \mu_0 \mathbf{H} = \mu_0(\mu - 1)\mathbf{H} = \frac{3\mu_0(\mu - 1)}{\mu + 2} \mathbf{H}'.$$

Using Eq. (14-9.10) and taking into account that $a \ll x$, so that the sphere may be regarded as a single dipole of moment $\frac{4}{3}\pi a^3\mathbf{M}$, we have

$$\mathbf{F} = \int (\mathbf{M} \cdot \nabla)\mathbf{H}'dv = \frac{4}{3}\pi a^3 M \frac{\partial}{\partial x}\mathbf{H}'$$

$$= -\frac{2a^3Mm}{\mu_0 x^4}\mathbf{i}.$$

Substituting M, we finally obtain

$$\mathbf{F} = -\frac{3a^3(\mu - 1)m^2}{\pi\mu_0(\mu + 2)x^7}\mathbf{i}.$$

Example 14-9.5   Determine the change in magnetic energy taking place when a magnetically linear and isotropic body is placed in a magnetic field whose sources are kept constant.

Let us assume that the magnetic field is produced by permanent magnets, and let the initial field be $\mathbf{H}_0$. The initial energy of the system is then by Eq. (14-9.6) (disregarding the magnetization energy of the magnets, which remains constant by supposition)

$$U_0 = \frac{1}{2}\int \mathbf{H}_0 \cdot \mathbf{B}_0 \, dv.$$

When the body is introduced into the field, the field changes to $\mathbf{H}$ and the energy becomes

$$U = \frac{1}{2}\int \mathbf{H} \cdot \mathbf{B} \, dv.$$

The change in energy is

$$\Delta U = \frac{1}{2}\int (\mathbf{H} \cdot \mathbf{B} - \mathbf{H}_0 \cdot \mathbf{B}_0)dv,$$

which can be written as

$$\Delta U = \overset{\circ}{\frac{1}{2}} \int (\mathbf{H} \cdot \mathbf{B}_0 - \mathbf{B} \cdot \mathbf{H}_0) \, dv + \overset{\circ}{\frac{1}{2}} \int (\mathbf{H} + \mathbf{H}_0) \cdot (\mathbf{B} - \mathbf{B}_0) \, dv$$

$$= \overset{\circ}{\frac{1}{2}} \int (\mathbf{H} \cdot \mathbf{B}_0 - \mathbf{B} \cdot \mathbf{H}_0) \, dv - \overset{\circ}{\frac{1}{2}} \int \mathbf{\nabla}(\varphi + \varphi_0) \cdot (\mathbf{B} - \mathbf{B}_0) \, dv,$$

where φ and φ_0 are the potentials corresponding to $\mathbf{H}$ and $\mathbf{H}_0$. We shall show now that the last integral is zero. Since

$$\mathbf{\nabla}(\varphi + \varphi_0) \cdot (\mathbf{B} - \mathbf{B}_0) = \mathbf{\nabla} \cdot [(\varphi + \varphi_0)(\mathbf{B} - \mathbf{B}_0)]$$
$$- (\varphi + \varphi_0)\mathbf{\nabla} \cdot (\mathbf{B} - \mathbf{B}_0),$$

and since $\mathbf{\nabla} \cdot (\mathbf{B} - \mathbf{B}_0) = \mathbf{\nabla} \cdot \mathbf{B} - \mathbf{\nabla} \cdot \mathbf{B}_0$ is zero by the divergence law, we can transform the last integral into a surface integral:

$$\overset{\circ}{\frac{1}{2}} \int \mathbf{\nabla}(\varphi + \varphi_0) \cdot (\mathbf{B} - \mathbf{B}_0) \, dv = \overset{\circ}{\frac{1}{2}} \oint (\varphi + \varphi_0)(\mathbf{B} - \mathbf{B}_0) \cdot d\mathbf{S}.$$

Since the field is regular at infinity and the surface of integration encloses all space, the surface integral vanishes, and so the last volume integral also vanishes. The change in the energy is then

$$\Delta U = \overset{\circ}{\frac{1}{2}} \int (\mathbf{H} \cdot \mathbf{B}_0 - \mathbf{B} \cdot \mathbf{H}_0) \, dv.$$

Now, outside the body inserted into the field, $\mathbf{B} = \mu_0\mathbf{H}$, so that $\mathbf{H} \cdot \mathbf{B}_0 - \mathbf{B} \cdot \mathbf{H}_0 = \mathbf{H} \cdot \mu_0\mathbf{H}_0 - \mu_0\mathbf{H} \cdot \mathbf{H}_0 = 0$. Therefore the last integral needs to be extended only over the volume occupied by the body. Thus we obtain

$$\Delta U = \overset{\circ}{\frac{1}{2}} \int_{\text{Body}} (\mathbf{H} \cdot \mathbf{B}_0 - \mathbf{B} \cdot \mathbf{H}_0) \, dv$$

$$= \overset{\circ}{\frac{1}{2}} \int_{\text{Body}} (\mathbf{H} \cdot \mu_0\mathbf{H}_0 - \mathbf{B} \cdot \mathbf{H}_0) \, dv$$

$$= -\overset{\circ}{\frac{1}{2}} \int_{\text{Body}} (\mathbf{B} - \mu_0\mathbf{H}) \cdot \mathbf{H}_0 \, dv,$$

or

$$\Delta U = -\overset{\circ}{\frac{1}{2}} \int_{\text{Body}} \mathbf{M} \cdot \mathbf{H}_0 \, dv. \tag{14-9.14}$$

Example 14-9.6   A liquid of permeability μ and density ρ is contained in a thin U-tube of circular cross section. When the tube is inserted between the flat poles of a permanent magnet, the liquid between the poles rises through a height h (Fig. 14.18). Neglecting all end effects, find h if the initial field between the poles is $\mathbf{H}_0$, the permeability of the tube is $\mu' = 1$, and the inner radius of the tube is a.

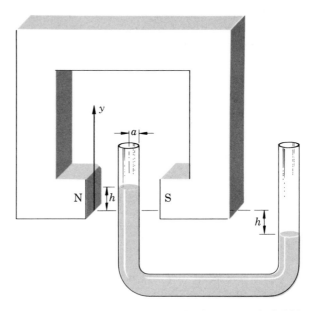

FIG. 14.18   Paramagnetic liquid is pulled in the magnetic field between the poles of a magnet. This effect can be used for determining μ of the liquid.

By the preceding example, the final energy of the system is

$$U = U_0 - \overset{\circ}{\frac{1}{2}} \int\limits_{\text{Liquid}} \mathbf{M} \cdot \mathbf{H}_0 dv.$$

Since all end effects are neglected, $\mathbf{M}$ may be assumed constant in the part of the tube located between the poles and zero elsewhere. If the height of the liquid between the poles as measured from the lower edge of the poles is y, the energy can then be written as

$$U = U_0 - \overset{\circ}{\frac{1}{2}} \mathbf{M} \cdot \mathbf{H}_0 \pi a^2 y.$$

The magnetic force on the liquid is then, by Eq. (14-9.7a),

$$F_y = -\frac{\partial U}{\partial y} = \overset{\circ}{\frac{1}{2}} \mathbf{M} \cdot \mathbf{H}_0 \pi a^2.$$

This force is kept in equilibrium by the weight of the liquid in the portion of the tube of length $2h$:

$$w = 2\pi a^2 h \rho g.$$

Combining the last two equations, we obtain

$$h = \frac{\overset{\circ}{\mathbf{M}} \cdot \mathbf{H}_0}{4\rho g}.$$

Since the tube has a circular cross section and is thin, the field in the liquid between the poles is (see Problem 14.9)

$$\mathbf{H} = \frac{2}{\mu + 1} \mathbf{H}_0,$$

so that

$$\mathbf{M} = \mathbf{B} - \mu_0\mathbf{H} = \mu_0(\mu - 1)\mathbf{H} = \frac{2\mu_0(\mu - 1)}{(\mu + 1)} \mathbf{H}_0.$$

Therefore we obtain for the height h

$$h = \frac{\mu_0(\mu - 1)}{2(\mu + 1)\rho g} H_0^2.$$

▲

PROBLEMS

14.1. Show that if an electric circuit is placed in an infinite medium of permeability μ, the inductance of the circuit will increase μ times.

14.2. A long coil of cross-sectional area A has along its axis a cylindrical core of cross-sectional area a and permeability μ. The core can be inserted into or withdrawn from the coil at will, so that the length of the core within the coil is adjustable. Neglecting end effects, show that the inductance of the coil can be changed by means of this core in the ratio

$$1 + (\mu - 1)(a/A).$$

14.3. A large slab of permeability μ and thickness t is inserted between the plates of a thin parallel-plate capacitor whose plates are rectangles of length a and width b and are separated from each other by a distance d. One plate carries a current I along its length, the other plate returns this current. The slab is parallel to the plates, and its edges are outside the capacitor. Neglecting edge effects, show that the inductance of the system is

$$L = \frac{\mu_0 a[d + (\mu - 1)t]}{b}.$$

14.4. A coaxial line is filled with insulating material of permeability $\mu = Kr$, where K is a constant and r is the distance from the axis of the line. The radius of the central wire is a, that of the sheath is b. Show that the external inductance of the line per unit length is

$$L_l = \frac{\mu_0 K(b - a)}{2\pi}.$$

14.5. A toroidal coil of n turns is wound on a ring of rectangular cross section and permeability μ. The inner radius of the ring is a, the outer radius is b, the width of the ring is w. The ring is not quite closed, so that there is a narrow gap in it. The end surfaces forming the gap are planes which, if extended, would intersect each other along the axis of the ring. They subtend an angle θ at the axis. Neglecting edge effects, show that the inductance of the system is

$$L = \frac{\mu_0 \mu n^2 w}{[2\pi + (\mu - 1)\theta]} \ln \frac{b}{a}.$$

14.6. A thin disk of permeability μ is placed in an initially uniform field **H**, the bases of the disk being normal to **H**. Neglecting edge effects, find the final field outside and inside the disk.

14.7. A thin cylinder of permeability μ is placed in an initially uniform field **H**, the axis of the cylinder being parallel to **H**. Neglecting end effects, find the final field inside and outside the cylinder.

14.8. Derive "Ohm's law for magnetism" and Eqs. (14-6.5), (14-6.6), and (14-6.7).

14.9. Show that an infinitely long circular cylinder of radius a and permeability μ placed with its axis perpendicular to a uniform magnetic field **H** modifies the field to

$$\mathbf{H}_1 = \mathbf{H} + H \frac{\mu - 1}{\mu + 1} \frac{a^2}{r^2} (\cos \theta \, \mathbf{r}_u + \sin \theta \, \mathbf{\theta}_u)$$

outside the cylinder and to

$$\mathbf{H}_2 = \frac{2}{\mu + 1} \mathbf{H}$$

inside the cylinder, where θ and r are cylindrical coordinates of the point of observation with respect to the axis of the cylinder.

14.10. A spherical shell of radii a and b is placed in an initially uniform magnetic field. Show that the ratio of the final field in the central cavity to the initial field ("shielding factor") is

$$f = \frac{9\mu}{9\mu - 2(\mu - 1)^2(a^3/b^3 - 1)}.$$

14.11. A long cylindrical shell of radii a and b and permeability μ is placed in an initially uniform magnetic field at a right angle to it. Show that the shielding factor of the shell (see the preceding problem) is

$$f = \frac{4\mu}{4\mu - (\mu - 1)^2(a^2/b^2 - 1)}.$$

14.12. A sphere of radius a and permeability μ_2 is placed in a liquid of infinite extent and permeability μ_1, $\mu_1 \ll \mu_2$. A uniform field Hi was originally present in the liquid. Show that the sphere modifies the field to

$$\mathbf{H}_1 = H\left(1 + 2\frac{a^3}{r^3}\right)\cos \theta \, \mathbf{r}_u - H\left(1 - \frac{a^3}{r^3}\right)\sin \theta \, \mathbf{\theta}_u$$

outside the sphere and to

$$\mathbf{H}_2 = \frac{3\mu_1}{\mu_2} \mathbf{H}$$

inside the sphere, where r and θ are the coordinates of the point of observation with respect to the center of the sphere.

14.13. A long straight wire carrying a current I is placed in a medium of permeability μ_1 a distance a from an infinite plane boundary with another medium of permeability μ_2. Show that the magnetic field **H** in medium 1 is the same as that due to the actual current I and an image current $I' = [(\mu_2 - \mu_1)/(\mu_1 + \mu_2)]I$ placed a distance a on the other side of the boundary (considering the entire space to be filled with the medium 1). Show that the field in medium 2 is the same as that due to an image current $I'' = [2\mu_1/(\mu_1 + \mu_2)]I$ at the position actually occupied by I (considering the entire space to be filled with the medium 2).

14.14. A long straight wire carrying a current I is placed in a medium of permeability μ_1 a distance d from the axis of a long circular cylinder of radius a and permeability μ_2. Show that the field outside the cylinder is the same as that due to the actual current and two image currents

$$I_1' = [(\mu_2 - \mu_1)/(\mu_1 + \mu_2)]I \quad \text{and} \quad I_2' = [(\mu_1 - \mu_2)/(\mu_1 + \mu_2)]I$$

located at distances $l = a^2/d$ and $l = 0$ from the axis of the cylinder, respectively (all currents are in one plane and the entire space is considered filled with the medium 1). Show that the field inside the cylinder is the same as that due to an image current $I'' = [2\mu_1/(\mu_1 + \mu_2)]I$ at the position actually occupied by I (considering the entire space filled with medium 2).

14.15. Show that the magnetic field measured in the center of a spherical cavity made in a uniformly magnetized medium is independent of the size of the cavity.

14.16. A right, cylindrical magnet of length $2l$ and radius a has constant magnetization **M** directed along the axis of the magnet. Find the magnetic field and induction produced by this magnet at all points of the axis.

14.17. Show that the magnetization potential φ_M due to the magnet described in the preceding problem reduces to

$$\varphi_M = \frac{a^2}{4\mu_0}\left(\frac{1}{r_1} - \frac{1}{r_2}\right)M$$

at distances that are large compared with the radius of the magnet, r_1 and r_2 being the distances from the ends of the magnet to the point of observation.

14.18. Assuming that the magnet described in Problem 14.16 is such that $l \gg a$ and using the method of axial expansion, find the potential at all points near one end of the magnet.

14.19. A spherical magnet of radius a is made from a permanently magnetized material of uniform magnetization **M**. Show that the internal and external fields of this magnet are, respectively,

$$\mathbf{H}_1 = -\frac{1}{3\mu_0}\mathbf{M}$$

and

$$\mathbf{H}_2 = \frac{1}{3\mu_0} M(a^3/r^3)(2\cos\theta\,\mathbf{r}_u + \sin\theta\,\mathbf{\theta}_u),$$

where r and θ are spherical coordinates of the point of observation with origin at the center of the sphere (the polar axis is parallel to $\mathbf{M}$). What is the corresponding induction field?

14.20. A spherical shell of inner radius a and outer radius b is made from a permanently magnetized material of uniform magnetization $\mathbf{M}$. Find the magnetization scalar potential produced by the shell at all points of space.

14.21. Two magnets of different shapes are made from equal quantities of material of the same uniform magnetization $\mathbf{M}$. Show that at large distances from the magnets the fields which the two magnets produce are equal, provided that the magnets are properly oriented.

14.22. Consider an interface between two media, 1 and 2, of permeability μ_1 and μ_2. At the interface, the magnetic field vector in the two media makes, respectively, angles α_1 and α_2 with the normal to the interface. Show that these angles satisfy the "law of refraction"

$$\mu_1 \cot \alpha_1 = \mu_2 \cot \alpha_2.$$

14.23. A small magnet of moment $\mathbf{m}$ is placed at a distance a from the plane face of a large slab of permeability μ. Show that the magnet is attracted to the slab with a force

$$F = \left(\frac{\mu-1}{\mu+1}\right) \frac{3m^2(1+\cos^2\theta)}{16\pi\mu_0 a^4},$$

where θ is the angle between $\mathbf{m}$ and the normal to the surface of the slab facing the magnet.

14.24. A small magnet of uniform magnetization M and volume v_1 is placed at a large distance r from a small, thin disk of permeability μ and volume v_2. The magnetization of the magnet is in the direction of the line joining the magnet with the disk. The flat surfaces of the disk are normal to this line. Neglecting edge effects, show that the disk is attracted to the magnet with a force

$$F = \frac{3(\mu-1)M^2 v_1^2 v_2}{4\pi^2\mu_0\mu r^7}.$$

14.25. A long straight wire carrying a current I is placed in a liquid of permeability μ_1 parallel to, and at a distance a from, the infinite-plane boundary with a large slab of permeability μ_2. Show that the wire is attracted to the slab with a force (per unit length)

$$F_l = \frac{\mu_0\mu_1(\mu_2-\mu_1)}{4\pi a(\mu_1+\mu_2)} I^2.$$

14.26. A long straight wire carries a current I. A second wire of radius a and permeability μ is placed at a distance $r \gg a$ parallel to the first. Show that the two wires attract each other with a force (per unit length)

$$F_l = \frac{°\mu_0(\mu - 1)a^2 I^2}{2(\mu + 1)\pi r^3} .$$

14.27. A ring magnet has the magnetization $\mathbf{M} = (A/r)\,\boldsymbol{\theta}_u$, where A is a constant, r is the distance from the axis of the ring, and $\boldsymbol{\theta}_u$ is a unit vector in circular direction, as in Fig. 8.17. The magnet has a narrow slot between two plane faces normal to $\boldsymbol{\theta}_u$ and forming an angle θ with each other. A small, short, thin cylinder of volume v and permeability μ is placed in the middle of the slot so as to point directly to the axis of the ring. Neglecting edge effects, show that a force

$$F = \frac{°2(\mu - 1)}{\mu_0(\mu + 1)r^3}\,vA^2$$

is required to keep the cylinder from moving toward the axis of the ring.

14.28. A U-shaped electromagnet of cross-sectional area A, average length l, and permeability μ has n turns of wire and carries a current I. The poles of the magnet are separated by a distance d. A flat bar, also of cross section A and permeability μ, is placed across the poles. Show that a force

$$F \approx \frac{°\mu_0\mu^2 n^2 I^2 A}{(l + d)^2}$$

is required to pull the bar away from the magnet.

14.29. Two small identical magnets are placed in a uniform field which is parallel to the magnets and perpendicular to the line joining their fixed centers. Show that the magnets are in equilibrium if

$$H > \frac{°3m}{4\pi\mu_0 r^3},$$

where m is the magnetic moment of the magnets and r is their separation.

14.30. Show that the dissipation of energy per unit volume of a magnetic material caused by hysteresis during each complete cycle in the change of $\mathbf{H}$ can be expressed as $\Delta U = °\oint \mathbf{H} \cdot d\mathbf{M}$ as well as $\Delta U = °\oint \mathbf{H} \cdot d\mathbf{B}$.

15

MAXWELL'S EQUATIONS
AND TIME-DEPENDENT
ELECTRIC AND
MAGNETIC FIELDS

In the preceding chapters the fundamental theory of the principal groups of electric and magnetic phenomena was developed. This theory has, however, two very important deficiencies. First, it is applicable only to time-independent phenomena. Second, it does not give a sufficiently full account of the relationships between the phenomena treated in different groups, although intimate relationships between all electromagnetic phenomena definitely exist as it is apparent, for instance, from the definitions of the basic electric and magnetic quantities as well as from the correlation between electric and magnetic fields measured in different reference frames.

In this chapter we shall concentrate our attention on these relationships between phenomena and shall utilize them for a unification and generalization of the fundamental laws already discussed, to obtain a set of generalized equations representing the most fundamental electromagnetic laws governing both the time-independent as well as the time-dependent phenomena. Then we shall investigate the basic consequences of these equations.

15-1. Conservation of Charge and Faraday's Law of Induction

As a preliminary step to formulating general electromagnetic laws we shall discuss two electromagnetic phenomena which were not treated in sufficient detail in the preceding chapters. The first of these phenomena is conservation of electric charge. The second is electromagnetic induction.

The conservation of charge is an effect already noted in Section 4-1. It can be expressed mathematically by the *continuity equation*

$$\mathbf{V} \cdot \mathbf{J} = -\frac{\partial \rho}{\partial t}. \qquad (15\text{-}1.1a)$$

This equation represents an experimentally established correlation and constitutes a fundamental law relating a time-variable charge distribution with electric current density.

By means of Gauss's theorem of vector analysis, the continuity equation can be written in an equivalent integral form

$$\oint \mathbf{J} \cdot d\mathbf{S} = -\frac{\partial}{\partial t} \int \rho \, dv. \qquad (15\text{-}1.1b)$$

This equation shows that whenever the total charge in a given region of space changes, there is a net electric current (conduction, convection, or both) through the surface enclosing the region. Since a conduction or convection current is merely an organized motion of electric charges, the equation also shows that any variation of electric charge within a closed surface is accompanied by an influx or an outflux of electric charges through this surface. The charge contained in the entire universe is thus conserved.

Under steady-state conditions the right-hand parts of Eqs. (15-1.1a) and (15-1.1b) become zero, and these equations reduce to Eqs. (9-2.2a) and (9-2.2b)

$$\mathbf{V} \cdot \mathbf{J} = 0, \qquad \oint \mathbf{J} \cdot d\mathbf{S} = 0.$$

Equations (9-2.2a) and (9-2.2b) are therefore merely the limiting cases of Eqs. (15-1.1a) and (15-1.1b).

Electromagnetic induction is an effect which, for moving systems, we have already discussed in Sections 10-2 and 12-2. Here, we shall consider electromagnetic induction in stationary systems.

It has been experimentally established that whenever the magnetic flux linking a stationary circuit changes, a voltage is induced in the circuit. Mathematically, this effect is expressed by the equation

$$V_{\text{ind}} = -\frac{\partial \Phi}{\partial t}. \qquad (15\text{-}1.2a)$$

The " $-$ " sign in this equation reflects the *Lenz law*, according to which the induced voltage causes a current whose magnetic field always counteracts the flux variation responsible for this voltage. Electromagnetic induction was discovered by Michael Faraday, and the correlation expressed by Eq. (15-1.2a) is called *Faraday's law of induction*.

The voltage between two points is equal to the line integral of the electric field $\mathbf{E}$ between the points. The voltage induced in a circuit is therefore equal to the line integral of the induced electric field, $\mathbf{E}_{ind}$, extended over the circuit. Since $\Phi = \int \mathbf{B} \cdot d\mathbf{S}$, Eq. (15-1.2a) can then be written in the integral form

$$\oint_{\text{Circuit}} \mathbf{E}_{ind} \cdot d\mathbf{l} = -\frac{\partial}{\partial t} \int \mathbf{B} \cdot d\mathbf{S}, \qquad (15\text{-}1.2b)$$

where the surface integral is extended over a surface bounded by the circuit under consideration.

The correlations expressed by Eqs. (15-1.1) and (15-1.2) are fundamental electromagnetic laws. They are what may be called the "connecting laws," correlating electric and magnetic quantities which we usually attribute to different types of electromagnetic phenomena.

It is clear that a complete set of general electromagnetic laws must contain not only the laws introduced in the preceding chapters, but also the connecting laws presented in this section.

▼
Example 15-1.1   At the time $t = 0$ there is a charge distribution ρ_0 in an infinite medium of dielectric constant ε and constant conductivity σ. Determine how this charge distribution changes with time.

Substituting $\mathbf{J} = \sigma\mathbf{E}$ in Eq. (15-1.1a), we have

$$\nabla \cdot \mathbf{J} = \nabla \cdot \sigma\mathbf{E} = \sigma\nabla \cdot \mathbf{E} = -\frac{\partial \rho}{\partial t}.$$

Substituting $\nabla \cdot \mathbf{E} = (1/\varepsilon_0\varepsilon)\nabla \cdot \mathbf{D} = (1/\varepsilon_0\varepsilon)\rho$ in this equation, we have

$$\frac{\sigma}{\varepsilon_0\varepsilon}\rho = -\frac{\partial \rho}{\partial t}.$$

Integrating and taking into account that at $t = 0$, $\rho = \rho_0$, we finally obtain

$$\rho = \rho_0 e^{-\frac{\sigma}{\varepsilon_0\varepsilon}t}.$$

Example 15-1.2   At the time $t = 0$ a battery of terminal voltage V_{max} is connected to two electrodes. The capacitance of the electrodes is C, and the resistance between the electrodes is R. Determine how the charge accumulating on the electrodes varies with time.

Applying Eq. (15-1.1b) to a surface enclosing one of the electrodes, we have

$$\oint \mathbf{J} \cdot d\mathbf{S} = I = -\frac{\partial}{\partial t} \int \rho \, dv = -\frac{\partial Q}{\partial t},$$

where I is the current leaving the electrode and Q is the charge carried by the electrode. Since $I = V/R$ and $V = Q/C$, where V is the voltage between the electrodes, we have

$$\frac{Q}{RC} = -\frac{\partial Q}{\partial t}.$$

Integrating and taking into account that at $t = 0$, $Q = 0$ while at $t \to \infty$, $Q = Q_{max}$, we have

$$Q = Q_{max}\left(1 - e^{-\frac{t}{RC}}\right).$$

Since $Q_{max} = V_{max}C$, we finally obtain

$$Q = V_{max}C\left(1 - e^{-\frac{t}{RC}}\right).$$

Example 15-1.3   A test loop is placed over a long coil of n turns, length l, resistance R, and cross-sectional area A as shown in Fig. 15.1. At $t = 0$ a voltage V is applied to the coil. Find the voltage impulse induced in the test loop.

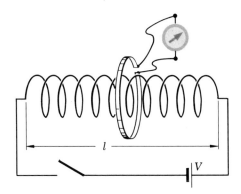

FIG. 15.1   If the switch closes, a voltage impulse is induced in the test loop enclosing the coil.

By Eq. (15-1.2a), we have for the voltage impulse

$$\int_0^\infty V_{ind}dt = -\int_0^\infty d\Phi.$$

Since at $t = 0$, $\Phi = 0$, while at $t = \infty$,

$$\Phi = BA = \mu_0 HA = \mu_0 \frac{nI}{l} A = \mu_0 \frac{nV}{lR} A,$$

we obtain

$$\int_0^\infty V_{\text{ind}} \, dt = -\mu_0 \frac{nV}{lR} A.$$

Note that as long as the end effects are neglected, the voltage impulse depends on the area of the coil but does not depend on the area of the loop which encloses the coil, because the magnetic flux through the loop outside the coil is zero in this case.

▲

15-2. Maxwell's Equations

Let us summarize the fundamental equations (representing the laws governing the electric and magnetic phenomena) which we have presented up to now.

(1) *The field equations.*
For the time-independent electric field in dielectrics and conductors we have

$$\mathbf{\nabla} \times \mathbf{E} = 0, \qquad \oint \mathbf{E} \cdot d\mathbf{l} = 0$$

$$\mathbf{\nabla} \cdot \mathbf{D} = \rho, \qquad \oint \mathbf{D} \cdot d\mathbf{S} = \int \rho \, dv.$$

For the time-independent current density field we have

$$\mathbf{\nabla} \cdot \mathbf{J} = 0, \qquad \oint \mathbf{J} \cdot d\mathbf{S} = 0.$$

For the time-independent magnetic field we have

$$\mathbf{\nabla} \times \mathbf{H} = \mathbf{J}, \qquad \oint \mathbf{H} \cdot d\mathbf{l} = \int \mathbf{J} \cdot d\mathbf{S}$$

$$\mathbf{\nabla} \cdot \mathbf{B} = 0, \qquad \oint \mathbf{B} \cdot d\mathbf{S} = 0.$$

(2) *The constitutive equations (linear isotropic media).*
For the displacement field we have

$$\mathbf{D} = \varepsilon_0 \varepsilon \mathbf{E}.$$

For the current density field we have

$$\mathbf{J} = \sigma \mathbf{E}.$$

For the induction field we have

$$\mathbf{B} = \mu_0 \mu \mathbf{H}.$$

(3) *The energy equations (linear isotropic media).*
For the electric field we have

$$U = \overset{\circ}{\frac{1}{2}} \int\limits_{\text{All space}} \mathbf{E} \cdot \mathbf{D} \, dv.$$

For the current density field we have

$$P = \overset{\circ}{} \int\limits_{\text{All space}} \mathbf{J} \cdot \mathbf{E} \, dv.$$

For the magnetic field we have

$$U = \overset{\circ}{\frac{1}{2}} \int\limits_{\text{All space}} \mathbf{H} \cdot \mathbf{B} \, dv.$$

(4) *The connecting equations.*
The continuity equations

$$\nabla \cdot \mathbf{J} = -\frac{\partial \rho}{\partial t}, \qquad \oint \mathbf{J} \cdot d\mathbf{S} = -\frac{\partial}{\partial t} \int \rho \, dv.$$

The electromagnetic induction equations

$$V_{\text{ind}} = -\frac{\partial \Phi}{\partial t}, \qquad \oint\limits_{\text{Circuit}} \mathbf{E}_{\text{ind}} \cdot d\mathbf{l} = -\frac{\partial}{\partial t} \int \mathbf{B} \cdot d\mathbf{S}.$$

As we shall now show, all field equations and connecting equations given above can be unified into a set of only four equations.

Let us first of all assume that the divergence (flux density) equations for $\mathbf{D}$ and $\mathbf{B}$ are always valid.

Let us then assume that the induction equations remain true even in the absence of a circuit, so that always

$$\oint \mathbf{E} \cdot d\mathbf{l} = -\frac{\partial}{\partial t} \int \mathbf{B} \cdot d\mathbf{S},$$

or, which is the same (by Stokes's theorem of vector analysis),

$$\nabla \times \mathbf{E} = -\frac{\partial \mathbf{B}}{\partial t}.$$

Note that for time-independent fields these equations reduce to $\nabla \times \mathbf{E} = 0$ and $\oint \mathbf{E} \cdot d\mathbf{l} = 0$, as required by the basic laws of time-independent electric fields.

Finally, let us modify the time-independent curl and circulation integral equations for $\mathbf{H}$ into

$$\nabla \times \mathbf{H} = \mathbf{J} + \frac{\partial \mathbf{D}}{\partial t}, \qquad \oint \mathbf{H} \cdot d\mathbf{l} = \int \mathbf{J} \cdot d\mathbf{S} + \frac{\partial}{\partial t} \int \mathbf{D} \cdot d\mathbf{S}.$$

The reason for this modification is that the equations so modified not only reduce to correct equations for the time-independent fields, but also contain the continuity equations as a consequence. Indeed, taking the divergence of the first equation and noting that the divergence of a curl is always zero and that $\mathbf{V} \cdot \mathbf{D} = \rho$, we have

$$\mathbf{V} \cdot \left(\mathbf{V} \times \mathbf{H}\right) = 0 = \mathbf{V} \cdot \mathbf{J} + \frac{\partial(\mathbf{V} \cdot \mathbf{D})}{\partial t},$$

or

$$\mathbf{V} \cdot \mathbf{J} = -\frac{\partial \rho}{\partial t}.$$

Similarly, applying Stokes's theorem to $\oint \mathbf{H} \cdot d\mathbf{l}$ and Gauss's theorem to $\oint \mathbf{D} \cdot d\mathbf{S}$, we have from the second equation

$$\oint \mathbf{V} \times \mathbf{H} \cdot d\mathbf{S} = \underset{\text{Zero path}}{\oint \mathbf{H} \cdot d\mathbf{l}} = 0 = \oint \mathbf{J} \cdot d\mathbf{S} + \frac{\partial}{\partial t} \oint \mathbf{V} \cdot \mathbf{D} \, dv,$$

or

$$\oint \mathbf{J} \cdot d\mathbf{S} = -\frac{\partial}{\partial t} \int \rho \, dv.$$

Thus all field and connecting equations given in the above summary can be unified into the following set of generalized field equations

(Ia) $\mathbf{V} \times \mathbf{E} = -\dfrac{\partial \mathbf{B}}{\partial t}$ (Ib) $\oint \mathbf{E} \cdot d\mathbf{l} = -\dfrac{\partial}{\partial t} \int \mathbf{B} \cdot d\mathbf{S}$

(IIa) $\mathbf{V} \cdot \mathbf{D} = \rho$ (IIb) $\oint \mathbf{D} \cdot d\mathbf{S} = \int \rho \, dv$

(IIIa) $\mathbf{V} \times \mathbf{H} = \mathbf{J} + \dfrac{\partial \mathbf{D}}{\partial t}$ (IIIb) $\oint \mathbf{H} \cdot d\mathbf{l} = \int \left(\mathbf{J} + \dfrac{\partial}{\partial t} \mathbf{D}\right) \cdot d\mathbf{S}$

(IVa) $\mathbf{V} \cdot \mathbf{B} = 0$ (IVb) $\oint \mathbf{B} \cdot d\mathbf{S} = 0.$

It was James Clerk Maxwell who first obtained this set of equations. Therefore they are called *Maxwell's equations*. It was also Maxwell who first introduced the terms $\partial \mathbf{D}/\partial t$ and $\partial(\int \mathbf{D} \cdot d\mathbf{S})/\partial t$ into the equations for $\mathbf{V} \times \mathbf{H}$ and $\oint \mathbf{H} \cdot d\mathbf{l}$. These terms are called, respectively, the *displacement current density* and the *displacement current*. Their significance will manifest itself clearly in Section 15-6.

Maxwell's equations form a remarkable set of physical equations. Their validity and applicability are apparently truly universal and unrestricted. Their simplicity is contrasted by the tremendous range and complexity of phenomena governed by the basic laws which they represent. In many a physicist they arouse aesthetic admiration.

Of course, Maxwell's equations are only the field equations and must be supplemented by the constitutive and energy equations for most practical applications. It has been found, however, that the constitutive equations and the basic energy equations obtained for the time-independent fields are valid for time-variable fields as well. Therefore, assuming linear isotropic media, we can always write

$$\mathbf{D} = \varepsilon_0 \varepsilon \mathbf{E}, \tag{15-2.1}$$

$$\mathbf{B} = \mu_0 \mu \mathbf{H}, \tag{15-2.2}$$

$$\mathbf{J} = \sigma \mathbf{E}; \tag{15-2.3}$$

and

$$P = \overset{\circ}{\int}_{\text{All space}} \mathbf{J} \cdot \mathbf{E} \, dv, \tag{15-2.4}$$

$$U = \overset{\circ}{\frac{1}{2}} \int_{\text{All space}} (\mathbf{E} \cdot \mathbf{D} + \mathbf{H} \cdot \mathbf{B}) \, dv, \tag{15-2.5}$$

where we have combined the energy equations for electric and magnetic fields into one *electromagnetic energy equation*.

▼
Example 15-2.1   A thin parallel-plate capacitor of plate separation d is filled with a medium of conductivity σ and dielectric constant ε. The plates of the capacitor are circular. A variable voltage $V = V_0 \sin \omega t$ is applied to the capacitor, as shown in Fig. 15.2. Assuming that the electric field between the plates is homogeneous, find the magnetic field in the capacitor.

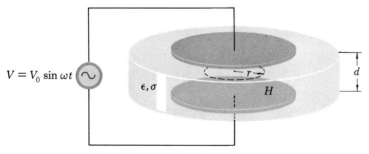

FIG. 15.2   Magnetic field is induced between the plates of a capacitor if a variable voltage is applied to the plates.

If the electric field is assumed homogeneous, it is equal to

$$E = \frac{V}{d} = \frac{V_0 \sin \omega t}{d}.$$

The displacement in the capacitor is then

$$D = \varepsilon_0 \varepsilon E = \varepsilon_0 \varepsilon \frac{V_0 \sin \omega t}{d}.$$

The current density is

$$J = \sigma E = \sigma \frac{V_0 \sin \omega t}{d}.$$

Applying Eq. (IIIb) to an Amperian circle of radius r drawn between the plates as shown in Fig. 15.2 and using the symmetry of the system, we then have

$$\oint \mathbf{H} \cdot d\mathbf{l} = H 2\pi r = \int \mathbf{J} \cdot d\mathbf{S} + \frac{\partial}{\partial t} \int \mathbf{D} \cdot d\mathbf{S}$$

$$= \sigma \frac{V_0 \sin \omega t}{d} \pi r^2 + \frac{\partial}{\partial t}\left(\varepsilon_0 \varepsilon \frac{V_0 \sin \omega t}{d} \pi r^2 \right)$$

$$= \sigma \frac{V_0 \sin \omega t}{d} \pi r^2 + \varepsilon_0 \varepsilon \omega \frac{V_0 \cos \omega t}{d} \pi r^2,$$

so that

$$H = \frac{V_0 r}{2d} (\sigma \sin \omega t + \varepsilon_0 \varepsilon \omega \cos \omega t).$$

Example 15-2.2   When dealing with time-dependent fields, it is customary to classify a material as a conductor or as an insulator depending on whether the conduction or the displacement current is dominant in Eq. (IIIa) when it is applied to the material under consideration. Assuming that the fields change appreciably during some characteristic time T, obtain an inequality in terms of σ, ε, and T to be used as the basis for such a classification.

By the statement of the problem, a material is considered a conductor if

$$J \gg \frac{\partial D}{\partial t} \approx \frac{D}{T}.$$

Since $J = \sigma E$ and $D = \varepsilon_0 \varepsilon E$, we then obtain for a "conductor"

$$\frac{\sigma T}{\varepsilon_0 \varepsilon} \gg 1$$

and, similarly, for an "insulator"

$$\frac{\sigma T}{\varepsilon_0 \varepsilon} \ll 1.$$

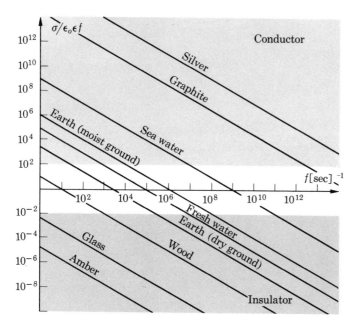

FIG. 15.3   A material in a time-periodic field is considered to be a conductor or an insulator depending on the frequency with which the field oscillates.

In the case of a time-periodic field, the characteristic time may be taken as $1/f$, where f is the frequency with which the field oscillates. We then have for a "conductor" and an "insulator," respectively,

$$\frac{\sigma}{\varepsilon_0 \varepsilon f} \gg 1 \quad \text{and} \quad \frac{\sigma}{\varepsilon_0 \varepsilon f} \ll 1.$$

For practical purposes a material can be usually classified as a conductor if $\sigma/\varepsilon_0 \varepsilon f \geq 10^2$, and as an insulator if $\sigma/\varepsilon_0 \varepsilon f \leq 10^{-2}$ (Fig. 15.3).

Example 15-2.3   Find the equations to which Maxwell's differential equations reduce for points within a perfect conductor ($\sigma \to \infty$) and discuss their significance.

Since in a perfect conductor **E** must be zero (otherwise **J** will be infinite), the first Maxwell equation reduces to

$$\frac{\partial \mathbf{B}}{\partial t} = 0,$$

so that only a time-independent magnetic field may be present within a perfect conductor. Similarly, the second equation reduces to $\rho = 0$, so that no charge may exist within a perfect conductor. The third equation, reduces to $\nabla \times \mathbf{H} = \mathbf{J}$. The last equation remains unchanged: $\nabla \cdot \mathbf{B} = 0$.

Since $\mathbf{H}$ in a perfect conductor must be time-independent (because $\partial\mathbf{B}/\partial t = 0$), $\mathbf{J}$ must be time-independent also (because $\mathbf{J} = \nabla \times \mathbf{H}$). Hence, a time-variable current cannot exist inside a perfect conductor and can be carried only on the surface of such a conductor ("skin effect," see Example 15-3.1).

▲

15-3. Boundary Conditions for Time-Dependent Electric and Magnetic Fields

As in the case of time-independent fields, the field equations (I), (II), (III), and (IV) can be replaced by more convenient equations for points of a boundary between different media.

Since the general flux integral equations (IIb) and (IVb) for $\mathbf{D}$ and $\mathbf{B}$ are the same as in the case of time-independent fields, the boundary conditions for $\mathbf{D}$ and $\mathbf{B}$ are the same as those obtained in Sections 8-5 and 14-5:

$$(\mathbf{D_2} - \mathbf{D_1}) \cdot \mathbf{n}_{12} = \sigma, \quad \text{or} \quad D_{n2} - D_{n1} = \sigma, \qquad (15\text{-}3.1a, b)$$

and

$$(\mathbf{B_2} - \mathbf{B_1}) \cdot \mathbf{n}_{12} = 0 \quad \text{or} \quad B_{n2} = B_{n1}. \qquad (15\text{-}3.2a, b)$$

Applying the continuity equation (15-1.1b) [which is a consequence of Eq. (IIIb)] to an infinitesimal pillbox enclosing a portion of the interface under consideration as in Fig. 8.5b, we obtain

$$(\mathbf{J_2} - \mathbf{J_1}) \cdot \mathbf{n}_{12} = -\frac{\partial \sigma}{\partial t}, \quad \text{or} \quad J_{n2} - J_{n1} = -\frac{\partial \sigma}{\partial t}, \qquad (15\text{-}3.3a, b)$$

where $\mathbf{n}_{12}$ is a unit vector normal to the interface and pointing from medium 1 to medium 2, while σ is the surface charge density residing on the interface.

Applying Eq. (Ib) to an infinitesimal loop enclosing a portion of the interface, as in Fig. 8.5a, we have

$$\oint \mathbf{E} \cdot d\mathbf{l} = -\frac{\partial}{\partial t} \int \mathbf{B} \cdot d\mathbf{S} = -\frac{\partial}{\partial t} \mathbf{B} \cdot \Delta\mathbf{S},$$

where $\Delta\mathbf{S}$ is the area of the loop. For a very narrow loop, however, $\Delta\mathbf{S}$ approaches zero, and we have

$$\oint \mathbf{E} \cdot d\mathbf{l} = 0,$$

which is the same equation as that obtained for the electrostatic field in Section 8-5. Therefore the general boundary condition for **E** is also the same as that obtained there:

$$(\mathbf{E}_2 - \mathbf{E}_1) \cdot \mathbf{t}_u = 0, \quad \text{or} \quad E_{t1} = E_{t2}. \qquad (15\text{-}3.4a, b)$$

Applying Eq. (IIIb) to an infinitesimal loop enclosing a portion of the interface, as in Fig. 14.5a, we have

$$\oint \mathbf{H} \cdot d\mathbf{l} = \int \mathbf{J} \cdot d\mathbf{S} + \frac{\partial}{\partial t} \int \mathbf{D} \cdot d\mathbf{S}$$

$$= \int \mathbf{J} \cdot d\mathbf{S} + \frac{\partial}{\partial t} \mathbf{D} \cdot \Delta\mathbf{S},$$

where $\Delta\mathbf{S}$ is the area of the loop. For a very narrow loop, however, $\Delta\mathbf{S}$ approaches zero, and we have

$$\oint \mathbf{H} \cdot d\mathbf{l} = \int \mathbf{J} \cdot d\mathbf{S},$$

which is the same equation as that used in Section 14-5. Therefore the general boundary condition for **H** is also the same as that obtained there:

$$(\mathbf{H}_2 - \mathbf{H}_1) \cdot \mathbf{t}_u = (\mathbf{J}^{(s)} \times \mathbf{n}_{12}) \cdot \mathbf{t}_u. \qquad (15\text{-}3.5)$$

▼

Example 15-3.1   Obtain the boundary conditions for time-variable fields at the surface of a perfect conductor.

Since in a perfect conductor $\mathbf{E} = 0$, and since E_t must be continuous across an interface, it follows that at the conductor's surface

$$E_t = 0.$$

Since, by Example 15-2.3, a time-variable B is zero inside a perfect conductor, and since B_n must be continuous across an interface, it follows that at the conductor's surface

$$B_n = 0.$$

But since, in general, there is a nonvanishing electric and magnetic field outside the conductor, we must have

$$E_{n \text{ outside}} \neq 0, \qquad B_{t \text{ outside}} \neq 0,$$

so that

$$D_{n \text{ outside}} \neq 0 \quad \text{and} \quad H_{t \text{ outside}} \neq 0.$$

By Eq. (15-3.1b), we then have

$$D_{n \text{ outside}} = \sigma,$$

and by Eq. (15-3.5), we have

$$H_{t \text{ outside}} = J^{(s)}.$$

Thus a perfect conductor in a time-variable electromagnetic field must carry a surface charge and a surface current, which "prevent" the field from penetrating into the conductor.

▲

15-4. Poynting's Vector

We shall now obtain several consequences of Maxwell's equations. In this section we shall obtain an equation indicating that all electric energy, or power, is transmitted through electromagnetic fields rather than through wires or other devices serving to conduct electric currents.

Let us consider a finite region of space containing linear isotropic media and bounded by some surface S. The curl equations for this region are Maxwell's equations

$$\mathbf{\nabla} \times \mathbf{E} = -\frac{\partial \mathbf{B}}{\partial t} \tag{Ia}$$

$$\mathbf{\nabla} \times \mathbf{H} = \mathbf{J} + \frac{\partial \mathbf{D}}{\partial t}. \tag{IIIa}$$

Dot-multiplying Eq. (Ia) by $\mathbf{H}$ and Eq. (IIIa) by $\mathbf{E}$, we have

$$\mathbf{H} \cdot (\mathbf{\nabla} \times \mathbf{E}) = -\mathbf{H} \cdot \frac{\partial \mathbf{B}}{\partial t} = -\mathbf{H} \cdot \frac{\partial \mu_0 \mu \mathbf{H}}{\partial t}$$

$$= -\frac{1}{2} \frac{\partial}{\partial t} (\mu_0 \mu H^2) = -\frac{\partial}{\partial t} \left(\frac{1}{2} \mathbf{H} \cdot \mathbf{B} \right)$$

and, similarly,

$$\mathbf{E} \cdot (\mathbf{\nabla} \times \mathbf{H}) = \mathbf{E} \cdot \mathbf{J} + \mathbf{E} \cdot \frac{\partial \mathbf{D}}{\partial t} = \mathbf{E} \cdot \mathbf{J} + \frac{\partial}{\partial t} \left(\frac{1}{2} \mathbf{E} \cdot \mathbf{D} \right).$$

Subtracting the second equation from the first and observing that $\mathbf{H} \cdot (\mathbf{\nabla} \times \mathbf{E}) - \mathbf{E} \cdot (\mathbf{\nabla} \times \mathbf{H}) = \mathbf{\nabla} \cdot (\mathbf{E} \times \mathbf{H})$ by vector identity (V-5), we have

$$\mathbf{\nabla} \cdot (\mathbf{E} \times \mathbf{H}) = -\frac{\partial}{\partial t} \left(\frac{1}{2} \mathbf{E} \cdot \mathbf{D} + \frac{1}{2} \mathbf{H} \cdot \mathbf{B} \right) - \mathbf{E} \cdot \mathbf{J}.$$

Integrating this equation over the volume of the region under consideration, we obtain

$$\int \mathbf{\nabla} \cdot (\mathbf{E} \times \mathbf{H}) \, dv = -\frac{\partial}{\partial t} \int \left(\frac{1}{2} \mathbf{E} \cdot \mathbf{D} + \frac{1}{2} \mathbf{H} \cdot \mathbf{B} \right) dv - \int \mathbf{E} \cdot \mathbf{J} \, dv.$$

Transforming the first integral by means of Gauss's theorem of vector analysis and multiplying the equation by $(-°)$, we finally obtain

$$- \oint^° (\mathbf{E} \times \mathbf{H}) \cdot d\mathbf{S} = \frac{°\partial}{\partial t} \int \left(\frac{1}{2} \mathbf{E} \cdot \mathbf{D} + \frac{1}{2} \mathbf{H} \cdot \mathbf{B} \right) dv + \int^° \mathbf{E} \cdot \mathbf{J} \, dv.$$

(15-4.1)

The first term on the right of this equation is, by Eq. (15-2.5), the rate of increase of the energy of the electromagnetic field in the region under consideration. The last term, by Eq. (15-2.4), is the rate of energy dissipation for Joule's heating of the media contained in the region. The principle of conservation of energy then requires that the term on the left be interpreted as the rate of energy influx into the region. Hence the vector

$$\mathbf{P} = {}°\mathbf{E} \times \mathbf{H}$$

(15-4.2)

may be regarded as the vector giving the direction and rate of electromagnetic energy flow per unit area at a point of space.

The vector $\mathbf{P}$ defined by Eq. (15-4.2) is called *Poynting's vector*, and Eq. (15-4.1) is frequently called *Poynting's theorem*.

The remarkable feature of Eq. (15-4.1) is that it indicates that electromagnetic energy is transported directly through space. Therefore special devices such as lead wires, transmission lines, etc., are needed not for transporting the energy, but rather for properly shaping the fields in the surrounding space to create in this space a *Poynting energy flow field* whose field lines (**P**-lines) connect the energy source with the consumer. It is interesting to note that since the **P**-lines are normal to $\mathbf{E}$ (because $\mathbf{P} = {}°\mathbf{E} \times \mathbf{H}$) they coincide in the case of time-independent fields with equipotential lines for the electric scalar potential φ drawn in a surface normal to $\mathbf{H}$.

▼

Example 15-4.1   Consider a coaxial cable carrying a current from a battery of terminal voltage V to a load resistance R and back. The length of the cable is l; the resistances of the central wire and the sheath are R_a and R_b, respectively; the radii of the central wire and the sheath are a and b (Fig. 15.4). Neglecting end effects, find Poynting's vector in the space between the wire and the sheath and analyze the energy flow in the cable.

The electric potential for this cable is given in Problem 9.34 and is

$$\varphi = \frac{V}{\ln (b/a)} \left\{ \left[1 - \frac{R_a z}{l(R_a + R_b + R)} \right] \ln (b/r) + \frac{R_b z}{l(R_a + R_b + R)} \ln (r/a) \right\}$$

(that this potential is correct can be verified easily by demonstrating that it satisfies Laplace's equation and the appropriate boundary conditions).

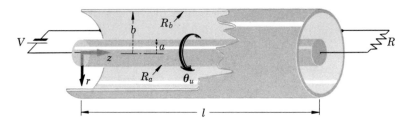

FIG. 15.4   A coaxial cable shapes the electric and magnetic fields so that the energy flux in these fields is confined to the tubular region between the core and the sheath and is directed mostly along the cable, from the source (V) to the load (R).

The electric field between the wire and the sheath is therefore

$$\mathbf{E} = -\nabla\varphi = \frac{V}{l(R_a + R_b + R)\ln(b/a)}[R_a\ln(b/r) - R_b\ln(r/a)]\mathbf{z}_u$$
$$+ \frac{V}{r\ln(b/a)}\left[1 - \frac{(R_a + R_b)z}{l(R_a + R_b + R)}\right]\mathbf{r}_u.$$

The magnetic field is, by Ampere's law,

$$H\cdot 2\pi r = I_{\text{enclosed}} = \frac{V}{R_a + R_b + R},$$

or, taking into account the direction of $\mathbf{H}$,

$$\mathbf{H} = \frac{V}{2\pi r(R_a + R_b + R)}\,\boldsymbol{\theta}_u.$$

The Poynting vector is then

$$\mathbf{P} = {}^{\circ}\mathbf{E}\times\mathbf{H} = {}^{\circ}\begin{vmatrix}\boldsymbol{\theta}_u & \mathbf{z}_u & \mathbf{r}_u \\ E_\theta & E_z & E_r \\ H_\theta & H_z & H_r\end{vmatrix}$$

$$= \frac{{}^{\circ}V^2}{2\pi r^2(R_a + R_b + R)\ln(b/a)}\left[1 - \frac{(R_a + R_b)z}{l(R_a + R_b + R)}\right]\mathbf{z}_u$$
$$- \frac{{}^{\circ}V^2}{2\pi rl(R_a + R_b + R)^2\ln(b/a)}[R_a\ln(b/r) - R_b\ln(r/a)]\mathbf{r}_u.$$

To investigate the energy flow in the cable, let us evaluate the integral

$$\int \mathbf{P}\cdot d\mathbf{S}$$

over the following four surfaces: the left end of the cable $(z = 0)$, the outer surface of the central wire $(r = a)$, the inner surface of the sheath $(r = b)$, and the right end of the cable $(z = l)$. By Poynting's theorem we expect the integral over the first surface to be ${}^{\circ}V^2/(R_a + R_b + R)$, which by Eq. (9-7.6) is the total power needed for Joule's heating of the cable and the load resistance R, and hence the total power that must enter the cable. We expect the integrals over the next two surfaces to be, respectively, $°V^2R_a/(R_a + R_b + R)^2$ and $°V^2R_b/(R_a + R_b + R)^2$, which by Eq. (9-7.5) are the powers needed for Joule's heating of the wire and the sheath, and hence the powers that must be delivered to them through their surfaces. Finally, we expect the integral over the last surface to be $°V^2R/(R_a + R_b + R)^2$, which by Eq. (9-7.5) is the power consumed in the load resistance outside the cable and hence the power that must leave the cable after being transported from the entrance end to the exit end of the cable.

Performing the integration, we obtain: For the left end of the cable $(z = 0)$,

$$\int \mathbf{P} \cdot d\mathbf{S} = \int P_z dS = \int_a^b P_z 2\pi r \, dr = °\int_a^b \frac{V^2 2\pi r \, dr}{2\pi r^2 (R_a + R_b + R) \ln (b/a)}$$

$$= \frac{°V^2}{(R_a + R_b + R)}.$$

For the inner wire $(r = a)$,

$$\int \mathbf{P} \cdot d\mathbf{S} = -\int P_r dS = -\int_0^l P_r 2\pi a \, dz = °\int_0^l \frac{V^2 R_a \ln (b/a) 2\pi a \, dz}{2\pi a l (R_a + R_b + R)^2 \ln (b/a)}$$

$$= \frac{°V^2 R_a}{(R_a + R_b + R)^2}.$$

For the sheath $(r = b)$,

$$\int \mathbf{P} \cdot d\mathbf{S} = \int P_r dS = \int_0^l P_r 2\pi b \, dz = °\int_0^l \frac{V^2 R_b \ln (b/a) 2\pi b \, dz}{2\pi b l (R_a + R_b + R)^2 \ln (b/a)}$$

$$= \frac{°V^2 R_b}{(R_a + R_b + R)^2}.$$

For the right end of the cable $(z = l)$,

$$\int \mathbf{P} \cdot d\mathbf{S} = \int P_z dS = \int_a^b P_z 2\pi r \, dr$$

$$= °\int_a^b \frac{V^2}{2\pi r^2 (R_a + R_b + R) \ln (b/a)} \left[1 - \frac{R_a + R_b}{R_a + R_b + R} \right] 2\pi r \, dr$$

$$= \frac{°V^2 R}{(R_a + R_b + R)^2}.$$

The results of the integration are thus in complete agreement with the expectations based on Poynting's theorem.   ▲

15-5. Maxwell's Stress Equation for Time-Dependent Fields and the Electromagnetic Momentum

As the second consequence of Maxwell's field equations we shall obtain Maxwell's stress equation for time-dependent fields, which indicates, among other things, that a definite amount of momentum is associated with an electromagnetic field.

Let us consider a region in an electromagnetic field where there is a charge distribution ρ and a current distribution $\mathbf{J}$. The force acting upon ρ and $\mathbf{J}$ is, by Eqs. (7-8.2) and (13-6.9),

$$\mathbf{F} = \overset{\circ}{\int} (\rho\mathbf{E} + \mathbf{J} \times \mathbf{B})\,dv$$

(although we have derived these equations for time-independent fields only, they must remain true for all electric and magnetic fields because these fields are *force fields* by definition). By Maxwell's Eq. (IIa) and Eq. (15-2.1), we have

$$\rho\mathbf{E} = (\mathbf{\nabla} \cdot \mathbf{D})\mathbf{E} = \varepsilon_0(\mathbf{\nabla} \cdot \mathbf{E})\mathbf{E}.$$

By Maxwell's Eq. (IIIa) and Eqs. (15-2.2) and (15-2.1), we have

$$\mathbf{J} \times \mathbf{B} = \left(\mathbf{\nabla} \times \mathbf{H} - \frac{\partial\mathbf{D}}{\partial t}\right) \times \mathbf{B} = \mu_0(\mathbf{\nabla} \times \mathbf{H}) \times \mathbf{H} - \varepsilon_0\frac{\partial\mathbf{E}}{\partial t} \times \mathbf{B}.$$

But

$$\varepsilon_0\frac{\partial\mathbf{E}}{\partial t} \times \mathbf{B} = \varepsilon_0\frac{\partial}{\partial t}(\mathbf{E} \times \mathbf{B}) - \varepsilon_0\mathbf{E} \times \frac{\partial\mathbf{B}}{\partial t} = \varepsilon_0\mu_0\frac{\partial}{\partial t}(\mathbf{E} \times \mathbf{H}) - \varepsilon_0\mathbf{E} \times \frac{\partial\mathbf{B}}{\partial t},$$

or, with Maxwell's Eq. (Ia),

$$\varepsilon_0\frac{\partial\mathbf{E}}{\partial t} \times \mathbf{B} = \varepsilon_0\mu_0\frac{\partial}{\partial t}(\mathbf{E} \times \mathbf{H}) + \varepsilon_0\mathbf{E} \times (\mathbf{\nabla} \times \mathbf{E}),$$

so that

$$\mathbf{J} \times \mathbf{B} = \mu_0(\mathbf{\nabla} \times \mathbf{H}) \times \mathbf{H} - \varepsilon_0\mathbf{E} \times (\mathbf{\nabla} \times \mathbf{E}) - \varepsilon_0\mu_0\frac{\partial}{\partial t}(\mathbf{E} \times \mathbf{H}).$$

Substituting these expressions for $\rho\mathbf{E}$ and $\mathbf{J} \times \mathbf{B}$ into the above force equation and replacing $\overset{\circ}{\mathbf{E} \times \mathbf{H}}$ by $\mathbf{P}$ (Poynting's vector), we have

$$\mathbf{F} = \overset{\circ}{\int} [\varepsilon_0(\mathbf{\nabla} \cdot \mathbf{E})\mathbf{E} - \mu_0\mathbf{H} \times (\mathbf{\nabla} \times \mathbf{H}) - \varepsilon_0\mathbf{E} \times (\mathbf{\nabla} \times \mathbf{E})]\,dv$$

$$- \varepsilon_0\mu_0\int \frac{\partial\mathbf{P}}{\partial t}\,dv.$$

Adding to the first integrand the term $\mu_0(\mathbf{\nabla} \cdot \mathbf{H})\mathbf{H}$ (which is zero because $\mathbf{\nabla} \cdot \mathbf{B} = 0$) and transforming the integral by means of the vector identity (V-22), we finally obtain for the force acting upon ρ and $\mathbf{J}$

$$\mathbf{F} = -\varepsilon_0\mu_0\frac{\partial}{\partial t}\int \mathbf{P}\,dv$$

$$- \overset{\circ}{\left[\frac{1}{2}\oint (\varepsilon_0 E^2 + \mu_0 H^2)d\mathbf{S} - \varepsilon_0\oint \mathbf{E}(\mathbf{E} \cdot d\mathbf{S}) - \mu_0\oint \mathbf{H}(\mathbf{H} \cdot d\mathbf{S})\right]}.$$

$$(15\text{-}5.1)$$

This is Maxwell's stress equation for time-dependent electromagnetic fields in vacuum. It differs from the stress equations (7-11.3) and (13-8.3) by the presence of the term involving Poynting's vector. If the fields do not vary in time, this term becomes zero and the equation reduces to the sum of Eqs. (7-11.3) and (13-8.3).

The new term in Maxwell's stress equation may be interpreted as follows. Each region of a time-dependent electromagnetic field is subjected to a volume force even when there are no charges or currents within the region. This force is given by

$$\mathbf{F}_0 = \varepsilon_0\mu_0 \frac{\partial}{\partial t} \int \mathbf{P} \, dv. \tag{15-5.2}$$

The total force experienced by a region of the field is given by the surface integral terms (brackets) of Eq. (15-5.1). The force experienced by charges and currents within the region is equal to the total force minus the force $\mathbf{F}_0$ experienced by the region as such (that is, by the field itself). This explains the presence of the new term (representing $-\mathbf{F}_0$) in Eq. (15-5.1).

Since the force experienced by an object is equal to the rate of change of the momentum of the object, Eq. (15-5.2) indicates that an electromagnetic field is associated with a definite amount of momentum $\mathbf{G}$ given by

$$\mathbf{G} = \varepsilon_0\mu_0 \int \mathbf{P} \, dv, \tag{15-5.3}$$

where the integration is over the volume of the region. The momentum per unit volume of the field is then

$$\mathbf{G}_v = \varepsilon_0\mu_0\mathbf{P}. \tag{15-5.4}$$

▼

Example 15-5.1   An electromagnetic radiation propagating with velocity $c = (\varepsilon_0\mu_0)^{-1/2}$ strikes a plane surface of a body at normal incidence and is then absorbed in the body. The energy density of the radiation is U_v. Find the pressure exerted by the radiation upon the body (radiation pressure).

The pressure is equal to the rate at which the momentum of the radiation is delivered to a unit area of the body. The momentum density of the radiation is, by Eq. (15-5.4), $\mathbf{G}_v = \varepsilon_0\mu_0\mathbf{P}$. The Poynting vector of the radiation is equal to the rate at which the energy is transmitted by the radiation per unit area of a surface normal to the direction of the radiation. Since the radiation propagates with velocity c and the energy density of the radiation is U_v, the Poynting vector of the radiation is

$$P = cU_v = \frac{1}{(\varepsilon_0\mu_0)^{1/2}} U_v.$$

The momentum density of the radiation is therefore

$$G_v = (\varepsilon_0\mu_0)^{1/2}U_v.$$

The pressure (rate of momentum transfer per unit area) is then

$$p = cG_v = \frac{(\varepsilon_0\mu_0)^{1/2}}{(\varepsilon_0\mu_0)^{1/2}}\,U_v,$$

or

$$p = U_v.$$

▲

15-6. Electromagnetic Wave Equations

Among the most important consequences of Maxwell's equations are the so-called *electromagnetic wave equations*, which show that electric and magnetic fields can propagate through space in the form of electromagnetic waves. In fact, the prediction of the existence of the electromagnetic waves by Maxwell was the most remarkable early achievement of the electromagnetic theory based on his equations.

The electromagnetic wave equations for linear isotropic media (the only media with which we are concerned in this book) can be obtained as follows.

Taking the curl of Maxwell's Eq. (Ia), we have

$$\mathbf{\nabla} \times \mathbf{\nabla} \times \mathbf{E} = -\frac{\partial}{\partial t}\mathbf{\nabla} \times \mathbf{B} = -\mu_0\mu\frac{\partial}{\partial t}\mathbf{\nabla} \times \mathbf{H}.$$

Eliminating $\mathbf{\nabla} \times \mathbf{H}$ by means of Maxwell's Eq. (IIIa), we obtain

$$\mathbf{\nabla} \times \mathbf{\nabla} \times \mathbf{E} = -\mu_0\mu\frac{\partial\mathbf{J}}{\partial t} - \mu_0\mu\frac{\partial^2\mathbf{D}}{\partial t^2} = -\mu_0\mu\frac{\partial\mathbf{J}}{\partial t} - \varepsilon_0\varepsilon\mu_0\mu\frac{\partial^2\mathbf{E}}{\partial t^2}.$$

Rearranging terms and replacing $\varepsilon_0\varepsilon\mu_0\mu$ by $1/c^2$, we finally obtain

$$\mathbf{\nabla} \times \mathbf{\nabla} \times \mathbf{E} + \frac{1}{c^2}\frac{\partial^2\mathbf{E}}{\partial t^2} = -\mu_0\mu\frac{\partial\mathbf{J}}{\partial t}. \qquad (15\text{-}6.1)$$

Taking now the curl of Maxwell's Eq. (IIIa), we have

$$\mathbf{\nabla} \times \mathbf{\nabla} \times \mathbf{H} = \mathbf{\nabla} \times \mathbf{J} + \frac{\partial}{\partial t}\mathbf{\nabla} \times \mathbf{D} = \mathbf{\nabla} \times \mathbf{J} + \varepsilon_0\varepsilon\frac{\partial}{\partial t}\mathbf{\nabla} \times \mathbf{E}.$$

Eliminating $\mathbf{\nabla} \times \mathbf{E}$ by means of Maxwell's Eq. (Ia), we obtain

$$\mathbf{\nabla} \times \mathbf{\nabla} \times \mathbf{H} = \mathbf{\nabla} \times \mathbf{J} - \varepsilon_0\varepsilon\frac{\partial^2\mathbf{B}}{\partial t^2} = \mathbf{\nabla} \times \mathbf{J} - \varepsilon_0\varepsilon\mu_0\mu\frac{\partial^2\mathbf{H}}{\partial t^2}.$$

Rearranging terms and replacing $\varepsilon_0 \varepsilon \mu_0 \mu$ by $1/c^2$, we finally obtain

$$\nabla \times \nabla \times \mathbf{H} + \frac{1}{c^2} \frac{\partial^2 \mathbf{H}}{\partial t^2} = \nabla \times \mathbf{J}. \tag{15-6.2}$$

Equations (15-6.1) and (15-6.2) are the electromagnetic wave equations for the electric and magnetic fields, respectively. They show that the time-dependent electric and magnetic fields are wave fields (see Section 2-14). Note the importance of Maxwell's displacement current density term for the derivation of these equations.

The properties and significance of the electromagnetic wave equations will be discussed in the next chapter.

15-7. Representation of Time-Dependent Electromagnetic Fields in Terms of Charges and Currents

According to the wave field theorem (Section 2-14), a vector field $\mathbf{V}$ vanishing at infinity and satisfying the general wave equation

$$\nabla \times \nabla \times \mathbf{V} + \frac{1}{c^2} \frac{\partial^2 \mathbf{V}}{\partial t^2} = \mathbf{K} \tag{2-14.1}$$

can be represented as

$$\mathbf{V} = -\frac{1}{4\pi} \int_{\text{All space}} \frac{[\nabla'(\nabla' \cdot \mathbf{V}) - \mathbf{K}]}{r} \, dv',$$

where the brackets are the retardation symbol.

Using the results of the preceding section, we can express time-variable electric and magnetic fields therefore as

$$\mathbf{E} = -\frac{1}{4\pi} \int_{\text{All space}} \frac{\left[\nabla'(\nabla' \cdot \mathbf{E}) + \mu_0 \mu \dfrac{\partial \mathbf{J}}{\partial t}\right]}{r} \, dv' \tag{15-7.1}$$

and

$$\mathbf{H} = -\frac{1}{4\pi} \int_{\text{All space}} \frac{[\nabla'(\nabla' \cdot \mathbf{H}) - \nabla' \times \mathbf{J}]}{r} \, dv', \tag{15-7.2}$$

where the quantities in the brackets are taken at the instant $t' = t - r/c = t - r\sqrt{\varepsilon_0 \varepsilon \mu_0 \mu}$ if $\mathbf{E}$ and $\mathbf{H}$ are to be found for the time t.

In the case of dielectric and magnetic media of constant ε and μ occupying all space, $\mathbf{\nabla} \cdot \mathbf{E} = \rho/\varepsilon_0\varepsilon$ and $\mathbf{\nabla} \cdot \mathbf{H} = 0$, so that the above equations reduce to

$$\mathbf{E} = -\frac{1}{4\pi\varepsilon_0\varepsilon} \int_{\text{All space}} \frac{\left[\mathbf{\nabla}'\rho + \dfrac{1}{c^2}\dfrac{\partial \mathbf{J}}{\partial t}\right]}{r}\, dv' \qquad (15\text{-}7.3)$$

and

$$\mathbf{H} = \frac{1}{4\pi} \int_{\text{All space}} \frac{[\mathbf{\nabla}' \times \mathbf{J}]}{r}\, dv'. \qquad (15\text{-}7.4)$$

As one can see, Eqs. (15-7.3) and (15-7.4) represent a generalization of Eqs. (4-5.1) and (10-6.1) and reduce to them in the case of time-independent fields in a vacuum.

There are several special forms into which Eqs. (15-7.3) and (15-7.4) can be transformed. One such special form is given below.

Writing Eq. (15-7.3) in terms of two integrals and using the vector identity (V-35) to transform the first integral, we have

$$\mathbf{E} = -\frac{1}{4\pi\varepsilon_0\varepsilon}\left\{\int \frac{[\mathbf{\nabla}'\rho]}{r}\, dv' + \frac{1}{c^2}\int \frac{1}{r}\left[\frac{\partial \mathbf{J}}{\partial t}\right] dv'\right\}$$

$$= -\frac{1}{4\pi\varepsilon_0\varepsilon}\left\{\int \mathbf{\nabla}\frac{[\rho]}{r}\, dv' + \int \mathbf{\nabla}'\frac{[\rho]}{r}\, dv' + \frac{1}{c^2}\int \frac{1}{r}\left[\frac{\partial \mathbf{J}}{\partial t}\right] dv'\right\},$$

where the integrals are extended over all space. The second integral in the last expression vanishes if there are no charges at infinity (see Example 2-14.3), which we assume to be the case. Differentiating the integrand in the first integral and using the vector identity (V-33), we then obtain

$$\mathbf{E} = \frac{1}{4\pi\varepsilon_0\varepsilon}\int\left\{\frac{[\rho]}{r^2} + \frac{1}{rc}\frac{\partial[\rho]}{\partial t}\right\}\mathbf{r}_u dv' - \frac{1}{4\pi\varepsilon_0\varepsilon c^2}\int \frac{1}{r}\left[\frac{\partial \mathbf{J}}{\partial t}\right] dv'. \quad (15\text{-}7.5)$$

Eq. (15-7.4) transforms similarly into

$$\mathbf{H} = \frac{1}{4\pi}\int\left\{\frac{[\mathbf{J}]}{r^2} + \frac{1}{rc}\frac{\partial[\mathbf{J}]}{\partial t}\right\} \times \mathbf{r}_u dv'. \qquad (15\text{-}7.6)$$

Equations (15-7.5) and (15-7.6) represent a generalization of Eqs. (4-5.4) and (10-6.4) and reduce to them in the case of time-independent fields in a vacuum.

These equations indicate that the sources of a time-dependent electric field are electric charges together with conduction and convection currents, while those of a time-dependent magnetic field are only the conduction and convection currents but not the displacement currents. This means that although a displacement current is associated with a magnetic field, this does not constitute a cause and effect relationship.

▼

Example 15-7.1 A thin, narrow ring of radius a carrying a uniformly distributed charge q oscillates about its axis with a frequency f, so that the angular velocity of the ring at a time t is $\omega = \omega_0 \sin 2\pi ft$ (Fig. 15.5). Find the electric and magnetic fields produced by the ring at the axial points far from the ring.

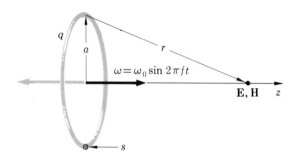

FIG. 15.5 A charged oscillating ring produces an electric and a magnetic field.

At large distances from the ring, the ring constitutes a point charge q, which does not depend on time, so that the contribution of the first integral in Eq. (15-7.5) is

$$\mathbf{E}_1 = \frac{q}{4\pi\varepsilon_0 z^2}\mathbf{k}.$$

Since the ring forms a convection line current $I = \dfrac{q}{2\pi a}\ \omega as = \dfrac{q}{2\pi}\ \omega_0 \sin 2\pi ft$, the contribution of the second integral in Eq. (15-7.5) is

$$\mathbf{E}_2 = -\frac{1}{4\pi\varepsilon_0 c^2}\oint_{\text{Ring}}\frac{1}{r}\left[\frac{\partial I}{\partial t}\right]d\mathbf{l}'$$

$$= -\frac{1}{4\pi\varepsilon_0 c^2}\oint_{\text{Ring}}\frac{1}{r}\left[\frac{q}{2\pi}\ \omega_0 2\pi f \cos 2\pi ft\right]d\mathbf{l}'$$

$$= -\frac{q\omega_0 f}{4\pi\varepsilon_0 c^2}\oint_{\text{Ring}}\frac{1}{r}\cos\{2\pi f(t-r/c)\}\,d\mathbf{l}',$$

$$= -\frac{q\omega_0 f}{4\pi\varepsilon_0 c^2}\cdot\frac{1}{r}\cos\{2\pi f(t-r/c)\}\oint_{\text{Ring}}d\mathbf{l}' = 0$$

(since $\oint d\mathbf{l} = 0$). The total electric field on the axis far from the ring is therefore

$$\mathbf{E} = \frac{q}{4\pi\varepsilon_0 z^2} \mathbf{k}.$$

Taking into account that the ring constitutes a line current, we have from Eq. (15-7.6) for the magnetic field

$$\mathbf{H} = -\frac{1}{4\pi} \oint_{\text{Ring}} \left(\frac{[I]}{r^2} + \frac{1}{cr} \frac{\partial[I]}{\partial t} \right) \mathbf{r}_u \times d\mathbf{l}'.$$

Since the point of observation is far from the ring $(r \to \infty)$, the first term in the integrand can be neglected, so that

$$\mathbf{H} = -\frac{1}{4\pi} \oint_{\text{Ring}} \frac{1}{cr} \frac{\partial[I]}{\partial t} \mathbf{r}_u \times d\mathbf{l}'$$

$$= -\frac{1}{4\pi} \oint_{\text{Ring}} \frac{1}{cr} \frac{\partial}{\partial t} \left(\frac{q\omega_0 \sin\{2\pi f(t - r/c)\}}{2\pi} \right) \mathbf{r}_u \times d\mathbf{l}'$$

$$= \frac{q\omega_0 f \cos\{2\pi f(t - r/c)\}}{4\pi c r^2} \oint_{\text{Ring}} d\mathbf{l}' \times \mathbf{r},$$

which, by Example 10-6.1, reduces to (we replace r by z)

$$\mathbf{H} = \frac{q\omega_0 f \cos\{2\pi f(t - z/c)\}}{2cz^2} a^2 \mathbf{k}.$$

Thus the direction and magnitude of the magnetic field on the axis change periodically with time and with the distance from the ring. The distance corresponding to one complete period in the variation of $\mathbf{H}$ is $d = c/f$. Note that $\mathbf{H}$ at infinity is proportional to r^{-2}, which can not happen for a magnetic field not varying in time (a time-independent magnetic field cannot decrease more slowly than r^{-3} when $r \to \infty$).

▲

15-8. Retarded Potentials for Electric and Magnetic Fields

The calculation of time-dependent electric and magnetic fields can usually be simplified by using the *retarded electromagnetic potentials*.

For the calculation of a magnetic field in a medium of constant ε and μ occupying all space it is convenient to use the potentials defined in Corollary I of Section 2-14. Substituting in Eqs. (2-14.3), (2-14.4), and (2-14.5) $\mathbf{V} = \mathbf{B}$, $\nabla \cdot \mathbf{V} = \nabla \cdot \mathbf{B} = 0$, $K_1 = 0$, and $\mathbf{K_2} = \mu_0 \mu \mathbf{J}$ [because by Eqs. (15-6.2) and (12-4.1) $\mathbf{K} = \nabla \times \mathbf{J}$ in the wave equation for **H**, so that $\mathbf{K} = \mu_0\mu\nabla \times \mathbf{J}$ in the wave equation for **B**], and dropping, as usual, $\varphi_\circ^*$ and $\mathbf{A}_\circ^*$, we have

$$\mathbf{B} = \nabla \times \mathbf{A}^*, \tag{15-8.1}$$

where

$$\mathbf{A}^* = \frac{\mu_0\mu}{4\pi} \int_{\text{All space}} \frac{[\mathbf{J}]}{r} \, dv'. \tag{15-8.2}$$

For the calculation of an electric field in a medium of constant ε and μ occupying all space it is convenient to use the potentials defined in Corollary II of Section 2-14. Substituting in Eqs. (2-14.6), (2-14.7), and (2-14.8) $\mathbf{V} = \mathbf{E}$, $\nabla \cdot \mathbf{V} = \nabla \cdot \mathbf{E} = \nabla \cdot (\mathbf{D}/\varepsilon_0\varepsilon) = \rho/\varepsilon_0\varepsilon$, $\mathbf{K} = -\mu_0\mu\partial\mathbf{J}/\partial t$ [see Eq. (15-6.1)], and dropping $\varphi_\circ^*$ and $\mathbf{W}_\circ^*$, we have

$$\mathbf{E} = -\nabla\varphi^* + \mathbf{W}^*, \tag{15-8.3}$$

where

$$\varphi^* = \frac{1}{4\pi\varepsilon_0\varepsilon} \int_{\text{All space}} \frac{[\rho]}{r} \, dv' \tag{15-8.4}$$

while

$$\mathbf{W}^* = -\frac{\mu_0\mu}{4\pi} \int_{\text{All space}} \frac{1}{r}\left[\frac{\partial\mathbf{J}}{\partial t}\right] dv'. \tag{15-8.5}$$

Since

$$-\frac{\mu_0\mu}{4\pi} \int \frac{1}{r}\left[\frac{\partial\mathbf{J}}{\partial t}\right] dv' = -\frac{\partial}{\partial t}\left\{\frac{\mu_0\mu}{4\pi} \int \frac{[\mathbf{J}]}{r} \, dv'\right\},$$

Eq. (15-8.3) can also be written as

$$\mathbf{E} = -\nabla\varphi^* - \frac{\partial\mathbf{A}^*}{\partial t}, \tag{15-8.6}$$

where $\mathbf{A}^*$ is the magnetic potential given by Eq. (15-8.2).

The potentials φ^* and $\mathbf{A}^*$ are the retarded electromagnetic potentials. As one can see, they represent a generalization of the potentials φ and $\mathbf{A}$ given by Eqs. (5-3.1) and (11-1.3) and reduce to them in the case of time-independent fields in a vacuum.

▼
Example 15-8.1   Prove that in an infinite medium of constant ε and μ

$$\nabla \cdot \mathbf{A}^* = -\varepsilon_0\varepsilon\mu_0\mu\frac{\partial\varphi^*}{\partial t}$$

(this relation is known as *Lorentz's condition*).

From Eq. (15-8.4) we have

$$-\varepsilon_0 \varepsilon \mu_0 \mu \frac{\partial \varphi^*}{\partial t} = -\frac{\mu_0 \mu}{4\pi} \int_{\text{All space}} \frac{\partial}{\partial t} \frac{[\rho]}{r} \, dv'$$

$$= -\frac{\mu_0 \mu}{4\pi} \int_{\text{All space}} \frac{\left[\dfrac{\partial \rho}{\partial t}\right]}{r} \, dv'.$$

But according to the continuity equation (15-1.1a),

$$-\left[\frac{\partial \rho}{\partial t}\right] = [\mathbf{\nabla}' \cdot \mathbf{J}],$$

so that

$$-\varepsilon_0 \varepsilon \mu_0 \mu \frac{\partial \varphi^*}{\partial t} = \frac{\mu_0 \mu}{4\pi} \int_{\text{All space}} \frac{[\mathbf{\nabla}' \cdot \mathbf{J}]}{r} \, dv'.$$

Transforming this integral by means of the vector identity (V-35), we have

$$-\varepsilon_0 \varepsilon \mu_0 \mu \frac{\partial \varphi^*}{\partial t} = \frac{\mu_0 \mu}{4\pi} \int_{\text{All space}} \mathbf{\nabla} \cdot \frac{[\mathbf{J}]}{r} \, dv' + \frac{\mu_0 \mu}{4\pi} \int_{\text{All space}} \mathbf{\nabla}' \cdot \frac{[\mathbf{J}]}{r} \, dv'.$$

The last integral can be transformed, however, into a surface integral by means of the vector identity (V-19), and since there is no current at infinity, the surface integral is zero, and so is this last integral. In the first integral, $\mathbf{\nabla}$ can be factored out from under the integral sign. Therefore we obtain

$$-\varepsilon_0 \varepsilon \mu_0 \mu \frac{\partial \varphi^*}{\partial t} = \mathbf{\nabla} \cdot \frac{\mu_0 \mu}{4\pi} \int_{\text{All space}} \frac{[\mathbf{J}]}{r} \, dv'.$$

Combining this equation with Eq. (15-8.2), we finally obtain

$$\mathbf{\nabla} \cdot \mathbf{A}^* = -\varepsilon_0 \varepsilon \mu_0 \mu \frac{\partial \varphi^*}{\partial t},$$

which was to be proved.

Example 15-8.2 Find the electric and magnetic fields at all points of space far from the oscillating ring described in Example 15-7.1 (Figs. 15.5 and 15.6).

Since at large distances from the ring, the ring constitutes a point charge q, which does not depend on time, the electric potential of the ring is simply

$$\varphi^* = \frac{q}{4\pi\varepsilon_0 r}.$$

Since the ring constitutes a convection line current

$$I = (q/2\pi)\omega_0 \sin 2\pi ft,$$

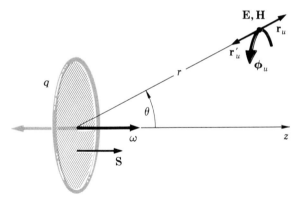

FIG. 15.6 Calculation of the electric and magnetic fields produced by a charged oscillating ring far from the ring.

the magnetic vector potential of the ring can be written as

$$\mathbf{A}^* = \frac{\mu_0}{4\pi} \oint_{\text{Ring}} \frac{q\omega_0 \sin\{2\pi f(t - r/c)\}}{2\pi r} \, d\mathbf{l}'.$$

To simplify the integration, we transform this integral into a surface integral by means of vector identity (V-16). We obtain, factoring out the constants,

$$\mathbf{A}^* = \frac{\mu_0 q \omega_0}{8\pi^2} \int_{\text{Ring}} d\mathbf{S}' \times \mathbf{\nabla}' \, \frac{\sin\{2\pi f(t - r/c)\}}{r}$$

$$= \frac{\mu_0 q \omega_0}{8\pi^2} \int_{\text{Ring}} \frac{\sin\{2\pi f(t - r/c)\} + r \dfrac{2\pi f}{c} \cos\{2\pi f(t - r/c)\}}{r^2} \, \mathbf{r}_u' \times d\mathbf{S}'.$$

Now, since the point of observation is far from the ring $(r \to \infty)$, the first term in the integrand can be neglected[1] and the integral can be replaced by a product, so that the vector potential is

$$\mathbf{A}^* = \frac{\mu_0 q \omega_0}{8\pi^2} \cdot \frac{2\pi f \cos\{2\pi f(t - r/c)\}}{cr} \, \mathbf{r}_u' \times \mathbf{S}',$$

where $\mathbf{S}'$ is a vector whose magnitude is equal to the area of the ring and whose direction is along the axis of the ring as shown in Fig. 15.6. Simplifying, we finally obtain

$$\mathbf{A}^* = \frac{\mu_0 q \omega_0 a^2 f \cos\{2\pi f(t - r/c)\}}{4cr} \sin\theta \, \mathbf{\phi}_u,$$

[1] See also Section 16-8.

where θ and $\boldsymbol{\phi}_u$ are as shown in Fig. 15.6. The electric field of the ring is therefore

$$\mathbf{E} = -\nabla\varphi^* - \frac{\partial \mathbf{A}^*}{\partial t}$$

$$= \frac{q}{4\pi\varepsilon_0 r^2}\,\mathbf{r}_u + \frac{\mu_0 q\omega_0\pi a^2 f^2 \sin\{2\pi f(t - r/c)\}}{2cr}\,\sin\theta\,\boldsymbol{\phi}_u.$$

The magnetic field is (see Table 2-I)

$$\mathbf{B} = \nabla \times \mathbf{A}^* = \frac{\mu_0 q\omega_0 a^2 f \cos\{2\pi f(t - r/c)\}}{2cr^2}\,\cos\theta\,\mathbf{r}_u$$

$$- \frac{\mu_0 q\omega_0\pi a^2 f^2 \sin\{2\pi f(t - r/c)\}}{2c^2 r}\,\sin\theta\,\boldsymbol{\theta}_u.$$

▲

Problems

15.1. At the time $t = 0$ a coil of resistance R and self-inductance L is connected to a battery of terminal voltage V. Show that the current I in the coil satisfies the differential equation

$$L\frac{dI}{dt} + RI = V$$

and find I as a function of t.

15.2. A poorly conducting spherical shell of inner radius a and outer radius b has dielectric constant ε and conductivity σ. At the time $t = 0$ a charge q_0 is sprayed with uniform density on the inner surface of the shell. Show that at any later time the charge on this surface will be

$$q = q_0 e^{-(\sigma/\varepsilon_0\varepsilon)t}.$$

15.3. Show that the electrostatic energy of the shell described in Problem 15.2 decreases by the amount

$$\Delta U = \frac{{}^\circ q_0^2}{8\pi\varepsilon_0\varepsilon}\left(\frac{1}{a} - \frac{1}{b}\right)$$

during the time interval between $t = 0$ and $t = \infty$. Then show by direct calculation that this energy decrease is equal to the energy dissipated in Joule's heating of the shell during the same time interval.

15.4. A circular loop of wire of radius a and resistance R is placed in a time-variable magnetic field

$$B = B_0 e^{-\alpha t}$$

which is normal to the plane of the loop. Show that the power dissipated in the loop in the form of Joule's heat is

$$P = {}^\circ\pi^2 a^4 B_0^2 \alpha^2 e^{-2\alpha t} \cdot \frac{1}{R}.$$

15.5. Two circuits have mutual inductance M. The resistances of the circuits are R_1 and R_2. Show that if a battery of terminal voltage V is connected in series with one of the circuits at time $t = 0$, a charge

$$q = \frac{VM}{R_1 R_2}$$

will flow in the other during the time interval between $t = 0$ and $t = \infty$.

15.6. Two circuits "a" and "b" are coupled. If the current in "a" changes at a certain rate, a certain voltage is induced in "b." Show that the same rate of change of current in "b" will result in the same voltage in "a."

15.7. Two infinite parallel conducting planes of very good conductivity carry equal and oppositely directed currents of density $\mathbf{J}^{(s)}$ per unit width. If $\mathbf{J}^{(s)}$ increases uniformly with time, find the electric field between the planes and the resulting surface charge on them.

15.8. A time-variable voltage V is applied to a capacitor of capacitance C. Show that the displacement current in the capacitor can be expressed as

$$I_d = C \frac{dV}{dt}$$

and show that this current is equal to the charging current of the capacitor.

15.9. Show that when a charged parallel-plate capacitor loses its charge through a leaky dielectric between its plates, the displacement current and the leakage current equalize one another and no magnetic field is produced.

15.10. In a betatron, charged particles are accelerated by the electric field produced by a time-varying magnetic field. Suppose that the magnetic field of a betatron is cylindrically symmetric so that the axial component of the field is

$$H_z = f(r, t).$$

Find the magnitude and the direction of the induced electric field.

15.11. A thin disk of conductivity σ, radius a, and thickness b is in a uniform magnetic field parallel to the axis of the disk. Show that if the field changes according to $B = B_0 \sin \omega t$, the power dissipated in the disk in consequence of induced currents is

$$P = {}^{\circ}\tfrac{1}{4} \pi \sigma^2 \omega^2 a^4 b B_0^2 \cos^2 \omega t.$$

15.12. Show that the time-dependent electric field in the capacitor discussed in Example 15-2.1 cannot be exactly homogeneous.

15.13. A charge q is distributed uniformly throughout a sphere whose radius R varies sinusoidally with time between the values $R_{\min}$ and $R_{\max}$. Find the electric and magnetic field for $r < R_{\min}$ and $r > R_{\max}$.

15.14. Show that the time-varying electric and magnetic fields in a vacuum can be expressed as

$$\mathbf{E} = -\nabla\varphi - \frac{\partial\mathbf{A}}{\partial t}$$
$$\mathbf{B} = \nabla \times \mathbf{A},$$

where φ is the electrostatic potential defined by

$$\varphi = \frac{1}{4\pi\varepsilon_0} \int\limits_{\text{All space}} \frac{\rho}{r}\, dv'$$

and $\mathbf{A}$ is a potential defined by

$$\mathbf{A} = \frac{\mu_0}{4\pi} \int\limits_{\text{All space}} \frac{\mathbf{J} + \dfrac{\partial\mathbf{D}}{\partial t}}{r}\, dv'.$$

15.15. Show that for the fields varying sinusoidally in time with a circular frequency ω, Maxwell's equations can be expressed as

$$\nabla \times \mathbf{E} = -i\omega\mathbf{B}, \qquad \nabla \times \mathbf{H} = \mathbf{J} + i\omega\mathbf{D},$$
$$\nabla \cdot \mathbf{D} = \rho, \qquad \nabla \cdot \mathbf{B} = 0,$$

where $i = \sqrt{-1}$.

15.16. Show that the current in a good conductor satisfies the equation

$$\nabla^2\mathbf{J} = \sigma\mu_0\mu\, \frac{\partial\mathbf{J}}{\partial t}\,.$$

15.17. A semi-infinite medium (good conductor) of conductivity σ and permeability μ is bounded by the plane $z = 0$. There is a uniform sinusoidal current of frequency f parallel to the plane. Show that the current density decreases with the depth of penetration into the conductor as

$$J = J_0 e^{-z/d},$$

where d ("skin depth") is equal to

$$1/\sqrt{\pi f \mu_0 \mu \sigma}.$$

15.18. A voltage V is applied to a long, thin conducting ribbon of conductivity σ, length l, width w, and thickness t. Neglecting edge effects, show by a direct calculation that Joule's heat generated in the ribbon is completely accounted for by the influx of the electromagnetic energy through the surface of the ribbon.

15.19. A long cylindrical wire of length l and resistance R carries a current I. Show by a direct calculation that Joule's heat generated in the wire is completely accounted for by the influx of the electromagnetic energy through the surface of the wire.

15.20. A parallel-plate capacitor with circular plates is being charged. Neglecting edge effects, show by a direct calculation that the rate at which the energy flows into the capacitor through the space between the edges of the plates is equal to the rate at which the energy of the capacitor increases.

15.21. Find the radius which a spherical particle of density $1 \text{ kg} \cdot \text{m}^{-3}$ should have in order to be in equilibrium under the action of the radiation pressure and gravitational attraction of the sun (the mass of the sun is $2 \cdot 10^{30}$ kg, the sun radiates electromagnetic energy at the rate $3.9 \cdot 10^{26}$ watts, the gravitational constant is $6.7 \cdot 10^{-11} \text{ m}^3 \text{ sec}^{-2} \text{ kg}^{-1}$; assume that the particle absorbs solar radiation).

15.22. Find the total radiation force exerted by the sun upon the earth (use numerical values given in Problem 15.21; the radius of the earth is $6.4 \cdot 10^6$ m, the distance from the sun to the earth is $1.5 \cdot 10^{11}$ m).

15.23. By what factor does the radiation pressure on a perfectly reflecting surface exceed that on a perfectly absorbing surface?

15.24. Show that two spherical particles of cosmical dust located in an isotropic field of electromagnetic radiation (light) are driven to each other by the radiation pressure with a force inversely proportional to the square of their separation (this is the starting point of the "dust cloud" cosmogonical hypothesis).

15.25. Show by a direct substitution that Eqs. (15-7.3) and (15-7.4) are compatible with Maxwell's equations.

15.26. A thin disk of radius a and surface charge density σ oscillates about its axis with a frequency f, so that the angular velocity of the disk is $\omega = \omega_0 \sin 2\pi f t$. Find the electric and magnetic fields at the axial points far from the disk.

15.27. Find the electric and magnetic fields, at all points of space far from the disk described in Problem 15.23.

15.28. Derive Eqs. (15-8.4) and (15-8.2) for the retarded potentials directly from Eqs. (15-7.3) and (15-7.4).

15.29. Show that in a medium of constant ε and μ the retarded potentials φ^* and $\mathbf{A}^*$ satisfy the wave equations

$$\nabla^2 \varphi^* - \frac{1}{c^2} \frac{\partial^2 \varphi^*}{\partial t^2} = -\frac{\rho}{\varepsilon_0 \varepsilon}$$

and

$$\nabla^2 \mathbf{A}^* - \frac{1}{c^2} \frac{\partial^2 \mathbf{A}^*}{\partial t^2} = -\mu_0 \mu \mathbf{J},$$

where $c = 1/\sqrt{\varepsilon_0 \varepsilon \mu_0 \mu}$. [Hint: start from Eqs. (15-8.1) and (15-8.6) and use Lorentz's condition].

15.30. The oscillating ring of Example 15-7.1 dissipates energy due to the outflux of the Poynting vector ("radiation damping"). Using the result of Example 15-8.2, find the power needed to maintain the oscillations of the ring.

15.31. Show that the fields due to sources periodically varying in time with frequency f can be found from the ordinary "unretarded" potentials if the distance d from the point of observation to the sources satisfies the relation $d \ll c/f$, where $c = (\varepsilon_0\mu_0)^{-1/2}$.

15.32. Show that the currents I_n leaving a junction of n conducting wires satisfy the equation

$$\Sigma I_n = -\frac{dQ}{dt},$$

where Q is the electric charge accumulated at the junction.

15.33. A circuit contains a resistance R, a capacitance C, and a self inductance L, connected in series. Show that the current in the circuit satisfies the equation

$$L\frac{d^2I}{dt^2} + R\frac{dI}{dt} + \frac{I}{C} = 0.$$

Then show that if the capacitor was given a charge q_0 at $t = 0$, the current in the circuit at any later time is

$$I = q_0 \frac{\omega_0^2}{\omega} e^{-\frac{R}{2L}t} \sin \omega t,$$

where

$$\omega_0 = \sqrt{\frac{1}{LC}} \quad \text{and} \quad \omega = \sqrt{\frac{1}{LC} - \left(\frac{R}{2L}\right)^2},$$

provided that

$$\left(\frac{R}{2L}\right)^2 < \frac{1}{LC}.$$

What are the equations for I if

$$\left(\frac{R}{2L}\right)^2 \geq \frac{1}{LC} \, ?$$

16

ELECTROMAGNETIC WAVES AND RADIATION

In the preceding chapter we learned that Maxwell's equations lead to the wave equations for $\mathbf{E}$ and $\mathbf{H}$. Thus Maxwell's equations predict the existence of electromagnetic waves. The velocity of propagation of these waves in vacuum is $c = 1/\sqrt{\varepsilon_0\mu_0} = 2.99 \cdot 10^8$ m/sec, which is equal to the velocity of light. This suggests that light consists of electromagnetic waves, and that the laws of optics are therefore derivable from the electromagnetic laws. Optics deals only with a narrow band of wave lengths. The wave equations for $\mathbf{E}$ and $\mathbf{H}$ do not, however, impose any restrictions on the length of electromagnetic waves. Electromagnetic waves longer than those of light were first produced and studied by Heinrich Hertz. The properties of these waves were exactly as predicted by theory. A successful derivation of the laws of optics from electromagnetic equations together with Hertz's experiments on electromagnetic waves constituted the first real proof of the Faraday-Maxwell theory of electric and magnetic fields.[1] Electromagnetic waves of lengths ranging from 10^{-15} m to 10^7 m have been observed and studied since Hertz's early experiments. These studies are responsible, directly or indirectly, for almost all major scientific and industrial achievements of the twentieth century. Recently a new kind of waves was predicted and observed, hydromagnetic waves. Like electromagnetic waves, hydromagnetic waves were predicted on the basis of Maxwell's equations. These waves play an important role in a rapidly developing new branch of physics known as magnetohydrodynamics.

[1] Faraday predicted the existence of electromagnetic waves in 1832.

In this chapter we shall study some of the basic properties of electromagnetic waves and, in conclusion, shall discuss the nature of hydromagnetic waves.

16-1. Electromagnetic Waves in Free Space

In free space there are neither electric charges nor electric currents. Since currents are absent, the wave equations (15-6.1) and (15-6.2) reduce to

$$\mathbf{V} \times \mathbf{V} \times \mathbf{E} + \frac{1}{c^2} \frac{\partial^2 \mathbf{E}}{\partial t^2} = 0 \qquad (16\text{-}1.1)$$

and

$$\mathbf{V} \times \mathbf{V} \times \mathbf{H} + \frac{1}{c^2} \frac{\partial^2 \mathbf{H}}{\partial t^2} = 0. \qquad (16\text{-}1.2)$$

Now, by the vector identity (V-12),

$$\mathbf{V} \times \mathbf{V} \times \mathbf{E} = \mathbf{V}(\mathbf{V} \cdot \mathbf{E}) - \nabla^2 \mathbf{E},$$

and since $\mathbf{V} \cdot \mathbf{E} = (1/\varepsilon_0) \mathbf{V} \cdot \mathbf{D} = (1/\varepsilon_0) \rho = 0$ in the absence of charges, we obtain

$$\nabla^2 \mathbf{E} - \frac{1}{c^2} \frac{\partial^2 \mathbf{E}}{\partial t^2} = 0. \qquad (16\text{-}1.3)$$

Similarly,

$$\mathbf{V} \times \mathbf{V} \times \mathbf{H} = \mathbf{V}(\mathbf{V} \cdot \mathbf{H}) - \nabla^2 \mathbf{H},$$

and since $\mathbf{V} \cdot \mathbf{H} = (1/\mu_0) \mathbf{V} \cdot \mathbf{B} = 0$ by the divergence law for $\mathbf{B}$, we obtain

$$\nabla^2 \mathbf{H} - \frac{1}{c^2} \frac{\partial^2 \mathbf{H}}{\partial t^2} = 0. \qquad (16\text{-}1.4)$$

Equations (16-1.3) and (16-1.4) are the electromagnetic wave equations for free space. To demonstrate that these equations are indeed wave equations, we shall consider a wave in which the field vectors depend only on one coordinate in a rectangular system of coordinates. Such a wave is called a *plane wave*. Let us assume that $\mathbf{E}$ and $\mathbf{H}$ depend only on the z-coordinate. In this case

$$\frac{\partial \mathbf{E}}{\partial x} = \frac{\partial \mathbf{E}}{\partial y} = 0 \quad \text{and} \quad \frac{\partial \mathbf{H}}{\partial x} = \frac{\partial \mathbf{H}}{\partial y} = 0,$$

so that Eqs. (16-1.3) and (16-1.4) become

$$\frac{\partial^2 \mathbf{E}}{\partial z^2} - \frac{1}{c^2} \frac{\partial^2 \mathbf{E}}{\partial t^2} = 0 \qquad (16\text{-}1.3\text{a})$$

and

$$\frac{\partial^2 \mathbf{H}}{\partial z^2} - \frac{1}{c^2}\frac{\partial^2 \mathbf{H}}{\partial t^2} = 0. \tag{16-1.4a}$$

The solution of each of these equations is the sum of the two arbitrary vector functions

$$\mathbf{f}_1(t - z/c) + \mathbf{f}_2(t + z/c) \tag{16-1.5}$$

as can be verified by direct substitution (see Problem 16.1).

The function $f_1(t - z/c)$ is, however, a mathematical expression for a wave propagating with velocity c in the positive direction of the z-axis. This can be seen from Fig. 16.1. Since the argument of the function is $t - z/c$, the value of the function at the time t_0 and point z_0 is the same as at a later time t_1 and a further point z_1, provided that

$$t_1 - z_1/c = t_0 - z_0/c.$$

Thus the function indeed represents a wave propagating in the direction of the positive z-axis. Solving the last equation for c, we have

$$c = \frac{z_1 - z_0}{t_1 - t_0}.$$

But $z_1 - z_0$ is the distance traveled by the wave during the time $t_1 - t_0$. Therefore c is the velocity with which the wave propagates.

Similarly, the function $f_2(t + z/c)$ is a mathematical expression for a wave propagating with velocity c in the negative direction of the z-axis.

In electromagnetic theory, especially important are *sinusoidal* plane waves—that is, waves for which the functions $\mathbf{f}_1$ and $\mathbf{f}_2$ in Eq. (16-1.5)

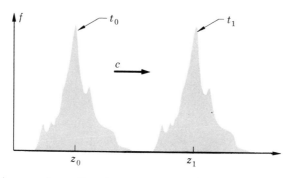

Fig. 16.1   A wave is a disturbance propagating through empty space or through a medium. The picture shown here is a superposition of two "photographs" of the same disturbance taken at the instants t_0 and t_1.

are sinusoids. Waves of this type are the most common ones, and, as it can be shown by means of the Fourier theorem of calculus, any plane wave can be regarded as a superposition of appropriately selected sinusoidal waves.

A sinusoidal electric plane wave propagating in the positive direction of the z-axis can be expressed as

$$\mathbf{E} = \mathbf{E}_0 \sin [\omega(t - z/c) + \delta], \qquad (16\text{-}1.6)$$

where $\mathbf{E}_0$, ω, and δ are constants characterizing the wave. The constant $\mathbf{E}_0$ is called *amplitude;* it represents the maximum value of $\mathbf{E}$ in the wave. The constant ω is called *circular frequency;* it is connected with the *frequency f* and the *period T* of the wave (frequency and period of the oscillation of $\mathbf{E}$ in the wave) by the relation

$$\omega = 2\pi f = 2\pi/T. \qquad (16\text{-}1.7)$$

The constant δ is called *phase angle;* its purpose is to allow for the fact that $\mathbf{E}$ need not be zero when t and z are zero or when $t - z/c$ is zero.

A sinusoidal magnetic plane wave propagating in the positive direction of the z-axis can be similarly expressed as

$$\mathbf{H} = \mathbf{H}_0 \sin [\omega(t - z/c) + \delta]. \qquad (16\text{-}1.8)$$

16-2. Direction of Electric and Magnetic Field Vectors in Plane Waves

For a plane electromagnetic wave which is a function of z and t only, all partial derivatives with respect to x and y vanish. Since

$$\mathbf{\nabla} \cdot \mathbf{B} = \frac{\partial B_x}{\partial x} + \frac{\partial B_y}{\partial y} + \frac{\partial B_z}{\partial z} = 0,$$

we then have $\partial B_z/\partial z = 0$. Therefore the magnetic field in a plane electromagnetic wave has no varying component along the direction of the propagation of the wave. Similarly, since

$$\mathbf{\nabla} \cdot \mathbf{D} = \frac{\partial D_x}{\partial x} + \frac{\partial D_y}{\partial y} + \frac{\partial D_z}{\partial z} = 0$$

(we are considering charge-free space), $\partial D_z/\partial z = 0$, so that the electric field in a plane electromagnetic wave has no varying component along the direction of the propagation. This means that the wave is *transverse*—that is, the electric and magnetic field vectors of the wave are in a plane perpendicular to the direction of the propagation of the wave.

We can obtain a more complete picture of the orientation of field vectors in a plane electromagnetic wave as follows. According to the preceding section, the field vectors in a plane wave propagating in the positive z-direction are a function of $t - z/c$. By the vector identity (V-9), we then have

$$\mathbf{\nabla} \times \mathbf{E} = \mathbf{\nabla}(t - z/c) \times \frac{\partial \mathbf{E}}{\partial(t - z/c)} = -\frac{\mathbf{k}}{c} \times \frac{\partial \mathbf{E}}{\partial(t - z/c)}.$$

Also, we have

$$\frac{\partial \mathbf{B}}{\partial t} = \frac{\partial \mathbf{B}}{\partial(t - z/c)}.$$

But according to Maxwell's Eq. (Ia),

$$\mathbf{\nabla} \times \mathbf{E} = -\frac{\partial \mathbf{B}}{\partial t}.$$

Therefore

$$-\frac{\mathbf{k}}{c} \times \frac{\partial \mathbf{E}}{\partial(t - z/c)} = -\frac{\partial \mathbf{B}}{\partial(t - z/c)}.$$

Integrating this equation, we obtain

$$\mathbf{B} = \frac{1}{c} \mathbf{k} \times \mathbf{E}. \tag{16-2.1}$$

Since $\mathbf{k} \perp \mathbf{E}$, Eq. (16-2.1) shows that in a plane wave the unit vector in the direction of propagation, the electric field vector, and the magnetic field vector (induction vector) are mutually perpendicular and form a right-handed system in the order stated (the "KEB" system).

Figure 16.2 shows these relations for a sinusoidal wave $\mathbf{E} = \mathbf{i}E_{0x} \sin \omega(t - z/c)$ and $\mathbf{H} = \mathbf{j}H_{0y} \sin \omega(t - z/c)$. The figure also shows the meaning of the *wave length*, λ. The wave length is the distance between two closest points in the wave after which the wave pattern repeats itself. As one can see from the figure, this distance corresponds to a difference of 2π in the argument of $\sin \omega(t - z/c)$. We thus have $\omega\lambda/c = 2\pi$, or

$$\lambda = \frac{c}{f}, \tag{16-2.2}$$

where f is the frequency of the wave $(f = \omega/2\pi)$.

A wave in which the electric field vector is always parallel to one direction, such as the wave shown in Fig. 16.2, is called a *plane-polarized wave*. In general, however, the electric field vector (and hence

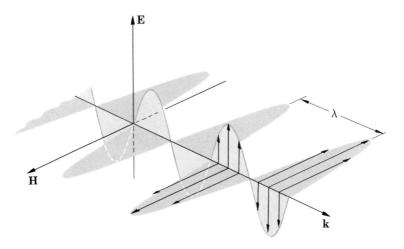

FIG. 16.2   Plane-polarized sinusoidal wave.

the magnetic field vector) constantly changes orientation in space as the wave propagates (this does not prevent the electric and magnetic field vectors from being mutually perpendicular and from staying in a plane normal to the direction of propagation). An example of such a wave is given in Fig. 16.3, where, for simplicity, only the electric component of the wave is shown. An observer moving with this wave would see the end point of vector **E** trace an ellipse in a plane normal to the direction of propagation. A wave of this type is therefore called an *elliptically polarized wave*. It represents the most general case of a sinusoidal plane wave.

There are two important special cases of an elliptically polarized wave. The first special case is a wave whose "polarization ellipse" (ellipse traced by the end point of vector **E**) is a circle. This wave is called a *circularly polarized wave*. The second special case is a wave whose polarization ellipse is a straight line. This wave is an ordinary plane-polarized wave.

An important property of an elliptically polarized wave is that such a wave can be regarded as a sum (superposition) of two plane-polarized waves. For example, an elliptically polarized wave propagating along the z-axis, as in Fig. 16.3, can be regarded as the sum of two waves whose electric field vectors are, respectively, $\mathbf{E_1} = \mathbf{i}E_{0x} \sin \omega(t - z/c)$ and $\mathbf{E_2} = \mathbf{j}E_{0y} \sin [\omega(t - z/c) + \delta]$. The resultant electric field vector in the wave is then

$$\mathbf{E} = \mathbf{i}E_{0x} \sin \omega(t - z/c) + \mathbf{j}E_{0y} \sin [\omega(t - z/c) + \delta].$$

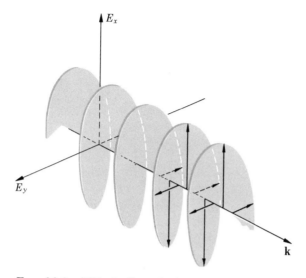

FIG. 16.3   Elliptically polarized sinusoidal wave.

As one can see from this equation, the shape of the polarization ellipse for this wave is determined by E_{0x}, E_{0y}, and δ. In particular, if $\delta = 0$, the ellipse is a straight line, and the wave is plane-polarized; if $E_{0x} = E_{0y}$ and $\delta = \pm\pi/2$, the ellipse is a circle, and the wave is circularly polarized.

16-3. Energy Relations in Plane Electromagnetic Waves

By the energy law (15-2.5), the energy density in a plane electromagnetic wave propagating through free space is

$$U_v = \frac{\varepsilon_0}{2} E^2 + \frac{\mu_0}{2} H^2. \tag{16-3.1}$$

By Eq. (16-2.1), however,

$$\mu_0 H^2 = \frac{1}{\mu_0} \cdot B^2 = \frac{1}{\mu_0} \cdot \frac{E^2}{c^2},$$

and since $c^2 = 1/\varepsilon_0\mu_0$, we have

$$\mu_0 H^2 = \varepsilon_0 E^2.$$

Therefore

$$\frac{\mu_0}{2} H^2 = \frac{\varepsilon_0}{2} E^2, \tag{16-3.2}$$

so that the energy of the wave is divided equally between the electric and the magnetic fields.

Let us now calculate the Poynting vector $\mathbf{P} = {}^{\circ}\mathbf{E} \times \mathbf{H}$ associated with a plane electromagnetic wave. Using Eq. (16-2.1) and noting that $c = 1/\sqrt{\varepsilon_0\mu_0}$, we have

$$\mathbf{P} = {}^{\circ}\mathbf{E} \times \mathbf{H} = {}^{\circ}\mathbf{E} \times \frac{1}{\mu_0}\mathbf{B} = \frac{{}^{\circ}1}{\mu_0}\left[\mathbf{E} \times \left(\frac{1}{c}\mathbf{k} \times \mathbf{E}\right)\right]$$

$$= \frac{{}^{\circ}1}{\mu_0 c}[\mathbf{E} \times (\mathbf{k} \times \mathbf{E})] = {}^{\circ}\sqrt{\frac{\varepsilon_0}{\mu_0}}[\mathbf{E} \times (\mathbf{k} \times \mathbf{E})].$$

Applying the "bac cab" expansion to the last expression, we have

$$\mathbf{P} = {}^{\circ}\sqrt{\frac{\varepsilon_0}{\mu_0}}[\mathbf{k}(\mathbf{E} \cdot \mathbf{E}) - \mathbf{E}(\mathbf{E} \cdot \mathbf{k})],$$

and since $\mathbf{E}$ is perpendicular to $\mathbf{k}$, we obtain

$$\mathbf{P} = {}^{\circ}\sqrt{\frac{\varepsilon_0}{\mu_0}}E^2\mathbf{k}, \tag{16-3.3}$$

or, with Eq. (16-3.2),

$$\mathbf{P} = {}^{\circ}\sqrt{\frac{\mu_0}{\varepsilon_0}}H^2\mathbf{k}. \tag{16-3.4}$$

Combining Eqs. (16-3.4), (16-3.3), and (16-3.1), and using $\mathbf{c} = \mathbf{k}/\sqrt{\varepsilon_0\mu_0}$, we can express $\mathbf{P}$ as

$$\mathbf{P} = U_v\mathbf{c}, \tag{16-3.5}$$

where U_v is the energy density, and $\mathbf{c}$ is the velocity vector of the wave. Hence, *energy is propagated by the wave* in the direction in which the wave propagates. The speed with which the energy is propagated is equal to the velocity of the wave (see Problem 16.8).

One frequently needs to know the average value of the Poynting vector over a complete period $T = 2\pi/\omega$ of the wave. For a plane-polarized wave, E in Eq. (16-3.3) can be expressed as $E = E_0 \times \sin\omega(t - z/c)$. The average $\mathbf{P}$ for such a wave is then

$$\mathbf{P}_{\text{av}} = {}^{\circ}\mathbf{k}\sqrt{\frac{\varepsilon_0}{\mu_0}}\frac{1}{T}\int_0^T E_0{}^2 \sin^2\omega(t - z/c)\,dt$$

$$= {}^{\circ}\mathbf{k}\sqrt{\frac{\varepsilon_0}{\mu_0}}\frac{E_0^2}{T}\left[\frac{1}{2}t - \frac{1}{4\omega}\sin 2\omega(t - z/c)\right]\Big|_0^T,$$

or

$$\mathbf{P}_{\text{av}} = \frac{{}^{\circ}1}{2}\sqrt{\frac{\varepsilon_0}{\mu_0}}E_0^2\mathbf{k} = \frac{{}^{\circ}1}{2}\sqrt{\frac{\mu_0}{\varepsilon_0}}H_0^2\mathbf{k}, \tag{16-3.6a, b}$$

where the last expression is obtained by using Eq. (16-3.4).

▼

Example 16-3.1   Consider an elliptically polarized electromagnetic wave whose electric component is given by

$$\mathbf{E} = \mathbf{i}E_0 \sin \omega(t - z/c) + \mathbf{j}E_0 \sin [\omega(t - z/c) + \pi/4].$$

Find the smallest and the largest value of the Poynting vector for this wave.
    Using Eq. (16-3.3) and designating $\omega(t - z/c)$ as α, for brevity, we have

$$\mathbf{P} = \sqrt[\circ]{\frac{\varepsilon_0}{\mu_0}} E^2 \mathbf{k} = \sqrt[\circ]{\frac{\varepsilon_0}{\mu_0}} [E_0^2 \sin^2 \alpha + E_0^2 \sin^2 (\alpha + \pi/4)] \mathbf{k}.$$

In order to find the values of α which make $\mathbf{P}$ a minimum or a maximum, we differentiate this expression with respect to α and set the derivative equal to zero. This gives

$$2 \sin \alpha \cdot \cos \alpha + 2 \sin (\alpha + \pi/4) \cdot \cos (\alpha + \pi/4) = 0,$$

or

$$\sin 2\alpha + \sin (2\alpha + \pi/2) = 0,$$

and hence

$$\sin 2\alpha = -\sin (2\alpha + \pi/2).$$

Therefore $4\alpha + \pi/2$ must be 0 or 2π (we need only two values), so that

$$\alpha_1 = -\pi/8 \qquad \text{and} \qquad \alpha_2 = 3\pi/8.$$

Substituting α_1 and α_2 into the above expression for $\mathbf{P}$, we have

$$\mathbf{P}_1 = \sqrt[\circ]{\frac{\varepsilon_0}{\mu_0}} E_0^2 \left[\sin^2 \left(\frac{\pi}{8} \right) + \sin^2 \left(\frac{\pi}{8} \right) \right] \mathbf{k} \approx {}^\circ 0.3 \sqrt{\frac{\varepsilon_0}{\mu_0}} E_0^2 \mathbf{k}$$

and

$$\mathbf{P}_2 = \sqrt[\circ]{\frac{\varepsilon_0}{\mu_0}} E_0^2 \left[\sin^2 \left(\frac{3\pi}{8} \right) + \sin^2 \left(\frac{5\pi}{8} \right) \right]$$

$$\approx {}^\circ 1.7 \sqrt{\frac{\varepsilon_0}{\mu_0}} E_0^2 \mathbf{k},$$

which are the smallest and the largest values of $\mathbf{P}$, respectively.

▲

16-4. Electromagnetic Origin of the Laws of Optics

All relations obtained in the preceding sections for electromagnetic waves in free space are obviously true for waves in nonconducting media of constant ε and μ as well, provided that ε_0 and μ_0 in these relations are replaced with $\varepsilon_0\varepsilon$ and $\mu_0\mu$. In particular, since the velocity of propagation of an electromagnetic wave in a vacuum is $c_{\text{vacuum}} = 1/\sqrt{\varepsilon_0\mu_0}$, the velocity of propagation of an electromagnetic wave in a material medium is $c_{medium} = 1/\sqrt{\varepsilon_0 \varepsilon \mu_0 \mu}$. This means that the optical index of refraction n, defined as $n = c_{vacuum}/c_{medium}$, is given by

$$n = \sqrt{\varepsilon \mu} \qquad (16\text{-}4.1)$$

and thus is determined by the electromagnetic properties of the medium under consideration.

For electromagnetic waves in gases, Eq. (16-4.1) is in good agreement with optical measurements of n. For the waves in liquids and solids, however, the agreement is usually quite poor. The reason for this discrepancy has been explained by the microscopic theory of electromagnetic phenomena and is a result of the absorption and re-emission of the wave by atoms and molecules in its path.

The fundamental laws of geometrical optics are the laws of reflection and refraction. We shall now show how these laws can be derived from the electromagnetic laws. For this purpose we shall need to consider a plane, sinusoidal electromagnetic wave propagating along an arbitrary unit vector $\mathbf{n}$. As it follows from Eqs. (16-1.6) and (16-1.8), the electric component of such a wave can be expressed as

$$\mathbf{E} = \mathbf{E}_0 \sin\left[\omega\left(t - \frac{\mathbf{n} \cdot \mathbf{r}}{c}\right) + \delta\right], \qquad (16\text{-}4.2)$$

and the magnetic component as

$$\mathbf{H} = \mathbf{H}_0 \sin\left[\omega\left(t - \frac{\mathbf{n} \cdot \mathbf{r}}{c}\right) + \delta\right], \qquad (16\text{-}4.3)$$

where $\mathbf{r}$ is a radius vector drawn from an arbitrary origin to the point at which $\mathbf{E}$ and $\mathbf{H}$ are being considered. [One can verify that Eqs. (16-4.2) and (16-4.3) represent plane waves propagating in the direction of $\mathbf{n}$ by using the same considerations as those used for explaining the meaning of the formula (16-1.5). Note that $\mathbf{n} \cdot \mathbf{r}$ represents the component of $\mathbf{r}$ in the direction of $\mathbf{n}$.]

Suppose that a plane electromagnetic wave (incident wave) whose electric component is

$$\mathbf{E}_i = \mathbf{E}_{0i} \sin \omega_i\left(t - \frac{\mathbf{n}_i \cdot \mathbf{r}}{c_1}\right) \qquad (16\text{-}4.4)$$

approaches an interface between two nonconducting media with a velocity $c_1 = 1/\sqrt{\varepsilon_0 \varepsilon_1 \mu_0 \mu_1}$ along a direction $\mathbf{n}_i$, as shown in Fig. 16.4. When the wave strikes the interface, a part of the wave is transmitted in the second medium, and a part is reflected in the first medium (since

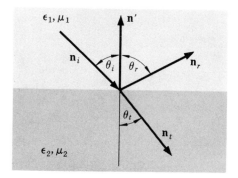

FIG. 16.4 Hypothetical directions of propagation for incident wave ($\mathbf{n}_i$), reflected wave ($\mathbf{n}_r$), and transmitted wave ($\mathbf{n}_t$).

the velocities and the energy densities of the wave in the two media are different, a reflected wave is demanded by the principle of conservation of energy to serve as an outlet for the part of the energy which cannot be accommodated in the transmitted wave). Let the electric component of the reflected wave be

$$\mathbf{E}_r = \mathbf{E}_{0r} \sin\left[\omega_r\left(t - \frac{\mathbf{n}_r \cdot \mathbf{r}}{c_1}\right) + \delta'\right], \qquad (16\text{-}4.5)$$

and that of the transmitted wave be

$$\mathbf{E}_t = \mathbf{E}_{0t} \sin\left[\omega_t\left(t - \frac{\mathbf{n}_t \cdot \mathbf{r}}{c_2}\right) + \delta''\right], \qquad (16\text{-}4.6)$$

where $c_2 = 1/\sqrt{\varepsilon_0 \varepsilon_2 \mu_0 \mu_2}$ is the velocity of the transmitted wave and $\mathbf{n}_r$ and $\mathbf{n}_t$ are as shown in Fig. 16.4 (the purpose of δ' and δ'' is to allow for possible phase differences of the reflected and the transmitted waves relative to the incident wave).

The electromagnetic laws require that the tangential component of $\mathbf{E}$ is continuous across the interface (see Section 15-3). This means that the sum of the tangential components of $\mathbf{E}_i$ and $\mathbf{E}_r$ just above the interface must be equal to the tangential component of $\mathbf{E}_t$ just below the interface. This condition must be satisfied at all times and at all points of the interface. Therefore all three vectors must be identical functions of the time t and of the position $\mathbf{r}$ on the interface.[1]

---

[1] It is plausible that the functions must be identical in order that they may vary in unison. The need for the identity, however, is not really obvious. The reader is referred to mathematical works discussing linearly independent functions for an analysis of the problem.

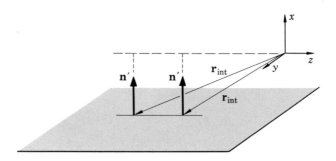

FIG. 16.5 Definition of $\mathbf{r}_{int}$. Equation $\mathbf{n}' \cdot \mathbf{r}_{int} = $ constant defines a constant vector $\mathbf{n}'$ normal to the interface.

We have then, disregarding an additive constant $\pm 2\pi$,

$$\omega_i\left(t - \frac{\mathbf{n}_i \cdot \mathbf{r}_{int}}{c_1}\right) = \omega_r\left(t - \frac{\mathbf{n}_r \cdot \mathbf{r}_{int}}{c_1}\right) + \delta' = \omega_t\left(t - \frac{\mathbf{n}_t \cdot \mathbf{r}_{int}}{c_2}\right) + \delta''$$

(16-4.7)

for all t and $\mathbf{r}_{int}$, where $\mathbf{r}_{int}$ is a radius vector terminating on the interface, as shown in Fig. 16.5. This relation can hold for all t and $\mathbf{r}_{int}$ only if

$$\omega_i = \omega_r = \omega_t. \tag{16-4.8}$$

Thus the frequency of the wave is not altered by reflection or transmission.

Let us now set $t = 0$ in Eq. (16-4.7). We have then with Eq. (16-4.8)

$$\frac{\mathbf{n}_i \cdot \mathbf{r}_{int}}{c_1} = \frac{\mathbf{n}_r \cdot \mathbf{r}_{int}}{c_1} - \frac{\delta'}{\omega_i} \tag{16-4.9}$$

and

$$\frac{\mathbf{n}_i \cdot \mathbf{r}_{int}}{c_1} = \frac{\mathbf{n}_t \cdot \mathbf{r}_{int}}{c_2} - \frac{\delta''}{\omega_i}. \tag{16-4.10}$$

Since δ'/ω_i and c_1 are constants, Eq. (16-4.9) can hold for all $\mathbf{r}_{int}$ only if

$$(\mathbf{n}_i - \mathbf{n}_r) \cdot \mathbf{r}_{int} = \text{constant}.$$

The equation

$$\mathbf{n}' \cdot \mathbf{r}_{int} = \text{constant} \tag{16-4.11}$$

defines, however, a constant vector $\mathbf{n}'$ normal to the interface, as can be seen from Fig. 16.5. Therefore $\mathbf{n}_i - \mathbf{n}_r$ must be constant and normal to the interface. The tangential components of $\mathbf{n}_i$ and $\mathbf{n}_r$, which are $|\mathbf{n}_i| \sin \theta_i$ and $|\mathbf{n}_r| \sin \theta_r$, respectively, must then be equal, and since the vectors are equal in magnitude (both are unit vectors), the angles θ_i and θ_r must be equal. We thus have

$$\theta_i = \theta_r, \tag{16-4.12}$$

which is the well-known law of optics stating that the angle of reflection is equal to the angle of incidence.

From Eq. (16-4.10) we likewise have

$$\left(\frac{\mathbf{n}_i}{c_1} - \frac{\mathbf{n}_t}{c_2}\right) \cdot \mathbf{r}_{\text{int}} = \text{constant}.$$

Therefore $\mathbf{n}_i/c_1 - \mathbf{n}_t/c_2$ must be parallel to $\mathbf{n}'$, and hence the tangential components of $\mathbf{n}_i/c_1$ and $\mathbf{n}_t/c_2$ must be equal. Thus we obtain

$$\frac{\sin \theta_i}{c_1} = \frac{\sin \theta_t}{c_2}. \tag{16-4.13}$$

Designating the angle of incidence θ_i as θ_1 and the angle of refraction θ_t as θ_2, and using the index of refraction relations $c_1 = c_{\text{vacuum}}/n_1$ and $c_2 = c_{\text{vacuum}}/n_2$, we obtain from Eq. (16-4.13)

$$n_1 \sin \theta_1 = n_2 \sin \theta_2, \tag{16-4.14}$$

which is the famous Snell's law of optics.

Finally, we note that since both $\mathbf{n}_i - \mathbf{n}_r$ and $\mathbf{n}_i/c_1 - \mathbf{n}_t/c_2$ are parallel to $\mathbf{n}'$, all three vectors $\mathbf{n}_i, \mathbf{n}_r$, and $\mathbf{n}_t$ representing the direction of the waves are coplanar and are in the plane of incidence defined by the vectors $\mathbf{n}_i$ and $\mathbf{n}'$.

Example 16-4.1   The index of refraction of the ionosphere for radio waves can be expressed as $n_{\text{ionosphere}} = \sqrt{1 - \lambda^2/A}$, where λ is the wavelength of a wave and A is a constant. Assuming that the ionosphere has a sharp lower boundary at an altitude h above the surface of the earth, find the wavelength of the shortest radio wave which can be totally reflected by the ionosphere when sent off from the surface of the earth at a given angle with respect to the vertical (this wavelength is called the *limiting wavelength*).

Consider a wave leaving the earth at an angle α with respect to the vertical, as shown in Fig. 16.6. Let the angle of incidence of this wave at the lower boundary of the ionosphere be θ_1. From Fig. 16.6 we see that

$$\sin \theta_1 = \frac{R \sin \alpha}{R + h} = \frac{\sin \alpha}{1 + h/R},$$

where R is the radius of the earth. Snell's law (16-4.14) for this wave can therefore be expressed as

$$n_{\text{atmosphere}} \cdot \frac{\sin \alpha}{1 + h/R} = n_{\text{ionosphere}} \cdot \sin \theta_2,$$

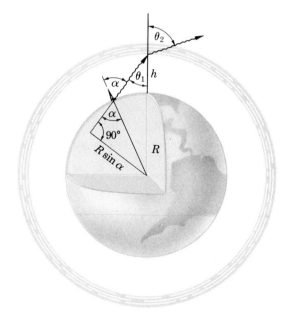

FIG. 16.6 A radio wave is refracted when entering the ionosphere (the wave then follows a curved path and is refracted once again when leaving the ionosphere, which, for simplicity, is not shown here). If α is properly chosen, however, the wave may be reflected from the ionosphere back to the earth. This effect is utilized for long-range radio communication.

where θ_2 is the angle of refraction of the wave in the ionosphere. With $n_{\text{atmosphere}} = 1$ and $n_{\text{ionosphere}} = \sqrt{1 - \lambda^2/A}$ we obtain from the last equation

$$1 - \lambda^2/A = \left(\frac{1}{\sin \theta_2} \cdot \frac{\sin \alpha}{1 + h/R}\right)^2,$$

and hence

$$\lambda^2 = A\left[1 - \left(\frac{1}{\sin \theta_2} \cdot \frac{\sin \alpha}{1 + h/R}\right)^2\right]. \tag{16-4.15}$$

The total reflection begins as soon as θ_2 becomes equal to $\pi/2$, because the transmitted wave disappears then. But $\theta_2 = \pi/2$ corresponds to the *largest* λ in Eq. (16-4.15) and hence to the *smallest* λ for the total reflection. Therefore the shortest wave which can be totally reflected for a given α has the wavelength

$$\lambda_{\text{lim}} = \left\{A\left[1 - \left(\frac{\sin \alpha}{1 + h/R}\right)^2\right]\right\}^{1/2}$$

(waves with $\lambda < \lambda_{\text{lim}}$ are transmitted into the ionosphere). The largest λ_{lim} corresponds to $\alpha = 0$, or to the wave sent off in the direction of the vertical:

$$\lambda_{\text{lim max}} = A^{1/2}.$$

The smallest $\lambda_{\lim}$ is called the *critical wavelength*. It corresponds to $\alpha = \pi/2$, or to the wave sent off in the direction of the horizon:

$$\lambda_{\text{crit}} = \left\{ A\left[1 - \left(\frac{1}{1 + h/R} \right)^2 \right] \right\}^{1/2}.$$

The numerical value for λ_{crit} is ≈ 10 m (see Problem 16.8); since long-range, short-wave radio communications between stations on the earth utilize the reflection of waves from the ionosphere, waves shorter than 10 m cannot ordinarily be used for such communications.

▲

16-5. Intensity Relations in Electromagnetic Waves at a Dielectric Interface

The laws of reflection and refraction which we derived in the preceding section are incomplete, because they give no information about the relations between the magnitudes of the field vectors in the reflected, transmitted, and incident waves. These relations, too, can be obtained from the basic electromagnetic laws, as will be shown in this section.

Let us consider the electric field vector in each wave as the sum of two components: $E_{\parallel}$ lying in the plane of incidence and $E_{\perp}$ perpendicular to this plane (Fig. 16.7). The continuity of the tangential component of **E** (see Section 15-3) requires that

$$E_{i\parallel} \cos \theta - E_{r\parallel} \cos \theta = E_{t\parallel} \cos \theta_t, \tag{16-5.1}$$

and

$$E_{i\perp} + E_{r\perp} = E_{t\perp}. \tag{16-5.2}$$

Let us likewise consider the magnetic field vector in each wave as the sum of $H_{\parallel}$ and $H_{\perp}$. The continuity of the tangential component of **H** (see Section 15-3) requires that

$$H_{i\parallel} \cos \theta - H_{r\parallel} \cos \theta = H_{t\parallel} \cos \theta_t \tag{16-5.3}$$

and

$$H_{i\perp} + H_{r\perp} = H_{t\perp}. \tag{16-5.4}$$

According to Eq. (16-2.1), the magnetic and electric vectors in a plane wave are connected by the relation

$$\mathbf{H} = \frac{1}{c\mu_0\mu} \mathbf{n} \times \mathbf{E}, \tag{16-5.5}$$

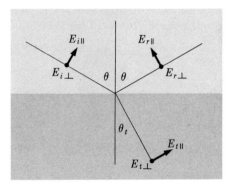

• points out of the page

FIG. 16.7   Geometrical relations for determining intensity relations in electromagnetic waves at a dielectric interface.

where **n** is a unit vector in the direction of the wave. Since $\mu \approx 1$ in most media dealt with in optics, we can write

$$\frac{1}{c\mu_0\mu} = \frac{\sqrt{\varepsilon_0\varepsilon\mu_0\mu}}{\mu_0\mu} = n\sqrt{\frac{\varepsilon_0}{\mu_0}},$$

where n is the index of refraction of the medium under consideration. Using this relation, we obtain from Eq. (16-5.5) for the incident, reflected, and transmitted waves, respectively,

$$\mathbf{H}_i = n_1\sqrt{\frac{\varepsilon_0}{\mu_0}}\,\mathbf{n}_i \times \mathbf{E}_i, \quad \mathbf{H}_r = n_1\sqrt{\frac{\varepsilon_0}{\mu_0}}\,\mathbf{n}_r \times \mathbf{E}_r, \quad \mathbf{H}_t = n_2\sqrt{\frac{\varepsilon_0}{\mu_0}}\,\mathbf{n}_t \times \mathbf{E}_t,$$

or, in terms of the parallel and perpendicular components,

$$-H_{i\parallel} = n_1\sqrt{\frac{\varepsilon_0}{\mu_0}}\,E_{i\perp}, \quad -H_{r\parallel} = n_1\sqrt{\frac{\varepsilon_0}{\mu_0}}\,E_{r\perp}, \quad -H_{t\parallel} = n_2\sqrt{\frac{\varepsilon_0}{\mu_0}}\,E_{t\perp},$$

and

$$H_{i\perp} = n_1\sqrt{\frac{\varepsilon_0}{\mu_0}}\,E_{i\parallel}, \quad H_{r\perp} = n_1\sqrt{\frac{\varepsilon_0}{\mu_0}}\,E_{r\parallel}, \quad H_{t\perp} = n_2\sqrt{\frac{\varepsilon_0}{\mu_0}}\,E_{t\parallel}.$$

With the aid of these relations we can eliminate H from Eqs. (16-5.3) and (16-5.4). This gives

$$n_1 E_{i\perp}\cos\theta - n_1 E_{r\perp}\cos\theta = n_2 E_{t\perp}\cos\theta_t \qquad (16\text{-}5.6)$$

and

$$n_1 E_{i\parallel} + n_1 E_{r\parallel} = n_2 E_{t\parallel}. \qquad (16\text{-}5.7)$$

The four equations (16-5.1), (16-5.2), (16-5.6), and (16-5.7) together with Snell's law (16-4.14) allow one to express $E_{r\parallel}$, $E_{r\perp}$, $E_{t\parallel}$, and $E_{t\perp}$ in terms of $E_{i\parallel}$ and $E_{i\perp}$.

Normal Incidence. If the incident wave strikes the interface at a right angle, θ and θ_t are zero. Equations (16-5.1), (16-5.2), (16-5.6), and (16-5.7) then reduce to

$$E_{i\parallel} - E_{r\parallel} = E_{t\parallel},$$

$$E_{i\perp} + E_{r\perp} = E_{t\perp},$$

$$n_1 E_{i\perp} - n_1 E_{r\perp} = n_2 E_{t\perp},$$

$$n_1 E_{i\parallel} + n_1 E_{r\parallel} = n_2 E_{t\parallel}.$$

From these equations we obtain immediately

$$E_{r\parallel} = -\frac{n_1 - n_2}{n_1 + n_2} E_{i\parallel}, \tag{16-5.8a}$$

$$E_{r\perp} = +\frac{n_1 - n_2}{n_1 + n_2} E_{i\perp}, \tag{16-5.8b}$$

$$E_{t\parallel} = \frac{2n_1}{n_1 + n_2} E_{i\parallel}, \tag{16-5.9a}$$

$$E_{t\perp} = \frac{2n_1}{n_1 + n_2} E_{i\perp}. \tag{16-5.9b}$$

As we can see from these equations, the relations for $E_\parallel$ and $E_\perp$ are identical in the case of normal incidence,[1] which means that the polarization of the wave is not affected by reflection or transmission in this case (compare with the case of oblique incidence below). Furthermore, as we can see from Eqs. (16-5.8a, b), if $n_1 < n_2$ the directions of the electric field vectors in the incident and reflected waves are opposite to each other,[1] which means that the phase of the reflected wave is shifted by π radians with respect to the incident wave in this case. Other consequences of these equations are stated in the caption to Fig. 16.8.

Oblique Incidence. The process of solving Eqs. (16-5.1), (16-5.2), (16-5.6), and (16-5.7) for the case of oblique incidence is somewhat longer than that for the case of normal incidence (see Problem 16.12).

---

[1] Note that in Fig. 16.7, $E_{r\perp}$ and $E_{i\perp}$ are assumed to be in the same direction, but $E_{r\parallel}$ and $E_{i\parallel}$ are assumed to be in opposite directions.

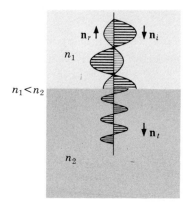
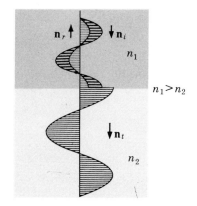

FIG. 16.8 Amplitude and phase relations for electric waves normally incident on a dielectric interface. If $n_1 < n_2$, the reflected wave changes phase by π radians upon reflection, and the amplitude of the transmitted wave is smaller than that of the incident one. If $n_1 > n_2$, the reflected wave does not change phase, and the amplitude of the transmitted wave is larger than that of the incident one. These relations are required by the continuity of the tangential component of **E** across the interface.

Since it presents little interest as far as electromagnetic theory is concerned, only the final results will be reproduced here. We obtain

$$E_{r\parallel} = E_{i\parallel} \frac{\tan (\theta - \theta_t)}{\tan (\theta + \theta_t)} \qquad (16\text{-}5.10a)$$

$$E_{r\perp} = - E_{i\perp} \frac{\sin (\theta - \theta_t)}{\sin (\theta + \theta_t)} \qquad (16\text{-}5.10b)$$

$$E_{t\parallel} = E_{i\parallel} \frac{2 \sin \theta_t \cos \theta}{\sin (\theta + \theta_t) \cos (\theta - \theta_t)} \qquad (16\text{-}5.11a)$$

$$E_{t\perp} = E_{i\perp} \frac{2 \sin \theta_t \cos \theta}{\sin (\theta + \theta_t)} \cdot \qquad (16\text{-}5.11b)$$

These equations are known as *Fresnel's equations* (Fresnel obtained similar equations in 1823 by assuming that light consisted of waves propagating in an elastic "ether").

As we can see from Fresnel's equations, the relations for $E_\parallel$ and $E_\perp$ are not identical for oblique incidence. This means that the polarization of the wave is affected by reflection and transmission in this case.

In particular, if the angle of incidence is such that $\theta + \theta_t = \pi/2$, the denominator of Eq. (16-5.10a) is infinite, and hence $E_{r\parallel} = 0$. Thus, for this angle of incidence, the reflected wave has no electric vector parallel to the plane of incidence, and is therefore completely polarized with electric vector normal to the plane of incidence. The angle of incidence for which such polarization occurs is called *Brewster's angle*. It is given by (see Problem 16.13)

$$\tan \theta_B = \frac{n_2}{n_1},\tag{16-5.12}$$

where n_1 and n_2 are the indices of refraction of the two media (the incident light is in medium 1).

Reflection and Transmission Coefficients. The intensity of an electromagnetic wave is defined as the magnitude of the time-averaged Poynting vector of the wave. According to Eq. (16-3.6a), the intensity I of a plane-polarized plane wave propagating in a nonconducting medium of dielectric constant ε, permeability $\mu = 1$, and index of refraction n is then

$$I = \frac{\overset{\circ}{1}}{2}\sqrt{\frac{\varepsilon_0\varepsilon}{\mu_0}}\,E_0^2 = \frac{\overset{\circ}{1}}{2}n\sqrt{\frac{\varepsilon_0}{\mu_0}}\,E_0^2.\tag{16-5.13}$$

The ratio of the intensity of the reflected wave to the intensity of incident wave is called the *reflection coefficient*. The ratio of the intensity of the transmitted wave to the intensity of the incident wave is called the *transmission coefficient*. Using Eqs. (16-5.13), (16-5.8a, b), and (16-5.9a, b), and designating the reflection coefficient as R and the transmission coefficient as T, we obtain for normal incidence

$$R = \left(\frac{n_1 - n_2}{n_1 + n_2}\right)^2\tag{16-5.14}$$

and

$$T = \frac{4n_1n_2}{(n_1 + n_2)^2}.\tag{16-5.15}$$

For oblique incidence the reflection and transmission coefficients depend on the magnitudes of the parallel and perpendicular components of the field vectors relative to each other. In the case of oblique incidence it is therefore customary to define these coefficients for the parallel and perpendicular components separately. Using Eqs. (16-5.13),

(16-5.10a,b), (16-5.11a,b), and Snell's law (16-4.14), we obtain after elementary transformations

$$R_\parallel = \frac{\tan^2 (\theta - \theta_t)}{\tan^2 (\theta + \theta_t)} \tag{16-5.16a}$$

$$R_\perp = \frac{\sin^2 (\theta - \theta_t)}{\sin^2 (\theta + \theta_t)} \tag{16-5.16b}$$

$$T_\parallel = \frac{2 \sin \theta_t \cos \theta \sin 2\theta}{\sin^2 (\theta + \theta_t) \cos^2 (\theta - \theta_t)} \tag{16-5.17a}$$

and

$$T_\perp = \frac{2 \sin \theta_t \cos \theta \sin 2\theta}{\sin^2 (\theta + \theta_t)} . \tag{16-5.17b}$$

▼
Example 16-5.1   A beam of monochromatic (that is, single frequency) electromagnetic radiation strikes a dielectric interface as shown in Fig. 16.9. What fraction of the time-averaged power of the beam is contained in the reflected beam and what fraction is contained in the transmitted beam if the electric field vector is (a) in the plane of incidence, (b) perpendicular to the plane of incidence?

The time-averaged power of a beam of electromagnetic radiation is equal to the product $P_{av}A$, where P_{av} is the magnitude of the time-averaged Poynting vector (intensity of the radiation) and A is the area of cross section of the beam. The ratio of the powers of two beams 1 and 2 is therefore

$$f = \frac{P_{1av}A_1}{P_{2av}A_2} .$$

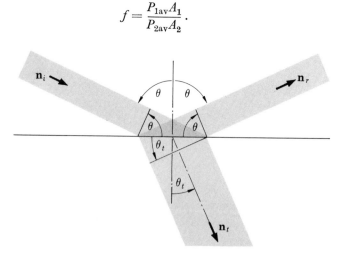

FIG. 16.9   Calculation of the radiation power relations in electromagnetic waves at a dielectric interface.

The ratio $P_{r\,av}/P_{i\,av}$ for the reflected and incident beams is equal to the reflection coefficient R, and the area of cross section of the reflected beam is equal to that of the incident beam. The fraction of the power of the incident beam contained in the reflected beam is therefore, by Eqs. (16-5.16a, b),

$$f_{r\|} = \frac{\tan^2 (\theta - \theta_t)}{\tan^2 (\theta + \theta_t)}$$

if the electric field vector is in the plane of incidence, and

$$f_{r\perp} = \frac{\sin^2 (\theta - \theta_t)}{\sin^2 (\theta + \theta_t)}$$

if the electric field vector is perpendicular to the plane of incidence. Likewise, the ratio $P_{t\,av}/P_{i\,av}$ for the transmitted and incident beams is equal to the transmission coefficient T, and the ratio of the areas of the beams is

$$\frac{A_t}{A_i} = \frac{\cos \theta_t}{\cos \theta},$$

as can be deduced from the geometrical relations of Fig. 16.9. The fraction of the power of the incident beam contained in the transmitted beam is therefore, by Eqs. (16-5.17a, b),

$$f_{t\|} = \frac{\sin 2\theta_t \sin 2\theta}{\sin^2 (\theta + \theta_t) \cos^2 (\theta - \theta_t)}$$

if the electric field vector is in the plane of incidence, and

$$f_{t\perp} = \frac{\sin 2\theta_t \sin 2\theta}{\sin^2 (\theta + \theta_t)}$$

if the electric field vector is perpendicular to the plane of incidence.

Example 16-5.2   A dielectric plate of index of refraction n_2, permeability $\mu_2 = 1$, and thickness l is inserted between two dielectric materials of index of refraction n_1 and n_3 and permeability $\mu_1 = \mu_3 = 1$. An electromagnetic wave is normally incident on the boundary between the first medium and the plate, as shown in Fig. 16.10. Under what conditions will there be no reflection from this boundary?

Equations (16-5.8a, b) and (16-5.9a, b) are not practicable for solving this problem because an infinite number of reflections in the plate would have to be considered if these equations were used. Therefore we shall make use of more general relations.

Let there be two sets of waves propagating in opposite directions with electric field vectors oriented as shown in Fig. 16.10. Let the first boundary be at $z = 0$, and the second at $z = l$. We shall now write the conditions which must be satisfied by electric field vectors at the two boundaries; note that because these conditions must be satisfied simultaneously at two different

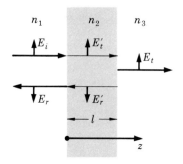

Fig. 16.10   Reflection from an interface between two media (n_1 and n_3) can be eliminated by inserting an appropriate layer of a third medium (n_2) between them.

boundaries, the time and space dependence of the fields must be made explicit. The continuity of E requires that at $z = 0$

$$E_{0i} \sin \omega t - E_{0r} \sin \omega t = E'_{0t} \sin \omega t - E'_{0r} \sin \omega t,$$

and at $z = l$

$$E'_{0t} \sin \omega \left(t - \frac{l}{c_2} \right) - E'_{0r} \sin \omega \left(t + \frac{l}{c_2} \right) = E_{0t} \sin \omega \left(t - \frac{l}{c_2} \right).$$

The continuity of H, together with Eqs. (16-2.1) and (16-4.1), requires that at $z = 0$

$$n_1 E_{0i} \sin \omega t + n_1 E_{0r} \sin \omega t = n_2 E'_{0t} \sin \omega t + n_2 E'_{0r} \sin \omega t,$$

and at $z = l$

$$n_2 E'_{0t} \sin \omega \left(t - \frac{l}{c_2} \right) + n_2 E'_{0r} \sin \omega \left(t + \frac{l}{c_2} \right) = n_3 E_{0t} \sin \omega \left(t - \frac{l}{c_2} \right).$$

We thus obtain the following system of equations:

$$E_{0r} + E'_{0t} - E'_{0r} + 0 = E_{0i}$$
$$n_1 E_{0r} - n_2 E'_{0t} - n_2 E'_{0r} + 0 = -n_1 E_{0i}$$
$$0 + E'_{0t} \sin \omega \left(t - \frac{l}{c_2} \right) - E'_{0r} \sin \omega \left(t + \frac{l}{c_2} \right) - E_{0t} \sin \omega \left(t - \frac{l}{c_2} \right) = 0$$
$$0 + n_2 E'_{0t} \sin \omega \left(t - \frac{l}{c_2} \right) + n_2 E'_{0r} \sin \omega \left(t + \frac{l}{c_2} \right) - n_3 E_{0t} \sin \omega \left(t - \frac{l}{c_2} \right) = 0.$$

For no reflection, E_{0r} must be zero, and therefore we must have

$$\begin{vmatrix} E_{0i} & 1 & -1 & 0 \\ -n_1 E_{0i} & -n_2 & -n_2 & 0 \\ 0 & \sin \omega \left(t - \frac{l}{c_2} \right) & -\sin \omega \left(t + \frac{l}{c_2} \right) & -\sin \omega \left(t - \frac{l}{c_2} \right) \\ 0 & n_2 \sin \omega \left(t - \frac{l}{c_2} \right) & n_2 \sin \omega \left(t + \frac{l}{c_2} \right) & -n_3 \sin \omega \left(t - \frac{l}{c_2} \right) \end{vmatrix} = 0,$$

or

$$\begin{vmatrix} 0 & n_1 - n_2 & -n_1 - n_2 & 0 \\ 1 & -n_2 & -n_2 & 0 \\ 0 & 2n_2 \sin \omega\left(t - \dfrac{l}{c_2}\right) & 0 & -n_2 - n_3 \\ 0 & 0 & 2n_2 \sin \omega\left(t + \dfrac{l}{c_2}\right) & n_2 - n_3 \end{vmatrix} = 0,$$

which is obtained from the first determinant by means of multiplication and addition. Evaluating the last determinant and cancelling common factors, we obtain

$$(n_2 + n_3)(n_1 - n_2) \sin \omega\left(t + \frac{l}{c_2}\right) + (n_1 + n_2)(n_2 - n_3) \sin \omega\left(t - \frac{l}{c_2}\right) = 0,$$

or, expanding the sines and rearranging terms,

$$(n_2 n_1 - n_2 n_3) \cos \omega \frac{l}{c_2} \cdot \sin \omega t + (n_1 n_3 - n_2^2) \sin \omega \frac{l}{c_2} \cdot \cos \omega t = 0.$$

This can be zero for all t only if

$$(n_2 n_1 - n_2 n_3) \cos \omega \frac{l}{c_2} = 0$$

and

$$(n_1 n_3 - n_2^2) \sin \omega \frac{l}{c_2} = 0.$$

The conditions for no reflection are therefore

$$\frac{\omega l}{c_2} = \frac{\pi}{2} \quad \text{and} \quad n_1 n_3 = n_2^2.$$

Note that the first condition implies that

$$l = \frac{\pi c_2}{2\omega} = \frac{\pi c_2}{4\pi f} = \frac{\lambda}{4},$$

where λ is the wave length of the wave in the plate ("quarter-wave" coating of optical lenses is a standard technique for decreasing the amount of reflected light and improving in this way the quality of optical systems). ▲

16-6. Reflection of Electromagnetic Waves from a Conducting Plane

Let a plane electromagnetic wave with electric field vector

$$\mathbf{E}_i = \mathbf{E}_{0i} \sin \omega\left(t - \frac{\mathbf{n}_i \cdot \mathbf{r}}{c}\right)$$

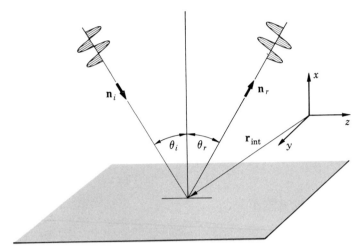

Fig. 16.11 Electromagnetic wave impinging on a perfect conductor is reflected at the same angle without change of amplitude.

impinge at an angle θ_i on a plane surface of a perfect conductor (Fig. 16.11). Since electromagnetic fields cannot exist in perfect conductors (see Example 15-2.3), there will be a reflected wave, but no transmitted one. Let the electric field vector in the reflected wave be

$$\mathbf{E}_r = \mathbf{E}_{0r} \sin \omega \left(t - \frac{\mathbf{n}_r \cdot \mathbf{r}}{c} \right),$$

and let the angle of reflection be θ_r. Using the same consideration as in Section 16-4, we conclude, that just as for a dielectric boundary,

$$\theta_i = \theta_r, \tag{16-6.1}$$

and that $\mathbf{n}_r$ is in the plane of incidence.

Since the tangential component of $\mathbf{E}$ is always continuous, and since inside the conductor $\mathbf{E}$ must be equal to zero, the sum of the tangential components of $\mathbf{E}_i$ and $\mathbf{E}_r$ must be equal to zero at the surface. But then, because of Eq. (16-6.1) and the fact that $\mathbf{n}_r$ is in the plane of incidence, this relation must hold:

$$E_{0i} = E_{0r}. \tag{16-6.2}$$

Thus the amplitudes of the electric fields in the incident and reflected wave are equal. Therefore the amplitudes of the magnetic fields are equal too. Hence the intensities of the incident and reflected wave are equal as well, so that a reflection of an electromagnetic wave from a perfect conductor occurs without a loss of intensity. Thus, a perfect conductor is a perfect reflector of electromagnetic waves. This explains why metallic surfaces (good conductors) are commonly used as reflectors and mirrors.

Let us now investigate the effect of superposition of the incident and reflected waves at a plane surface of a perfect conductor. For this purpose we shall assume that $\mathbf{n}_i$ and $\mathbf{n}_r$ are in the xz-plane (plane of incidence), while the surface of the conductor is in the yz-plane. Also, we shall separate the discussion in two cases: the electric field vector normal to the plane of incidence, and the electric field vector in the plane of incidence. Other cases may then be considered as a combination of these two.

Electric Field Vector Normal to the Plane of Incidence. In this case (Fig. 16.12) the electric field vector of the incident wave can be written as

$$\mathbf{E}_i = \mathbf{j}E_0 \sin \omega \left(t - \frac{z \sin \theta - x \cos \theta}{c} \right), \tag{16-6.3}$$

and that of the reflected wave as

$$\mathbf{E}_r = -\mathbf{j}E_0 \sin \omega \left(t - \frac{z \sin \theta + x \cos \theta}{c} \right). \tag{16-6.4}$$

The corresponding magnetic field vectors can be written as

$$\mathbf{H}_i = -H_0(\mathbf{i} \sin \theta + \mathbf{k} \cos \theta) \sin \omega \left(t - \frac{z \sin \theta - x \cos \theta}{c} \right), \tag{16-6.5}$$

and

$$\mathbf{H}_r = H_0 (\mathbf{i} \sin \theta - \mathbf{k} \cos \theta) \sin \omega \left(t - \frac{z \sin \theta + x \cos \theta}{c} \right). \tag{16-6.6}$$

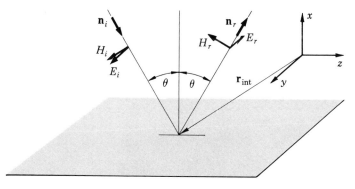

FIG. 16.12   Electromagnetic wave incident on a perfect conductor. The electric field vector is normal to the plane of incidence.

Adding $\mathbf{E}_i$ to $\mathbf{E}_r$ and $\mathbf{H}_i$ to $\mathbf{H}_r$ and using the relation $\sin \alpha \pm \sin \beta = 2 \sin \dfrac{\alpha \pm \beta}{2} \cos \dfrac{\alpha \mp \beta}{2}$, we obtain for the total electric and magnetic fields

$$\mathbf{E} = \mathbf{j}2E_0 \sin 2\pi \left(\frac{x \cos \theta}{\lambda} \right) \cos \omega \left(t - \frac{z \sin \theta}{c} \right), \qquad (16\text{-}6.7)$$

and

$$\mathbf{H} = -\mathbf{i}2H_0 \sin \theta \sin 2\pi \left(\frac{x \cos \theta}{\lambda} \right) \cos \omega \left(t - \frac{z \sin \theta}{c} \right)$$
$$-\mathbf{k}2H_0 \cos \theta \cos 2\pi \left(\frac{x \cos \theta}{\lambda} \right) \sin \omega \left(t - \frac{z \sin \theta}{c} \right), \qquad (16\text{-}6.8)$$

where $\lambda = \dfrac{2\pi c}{\omega}$ is the wave length.

As one can see, these equations represent a "standing wave" along the direction normal to the conducting surface, but a traveling wave along the direction parallel to the surface and to the plane of incidence of the original wave.

An important characteristic of this complex new wave is that the wave is transverse only as far as the electric field is concerned. As far as the magnetic field is concerned the wave is not transverse, because there is a magnetic field component in the direction of propagation. Waves of this type are called therefore *transverse electric*, or *TE*, *waves*. Sometimes they are also called *H waves* or *magnetic waves*.

Electric Field Vector in the Plane of Incidence. In this case (Fig. 16.13) the electric field vector of the incident wave can be written as

$$\mathbf{E}_i = E_0(\mathbf{i} \sin \theta + \mathbf{k} \cos \theta) \sin \omega \left(t - \frac{z \sin \theta - x \cos \theta}{c} \right), \qquad (16\text{-}6.9)$$

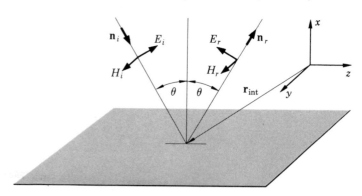

Fig. 16.13 Electromagnetic wave incident on a perfect conductor. The electric field vector is in the plane of incidence.

and that of the reflected wave as

$$\mathbf{E}_r = E_0(\mathbf{i} \sin \theta - \mathbf{k} \cos \theta) \sin \omega \left(t - \frac{z \sin \theta + x \cos \theta}{c} \right). \quad (16\text{-}6.10)$$

The corresponding magnetic field vectors can be written as

$$\mathbf{H}_i = \mathbf{j} H_0 \sin \omega \left(t - \frac{z \sin \theta - x \cos \theta}{c} \right), \quad (16\text{-}6.11)$$

and

$$\mathbf{H}_r = \mathbf{j} H_0 \sin \omega \left(t - \frac{z \sin \theta + x \cos \theta}{c} \right). \quad (16\text{-}6.12)$$

Adding $\mathbf{E}_i$ to $\mathbf{E}_r$ and $\mathbf{H}_i$ to $\mathbf{H}_r$, we now obtain for the total electric and magnetic fields

$$\mathbf{E} = \mathbf{i} 2 E_0 \sin \theta \cos 2\pi \left(\frac{x \cos \theta}{\lambda} \right) \sin \omega \left(t - \frac{z \sin \theta}{c} \right)$$

$$+ \mathbf{k} 2 E_0 \cos \theta \sin 2\pi \left(\frac{x \cos \theta}{\lambda} \right) \cos \omega \left(t - \frac{z \sin \theta}{c} \right) \quad (16\text{-}6.13)$$

and

$$\mathbf{H} = \mathbf{j} 2 H_0 \cos 2\pi \left(\frac{x \cos \theta}{\lambda} \right) \sin \omega \left(t - \frac{z \sin \theta}{c} \right). \quad (16\text{-}6.14)$$

These equations, too, represent a standing wave along a direction normal to the conducting surface, but a traveling wave along the direction parallel to the surface and to the plane of incidence.

In this wave, however, it is the magnetic field which is transverse; the electric field has a component in the direction of propagation. Waves of this type are therefore called *transverse magnetic*, or *TM*, *waves*. Sometimes they are also called *E waves* or *electric waves*.

Thus a conducting surface has a directional action on plane electromagnetic waves impinging on it, causing the waves to propagate along the surface in the form of *TE* or *TM* waves.

It is interesting to note that the velocity with which these waves propagate, or their *phase velocity* v_p is, by Eqs. (16-6.7), (16-6.8), (16-6.13), and (16-6.14),

$$v_p = \frac{c}{\sin \theta} \quad (16\text{-}6.15)$$

and thus is greater than the velocity of light. The velocity with which the energy is propagated by these waves, or their *signal velocity* v_s is, however, smaller than the velocity of light. Indeed, the velocity with which the energy is propagated along the conducting surface is simply the component of the velocity of the original wave along the surface, so that

$$v_s = c \sin \theta. \tag{16-6.16}$$

Let us now consider two limiting cases of wave reflection at a perfectly conducting surface: the case of normal incidence and the case of grazing incidence.

Normal Incidence. In this case the angle of incidence is zero, and Eqs. (16-6.7) and (16-6.8) reduce to

$$\mathbf{E} = \mathbf{j}2E_0 \sin 2\pi \frac{x}{\lambda} \cos \omega t, \tag{16-6.17}$$

$$\mathbf{H} = -\mathbf{k}2H_0 \cos 2\pi \frac{x}{\lambda} \sin \omega t, \tag{16-6.18}$$

while Eqs. (16-6.13) and (16-6.14) reduce to

$$\mathbf{E} = \mathbf{k}2E_0 \sin 2\pi \frac{x}{\lambda} \cos \omega t, \tag{16-6.19}$$

$$\mathbf{H} = \mathbf{j}2H_0 \cos 2\pi \frac{x}{\lambda} \sin \omega t. \tag{16-6.20}$$

These equations represent standing waves. The nodes (zero values) of the electric field vectors in these waves are at the surface of the conductor and at distances $n(\lambda/2)$ from the surface, where $n = 1, 2, 3$, etc. The nodes of the electric field vector coincide with the loops (maximum values) of the magnetic field vector, so that the wave patterns for the electric and magnetic fields are out of phase by $\pi/2$ radians. Furthermore, the electric and magnetic fields are also out of phase by $\pi/2$ radians in time, so that at the instant when the electric field is a maximum the magnetic field is zero, and vice versa. As a result of this latter relation the energy of the wave fluctuates between the electric and the magnetic fields instead of being divided equally between them, as was the case with plane electromagnetic waves discussed in Section 16-3.

The average value of the Poynting vector in these waves is zero (see Example 16-6.1), a consequence of the fact that as much energy is carried away by the reflected wave as is delivered by the incident wave.

The phase velocity of the waves, by Eq. (16-6.15), is infinite. But the signal velocity, by Eq. (16-6.16), is zero (which emphasizes the fact that no net energy is transported by the waves).

Finally, we note that at the surface of the conductor there is a magnetic field

$$H = 2H_0 \sin \omega t. \tag{16-6.21}$$

By Example 15-3.1, the conductor must then have a surface current

$$J^{(s)} = 2H_0 \sin \omega t \tag{16-6.22}$$

directed at a right angle to **H**. (In real conductors the current is not confined to the surface but penetrates more or less deeply into the conductor, where it causes a dissipation of energy for Joule's heating. The intensity of the reflected wave is then smaller than that of the incident wave by an amount corresponding to the energy dissipated in the conductor).

Grazing Incidence. In this case the angle of incidence is $\pi/2$, and the fields described by Eqs. (16-6.7) and (16-6.8) vanish. The fields described by Eqs. (16-6.13) and (16-6.14) become

$$\mathbf{E}' = \mathbf{i}E_0' \sin \omega\left(t - \frac{z}{c}\right) \tag{16-6.23}$$

$$\mathbf{H}' = \mathbf{j}H_0' \sin \omega\left(t - \frac{z}{c}\right), \tag{16-6.24}$$

where $E_0' = 2E_0$ and $H_0' = 2H_0$.

As one can see, these equations represent an ordinary transverse, plane electromagnetic wave. When dealing with waves of this type in the presence of metallic boundaries it is customary to call them *transverse electromagnetic*, or *TEM*, *waves*.

As we already know, a wave of this type propagates energy. The signal velocity of such a wave is c and is equal to the phase velocity.

Note that, by Eq. (16-6.24), there is again a magnetic field at the surface of the conductor, so that the conductor must have a surface current. This current is

$$\mathbf{J}^{(s)} = \mathbf{k}H_0' \sin \omega\left(t - \frac{z}{c}\right) \tag{16-6.25}$$

and constitutes a surface wave propagating along the conductor.

Note also that, by Eq. (16-6.23) and the displacement law, there must be a surface charge

$$\sigma = \varepsilon_0 E_0' \sin \omega\left(t - \frac{z}{c}\right) \tag{16-6.26}$$

on the surface of the conductor. This charge, too, constitutes a surface wave propagating along the conductor.

▼

Example 16-6.1   Find the time-averaged value of the Poynting vector for the waves described by Eqs. (16-6.17) and (16-6.18).

We have

$$\mathbf{P}_{av} = {}^{\circ}(\mathbf{E} \times \mathbf{H})_{av} = -{}^{\circ}\mathbf{i}4E_0H_0 \sin 2\pi \frac{x}{\lambda} \cos 2\pi \frac{x}{\lambda} \cdot \frac{1}{T} \int_0^T \cos \omega t \sin \omega t \, dt$$

$$= -{}^{\circ}\mathbf{i}4E_0H_0 \sin 2\pi \frac{x}{\lambda} \cos 2\pi \frac{x}{\lambda} \cdot \frac{1}{T} \cdot \frac{\sin^2 \omega t}{2\omega} \bigg|_0^T$$

and since $T = 2\pi/\omega$, $\mathbf{P}_{av} = 0$. The same result would be obtained if Eqs. (16-6.19) and (16-6.20) were used.

▲

16-7. Guided Electromagnetic Waves

Examining Eqs. (16-6.7) and (16-6.13), we note that the tangential component of the electric field vector vanishes not only at the surface of the conductor, $x = 0$, but also at the surfaces

$$x = \frac{n\lambda}{2 \cos \theta}, \qquad (16\text{-}7.1)$$

where n is an integer. Therefore a second perfectly conducting surface can be placed at a distance $n\lambda/2 \cos \theta$ from the surface considered in the preceding section, and all equations obtained in the preceding section, will remain valid for the fields resulting from a plane wave reflected back and forth from one surface to the other. This means that waves of the types *TE*, *TM*, and *TEM* (grazing incidence) can be propagated, or *guided*, between two parallel conducting planes. Let us consider such guided waves in some details.

TE and TM Waves between Parallel Planes. Suppose that the distance between the planes is a. By Eq. (16-7.1), plane waves of wave length λ can be reflected back and forth, or guided, between these

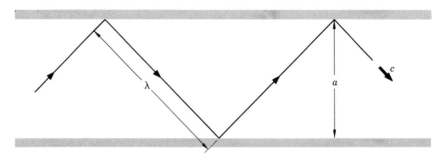

FIG. 16.14 Zig-zag path followed by an electromagnetic wave between parallel conducting planes for the case of a TM_1 wave with $\lambda = \sqrt{2} \, a$.

planes only if

$$\lambda = \frac{2a \cos \theta}{n}.$$ (16-7.2)

Since the smallest value of n and the largest value of $\cos \theta$ is one, the longest wave which can be so guided has the wave length

$$\lambda_{\text{max}} = 2a.$$ (16-7.3)

The corresponding lowest frequency of the wave is

$$f_{\text{min}} = \frac{c}{2a}.$$ (16-7.4)

This wave length and frequency are called *cut-off wave length* and *cut-off frequency*.

The phase velocity of TE or TM waves between parallel planes is, by Eq. (16-6.15),

$$v_p = \frac{c}{\sin \theta},$$ (16-7.5)

and the signal velocity is, by Eq. (16-6.16),

$$v_s = \sin \theta.$$ (16-7.6)

In specifying TE and TM waves between parallel planes, it is desirable to state the number of half-waves ($\lambda_{\text{standing}}/2$) contained in the standing wave pattern between the planes. This is done by affixing n of Eq. (16-7.2) as a subscript to the symbols denoting the waves. For

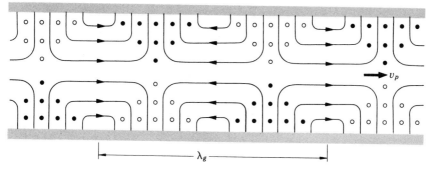

FIG. 16.15   Electric and magnetic field pattern formed by superposition of reflected waves between parallel conducting planes for the case of a TM_1 wave. The **E**-field is represented by lines. The **H**-field is represented by dots and circles. This pattern constitutes a "guided wave" described by Eqs. (16-6.13) and (16-6.14).

example, TE_2 means "a transverse electric wave with two half-waves in the standing wave pattern."

A schematic drawing of an electromagnetic wave propagating between parallel planes is given in Fig. 16.14. The corresponding field pattern is shown in Fig. 16.15.

The shortest distance along the planes after which the field pattern repeats itself is called *guide wave length*, λ_g. As it follows from Eqs. (16-7.5) and (16-2.2), this distance is given by

$$\lambda_g = \frac{\lambda}{\sin \theta}. \tag{16-7.7}$$

TEM Waves between Parallel Planes. Waves of this type are characterized by the same properties as the transverse plane waves in free space. It is interesting to note that in contrast to TE and TM waves TEM waves of any wave length or frequency can be propagated between parallel planes.

Wave Guides and Transmission Lines. The conducting parallel planes discussed above represent a special case of devices known as *wave guides* and *transmission lines*. They are used for confining and guiding electromagnetic waves.

A typical example of a wave guide is a hollow, conducting rectangular tube, or a *rectangular wave guide*. Electromagnetic fields in such a guide are similar to those between parallel planes, except that they form a standing wave pattern along the width as well as along the height of the guide, because the boundary conditions for **E** (continuity of the tangential component) must be satisfied at all four walls.

A common characteristic of all hollow-tube wave guides is that they cannot transmit waves whose length in free space exceeds a certain cut-off wave length, and can transmit only the TE and TM, but not the TEM, waves.

Transmission lines, however, can transmit the TEM waves (as well as waves of other types), and usually impose no restrictions upon the length of the waves. Typical examples of transmission lines are a pair of parallel wires and a coaxial cable.

16-8. Generation of Electromagnetic Waves

Having made ourselves familiar with the basic properties of electromagnetic waves, we shall now discuss how macroscopic electromagnetic waves can be generated.

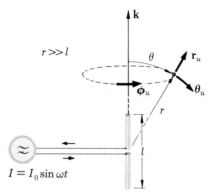

FIG. 16.16 One of the simplest systems capable of generating electromagnetic waves is an electric dipole antenna.

$I = I_0 \sin \omega t$

Electric Dipole Antenna. One of the simplest systems capable of generating electromagnetic waves is the *electric dipole antenna*, shown in Fig. 16.16. It consists of a piece of open wire which carries a current[1]

$$I = I_0 \sin \omega t. \tag{16-8.1}$$

By the continuity law (15-1.1b), the ends of the wire must carry electric charges [assuming that Eq. (16-8.1) holds at the ends]

$$q_+ = \frac{I_0}{\omega} \cos \omega t \quad \text{and} \quad q_- = -\frac{I_0}{\omega} \cos \omega t, \tag{16-8.2a, b}$$

so that the wire constitutes an oscillating electric dipole. That is why such a wire is called an "electric dipole" antenna. The amplitude of the dipole moment of this dipole is

$$p_0 = \frac{I_0 l}{\omega}, \tag{16-8.3}$$

where l is the length of the antenna.

An electric dipole antenna whose length is much smaller than $\lambda = 2\pi c/\omega$, where c is the velocity of light and ω is the frequency of current in the antenna is called a *Hertzian dipole*. In a Hertzian dipole the current is the same along the entire length of the antenna, so that Eq. (16-8.1) holds for all points of the antenna simultaneously. Let us calculate the electric and magnetic fields produced by a Hertzian dipole at large distances $r \gg \lambda$ from it.

The magnetic field is, by Eq. (15-7.6),

$$\mathbf{H} = -\frac{1}{4\pi} \int_{\text{Antenna}} \left\{ \frac{I_0 \sin \omega(t - r/c)}{r^2} + \frac{I_0 \omega \cos \omega(t - r/c)}{rc} \right\} \mathbf{r}_u \times d\mathbf{l}'.$$

---

[1] The current is produced by cutting the wire in the middle and connecting the two parts to a current source.

Since $r \gg \lambda = 2\pi c/\omega$, the first term in this integral may be neglected, and since $r \gg l$, r may be considered constant. We obtain, therefore, using Eq. (16-8.3),

$$\mathbf{H} = -\mathbf{r}_u \times \mathbf{p}_0 \frac{\omega^2 \cos \omega(t - r/c)}{4\pi rc},$$

or in terms of the coordinates shown in Fig. 16.16,

$$\mathbf{H} = \frac{p_0\omega^2 \cos \omega(t - r/c)}{4\pi rc} \sin \theta \, \boldsymbol{\phi}_u. \tag{16-8.4}$$

To find the electric field, we use Maxwell's Eq. (IIIa). Taking the curl of $\mathbf{H}$ given by Eq. (16-8.4), integrating with respect to t, and dividing the result by ε_0, we obtain[1]

$$\mathbf{E} = \frac{p_0\omega^2 \cos \omega(t - r/c)}{4\pi\varepsilon_0 rc^2} \sin \theta \, \boldsymbol{\theta}_u. \tag{16-8.5}$$

Equations (16-8.4) and (16-8.5) represent *spherical* electromagnetic waves propagating in the direction of increasing r. For a very large r and a small region where the waves are observed they may be considered as plane waves. The amplitudes of the waves are a function of the polar angle θ. The largest amplitudes are associated with the waves

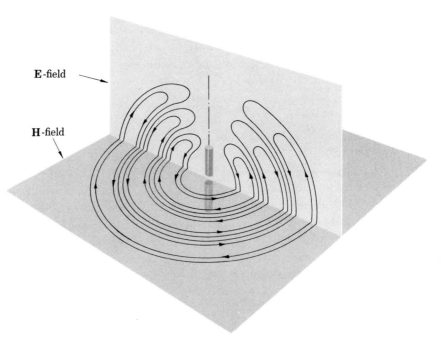

E-field

H-field

FIG. 16.17   Radiation field of an electric dipole antenna.

[1] The details of this calculation are left to Problem 16.24.

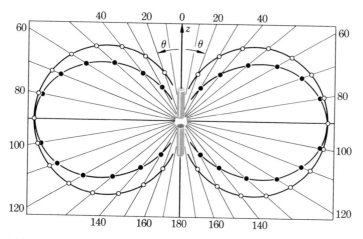

FIG. 16.18   Wave amplitude (circles) and time-averaged power (dots) in the radiation field of an electric dipole antenna as a function of polar angle.

propagating in the equatorial plane of the dipole (Figs. 16.17 and 16.18).

Let us calculate the Poynting vector for these waves. From Eqs. (16-8.4) and (16-8.5) we have

$$\mathbf{P} = {}^{\circ}\mathbf{E} \times \mathbf{H} = \frac{{}^{\circ}p_0{}^2\omega^4 \cos^2\omega(t - r/c)}{16\pi^2\varepsilon_0 r^2 c^3} \sin^2\theta \, \mathbf{r}_u. \qquad (16\text{-}8.6)$$

Integrating $\mathbf{P}$ over the surface of a sphere of radius r, we find the total power W radiated by a Hertzian dipole:

$$W = \oint \mathbf{P} \cdot d\mathbf{S} = \frac{{}^{\circ}p_0{}^2\omega^4 \cos^2\omega(t - r/c)}{16\pi^2\varepsilon_0 c^3} \int_0^\pi \frac{\sin^2\theta}{r^2} 2\pi r^2 \sin\theta \, d\theta,$$

or

$$W = \frac{{}^{\circ}p_0{}^2\omega^4 \cos^2\omega(t - r/c)}{6\pi\varepsilon_0 c^3}. \qquad (16\text{-}8.7)$$

This is the instantaneous power. For practical purposes one usually needs the time-averaged power. The average value of $\cos^2\omega(t - r/c)$ is $\frac{1}{2}$. Therefore the average power radiated by a Hertzian dipole is

$$W_{\mathrm{av}} = \frac{{}^{\circ}p_0^2\omega^4}{12\pi\varepsilon_0 c^3}. \qquad (16\text{-}8.8)$$

The overall efficiency of an antenna can be characterized by means of the *radiation resistance* R_{rad}, defined as

$${}^{\circ}R_{\mathrm{rad}} = 2\frac{W_{\mathrm{av}}}{I_0^2}, \qquad (16\text{-}8.9)$$

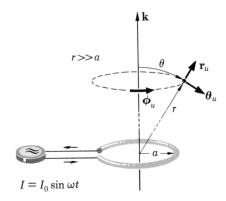

$I = I_0 \sin \omega t$

FIG. 16.19 Another simple system capable of generating electromagnetic waves is a magnetic dipole antenna.

where I_0 is the amplitude of the current in the antenna. The higher the radiation resistance of an antenna, the more power does the antenna radiate for a given current.

The radiation resistance of the Hertzian dipole can be found from Eqs. (16-8.9), (16-8.8), and (16-8.3). Combining these equations, we obtain

$$R_{\text{rad}} = \frac{l^2 \omega^2}{6 \pi \varepsilon_0 c^3}, \tag{16-8.10}$$

or, in terms of the wave length λ of the radiated wave,

$$R_{\text{rad}} = \frac{2\pi}{3} \sqrt{\frac{\mu_0}{\varepsilon_0}} \frac{l^2}{\lambda^2}, \tag{16-8.11}$$

where we have used the relations $\lambda = 2\pi c/\omega$ and $c = 1/\sqrt{\varepsilon_0 \mu_0}$.

Magnetic Dipole Antenna. Another simple system capable of generating electromagnetic waves is the *magnetic dipole antenna*, shown in Fig. 16.19. It consists of a circular loop of wire carrying a current

$$I = I_0 \sin \omega t, \tag{16-8.12}$$

and from large distances may be regarded as an oscillating magnetic dipole. That is why such an antenna is called a "magnetic dipole" antenna. The amplitude of the magnetic moment of this dipole is

$$m_0 = \mu_0 I_0 \pi a^2, \tag{16-8.13}$$

where a is the radius of the loop.

Let us calculate the electric and magnetic fields of a magnetic dipole antenna at large distances $r \gg \lambda \gg a$ from it.

The electric field produced by this antenna is, by Eq. (15-7.5),

$$\mathbf{E} = -\frac{1}{4\pi\varepsilon_0 c^2} \oint_{\text{Antenna}} \frac{I_0 \omega \cos \omega(t - r/c)}{r} \, d\mathbf{l}'. \tag{16-8.14}$$

Transforming this integral by means of the vector identity (V-16), factoring out the constants, and using the vector identity (V-28), we have

$$\mathbf{E} = -\frac{I_0\omega}{4\pi\varepsilon_0 c^2} \int_{\text{Antenna}} d\mathbf{S}' \times \nabla' \frac{\cos \omega(t - r/c)}{r}$$

$$= +\frac{I_0\omega}{4\pi\varepsilon_0 c^2} \int_{\text{Antenna}} \left\{ \frac{1}{r^2} \cos \omega(t - r/c) - \frac{\omega}{rc} \sin \omega(t - r/c) \right\} \mathbf{r}_u \times d\mathbf{S}'.$$

But $\omega/c = 2\pi/\lambda$, so that if $r \gg \lambda$, which we assume to be the case, the first term in the integrand may be neglected, and we obtain

$$\mathbf{E} = -\frac{I_0\omega^2}{4\pi\varepsilon_0 c^3} \int_{\text{Antenna}} \frac{\sin \omega(t - r/c)}{r} \mathbf{r}_u \times d\mathbf{S}'.$$

Now, since r is large compared with the radius a of the antenna, we can write

$$\mathbf{E} = -\frac{I_0\omega^2}{4\pi\varepsilon_0 c^3} \cdot \frac{\sin \omega(t - r/c)}{r} \mathbf{r}_u \times \int_{\text{Antenna}} d\mathbf{S}',$$

or

$$\mathbf{E} = \frac{m_0\omega^2 \sin \omega(t - r/c)}{4\pi rc} \sin \theta \, \boldsymbol{\phi}_u, \tag{16-8.15}$$

where $m_0 = \mu_0 I_0 \pi a^2$ is the amplitude of the dipole moment of the antenna, and θ and $\boldsymbol{\phi}_u$ are as shown in Fig. 16.19.

The magnetic field is, by Eq. (15-7.6),

$$\mathbf{H} = -\frac{1}{4\pi} \oint_{\text{Antenna}} \left\{ \frac{1}{r^2} I_0 \sin \omega(t - r/c) + \frac{\omega}{rc} I_0 \cos \omega(t - r/c) \right\} \mathbf{r}_u \times d\mathbf{l}'.$$

Neglecting the first term in the integrand and factoring out the constants, we have

$$\mathbf{H} = -\frac{I_0\omega}{4\pi c} \oint_{\text{Antenna}} \frac{\cos \omega(t - r/c)}{r} \mathbf{r}_u \times d\mathbf{l}'.$$

Since the point of observation is far from the antenna and the antenna is small, we can write

$$\mathbf{H} = -\frac{I_0\omega}{4\pi c} \mathbf{r}_u \times \oint_{\text{Antenna}} \frac{\cos \omega(t - r/c)}{r} d\mathbf{l}'.$$

But this is the same integral as that in Eq. (16-8.14) for $\mathbf{E}$. By Eqs. (16-8.14) and (16-8.15), we then have, using $c^2 = 1/\varepsilon_0\mu_0$,

$$\mathbf{H} = \frac{m_0\omega^2 \sin \omega(t - r/c)}{4\pi\mu_0 rc^2} \sin \theta \, \mathbf{r}_u \times \boldsymbol{\phi}_u,$$

or

$$\mathbf{H} = -\frac{m_0\omega^2 \sin \omega(t - r/c)}{4\pi\mu_0 rc^2} \sin \theta \, \boldsymbol{\theta}_u. \qquad (16\text{-}8.16)$$

Equations (16-8.15) and (16-8.16) represent spherical waves propagating in the direction of increasing r. The amplitudes of these waves are a function of the polar angle θ. The largest amplitudes are associated with the waves propagating in the plane of the antenna. The radiation pattern is the same as for the electric dipole antenna (Fig. 16.17), but with $\mathbf{E}$ and $\mathbf{H}$ fields interchanged and with the direction of one field reversed. The intensity diagram is the same as for the electric dipole antenna (Fig. 16.18).

Let us now calculate Poynting's vector for this antenna. From Eqs. (16-8.15) and (16-8.16), we have

$$\mathbf{P} = {}^\circ\mathbf{E} \times \mathbf{H} = \frac{{}^\circ m_0^2\omega^4 \sin^2 \omega(t - r/c)}{16\pi^2\mu_0 r^2 c^3} \sin^2 \theta \, \mathbf{r}_u. \qquad (16\text{-}8.17)$$

Integrating $\mathbf{P}$ over the surface of a sphere of radius r, we find the total power W radiated by the antenna:

$$W = \oint \mathbf{P} \cdot d\mathbf{S} = \frac{{}^\circ m_0^2\omega^4 \sin^2 \omega(t - r/c)}{16\pi^2\mu_0 c^3} \int_0^\pi \frac{\sin^2 \theta}{r^2} 2\pi r^2 \sin \theta \, d\theta$$

or

$$W = \frac{{}^\circ m_0^2\omega^4 \sin^2 \omega(t - r/c)}{6\pi\mu_0 c^3}. \qquad (16\text{-}8.18)$$

This is the instantaneous power. The average power is

$$W_{\text{av}} = \frac{{}^\circ m_0{}^2\omega^4}{12\pi\mu_0 c^3}. \qquad (16\text{-}8.19)$$

The radiation resistance of the magnetic dipole antenna can be found from Eqs. (16-8.9), (16-8.19), and (16-8.13). Combining these equations, we have

$$R_{\text{rad}} = \frac{\mu_0\pi a^4\omega^4}{6c^3}, \qquad (16\text{-}8.20)$$

or, in terms of the wave length λ,

$$R_{\text{rad}} = \frac{8\pi^5}{3}\sqrt{\frac{\mu_0}{\varepsilon_0}}\frac{a^4}{\lambda^4}. \qquad (16\text{-}8.21)$$

It is interesting to calculate the ratio of the radiation resistances of an electric and a magnetic dipole of similar dimensions radiating waves of the same length. If $l = a$, we have from Eqs. (16-8.11) and (16-8.21)

$$\frac{R_{\text{rad e.d.}}}{R_{\text{rad m.d.}}} = \frac{\lambda^2}{4\pi^4 l^2}.$$

Since by supposition $\lambda \gg l$, this relation shows than an electric dipole is a more efficient radiator than a magnetic dipole. That is why radio antennas are usually built in the form of electric, rather than magnetic, dipoles.

16-9. Hydromagnetic Waves

The possibility of hydromagnetic waves was first suggested by Alfvén in 1942. They were first produced in a laboratory by Lundquist in 1959. Hydromagnetic waves are an important phenomenon in plasma physics, space physics, and astrophysics.

The phenomenon of hydromagnetic waves can be explained qualitatively as follows. Consider a conducting liquid in which there is a homogeneous magnetic field $\mathbf{B}_0$ as shown in Fig. 16.20a. Suppose that a portion $ABCD$ of the liquid is set in motion perpendicular to the direction of $\mathbf{B}_0$. An induced electric field similar to that shown in Fig. 16.20b will then appear in the liquid (see Section 12-2). The electric field will cause electric currents in the liquid. These currents will be subjected to a magnetic force $\mathbf{F} = {}^{\circ}\mathbf{J} \times \mathbf{B}_0$, which will slow down the liquid in the portion $ABCD$ (induction drag), and will accelerate the liquid in the adjacent regions. Thus the induced current

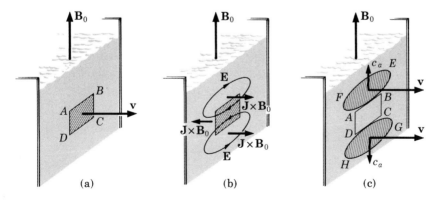

FIG. 16.20   Generation of hydromagnetic waves.

system transfers the initial motion of the liquid to the adjacent regions. As a result, after some time the portion *ABCD* will be at rest, while the portions *AFEB* and *DHGC* (Fig. 16.20c) will be set in motion. In this manner a hydromagnetic wave is produced.

Let us now consider the problem quantitatively. Suppose that we have an incompressible liquid of high conductivity σ, permeability μ, and density ρ moving with velocity $\mathbf{v}$. The following electromagnetic equations must be then satisfied by electric and magnetic fields in the liquid[1]:

$$\nabla \times \mathbf{E} = -\frac{\partial \mathbf{B}}{\partial t} \tag{16-9.1}$$

$$\nabla \times \mathbf{H} = \mathbf{J} \tag{16-9.2}$$

$$\mathbf{J} = \sigma(\mathbf{E} + \mathbf{v} \times \mathbf{B}). \tag{16-9.3}$$

Note that Eq. (16-9.2) does not contain the displacement current because the liquid is assumed to be a good conductor (see Example 15-2.2). In addition, the hydrodynamic continuity equation and hydrodynamic equation of motion (Newton's second law) must be satisfied, so that

$$\nabla \cdot \mathbf{v} = 0 \tag{16-9.4}$$

and

$$\rho \frac{\partial \mathbf{v}}{\partial t} = {}^{\circ}\mathbf{J} \times \mathbf{B} - \nabla p, \tag{16-9.5}$$

where p is the mechanical pressure within the liquid (the first equation is the continuity equation, the second equation is the equation of motion "per unit volume" of the liquid—this latter equation is an approximate one).

Let us assume that the liquid is originally at rest and is located in an external magnetic field

$$\mathbf{B}_0 = B_0\mathbf{k}. \tag{16-9.6}$$

Suppose now that as a result of some disturbance a part of the liquid is set in motion so that a velocity field $\mathbf{v}$ is produced in the liquid. This motion will produce an induced current $\mathbf{J}$ in the liquid (see Section 12.2). As a result, an electric field

$$\mathbf{E} = \frac{\mathbf{J}}{\sigma} - \mathbf{v} \times \mathbf{B} \tag{16-9.7}$$

---

[1] Strictly speaking, we should use the vectors $\mathbf{E}_m$, $\mathbf{D}_m$, $\mathbf{H}_m$, and $\mathbf{B}_m$, in accordance with the definitions of Section 12-3. Inasmuch as all vectors refer to fields in moving media, however, the subscripts can be omitted without introducing an ambiguity in the calculations. The special case $\mathbf{B} = \mu_0\mu\mathbf{H}$ will be assumed to hold.

will appear in the liquid (this field is associated with accumulations of charges in the regions where $\mathbf{v}$ experiences a change, much like the accumulation of charges on the surface of the artificial satellite discussed in Example 12-2.1). Also, an additional magnetic field $\mathbf{B}'$ will appear in the liquid, as required by Eq. (16-9.2). The total magnetic field will then be

$$\mathbf{B} = \mathbf{B}_0 + \mathbf{B}'. \qquad (16\text{-}9.8)$$

Combining Eqs. (16-9.8), (16-9.7), and (16-9.1), and noting that $\mathbf{B}_0$ is a constant, we have

$$\frac{\partial \mathbf{B}'}{\partial t} = \nabla \times [\mathbf{v} \times (\mathbf{B}_0 + \mathbf{B}')] - \nabla \times \frac{\mathbf{J}}{\sigma}.$$

If σ is sufficiently large, which we assume to be the case, the last term may be neglected, and we obtain

$$\frac{\partial \mathbf{B}'}{\partial t} = \nabla \times [\mathbf{v} \times (\mathbf{B}_0 + \mathbf{B}')].$$

But $\mathbf{B}'$, being an induced field, is much smaller than the external field $\mathbf{B}_0$. Taking this into account, we have

$$\frac{\partial \mathbf{B}'}{\partial t} = \nabla \times (\mathbf{v} \times \mathbf{B}_0). \qquad (16\text{-}9.9)$$

Combining Eqs. (16-9.5) and (16-9.2) we can write

$$\rho \frac{\partial \mathbf{v}}{\partial t} = [°(\nabla \times \mathbf{H}) \times \mathbf{B} - \nabla p],$$

and using Eq. (16-9.8) we obtain

$$\rho \frac{\partial \mathbf{v}}{\partial t} = \frac{1}{\mu_0 \mu} \{°[\nabla \times (\mathbf{B}_0 + \mathbf{B}')] \times (\mathbf{B}_0 + \mathbf{B}') - \mu_0 \mu \nabla p\}.$$

But $\mathbf{B}_0$ is constant, and $\mathbf{B}'$ is small. Therefore

$$\rho \frac{\partial \mathbf{v}}{\partial t} = \frac{1}{\mu_0 \mu} [°(\nabla \times \mathbf{B}') \times \mathbf{B}_0 - \mu_0 \mu \nabla p]. \qquad (16\text{-}9.10)$$

Using the vector identity (V-2) and noting that $\mathbf{B}_0$ is constant, we can transform Eq. (16-9.10) into

$$\rho \frac{\partial \mathbf{v}}{\partial t} = \frac{1}{\mu_0 \mu} [°(\mathbf{B}_0 \cdot \nabla)\mathbf{B}' - °\nabla(\mathbf{B}' \cdot \mathbf{B}_0) - \mu_0 \mu \nabla p]. \qquad (16\text{-}9.11)$$

Suppose now that the pressure p in the liquid is so adjusted that (see Problem 16.29)

$$\nabla[(°\mathbf{B}' \cdot \mathbf{B}_0) + \mu_0 \mu p] = 0.$$

In this case Eq. (16-9.11) reduces to

$$\rho \frac{\partial \mathbf{v}}{\partial t} = \frac{^{\circ}1}{\mu_0 \mu}(\mathbf{B}_0 \cdot \nabla)\mathbf{B}'. \tag{16-9.12}$$

By supposition, however, $\mathbf{B}_0 = B_0 \mathbf{k}$. Therefore

$$\rho \frac{\partial \mathbf{v}}{\partial t} = \frac{^{\circ}1}{\mu_0 \mu} B_0 \frac{\partial \mathbf{B}'}{\partial z}. \tag{16-9.13}$$

Using the vector identity (V-8) and taking into account that $\nabla \cdot \mathbf{v} = 0$ and that $\mathbf{B}_0$ is constant, we can transform Eq. (16-9.9) into

$$\frac{\partial \mathbf{B}'}{\partial t} = (\mathbf{B}_0 \cdot \nabla)\mathbf{v},$$

and since $\mathbf{B}_0 = B_0 \mathbf{k}$, we obtain

$$\frac{\partial \mathbf{B}'}{\partial t} = B_0 \frac{\partial \mathbf{v}}{\partial z}. \tag{16-9.14}$$

If we now differentiate Eq. (16-9.13) with respect to z, and Eq. (16-9.14) with respect to t, we obtain upon eliminating $\mathbf{v}$

$$\frac{\partial^2 \mathbf{B}'}{\partial z^2} - \frac{1}{c_a^2}\frac{\partial^2 \mathbf{B}'}{\partial t^2} = 0, \tag{16-9.15}$$

where we are using the abbreviation $c_a^2 = {}^{\circ}B_0^2/\mu_0\mu\rho$. Similarly, differentiating Eq. (16-9.13) with respect to t, and Eq. (16-9.14) with respect to z, we obtain upon eliminating $\mathbf{B}'$

$$\frac{\partial^2 \mathbf{v}}{\partial z^2} - \frac{1}{c_a^2}\frac{\partial^2 \mathbf{v}}{\partial t^2} = 0. \tag{16-9.16}$$

Equations (16-9.15) and (16-9.16) are the hydromagnetic wave equations. As we can see from these equations, a hydromagnetic wave is a mechanical wave ($\mathbf{v}$) and a magnetic wave ($\mathbf{B}'$) both propagating with the same *hydromagnetic wave velocity*, or *Alfvén wave velocity*,

$$c_a = B_0 \sqrt{\frac{^{\circ}1}{\mu_0\mu\rho}}. \tag{16-9.17}$$

Since the velocity of hydromagnetic waves is inversely proportional to the density ρ, the waves are especially important in media of low density, such as ionized gases. In the sun, for example, the velocity of these waves approaches the velocity of sound. Therefore in cosmical physics the phenomenon of hydromagnetic waves is at least as important as the phenomenon of purely mechanical waves.

The prediction and subsequent discovery of hydromagnetic waves is a new example of the vitality, productiveness, and universality of the Faraday-Maxwell theory of electromagnetic fields.

PROBLEMS

16.1. Show by differentiation and substitution that

$$\mathbf{W} = \mathbf{f}_1(t - z/c) + \mathbf{f}_2(t + z/c)$$

satisfies the wave equation

$$\frac{\partial^2 \mathbf{W}}{\partial z^2} - \frac{1}{c^2} \frac{\partial^2 \mathbf{W}}{\partial t^2} = 0.$$

16.2. Sinusoidal waves are frequently expressed in an exponential form. What is the exponential form of Eqs. (16-1.6) and (16-1.8) ?

16.3. A standing wave can be produced by two progressing waves of equal amplitudes and frequencies propagating in opposite directions. (a) Show that the superposition (sum) of the waves

$$\mathbf{W}_1 = \mathbf{W}_0 \sin \omega(t - z/c) \quad \text{and} \quad \mathbf{W}_2 = \mathbf{W}_0 \sin \omega(t + z/c)$$

produces the standing wave

$$\mathbf{W}_s = 2\mathbf{W}_0 \cos 2\pi \left(\frac{z}{\lambda}\right) \sin \omega t,$$

where $\lambda = 2\pi c/\omega$. (b) Represent all three waves graphically.

16.4. Show that a plane polarized wave can be regarded as a superposition (sum) of two circularly polarized waves.

16.5. Construct polarization ellipses for the wave

$$\mathbf{W} = \mathbf{i}W_0 \sin \omega(t - z/c) + \mathbf{j}W_0 \sin [\omega(t - z/c) + \delta]$$

if $\delta = 0$, $\pi/6$, $\pi/2$, $5\pi/6$, π, and $7\pi/6$, respectively.

16.6. Find the maximum and minimum values of the Poynting vector in an electromagnetic wave whose electric field vector is given by

$$\mathbf{E} = \mathbf{i}E_{ox} \sin \omega(t - z/c) + \mathbf{j}E_{oy} \sin \omega(t - z/c).$$

16.7. Prove that in an elliptically polarized electromagnetic wave the magnitude of the time-averaged Poynting vector is equal to the arithmetic mean of the largest and smallest magnitudes of this vector:

$$P_{av} = \tfrac{1}{2}(P_{max} + P_{min}).$$

16.8. Show that a plane electromagnetic wave propagates energy with velocity equal to the velocity of the wave.

16.9. Show that the phase angles δ' and δ'' in Eqs. (16-4.5) and (16-4.6) are

$$\delta' = -\frac{2r_{int}}{\omega c_1} \sin \alpha \cos \theta_i$$

and

$$\delta'' = \frac{r_{int} \sin \alpha}{\omega c_1 c_2} (\sqrt{c_1^2 - c_2^2 \sin^2 \theta_i} - c_2 \cos \theta_i),$$

where r_{int} is as shown in Fig. 16.5, α is the angle between r_{int} and the interface, and θ_i is the angle of incidence.

16.10. The ionospheric layer making possible a stable, long-range radio communication (F_2 layer) is located at an altitude $h \approx 300$ km above the surface of the earth. The index of refraction of this layer can be expressed as $n = \sqrt{1 - \lambda^2/A}$, where $A = 10^3$ m². Show that the shortest radio wave which can be reflected from this layer has the wave length

$$\lambda_{crit} \approx \sqrt{\frac{2Ah}{R}},$$

where R is the radius of the earth, and find the numerical value of this wave length.

16.11. Show that if an electromagnetic wave propagating in a medium whose index of refraction is n_1 impinges at a right angle on an interface with a medium whose index of refraction is n_2, the magnetic field vector changes phase by π radians upon reflection from the interface provided that $n_1 > n_2$.

16.12. Complete the derivation of Fresnel's equations given in the text. [Hint: $\sin (\alpha \pm \beta) \cos (\alpha \mp \beta) = \sin \alpha \cos \alpha \pm \sin \beta \cos \beta$].

16.13. Derive Brewster's formula

$$\tan \theta_B = \frac{n_2}{n_1}.$$

16.14. An electromagnetic wave is incident on a dielectric boundary. (a) Under what conditions is the amplitude of the electric field vector in the transmitted wave larger than that in the incident wave? (b) Under what conditions is the amplitude of the magnetic field vector larger?

16.15. A plane electromagnetic wave is incident normally on a plane boundary between two dielectrics. Show that the rate at which energy leaves the boundary in the refracted and reflected beams is equal to the rate at which energy is incident on the boundary.

16.16. Electromagnetic radiation approaches a glass surface at normal incidence. The index of refraction of the glass is 1.41. Determine the ratio of the power reflected from the glass to the power transmitted into the glass.

16.17. According to Eqs. (16-5.8) and (16-5.9), the amplitude of the electric field in a transmitted wave can be larger than the amplitude of the electric field in the incident wave. Show that in spite of this, the power carried by a transmitted beam of electromagnetic radiation is never larger than the power carried by the incident beam.

16.18. Show that for a beam of unpolarized (natural) light, the power W of the beam can be written as

$$W = \tfrac{1}{2}W_{\parallel} + \tfrac{1}{2}W_{\perp},$$

where $W_{\parallel}$ and $W_{\perp}$ are the powers associated with electric field components along two mutually perpendicular directions in the beam.

16.19. A beam of natural light strikes a dielectric boundary. The angle of incidence is θ. Show that the reflected beam carries off a fraction

$$f_r = \frac{1}{2}\left[\frac{\sin^2(\theta - \theta_t)}{\sin^2(\theta + \theta_t)} + \frac{\tan^2(\theta - \theta_t)}{\tan^2(\theta + \theta_t)}\right]$$

of the time-averaged power of the incident beam, and the transmitted beam carries off a fraction

$$f_t = \frac{1}{2}\left[\frac{\sin 2\theta \sin 2\theta_t}{\sin^2(\theta + \theta_t)} + \frac{\sin 2\theta \sin 2\theta_t}{\sin^2(\theta + \theta_t)\cos^2(\theta - \theta_t)}\right].$$

16.20. Show that the formulas of the preceding problem satisfy the principle of conservation of energy.

16.21. A beam of monochromatic electromagnetic radiation strikes a dielectric interface at a right angle to the interface. What fraction of the time-averaged power of the beam is contained in the reflected beam and what fraction is contained in the transmitted beam?

16.22. By direct calculation show that the intensity of the transmitted beam for the system discussed in Example 16-5.2 is equal to the intensity of the incident beam if the reflection is eliminated.

16.23. Show that an electromagnetic wave guided between infinite, parallel conducting plates satisfies the relation

$$\frac{1}{\lambda_g^2} + \frac{1}{\lambda_c^2} = \frac{1}{\lambda^2},$$

where λ_g is guide wave length, λ_c is the cut-off wave length, and λ is the wave length of the wave bouncing between the plates.

16.24. Derive Eq. (16-8.5) by substituting the expression for **H** given by Eq. (16-8.4) into the current-free Maxwell's Eq. (IIIa),

$$\frac{\partial \mathbf{D}}{\partial t} = \nabla \times \mathbf{H}.$$

16.25. (a) What current is required to radiate 1000 watts from an electric dipole of length equal to 0.1 wave length? (b) What current is required to radiate the same power from a magnetic dipole of radius equal to 0.1 wave length?

16.26. Calculate the electric field intensity at a distance of 10 km in the equatorial plane of a Hertzian dipole radiating 1 kilowatt of power. Assume that $\lambda \ll 10$ km.

16.27. Calculate retarded potentials for an electric dipole antenna and derive Eqs. (16-8.4) and (16-8.5) from these potentials.

16.28. Calculate retarded potentials for a magnetic dipole antenna and derive Eqs. (16-8.15) and (16-8.16) from these potentials.

16.29. Show that in a liquid whose surface is not subjected to pressure the relation

$$\nabla[°(\mathbf{B}' \cdot \mathbf{B}_0) + \mu_0 \mu p] = 0$$

is satisfied automatically. [Hint: take the divergence of Eq. (16-9.11), then use vector identity (V-24).]

16.30. Calculate the velocity of hydromagnetic waves in mercury, the earth's core, interstellar plasma, and the sun. Use the following table and assume that $\mu \approx 1$ in all four media.

	Mercury	Earth's Core	Interstellar Plasma	Sun
ρ [kg/m³]	$1.36 \cdot 10^4$	10^4	10^{-21}	10^{-4}
B_0 [Vs/m²]	1	10^{-1}	10^{-9}	10^{-1}

16.31. In electromagnetic waves the energy is divided equally between electric and magnetic fields. If a wave were associated with a beam of charged particles, what should be their velocity to produce such equipartitioning of energy?

APPENDIX 1

Tables for Conversion of Measurables and Units

TABLE A-1

Relationship between Symbols in
Different Systems of Measurables[a]

Quantity	$LMTVI, LMTQ,$ $LMTI$	LMT (esu), LMT (emu) LMT (Gaussian)
Displacement	D	$\dfrac{D}{4\pi}$
Magnetic field	H	$\dfrac{H}{4\pi}$
Magnetic scalar potential	φ	$\dfrac{\varphi}{4\pi}$
Magnetization[b]	M	$4\pi M$
Magnetic moment[c]	m	$4\pi m$

[a] Symbols for quantities not listed in this table but listed in Table A-3 remain unchanged in all six systems of measurables.
[b] If **M** is defined as $\mathbf{M} = \mathbf{B} - \mu_0\mathbf{H}$.
[c] If m is defined as $m = \mu_0 IS$.

TABLE A-2

Relationship between Dimensional Constants
in Different Systems of Measurables[a]

$LMTVI$	$LMTI$	$LMTQ$	LMT (esu)	LMT (emu)	LMT (Gaussian)
ε_0	ε_0	ε_0	$\dfrac{1}{4\pi}$	$\dfrac{1}{4\pi c^2}$	$\dfrac{1}{4\pi}$
μ_0	μ_0	μ_0	$\dfrac{4\pi}{c^2}$	4π	4π
$\circ$	1	1	1	1	1
1	1	1	1	1	c

[a] The symbol c stands for the velocity of light in vacuum.

TABLE A-3

Dimensions of Electric and Magnetic Quantities
in Different Systems of Measurables[a,b]

Quantity		$LMTVI$	$LMTQ$	LMT (esu)	LMT (emu)
Capacitance	C	$TV^{-1}I$	$L^{-2}M^{-1}T^2Q^2$	$\mathbf{L}$	$L^{-1}T^2$
Charge	q	TI	Q	$\mathbf{L^{3/2}M^{1/2}T^{-1}}$	$L^{1/2}M^{1/2}$
Charge density	ρ	$L^{-3}TI$	$L^{-3}Q$	$\mathbf{L^{-3/2}M^{1/2}T^{-1}}$	$L^{-5/2}M^{1/2}$
Charge density	σ	$L^{-2}TI$	$L^{-2}Q$	$\mathbf{L^{-1/2}M^{1/2}T^{-1}}$	$L^{-3/2}M^{1/2}$
Charge density	λ	$L^{-1}TI$	$L^{-1}Q$	$\mathbf{L^{1/2}M^{1/2}T^{-1}}$	$L^{-1/2}M^{1/2}$
Conductance	G	$V^{-1}I$	$L^{-2}M^{-1}TQ^2$	$\mathbf{LT^{-1}}$	$L^{-1}T$
Conductivity	σ	$L^{-1}V^{-1}I$	$L^{-3}M^{-1}TQ^2$	$\mathbf{T^{-1}}$	$L^{-2}T$
Current	I	I	$T^{-1}Q$	$\mathbf{L^{3/2}M^{1/2}T^{-2}}$	$L^{1/2}M^{1/2}T^{-1}$
Current density	J	$L^{-2}I$	$L^{-2}T^{-1}Q$	$\mathbf{L^{-1/2}M^{1/2}T^{-2}}$	$L^{-3/2}M^{1/2}T^{-1}$
Current density	$J^{(s)}$	$L^{-1}I$	$L^{-1}T^{-1}Q$	$\mathbf{L^{1/2}M^{1/2}T^{-2}}$	$L^{-1/2}M^{1/2}T^{-1}$
Displacement	D	$L^{-2}TI$	$L^{-2}Q$	$\mathbf{L^{-1/2}M^{1/2}T^{-1}}$	$L^{-3/2}M^{1/2}$
Electric field	E	$L^{-1}V$	$LMT^{-2}Q^{-1}$	$\mathbf{L^{-1/2}M^{1/2}T^{-1}}$	$L^{1/2}M^{1/2}T^{-2}$
Electric dipole moment	p	LTI	LQ	$\mathbf{L^{3/2}M^{1/2}T^{-1}}$	$L^{3/2}M^{1/2}$
Electrostatic potential	φ	V	$L^2MT^{-2}Q^{-1}$	$\mathbf{L^{1/2}M^{1/2}T^{-1}}$	$L^{3/2}M^{1/2}T^{-2}$
Energy	U	L^2MT^{-2}	L^2MT^{-2}	L^2MT^{-2}	L^2MT^{-2}
Energy constant	$^\circ$	$L^2MT^{-3}V^{-1}I^{-1}$	1	1	1
Force	F	LMT^{-2}	LMT^{-2}	LMT^{-2}	LMT^{-2}
Inductance	L	TVI^{-1}	L^2MQ^{-2}	$L^{-1}T^2$	$\mathbf{L}$
Induction	B	$L^{-2}TV$	$MT^{-1}Q^{-1}$	$L^{-3/2}M^{1/2}$	$\mathbf{L^{-1/2}M^{1/2}T^{-1}}$
Magnetic dipole moment[c]	m	LTV	$L^3MT^{-1}Q^{-1}$	$L^{3/2}M^{1/2}$	$\mathbf{L^{5/2}M^{1/2}T^{-1}}$
Magnetic field	H	$L^{-1}I$	$L^{-1}T^{-1}Q$	$L^{1/2}M^{1/2}T^{-2}$	$\mathbf{L^{-1/2}M^{1/2}T^{-1}}$
Magnetic flux	Φ	TV	$L^2MT^{-1}Q^{-1}$	$L^{1/2}M^{1/2}$	$\mathbf{L^{3/2}M^{1/2}T^{-1}}$
Magnetic scalar potential	φ	I	$T^{-1}Q$	$L^{3/2}M^{1/2}T^{-2}$	$\mathbf{L^{1/2}M^{1/2}T^{-1}}$
Magnetic vector potential	A	$L^{-1}TV$	$LMT^{-1}Q^{-1}$	$L^{-1/2}M^{1/2}$	$\mathbf{L^{1/2}M^{1/2}T^{-1}}$
Magnetization[d]	M	$L^{-2}TV$	$MT^{-1}Q^{-1}$	$L^{-3/2}M^{1/2}$	$\mathbf{L^{-1/2}M^{1/2}T^{-1}}$
Permeability of space	μ_0	$L^{-1}TVI^{-1}$	LMQ^{-2}	1	1
Permittivity of space	ε_0	$L^{-1}TV^{-1}I$	$L^{-3}M^{-1}T^2Q^2$	1	1
Polarizability[e]	α	$L^2TV^{-1}I$	$M^{-1}T^2Q^2$	$\mathbf{L^3}$	LT^2
Polarization	P	$L^{-2}TI$	$L^{-2}Q$	$\mathbf{L^{-1/2}M^{1/2}T^{-1}}$	$L^{-3/2}M^{1/2}$
Resistance	R	VI^{-1}	$L^2MT^{-1}Q^{-2}$	$\mathbf{L^{-1}T}$	LT^{-1}
Resistivity	ρ	LVI^{-1}	$L^3MT^{-1}Q^{-2}$	$\mathbf{T}$	L^2T^{-1}
Voltage	V	V	$L^2MT^{-2}Q^{-1}$	$\mathbf{L^{1/2}M^{1/2}T^{-1}}$	$M^{1/2}L^{3/2}T^{-2}$

[a] Dimensions of quantities in the $LMTI$ system are obtained from those in the $LMTQ$ system by replacing Q by TI.

[b] Dimensions of quantities in the Gaussian system are shown in bold face in the columns for the LMT systems.

[c] Defined as $m = \mu_0 IS$.

[d] Defined as $\mathbf{M} = \mathbf{B} - \mu_0\mathbf{H}$.

[e] Defined by $\mathbf{p} = \alpha\mathbf{E}$.

TABLE A-4

Relationship between Electric and Magnetic Quantities in Different Systems of Units[a]

Quantity		mksva	cgs (esu)	cgs (emu)	cgs (Gaussian)
Capacitance	C	$1 \dfrac{amp \cdot s}{volt} = 1$ farad	$9 \cdot 10^{11}$ cm	10^{-9} cm^{-1} s^2	$9 \cdot 10^{11}$ cm
Charge	q	1 amp $\cdot$ s $= 1$ coulomb	$3 \cdot 10^9$ cm$^{3/2}$ g$^{1/2}$ s^{-1}	10^{-1} cm$^{1/2}$ g$^{1/2}$	$3 \cdot 10^9$ cm$^{3/2}$ g$^{1/2}$ s^{-1}
Charge density	ρ	$1 \dfrac{amp \cdot s}{m^3}$	$3 \cdot 10^3$ cm$^{-3/2}$ g$^{1/2}$ s^{-1}	10^{-7} cm$^{-5/2}$ g$^{1/2}$	$3 \cdot 10^3$ cm$^{-3/2}$ g$^{1/2}$ s^{-1}
Charge density	σ	$1 \dfrac{amp \cdot s}{m^2}$	$3 \cdot 10^5$ cm$^{-1/2}$ g$^{1/2}$ s^{-1}	10^{-5} cm$^{-3/2}$ g$^{1/2}$	$3 \cdot 10^5$ cm$^{-1/2}$ g$^{1/2}$ s^{-1}
Charge density	λ	$1 \dfrac{amp \cdot s}{m}$	$3 \cdot 10^7$ cm$^{1/2}$ g$^{1/2}$ s^{-1}	10^{-3} cm$^{-1/2}$ g$^{1/2}$	$3 \cdot 10^7$ cm$^{1/2}$ g$^{1/2}$ s^{-1}
Conductance	G	$1 \dfrac{amp}{volt} = 1$ mho	$9 \cdot 10^{11}$ cm s^{-1}	10^{-9} cm^{-1} s	$9 \cdot 10^{11}$ cm s^{-1}
Conductivity	σ	$1 \dfrac{amp}{volt \cdot m}$	$9 \cdot 10^9$ s^{-1}	10^{-11} cm^{-2} s	$9 \cdot 10^9$ s^{-1}
Current	I	1 amp	$3 \cdot 10^9$ cm$^{3/2}$ g$^{1/2}$ s^{-2}	10^{-1} cm$^{1/2}$ g$^{1/2}$ s^{-1}	$3 \cdot 10^9$ cm$^{3/2}$ g$^{1/2}$ s^{-2}
Current density	J	$1 \dfrac{amp}{m^2}$	$3 \cdot 10^5$ cm$^{-1/2}$ g$^{1/2}$ s^{-2}	10^{-5} cm$^{-3/2}$ g$^{1/2}$ s^{-1}	$3 \cdot 10^5$ cm$^{-1/2}$ g$^{1/2}$ s^{-2}
Current density	$J^{(s)}$	$1 \dfrac{amp}{m}$	$3 \cdot 10^7$ cm$^{1/2}$ g$^{1/2}$ s^{-2}	10^{-3} cm$^{-1/2}$ g$^{1/2}$ s^{-1}	$3 \cdot 10^7$ cm$^{1/2}$ g$^{1/2}$ s^{-2}
Displacement	D	$1 \dfrac{amp \cdot s}{m^2}$	$4\pi \, 3 \cdot 10^5$ cm$^{-1/2}$ g$^{1/2}$ s^{-1}	$4\pi 10^{-5}$ cm$^{-3/2}$ g$^{1/2}$	$4\pi \, 3 \cdot 10^5$ cm$^{-1/2}$ g$^{1/2}$ s^{-1}
Electric field	E	$1 \dfrac{volt}{m}$	$\dfrac{10^{-4}}{3}$ cm$^{-1/2}$ g$^{1/2}$ s^{-1}	10^6 cm$^{1/2}$ g$^{1/2}$ s^{-2}	$\dfrac{10^{-4}}{3}$ cm$^{-1/2}$ g$^{1/2}$ s^{-1}
Electric dipole moment	p	1 amp $\cdot$ s $\cdot$ m	$3 \cdot 10^{11}$ cm$^{5/2}$ g$^{1/2}$ s^{-1}	10 cm$^{3/2}$ g$^{1/2}$	$3 \cdot 10^{11}$ cm$^{5/2}$ g$^{1/2}$ s^{-1}
Electrostatic potential	φ	1 volt	$\dfrac{1}{300}$ cm$^{1/2}$ g$^{1/2}$ s^{-1}	10^8 cm$^{3/2}$ g$^{1/2}$ s^{-2}	$\dfrac{1}{300}$ cm$^{1/2}$ g$^{1/2}$ s^{-1}
Energy	U	1 m^{2}ks^{-2} = 1 joule	10^7 cm^2 g s^{-2}	10^7 cm^2 g s^{-2}	10^7 cm^2 g s^{-2}

Quantity	Symbol	MKS definition			
Force	F	$1\ \mathrm{mks^{-2}} = 1$ newton	10^7 cm g s^{-2}	10^7 cm g s^{-2}	10^7 cm g s^{-2}
Inductance	L	$1\ \dfrac{\mathrm{volt\cdot s}}{\mathrm{amp}} = 1$ henry	$\dfrac{10^{-11}}{9}$ cm^{-1} s^2	10^9 cm	10^9 cm
Induction	B	$1\ \dfrac{\mathrm{volt\cdot s}}{\mathrm{m}^2}$	$\dfrac{10^{-6}}{3}$ cm$^{-\frac12}$ g$^{\frac12}$	10^4 cm$^{-\frac12}$ g$^{\frac12}$ s^{-1} $=10^4$ gauss	10^4 cm$^{-\frac12}$ g$^{\frac12}$ s^{-1} $=10^4$ gauss
Magnetic dipole moment[b]	m	1 volt · s · m	$\dfrac{1}{4\pi}\cdot\dfrac13$ cm$^{\frac52}$ g$^{\frac12}$	$\dfrac{1}{4\pi}10^{10}$ cm$^{\frac52}$ g$^{\frac12}$ s^{-1}	$\dfrac{1}{4\pi}10^{10}$ cm$^{\frac52}$ g$^{\frac12}$ s^{-1}
Magnetic field	H	$1\ \dfrac{\mathrm{amp}}{\mathrm{m}}$	$4\pi\,3\cdot10^7$ cm$^{-\frac12}$ g$^{\frac12}$ s^{-2}	$4\pi\,10^{-3}$ cm$^{-\frac12}$ g$^{\frac12}$ s^{-1} $=4\pi\,10^{-3}$ oersted	$4\pi\,10^{-3}$ cm$^{-\frac12}$ g$^{\frac12}$ s^{-1} $=4\pi\,10^{-3}$ oersted
Magnetic flux	Φ	1 volt · s $= 1$ weber	$\dfrac{1}{300}$ cm$^{\frac12}$ g$^{\frac12}$	10^8 cm$^{\frac32}$ g$^{\frac12}$ s^{-1} $=10^8$ maxwell	10^8 cm$^{\frac32}$ g$^{\frac12}$ s^{-1} $=10^8$ maxwell
Magnetic scalar potential	φ	1 amp	$4\pi\,3\cdot10^9$ cm$^{\frac32}$ g$^{\frac12}$ s^{-2}	$4\pi\,10^{-1}$ cm$^{\frac12}$ g$^{\frac12}$ s^{-1}	$4\pi\,10^{-1}$ cm$^{\frac12}$ g$^{\frac12}$ s^{-1}
Magnetic vector potential	A	$1\ \dfrac{\mathrm{volt\cdot s}}{\mathrm{m}}$	$\dfrac{10^{-4}}{3}$ cm$^{-\frac12}$ g$^{\frac12}$	10^6 cm$^{\frac12}$ g$^{\frac12}$ s^{-1}	10^6 cm$^{\frac12}$ g$^{\frac12}$ s^{-1}
Magnetization[c]	M	$1\ \dfrac{\mathrm{volt\cdot s}}{\mathrm{m}^2}$	$\dfrac{1}{4\pi}\dfrac{10^{-6}}{3}$ cm$^{-\frac12}$ g$^{\frac12}$	$\dfrac{1}{4\pi}10^4$ cm$^{-\frac12}$ g$^{\frac12}$ s^{-1}	$\dfrac{1}{4\pi}10^4$ cm$^{-\frac12}$ g$^{\frac12}$ s^{-1}
Polarizability[d]	α	$1\ \dfrac{\mathrm{amp\cdot s\cdot m}^2}{\mathrm{volt}}$	$9\cdot10^{15}$ cm^3	10^{-5} cm s^2	$9\cdot10^{15}$ cm^3
Polarization	P	$1\ \dfrac{\mathrm{amp\cdot s}}{\mathrm{m}^2}$	$3\cdot10^5$ cm$^{-\frac12}$ g$^{\frac12}$ s^{-1}	10^{-5} cm$^{-\frac32}$ g$^{\frac12}$	$3\cdot10^5$ cm$^{-\frac12}$ g$^{\frac12}$ s^{-1}
Power	$P,\ W$	$1\ \dfrac{\mathrm{joule}}{\mathrm{sec}} = 1$ watt	10^7 cm^2 g s^{-3}	10^7 cm^2 g s^{-3}	10^7 cm^2 g s^{-3}
Resistance	R	$1\ \dfrac{\mathrm{volt}}{\mathrm{amp}} = 1$ ohm	$\dfrac{10^{-11}}{9}$ cm^{-1} s	10^9 cm^{-1} s	$\dfrac{10^{-11}}{9}$ cm^{-1} s
Resistivity	ρ	$1\ \dfrac{\mathrm{volt\cdot m}}{\mathrm{amp}}$	$\dfrac{10^{-9}}{9}$ s	10^{11} cm^2 s^{-1}	$\dfrac{10^{-9}}{9}$ s
Voltage	V	1 volt	$\dfrac{1}{300}$ cm$^{\frac12}$ g$^{\frac12}$ s^{-1}	10^8 cm$^{\frac32}$ g$^{\frac12}$ s^{-1}	$\dfrac{1}{300}$ cm$^{\frac12}$ g$^{\frac12}$ s^{-1}

[a] Numerical values of quantities in the *mksa* and *mksc* systems are the same as in the *mksva* system.   [b] Defined as $m = \mu_0 IS$.

[c] Defined as $\mathbf{M} = \mathbf{B} - \mu_0\mathbf{H}$.   [d] Defined by $\mathbf{p} = \alpha\mathbf{E}$.

APPENDIX 2

Electric and Magnetic Properties
of Common Substances

TABLE A-5[a]

Electric and Magnetic Properties of Common Substances

Substance	Classification	Permit-tivity	Conductivity[b] amp/volt · m	Permeability
Air (1 atm, 20°C)	dielectric paramagnetic	1.0006		1.0000004
Alcohol (ethyl, 20°C)	dielectric	28	$3.3 \cdot 10^{-5}$	
Aluminum	conductor paramagnetic		$3.5 \cdot 10^7$	1.00002
Amber	dielectric	2.8	$2 \cdot 10^{-15}$	
Bakelite	dielectric	5	10^{-9}	
Barium titanate ($BaTiO_3$)	dielectric	1200		
Barium strontium titanate ($2BaTiO_3:1SrTiO_3$)	dielectric	10000		
Bismuth	conductor diamagnetic		$8.3 \cdot 10^5$	0.99983
Brass	conductor		$1.1 \cdot 10^7$	
Castor oil	dielectric	4.3	$1.7 \cdot 10^{-9}$	
Ceresin wax	dielectric	2.2	$2 \cdot 10^{-17}$	
Cobalt	conductor ferroelectric		$1.1 \cdot 10^7$	250
Constantan	conductor		$2 \cdot 10^6$	
Copper	conductor diamagnetic		$5.7 \cdot 10^7$	0.999991
Glass	dielectric	5–10	10^{-10}–10^{-14}	
Germanium (pure)	conductor		2.2	
Glycerin	dielectric	10		
Gold	conductor paramagnetic		$4.1 \cdot 10^7$	0.999964
Graphite	conductor		10^4–10^5	
Iron (cast)	conductor ferromagnetic		$1.2 \cdot 10^7$	5000
Lead	conductor diamagnetic		$5 \cdot 10^6$	0.999983
Mercury	conductor		$1.04 \cdot 10^6$	
Mica	dielectric	6	10^{-11}–10^{-15}	
Nichrome	conductor		10^6	
Nickel	conductor ferromagnetic		$1.28 \cdot 10^7$	600
Nylon	dielectric	8		
Paper	dielectric	3.7	10^{-11}	
Paraffin	dielectric	2.1	10^{-15}	
Permalloy (2Mo, 81Ni)	conductor ferromagnetic			130
Permalloy (78.5 Ni)	conductor ferromagnetic			100000
Plexiglass	dielectric	3.4	10^{-14}	
Porcelain	dielectric	7	10^{-12}	
Quartz (fused)	dielectric	4	10^{-16}	
Rubber (hard)	dielectric	3	10^{-13}–10^{-16}	
Rutile (TiO_2)	dielectric	89		

TABLE A-5^a (*Continued*)

Substance	Classification	Permittivity	Conductivity^b amp/volt · m	Permeability
Silver	conductor diamagnetic		6.1 · 10^7	0.99997
Silicon (pure)	conductor or dielectric	12	1.6 · 10^{-3}	
Sulphur	dielectric	3.44	10^{-15}	
Supermalloy (5Mo, 79Ni)	conductor ferromagnetic			1000000
Tungsten	conductor diamagnetic		1.8 · 10^7	0.999932
Water (distilled)	dielectric diamagnetic	81	2 · 10^{-4}	0.999991
Water (sea)	conductor		5	
Wood	dielectric	2.5–8.0	10^{-8}–10^{-12}	
Zinc	conductor		1.7 · 10^7	

^{a} Numerical values given in this table are to be regarded as representative rather than exact ones.

^{b} The volume conductivities are given. The surface conductivities of dielectrics may be considerably higher due to moisture and impurities on the surface.

INDEX